THE DIRECTORY OF GRANT MAKING TRUSTS 1997–98

15TH EDITION

VOLUME ONE

The Indices

EDITORIAL TEAM
JOHANNA DAVIS
JILL GOLDSWORTHY
DAVID MONCRIEFF

© 1997 Charities Aid
Foundation

Published by the Charities Aid
Foundation

Kings Hill
West Malling
Kent ME19 4TA

Telephone
+44 (0)1732 520000

Fax
+44 (0)1732 520001

Web address
http://www.charitynet.org

E-mail address
cafpubs@caf.charitynet.org

Database management
and typesetting
BPC Whitefriars Ltd

Design
Eugenie Dodd Typographics

Printed and bound
in Great Britain by Bell & Bain
Ltd, Glasgow

A catalogue record for this
book is available from
the British Library.

ISBN 1–85934–025–3
(two volumes)

Acknowledgements

The publication of a new
edition of *The Directory of
Grant Making* Trusts has
always been demanding.
The development of the
1997–98 edition has been
particularly challenging
owing to the introduction
of the new indexing system
and the comprehensive
overhaul of the master
database which services
the directory. In particular,
CAF would like to thank
and acknowledge the
contributions of: the Charity
Commission, Elinor Denman,
Eugenie Dodd, the Factary,
Jo Habib, Caroline Hartnell,
Les Hems, Margo Horsley,
Marion Peat, Jacqueline Rae,
Ben Richards, Nigel Siederer,
and Allan and Mary Wyatt.

Contents

VOLUME ONE

Introduction   v
Criteria for inclusion

Structure and content   vii

How to use the directory   xiii

The National Lottery   xvii

BLUE PAGES
Trusts by beneficial area   2

GREEN PAGES
Trusts by field of interest and type of beneficiary   54

PINK PAGES
The directory of products and services   318

Introduction

Grant-making trusts are a major source of funding that is available to the voluntary sector in the UK and overseas. The figures published by CAF in the 1996 edition of *Dimensions of the Voluntary Sector* indicate that the top 500 trusts had an income of around £865 million and made grants of £705 million.

Many of the major grant-making trusts are household names. Others are less well known. Yet the vast majority, large and small, are open to funding applications from voluntary organisations for a wide range of projects and activities.

CAF published the first edition of *The Directory of Grant Making Trusts* (*DGMT*) in 1968. Since that time the title has gained a pre-eminent reputation among grant-seekers as the definitive guide to UK grant-making trusts and their funding priorities. Today it is hard to imagine the difficulties which must have been encountered in trying to obtain funds from trusts before the *DGMT* threw a spotlight on to their existence and provided a mechanism by which fundraisers could identify the trusts most likely to be in sympathy with their needs.

Predictably, some trusts continue to be unhappy at the loss of their anonymity. Nor are established beneficiaries always eager to share information on a rich vein of financial support into which they have tapped for years and about which they may have come to feel distinctly proprietorial. Over a period of time, however, it has become accepted that the *DGMT* provides a significant bridge between grant-makers and grant-seekers and has helped to make the workload of both types of organisation less onerous.

With a new editorial team in place, and in response to constructive criticism received, the 1997–98 edition of the *DGMT*, published in two volumes for the first time, has undergone a complete design overhaul in order to make the information presented even more straightforward and accessible. The indices which 'lead' the user to the most relevant trusts have also been radically amended, using the new Charity Commission classification system as a basic model. Particularly significantly, the listing of trusts by beneficial area has been reorganised in order to highlight trusts' geographical funding preferences more clearly and a new classification of types of beneficiary has been introduced.

The new indices have been developed following a comprehensive survey of grant-making trusts in the UK. Every trust appearing on the master database was sent a detailed questionnaire seeking information on its future funding preferences. These questionnaires were analysed in order to create the beneficial area, activity and beneficiary headings seen in the indices in the blue and green pages. Where trusts failed to return the questionnaires, or to supply the necessary information, the editorial team determined their classification on the basis of either the amended proof of their entry in the main register that they returned to CAF or the data available on the Charity Commission files.

The core data appearing in this title have been either checked by the trust concerned or verified at the Charity Commission within an established timeframe.

These improvements will enable fundraisers to obtain an even more detailed understanding of the future funding policies of the trusts listed and thereby to tailor their requests for support more accurately – so reducing the time and money wasted on inappropriate appeals.

Criteria for inclusion

The details of trusts registered under the law of England and Wales which appear in this *DGMT* are recorded on the public register at the Charity Commission and are consequently available for publication. As there is no register open to the public in Scotland or Northern Ireland, the publishers have relied on direct contact with the Scottish and Irish trusts listed in order to obtain the latest information.

Prior to publication, every trust listed was contacted by phone, fax or post and asked to verify the information appearing in its entry and to amend the details in such a way that they would accurately reflect its grant-making policy and preferences for 1997–98.

In responding to our approach, some trusts indicated that they did not wish to be included in this publication. While the editorial team has reviewed each case individually, in general it has excluded only those trusts which have been wound up or are not open to unsolicited applications in any circumstances.

Where it has been judged, on the basis of the information available, that a speculative application could be successful, either currently or at some future date, the trust's details have been included. Naturally, the team has endeavoured to be entirely accurate in this process, but inevitably, in certain circumstances, a subjective judgement has had to be made, primarily owing to the non-availability of up-to-date or reliable information.

Trusts which fund individuals *exclusively* have not been included in this edition of the *DGMT*.

Structure and content

The aim of the *DGMT* is to enable grant-seekers to identify as accurately as possible those trusts which are likely to be sympathetic to their cause. Volume One of the *DGMT* contains two indices. If readers use these indices correctly, they should end up with a shortlist of trusts whose funding preferences closely match their needs. They can then look these trusts up in the main register of trusts in Volume Two.

The Indices (Volume One)

A step-by-step explanation of how to use the indices in order to draw up a 'hit list' of trusts is given on pages xiii–xvi. What follows immediately is a description of the two indices contained in Volume One.

BLUE PAGES
Trusts by beneficial area

The blue pages enable you to see which trusts will consider applications from a charity or project in a particular geographical area. They list trusts under the areas for which the trust has expressed a funding preference either in the survey questionnaire or in the amended proof of their entry in the main register that they returned to CAF.

The survey questionnaire asked trusts to tick the geographical areas from which they will consider funding applications. They were given the following options and invited to tick as many of them as they wished:

- the whole UK;
- a specific UK country – England, Scotland, Wales, Northern Ireland;
- a region of the UK, eg the North West or the South East;
- a county;
- a large metropolitan area such as Birmingham (in general the UK has been divided according to county council boundaries, but certain large metropolitan areas have been listed separately);
- overseas.

The titles of the new unitary authorities have not been included following advice that they are still in a state of transition.

The blue pages contain two separate listings.

LIST OF GEOGRAPHICAL AREA HEADINGS

This is a complete list of all the geographical area headings used in the *DGMT*. These are the options that trusts were invited to tick. Counties are shown under the relevant region and regions under the relevant UK country. If you are unsure which region a particular county will appear under, this list will provide the answer.

Page numbers relate to the position of headings in the list of trusts by beneficial area that follows.

LIST OF TRUSTS BY BENEFICIAL AREA

The second part of the blue pages lists trusts under the geographical areas they ticked.

Berkshire

Counties and metropolitan areas are shown in small bold type under the appropriate region.

■ South East

The region headings appear in larger bold type preceded by a black square and with a dotted line above.

England

The regions in turn appear under the appropriate UK country; country headings are in white against a black strip.

Where a trust has stated that it prefers to concentrate its work in a particular region or county (eg Cornwall) but will consider grant applications from a larger geographical area (eg the whole of the UK), the trust is listed under both headings (UK and Cornwall). Users of the *DGMT* should note that a trust listed as considering funding applications from anywhere in the UK may be just as likely to provide funding for a Cornish project as a trust which states that it prefers to fund activity only in Cornwall.

The page references by each trust's name relate to the position of the trust's entry in the main register in Volume Two.

**GREEN PAGES
Trusts by field of interest and type of beneficiary**

The green pages enable you to see which trusts are likely to fund projects doing a particular type of work to benefit a particular type of person. They list trusts according to:

a the type of activity or work they are likely to fund – their 'field of interest';

b who they want to benefit – their preferred 'beneficiaries'.

In order to compile the green pages, CAF's researchers asked the trusts appearing in the *DGMT* to provide information on their field of interest and their preferred beneficiaries. This information was collected via the survey questionnaire and the amended proofs of the entries in the main register returned to CAF by the trusts. Where a trust did not respond, its classification (and consequent listing in the green pages) has been determined on the basis of information held at the Charity Commission.

The green pages contain two separate listings.

CATEGORISATION OF FIELDS OF INTEREST AND TYPES OF BENEFICIARY

This lists all the headings used in the *DGMT* to categorise fields of interest and types of beneficiary. Before you can identify the trusts that are most likely to fund your project, you will have to decide which heading or headings your project falls under. If this is not immediately obvious, this listing should help you to match your project with one – or some – of the categories used in the *DGMT*.

'Fields of interest' – the types of activity or work that trusts may want to fund – are grouped under nine main headings, eg 'Social Care & Development', 'Education & Training'. These are the most general headings; they appear in white against a black strip. With the exception of 'General Charitable Purposes', the *DGMT* does not list trusts under these very general headings; they are included here so that you can see how the fields of interest have been grouped together.

Education & Training

These nine main areas are further divided. Thus 'Education & Training' is divided into 'Schools & colleges', 'Education & training', 'Costs of study' and 'Academic subjects, sciences & research'. These headings are in bold type preceded by a black square and with a dotted line above.

■ **Costs of study**

Each of these categories is subdivided still further. Thus 'Costs of study' is divided into 'Bursaries & fees', 'Fellowships' and 'Scholarships'. These are the most specific categories; they are shown in ordinary roman type.

Bursaries & fees

'Beneficiaries' are grouped under six main headings, eg 'Beneficiaries by age', 'Beneficiaries by disease & medical condition'; these are again in bold type preceded by a black square and with a dotted line above. The different age groups, specific diseases, etc, are listed under them in ordinary roman type.

The page numbers relate to the position of headings in the listing of trusts that follows.

This list of headings is the equivalent of the 'classification of charitable purposes' index (the white pages) in previous editions of the *DGMT*.

LIST OF TRUSTS BY FIELD OF INTEREST AND TYPE OF BENEFICIARY

The second part of the green pages lists the names of all the trusts appearing in the *DGMT* under the fields of interest and types of beneficiary which they have indicated they might be willing to support. Both the field of interest and type of beneficiary headings and the trusts that are listed beneath them appear in alphabetical order.

When ticking a field of interest or type of beneficiary, trusts were asked to indicate whether projects working in that area/for that type of beneficiary

a are a funding priority;

b will be considered.

The green pages list separately for each field of interest/beneficiary those trusts for which the field/beneficiary is a 'funding priority' and those that 'will consider' an application.

Headings that appear in ordinary roman type in the categorisation of headings on pages 54–58 are followed in this list of trusts by a cross-reference to the more general heading which they fall under in the earlier listing. These cross-references appear immediately after the heading before the 'Funding priority' trusts. If, for example, you look up 'Music', you will find a cross-reference '*see also* Arts & arts facilities'. This is to remind you that even if your project falls under a specific heading such as 'Music', it may still be worth applying to trusts that have expressed a general interest in funding the arts.

This list of trusts also includes headings which are not used in the *DGMT* classification (and are not therefore included on pages 54–58), with cross-references to the appropriate headings that are used. This may be helpful if your project does not seem to fit under any of the headings listed on pages 54–58. 'Blindness', for example, is not one of the specific disabilities listed there under 'Beneficiaries by disease & medical condition'. However, if you look up 'Blindness' here, you will find a cross-reference to 'Sight loss', which is a heading used in the *DGMT* and therefore included in this listing.

These cross-references have been determined on the basis of the descriptions which emerged most commonly from the survey questionnaire but which were not adopted into the main classification model.

The page references relate to the position of the trust's main entry in Volume Two.

This list of trusts serves the same purpose as the original green pages in past editions of the *DGMT*.

The directory of products and services

This is a service CAF has provided to advertisers wishing to address the fundraising community. Every company or organisation appearing in the listing has paid a fee to be included. CAF does not, and cannot, endorse any products and services advertised in *The Directory of Grant Making Trusts 1997–98* for which it is not directly responsible.

The main register of grant-making charitable trusts (Volume Two)

The main register of trusts, which appears in Volume Two of *The Directory of Grant Making Trusts 1997–98*, contains the core data about the individual trusts held on the CAF database. Trusts are listed in alphabetical order. A complete entry should contain information under the headings listed below; an explanation of the content of some of these is given in italics.

Trust name

Objects	*Generally, the legal charitable purposes of the trust required for registration at the Charity Commission.*
Funding priorities	*The main and/or specialist areas of interest of the trust in more detail.*
Type of grant	*The type of expenditure the trust will support, eg recurrent, capital, running costs, etc.*
Type of beneficiary	*The types of organisation, project or group of people most likely to succeed with an application.*
Restrictions	*The types of project/cause to which trustees will **not** make grants.*
Beneficial area	*The geographical areas where the trust prefers to direct its funding.*
Finances	*The most up-to-date details of the trust's income, assets and grants made for which details are available.*

Trustees

Submission of applications	*The trust's rules for the submission of funding requests (including the availability of guidelines) and practice in responding to applications.*
Correspondent	*The name and address of the person (or company) to whom correspondence relating to the activities of the trust should be directed.*
Charity Commission number*	
Established	*The year of the trust's foundation.*

*The abbreviation 'CC' is used in relation to trusts registered in England and Wales. 'SC' is used in relation to Scottish trusts, and 'IR' in relation to Irish trusts.

How to use the directory

This directory is designed to enable fundraisers to draw up their 'hit list' of trusts in six easy steps.

STEP 1

Define the project, programme or work for which you are seeking funding in as much detail as possible.

The following checklist has been devised to help you to assemble the information you will need about the project for which you require funding.

- What is the geographical location of the people who will benefit from any funding received?

  Do they live in the UK or abroad?

  In which of the UK countries do they live – England, Scotland, Wales or Northern Ireland?

  In which region of that country do they live?

  In which county or metropolitan borough do they live?

- What facilities or services will the funding provide? In particular, what is new or unusual about the project?

- What are the characteristics which best describe the people who will benefit from any funding received?

EXAMPLE

Funding is being sought for a scheme for carers in Newcastle which enables them to take a break from looking after a disabled relative or friend.

*The geographical location is: UK > England > the North East > **Tyne & Wear**.*

*The service to be provided is: **respite care**.*

*The key characteristic of the people to benefit is that they are: **carers**.*

STEP 2 | **Turn to the blue pages – which list trusts by beneficial area.**

First look up the area where your project is based in the list of geographical area headings on pages 2–3. Note down the page reference; this refers to the list of trusts by beneficial area.

Turn to the relevant pages and note down the names of the trusts that will consider funding projects in your area.

See pages vii–viii for an explanation of how this index is organised.

EXAMPLE | *First look up the area most local to your requirements (Tyne & Wear) in the list of geographical area headings. Then turn to the relevant page of the list of trusts by beneficial area and look up the names of the trusts listed under Tyne & Wear. You will probably want to look at trusts listed under the broader region heading (the North East) as well. Note down the names of all these trusts so that they can be compared with the lists produced through the green pages.*

It is also worth looking at trusts listed under 'England' or 'UK'. A trust listed under a more general heading may be just as ready to fund activity in a specific region as another which states that it has a specific interest in that region.

STEP 3 | **Turn to the green pages.**

Using the categorisation of fields of interest and types of beneficiary on pages 54–58, identify all the categories that match the project, programme or work for which you are seeking funding.

This categorisation is based on the Charity Commission classification model and so groups similar types of activity together. This should help you to identify the fields of interest and beneficiaries most relevant to your own project. It may also suggest links which you could make between your own project and other types of activity. This could enable a small list of potential funders to be expanded.

Note down the relevant page references; these relate to the position of the heading in the list of trusts by field of interest and type of beneficiary.

See page ix for an explanation of how this listing is organised.

With a project to provide respite care, you will probably look first under 'Health'. Under 'Health' you will find 'Health care' (in bold type preceded by a black square) and under 'Health care' you will find the heading 'Respite care, care for carers' (in ordinary roman type). Note down the page numbers beside 'Health care' and 'Respite care, care for carers'. (Remember that trusts are not listed under the most general headings – those in white against a black strip.) Trusts that have expressed a specific interest in funding respite care may represent your best prospects, but trusts with a more general interest in health care may be worth approaching – particularly if they like to fund projects in your area.

If you look under 'Beneficiaries', you will find 'Carers' under the general heading 'Beneficiaries by social circumstances'. Note down this page number too.

Another general heading that might be worth looking at is 'Social Care & Development'. Under the subheading 'Community services' you will find 'Care in the community'; again the page number is worth noting down.

STEP 4 | **Turn to the list of trusts by field of interest and type of beneficiary which starts on page 59.**

Using the page references obtained through step 3, look up the headings identified; you might want to start with the headings for field of interest and type of beneficiary that most closely match your type of work. Note down the names of the trusts appearing under these headings so that you can compare them with the names identified through the blue pages.

Look first at the trusts that appear under the heading 'Funding priority', as they have stated that the particular field of interest/beneficiary is a funding priority. Then look under the heading 'Will consider'. You are clearly more likely to be successful if you apply to a trust that regards your type of work as a funding priority.

Under the more specific headings (those that appear in ordinary roman type on pages 59–315), cross-references to the more general headings are included. This is to remind you that it may well be worth applying to trusts with a general interest in funding your area of work.

Common alternative descriptions of an activity or group of beneficiaries have also been included in this listing in order to enable you to make appropriate links between these and the headings used in the *DGMT* classification.

The page references given relate to the position of a trust's main entry in Volume Two of the *DGMT*.

See page x for more details of how this index is organised.

STEP 5 Collate the lists of trust names produced via steps 2 and 4.

This will produce a list of trusts whose funding objectives most closely match the characteristics of the project for which you are seeking funding. In order to achieve a ranking, you could assign a certain number of points to each element of the criteria you have devised and then 'score' each trust identified on the basis of the number of 'matches'.

If the list turns out to be too long or too short, it can easily be adjusted.

EXAMPLE *You find that you have ended up with a list of 150 trusts. Going back to step 4, you could limit yourself to trusts that regard your particular area of activity as a 'funding priority' and leave out those that 'will consider' applications. You could also discard the names of trusts that have a general interest in funding health care and confine your list to trusts that are interested in funding respite care or projects for carers. Conversely, if your list is too short, you could, for example, include trusts that come under 'Care in the community'.*

STEP 6 Turn to the main register of trusts in Volume Two.

Look up the entries for the trusts identified via step 5 and study their details carefully, paying particular attention to the funding priorities and the restrictions listed.

If you feel that there is a good match between the characteristics of the project for which you require support and the funding objectives of the trust identified, you could submit an application.

If there appears to be a contradiction you might like to consider contacting the trust concerned for further information. Where possible, the publishers have attempted to eliminate inconsistencies between the data provided by a trust for the indices and the information in the main entry; however, this has not always been possible.

☎ DGMT Helpline

In order to help people who have queries about how to use the *DGMT*, a helpline will be open from 9.30 to 10.30 every weekday morning. Tel: 01732 520110.

Users of the *DGMT* will understand that CAF *cannot* assist with individual searches, but the publishing team will be happy to assist anyone having difficulty understanding how the directory works.

The National Lottery

The National Lottery was set up in response to the National Lottery Act etc 1993.

OFLOT, the Office of the National Lottery, regulates the Lottery. Its Director General is responsible for awarding the operating licence to run the National Lottery, subject to any terms and conditions imposed by the Secretary of State for National Heritage. His/her remit is to ensure that the National Lottery is run with due propriety, to protect the interests of every participant and to ensure the maximum amount is raised for good causes. In 1994 OFLOT selected Camelot Group plc from eight contenders to run the National Lottery for the first seven years. At the time of writing the Labour Party has stated that it believes the National Lottery should be run by a non-profit organisation when the existing licence expires.

The first National Lottery draw took place on 14 November 1994. A second weekly draw was introduced early in 1997.

How is the money raised from sales of Lottery tickets divided up?

The Act also explains how the proceeds of the Lottery should be distributed. It says that five good causes should each receive a 20 per cent share of the 'profits' of the National Lottery (the 'profits' are 28 per cent of the money raised, as shown in the table below). The Secretary of State has the power to vary these proportions but each good cause must receive at least five per cent of the proceeds.

Tax Returned to the public in prizes	50%
Tax on ticket sales paid to government	12%
Profits to Camelot after operating cost	5%
Retailers' commission on ticket sales	5%
National Lottery Distribution Fund for the five good causes	28%
	100%

In the first 13 months £1.4 billion were available for distribution. It is anticipated that £8.96 billion will be available over the first seven years. The five good causes funded through the National Lottery are:

- Arts
- Charities
- Heritage
- Millennium
- Sports

There are 11 independent 'distributing bodies' making grants.

ARTS
- Arts Council of England
- Arts Council of Northern Ireland
- Arts Council of Wales
- Scottish Arts Council

CHARITIES
- National Lottery Charities Board

HERITAGE
- Heritage Lottery Fund

MILLENNIUM
- Millennium Commission

SPORTS
- Scottish Sports Council
- Sports Council for England
- Sports Council for Northern Ireland
- Sports Council for Wales

It is likely that on 31 December 2000 money from the Lottery will cease to be allocated to the celebration of the Millennium. It is possible, however, that funding will continue for an extra year if there is an overspend on the Millenium celebration. This 20 per cent proportion of the funds will subsequently be shared between the remaining four good causes.

Each distributing body provides more detailed information about the types of grant it makes and its grants process. This information is available free of charge direct from the distributing body.

The distributing bodies are all included in the main register of grant-making charitable trusts in Volume Two of the *DGMT* and they are indexed in this volume.

Trusts by beneficial area

The blue pages contain two separate listings.

Geographical area headings This lists all the geographical area headings used in the *DGMT*.

Trusts by beneficial area This lists the trusts appearing in the *DGMT* under the geographical areas for which they have expressed a funding preference.

Geographical area headings

United Kingdom

Full area *4*

■ England
Full area *18*

North East *19*
Cleveland *19*
Durham *20*
Hartlepool *20*
Middlesborough *20*
Northumberland *20*
Stockton-on-Tees *20*
Tyne & Wear *20*

North West *20*
Cheshire *21*
Cumbria *21*
Greater Manchester *22*
Isle of Man *22*
Knowsley *22*
Lancashire *22*
Liverpool *22*
Merseyside *22*
Sefton *23*
St Helens *23*
Wirral *23*

East Midlands *23*
Derbyshire *24*
Leicestershire *24*
Lincolnshire *24*
Northamptonshire *24*
Nottinghamshire *24*

West Midlands *25*
Hereford & Worcester *26*
Shropshire *26*
Staffordshire *26*
Warwickshire *26*
West Midlands *26*

Eastern *26*
Bedfordshire *27*
Cambridgeshire *27*
Essex (not London Boroughs) *27*
Hertfordshire (not London Boroughs) *27*
Norfolk *28*
Suffolk *28*

Yorks & Humberside *28*
East Riding of Yorkshire *29*
Kingston upon Hull *29*
North Lincolnshire *29*
North East Lincolnshire *29*
North Yorkshire *29*
South Yorkshire *29*
York *30*
West Yorkshire *30*

South East *30*
Berkshire *31*
Buckinghamshire *31*
East Sussex *31*
Hampshire *31*
Isle of Wight *31*
Kent (not London Boroughs) *32*
Oxfordshire *32*
Surrey (not London Boroughs) *32*
West Sussex *32*

South West & Channel Islands *32*
Bath & North East Somerset *33*
Bristol *33*
Channel Islands (Jersey & Guernsey) *34*
Cornwall *34*
Devon *34*
Dorset *34*
Gloucestershire *34*
Isles of Scilly *34*
North West Somerset *34*
Somerset *35*
South Gloucestershire *35*
Wiltshire *35*

London *35*

Page references refer to the list of trusts by beneficial area that begins on page 4

■ Northern Ireland

Full area *37*

Antrim *37*
Armagh *37*
Down *38*
Fermanagh *38*
Londonderry *38*
Tyrone *38*

■ Scotland

Full area *39*

North Scotland *39*
Grampian *40*
Highland *40*
Orkney *40*
Shetland *40*
Western Isles *40*

South Scotland *40*
Borders *41*
Central *41*
Dumfries & Galloway *41*
Fife *41*
Lothian *41*
Strathclyde *41*
Tayside *41*

■ Wales

Full area *42*

North Wales *43*
Gwynedd *43*
Clwyd *43*

South Wales *43*
Powys *44*
Dyfed *44*
Mid Glamorgan *44*
West Glamorgan *44*
South Glamorgan *44*
Gwent *44*

Overseas *45*

All trusts that support work overseas have been grouped together

Trusts by beneficial area

United Kingdom

Full area
AB Charitable Trust *3*
AFC Charitable Trust *3*
AGF Charitable Trust *3*
AHJ Charitable Trust, The *3*
AIIT (The Ancient India and Iran Trust) *3*
AM Charitable Trust *4*
AMEC Charitable Trust *4*
ATP Charitable Trust, The *4*
AW Charitable Trust *4*
Abbey National Charitable Trust *4*
Abbeydale Trust *5*
Abraham Charitable Trust, Keith & Freda *5*
Abrahams 2nd Charitable Foundation, The Henry and Grete *5*
Access 4 Trust *6*
Achiezer Association Limited *6*
Acorn Foundation, The *6*
Action Research *6*
Adint Charitable Trust, The *7*
Adler Foundation, The *7*
Aga Khan Foundation (UK) *7*
Agricola Trust, The *8*
Aid to the Church in Need (United Kingdom) *8*
Airflow Community Ltd, The *9*
Albright Charitable Trust, D G *9*
Alchemy Foundation, The *9*
Alcohol Education and Research Council *9*
Alecto Trust, The *10*
Aleh Charitable Foundation, The *10*
Alexander Charitable Trust, Mrs K L *11*
Alexandra Rose Day *11*
Alexis Trust, The *11*
Al-Fayed Charitable Foundation, The *11*
Alglen Ltd *11*
All Saints Educational Trust *12*
Allachy Trust, The *12*
Allen Charitable Trust, D C R *12*
Allen Charitable Trust, The H B *12*
Allen Charitable Trust, The Rita *12*
Allen Memorial Fund, Dorothy Gertrude *13*
Allen Trust, Mrs M H *13*
Alliance Family Foundation Limited *13*
Allied Domecq Trust *13*
Allied Dunbar Staff Charity Fund *13*
Allnatt Charitable Foundation, Angus *14*
Allsop Charitable Trust, Pat *14*
Almond Trust, The *14*

Ambika Paul Foundation *15*
Amelan Charitable Trust, The Harold *15*
Amis Charitable Trust, Richard *15*
Ammco Trust, The *15*
Amory's Charitable Trust, Sir John and Lady *16*
Ancaster Trust, The *16*
Andersen Consulting Foundation, The *16*
Anderson Trust, Andrew *16*
Andrew Charitable Trust, The Prince *16*
Andrew Convalescent Trust, The Frederick *17*
Anglo Hong Kong Trust, The *17*
Anglo-Arab Aid Ltd *17*
Anglo-Catholic Ordination Candidates Fund, The *18*
Anglo-German Foundation for the Study of Industrial Society *18*
Animal Defence Trust, The *18*
Anne's Charities, The Princess *18*
Anstey Charitable Settlement, J C W *18*
Appelbe Trust, Ambrose & Ann *19*
Aquarian Healing Trust *19*
Aquinas Trust *20*
Arbib Foundation *20*
Arbib Trust, The Annie *20*
Archer Trust, The *20*
Ardwick Trust, The *20*
Arihant Charitable Trust *21*
Arkleton Trust, The *21*
Armourers' & Brasiers' Gauntlet Trust, The *21*
Army Benevolent Fund, The *22*
Arno Bequest, Thomas *22*
Arnopa Trust, The *22*
Artemis Charitable Trust, The *22*
Arthritis and Rheumatism Council for Research in Great Britain and the Commonwealth, The *22*
Ashby Charitable Trust, The *23*
Ashcroft Charitable Trust, The *23*
Ashden Charitable Trust, The *24*
Ashdown Charitable Settlement, The Lord *24*
Ashley Foundation, The Laura *24*
Assheton-Smith Charitable Trust *25*
Asthma Allergy and Inflammation Research Trust *25*
Astor Foundation, The *26*
Astor's 1969 Charity, The Hon M L *26*
Astra Foundation, The *26*

Atwell's Charity (Skinner's Company), Lawrence 27
Avenal 27
Avenue Charitable Trust, The 27
AXA Equity & Law Charitable Trust 28
BBC Children in Need Appeal, The 29
BP Conservation Programme 29
BUPA Foundation, The 29
Bachad Fellowship – Friends of Bnei Akiva 30
Bagri Foundation 30
Bain Memorial Trust Fund, Dr James and Dr Bozena 30
Baker Charitable Trust, The 30
Baker Trust, The C Alma 31
Balfour Trust, The Nancy 31
Balint Charitable Trust, Andrew 31
Balint Charitable Trust, The George 31
Balint Charitable Trust, Paul 31
Ball Charitable Trust, The Bruce 31
Baltic Charitable Fund, The 32
Bancroft (No 2) Charitable Trust and Jenepher Gillett Trust, William P 32
Bancroft Trust, The 33
Banks Educational Trust, The 33
Barbour Paton Charitable Trust 33
Barclay Charitable Fund, The 33
Barclay Jewish Trust 34
Baring Foundation, The 34
Barleycorn Trust, The 34
Barnby's Foundation Appointed Fund, Lord 35
Barnby's Foundation, Lord 35
Barnsbury Charitable Trust 35
Baronets Trust, The 35
Barrie Charitable Trust, The Misses 36
Bartholomew Christian Trust 36
Bartlett Charitable Trust, Doris and Rendell 36
Bartlett Taylor Charitable Trust 36
Barton Trust, Eleanor 37
Batchworth Trust, The 37
Bateman Charitable Trust, Lady Margaret 37
Bates Charitable Trust, The 37
Beacon Trust 38
Bealey Foundation, The 38
Bear Charitable Trust Fund, The 38
Bear Mordechai Ltd 39
Beaufort Charitable Trust 39
Beaverbrook Foundation, The 39

Beckwith Charitable Settlement, The Heather 39
Beckwith Charitable Trust, The John 40
Beckwith Charitable Trust, The Peter 40
Beecham Charitable Settlement, The Patricia 40
Behrens Charitable Trust, E M 40
Bell Charity, The Sylvia 41
Bell Trust and Additional Fund, The Barron 41
Bellinger Donnay Trust, The 42
Belljoe Tzedoko Ltd 42
Belsize Charitable Trust No1 43
Benesco Charity Limited 43
Bengough Trust, The 43
Benham Charitable Settlement 43
Benlian Trust, The 44
Beresford Trust, The 44
Bergqvist Charitable Trust 44
Bernheim Charitable Trust, Andre 45
Berris Charitable Trust 45
Berthoud Charitable Trust, Patrick 45
Bestway Foundation, The 46
Betard Bequest 46
Bexleyheath Community Church 47
Bibby 1981 Trust, The Mason 47
Bier Charitable Settlement 47
Biggs Charitable Trust, The Ken 47
Biggs Charity, The Elizabeth Emily 48
Billingsgate Christian Mission Charitable Trust 48
Billmeir Charitable Trust, The 48
Bilton Charity, The Percy 48
Biological Trust, The 49
Bircham and Company Charitable Trust, The 49
Birmingham's Charity, Lord Mayor of 50
Bisgood Trust, The 50
Bisgood's Charitable Trust, Miss Jeanne 50
Black Charitable Trust, The Cyril W 51
Black Charitable Trust, Peter 51
Black Foundation, The Bertie 51
Blackford Charitable Trust, The 52
Blake Charitable Trust, The Morgan 53
Blakenham's Charity Trust, Lady 53
Blank Donations Ltd, The David 54

Blankstone Charitable Trust, The Solomon & Isobel 54
Blay Trust, The Robert 54
Blond Charitable Trust, Neville & Elaine 54
Bloom Charitable Trust, The Patsy 54
Bluston Charitable Settlement, The 55
Body Shop Foundation, The 55
Boltons Trust, The 55
Bonar Charitable Trust, Andrew 55
Bonham-Carter Charitable Trust, The Charlotte 55
Bornstein Charitable Trust, M & S 56
Borthwick Memorial Trust, The Oliver 56
Botteley Charitable Settlement, H E & E L 56
Bourne Charitable Trust, The M 57
Bourne Foundation, The Anthony 57
Bowland Charitable Trust, The 57
Bowring (Charities Fund) Ltd, C T 57
Bradford's 1981 Charitable Trust, The Seventh Earl of 58
Bradman Charitable Foundation Limited 58
Bramall Charitable Trust, The Tony 58
Bramble Charitable Trust 58
Brand Charitable Trust 58
Brand Trust, The 59
Brandt Charitable Trust, Tim 59
Branford Charitable Trust, The Jan 59
Breast Cancer Research Trust, The 59
Brecher & Co Charitable Trust, The 59
Bridge Will Trust, The Elsie Talbot 60
Briess Family Charitable Trust 60
Brinton Foundation, Lady Mary 61
British Council for Prevention of Blindness 61
British Diabetic Association, The 61
British Dietetic Association General and Education Trust Fund, The 61
British Friends of Chinuch Atzmai Trust, The 62
British Heart Foundation 62
British Humane Association 62
British Institute of Archaeology at Ankara 62
British Schools and Universities Foundation (Inc) 62

British Sugar Foundation 63
Britland Charitable Trust, The 63
Brixton Estate Charitable Trust, The 63
Broackes 1993 Charitable Trust, Sir Nigel 63
Broadfield Trust 64
Broadley Charitable Trust, The 64
Brocklebank Charitable Trust, Charles 64
Brook Charitable Settlement, R E 64
Brook Charitable Trust 64
Brookhouse's Will Trust, Mr John Charles 65
Brown Charitable Settlement, Mrs E E 65
Brownless Charitable Trust, R S 66
Brown's Charitable Settlement, Bill 66
Brunner's Charitable Trust, T B H 66
Brunner's Sons' Charitable Trust, Sir Felix 66
Brushmill Ltd 66
Buckingham Trust 67
Buckle Family Charitable Trust, The 67
Bulldog Trust, The 68
Bullough Tompson Settlement, The 68
Bunney Reckitt Trust 68
Bunzl Charitable Foundation, G G 69
Burden Trust, The 69
Burden's Charitable Foundation 69
Burgess Trust, The Michael 69
Burns Charity, The Dorothy 70
Burrough Charitable Trust, The Alan & Rosemary 70
Burry Charitable Trust, The 70
Burton Charitable Trust, The Harriet 71
Burton Charitable Trust, R M 71
Butler Charitable Trust, The A S 71
Butler's Trust, Lord 71
Butlin Charity Trust, Bill 72
CAF (Charities Aid Foundation) 73
CB Charitable Trust, The 73
CfBT Education Services 74
CHK Charities Limited 74
CMB Charities Limited 74
Cadbury Charity, C James 76
Cadbury Schweppes Foundation, The 76
Cadbury Trust, The Barrow 76
Cadbury Trust, A Account, The George 77
Cadbury Trust, B Account, The George 77

Cadell-Samworth Foundation, The 77
Cadman Charitable Trust, The Beatrice A V 77
Cairns Charitable Trust, The 78
Caledonian Charitable Foundation 78
Callingham Foundation, Roland 78
Calypso Browning Trust 78
Camelot Foundation, The 78
Cancer Relief Macmillan Fund 79
Candap Trust, The 80
Canine Supporters Charity, The 80
Canning Trust, The 80
Caplin Foundation, The Fay and Robert 80
Careers Services Trust 81
Carmichael-Montgomery Charitable Trust, The 81
Carnegie United Kingdom Trust, The 82
Carpenter Charitable Trust 82
Carpenters' Company Charitable Trust, The 83
Carroll-Marx Charitable Foundation, The 83
Carron Charitable Trust, The 83
Cassel Educational Trust (Overseas Research Grants), Sir Ernest 84
Cassel Educational Trust (Grants for Educational Purposes), Sir Ernest 84
Cassel Educational Trust (Mountbatten Memorial Grants to Commonwealth Students), The Sir Ernest 84
Castang Charitable Trust, H and M 85
Cathedral Amenities Fund, The 85
Catholic Charitable Trust 86
Catholic Foreign Missions 86
Catto Charitable Settlement, The Thomas Sivewright 86
Cazalet Charitable Trust, The Raymond 87
Celebrities Guild of Great Britain, The 87
Cen Foundation, The Hyman 87
Chamberlain Charity, June 87
Champion Foundation, The Pamela 87
Chandaria Foundation, The 88
Chandris Foundation, The 88
Chapman Charitable Trust 88
Charipot Trust 88
Charitable Fund Administered by The Russia Company 89
Charities Fund 89
Charity for Change 89
Charity Projects 90

Chartered Institute of Management Accountants' General Charitable Trust, The 90
Chase Charity, The 91
Chesters Settlement for Methodist Church Purposes, Mr H G 91
Chevras Ezras Nitzrochim Trust, The 91
Chickadee Trust, The 91
Chiddick Charitable Trust 92
Child Growth Foundation 92
Children's Research Fund, The 92
Childs Charitable Trust, The 92
Childtime Trust, The 92
Childwick Trust, The 93
Chippindale Foundation, Sam 93
Chiron Trust, The 93
Christabella Charitable Trust 93
Christendom Trust, The 94
Christian Renewal Trust, The 94
Christian Trust, The Andre 94
Christian Vision 94
Ciba Fellowship Trust, The 95
Cinderford Charitable Trust, The 96
City of London School Charitable Trust, The 96
Civil Service Benevolent Fund, The 97
Clapman Charitable Trust 97
Clark Charitable Trust 98
Clark Charitable Trust, J Anthony 98
Clark Charitable Trust, Elizabeth 98
Clark Charitable Trust, Hilda & Alice 98
Clark Charitable Trust, Roger and Sarah Bancroft 98
Clark 1965 Charitable Trust, Stephen 98
Clarke's Charitable Trust, The Late Miss Doris Eveleyn 99
Classic FM Charitable Trust, The 99
Clemence Charitable Settlement, The John & Heather 99
Cleopatra Trust 99
Clifford Charity Oxford, The 100
Clifton Charitable Trust 100
Clore Foundation, The 101
Clore's 1967 Charitable Trust, Miss V L 101
Closehelm Ltd 101
Clothworkers' Foundation, The 101
Clover Trust 102
Clutterbuck Charitable Trust, Robert 102
Clydpride Ltd 102

Coates Charitable Settlement, The *102*

Coates Charitable Trust 1969, Lance *103*

Cobb Charity *103*

Cockenzie Charitable Trust, The *103*

Cohen and William Leech Foundation, Sebag *103*

Cohen Charitable Foundation, The Lucy and Henry *103*

Cohen Charitable Trust, The *104*

Cohen Charitable Trust, The Andrew *104*

Cohen Charitable Trust, The Vivienne and Samuel *104*

Cohen Charity Trust, Lucy *104*

Cohen Foundation, The Alfred S *104*

Cohen Foundation, The John S *104*

Cohen's Charitable Settlement, The Hon L H L *105*

Collier Charitable Trust, The *105*

Collier Charitable Trust, The *105*

Colline Trust Fund, Lucy Ann *105*

Collinson Charitable Settlement, R F *106*

Collis Charity, Robert Hickson *106*

Colman Charitable Fund Ltd, The E Alec *106*

Colman Charitable Trust, O J *106*

Colston Educational Foundation *107*

Colt Foundation, The *107*

Comino Foundation *107*

Company of Chartered Surveyors Charitable Trust Fund, The *108*

Company of Chartered Surveyors Charitable Trust Fund 1992, The *109*

Condon Family Trust *109*

Conrad Charitable Trust, Neville and Carole *109*

Conservation Foundation, The *110*

Cook Trust, The Ernest *110*

Cooks Charity, The *111*

Cooper Charitable Trust *111*

Cooper Dean Charitable Foundation, Alice Ellen *111*

Cooper Gay Charitable Trust *111*

Coote Animal Charity Fund, The Marjorie *111*

Cope Charitable Trust, Alfred *112*

Copperfield Trust, David *112*

Corage Charitable Trust, The *112*

Coren Charitable Foundation, The Muriel and Gershon *113*

Corfield Charitable Settlement, The Holbeche *113*

Corman Charitable Trust, Molly *113*

Corman Charitable Trust, Ruth and Charles *113*

Cornerstone Charitable Trust *114*

Cornforth 1983 Charity Trust, Edwin *114*

Cotton Trust, The *114*

Courtauld Charitable Trust, The Peter *115*

Courtauld Trust for the Advancement of Music, The *116*

Cowan Foundation, The John *116*

Cowley Charitable Foundation, The *116*

Cozens-Hardy Trust, The Lord *117*

Cranfield Charitable Trust (1971) *117*

Crawford Children's Charity, Michael *117*

Crawley Warren Charitable Trust *117*

Crescent Trust, The *117*

Cripps Charitable Trust, The Violet & Milo *118*

Croft Foundation, Annie *118*

Crossfield Charitable Fund *118*

Crowson Charitable Settlement, The Derek *119*

Cruse Trust, The *119*

Curry Charitable Trust, Dennis *119*

Curry's Charitable Trust, D A *119*

Curtis Charitable Trust *119*

Curzon Charitable Trust, The Wallace *120*

Cussins Foundation, The Manny *120*

Cutforth Charitable Trust, The David *120*

Cymerman Trust Limited, Itzchok Meyer *120*

Cystic Fibrosis Trust *121*

DCW Trust *121*

DLM Charitable Trust, The *121*

Dahl Foundation, The Roald *122*

Daily Telegraph Charitable Trust *122*

Daiwa Anglo-Japanese Foundation, The *122*

Dalmia Foundation, The *123*

Dandeen Charitable Trust *123*

Daniell Charitable Trust, The Sir Peter *123*

Darell Charitable Trust *124*

Dashe Trust, The *124*

Datnow Limited *124*

Davies Charities Limited, J *125*

Davis Charitable Foundation, Lily & Henry *125*

Davis Charitable Settlement, Michael *125*

Davy Foundation, The J *126*

De Avenley Foundation, The *126*

De Clermont Charitable Company Limited, The *126*

de Freitas Charitable Trust, The Helen and Geoffrey *126*

De Groot Charitable Trust, Zena and Ralph *127*

De Haan Charitable Trust *127*

De La Rue Charitable Trust *127*

De Rothschild Charitable Trust, Edmund *127*

De Rothschild Charitable Trust, The Leopold *127*

De Rothschild 1980 Charitable Trust, The Leopold *127*

De Vere Hunt Charitable Trust, The *128*

De Yong Charitable Trust, The Emma *128*

De Yong's Charitable Trust 1984, Nicholas *128*

Delafield Charitable Trust, The William *129*

Delfont Foundation, The *129*

Delius Trust, The *129*

Dellal Foundation, The *129*

Denby Charitable Foundation, The *130*

Denton Charitable Trust, The *130*

Derby's Charitable Trust, The Right Hon The Earl of *130*

Desmond Charitable Trust, The Richard *131*

Deutsch Charitable Trust, The H & M *131*

Devonport Charitable Trust *131*

Devonshire's Charitable Trust, The Duke of *131*

Diamond Charitable Trust, The Alan & Sheila *132*

Diamond Industry Educational Charity, The *132*

Diana Memorial Trust, The *132*

Dibb Lupton Broomhead Charitable Trust *132*

Dibdin Foundation, Thomas Peter *132*

Dibs Charitable Trust, The *133*

Digby Charitable Trust, The Marcella and Claude *133*

Dimbleby Cancer Fund, The Richard *134*

Direct Response *134*

Dixon Charitable Trust, C H *134*

Djanogly Foundation, The *135*

Dodd Charitable Trust, The Dudley *135*

Dolphin Charitable Trust, The *136*
Donatewell Ltd *136*
Dorus Trust *136*
Double 'O' Charity Ltd *136*
Douglas Charitable Trust, R M *137*
Douglas Valley Evangelical Trust *137*
Dove-Bowerman Trust *137*
D'Oyly Carte Charitable Trust, The *137*
Drapers' Charitable Fund *137*
Drayton Trust, The *138*
Drexler Foundation, The George *138*
Drummond Trust, The *138*
du Boulay Charitable Trust, The Anthony *138*
Duffield Foundation, The Vivien *138*
Dulverton Trust, The *139*
Duncan Literary Fund, Ronald *139*
Dunecht Charity Trust *140*
Dunhill Medical Trust, The *140*
Dunn Foundation, The Mrs C T M *140*
Duveen Trust, The *141*
Dzienisiewicz Trust, Jan *141*
EAGA Charitable Trust *141*
ED Charitable Trust, The *141*
E D B Memorial Charitable Trust *141*
Earmark Trust, The *142*
East Charitable Trust, B D *142*
Eastwood Memorial Trust, Sybil *143*
Eaton Fund for Artists, Nurses and Gentlewomen *144*
Ebb and Flow Charitable Trust *144*
Ebenezer Trust *144*
Ecclesiastical Music Trust, The *144*
Edgar Foundation, The Gilbert and Eileen *145*
Edgar Trust, The Gilbert *145*
Edinburgh Trust, No 2 Account *145*
Education Services *145*
Elanore Ltd *146*
Elephant Trust, The *146*
Elias Charitable Settlement, E V *146*
Elijah Trust *147*
Eling Trust *147*
Ellador Ltd *147*
Ellerman Foundation, The John *148*
Ellinson Foundation Limited *148*
Ellis 1985 Charitable Trust, Edith M *148*
Elshore Limited *149*
Elton John Aids Foundation, The *149*

Elton's Charitable Settlement, Mr & Mrs *149*
Ely Charitable Trust, The Vernon N *149*
Emanuel Charitable Settlement, Ralph and Muriel *150*
Emerton-Christie Charity *150*
Emily Appeal Fund, The *150*
Emmaus Christian Foundation *150*
Emmott Foundation Limited, The *151*
Englass Charitable Trust, The *151*
Englefield Charitable Trust, The *151*
English Bowling Association Charitable Trust *151*
Epigoni Trust *152*
Equity Charity Fund, The *152*
Eranda Foundation, The *152*
Ericson Trust *152*
Erycinus Charitable Trust *153*
Esher House Charitable Trust, The *153*
Esperanza Charitable Trust, The *153*
Essame Charitable Trust, The Guthrie *153*
Essefian Charitable Trust, The Mihran *153*
Eton Action *154*
Euroclydon Trust *154*
European Cultural Foundation (UK Committee) *154*
Evans Memorial Trust, The Alan *155*
Evershed Trust, The Norman *155*
Eves Charitable Trust, The Douglas Heath *155*
Evetts & Robert Luff Animal Welfare Trust, Beryl *156*
Eyre Charitable Trust, G F *156*
FBT Charitable Fund, The *157*
FR 1978 Charitable Trust, The *157*
Fairbairn Charitable Trust, The Esmee *157*
Fairbairn Trust, The Lady Mary *157*
Fairway Trust, The *158*
Falkner Charitable Trust, The Daniel *158*
Family Foundations Trust, The *158*
Famos Foundation Trust *158*
Farmers' Company Charitable Fund, The *159*
Farmer's Trust, Samuel William *159*
Farne Trust, The *159*
Farthing Trust, The *159*
Fattorini Charitable Trust, James J *160*
Fawkes Charitable Trust, The Guy *160*
Felicitas Trust, The *161*

Fencewood Trust, The *161*
Fenton Trust, The A M *161*
Ferraris Charitable Trust, The *162*
Fidelity UK Foundation, The *162*
Finzi Charitable Trust, Gerald *162*
Firdale Christian Trust, The *162*
Firtree Trust, The *163*
Fisher Foundation, The Sir John *163*
Fitton Trust, The *163*
Fitzwilliam Charitable Trust, The Earl *164*
Flanagan Leukaemia Fund, Bud *164*
Fleisher Deceased, The Will of Sydney *164*
Fleming Charitable Trust, The Ian *164*
Fleurus Trust, The *165*
Floyd Charitable Trust, John Anthony *165*
Follett Trust, The *166*
Forbes Trust, The *166*
Forbesville Limited *166*
Ford Foundation, Oliver *166*
Fordeve Limited *167*
Foreman 1980 Charitable Trust, The Russell and Mary *167*
Foreman Foundation, The Carl & Eve *167*
Foresters' Charity Stewards UK Trust, The *167*
Foster Settlement, Alfred *168*
Foundation for Management Education *168*
Fourth Settlement Charity *168*
Fox Memorial Trust *169*
Foyle Trust, Charles Henry *169*
Frampton Charitable Trust, The David *169*
Frankel Memorial Charitable Trust, The Isaac & Freda *169*
Franklin Bequest, The Rosalind *169*
Franklin Deceased's New Second Charity, Sydney E *170*
Franklin Trust, Jill *170*
Fraser Trust, The *170*
Frazer Charities Trust, The *171*
Freedman Charitable Trust, The Louis *171*
Friday Charitable Trust, The *172*
Friends of Biala Ltd *172*
Friends of Friendless Churches, The *173*
Friends of the Animals *173*
Friends of Wiznitz Limited *173*
Frigenti Charitable Trust, The Nina *174*
Frognal Trust *174*
Frome Christian Fellowship *174*

Frost Charitable Trust, T F C *174*

Frost Foundation, The Patrick *174*

Fry Charitable Trust, Maurice *174*

GABO Trust for Sculpture Conservation *175*

GMC Trust, The *175*

GNC Trust *175*

GRP Charitable Trust *176*

GW Trust, The *176*

Galinski Charitable Trust *177*

Gallagher Memorial Fund, Angela *177*

Garnett Charitable Trust, The *178*

Garrod Memorial Charitable Trust, The John and Daisy *179*

Gatsby Charitable Foundation, The *179*

Gee Charitable Trust, The Cecil *179*

Gelston Charitable Trust, The *179*

Gem Charitable Trust *179*

George's Fund for Sailors, King *180*

Gibbs Charitable Trusts, The *181*

Gibson Charitable Trust, The G C *182*

Gibson Charitable Trust, The Simon *182*

Gibson's Charitable Trust, Mrs E D *182*

Gibson's Charity Trust, The Hon Mr & Mrs Clive *182*

Gibson's Charity Trust, The Hon H M T *182*

Gibson's Charity Trust, The Hon P N *183*

Gibson's Charity Trust, The Hon W K *183*

Gilchrist Educational Trust *183*

Gillett Charitable Trust, J A *183*

Gill's Charitable Trust, Mrs M M *184*

Girdlers' Company Charitable Trust, The *184*

Glasser Charitable Trust, The B & P *184*

Glebe Charitable Trust *185*

Glencore Foundation for Education and Welfare *185*

Gluck Charitable Trust, Avraham Yitzchak *185*

Gluckstein Charitable Settlement, The Penelope *185*

Glyn Charitable Trust, James *186*

Goldberg Charitable Trust, The Lewis *186*

Goldberg Charity Trust, The Isaac *187*

Golden Bottle Trust *187*

Golden Charitable Trust *187*

Golders Green Foundation *187*

Golding Fund, The Sir John *187*

Good Neighbours Trust, The *188*

Goodacre Benevolent Fund *188*

Goodisons Charitable Settlement, Sir Nicholas & Lady *188*

Goodman Charitable Foundation, The Everard and Mina *188*

Goodman Trust, The S & F *189*

Gosling Foundation Limited, The *189*

Gradel Foundation, The *189*

Gradel Trust, The Leon and Bertha *189*

Grahame Charitable Foundation, The *190*

Grand Metropolitan Charitable Trust, The *191*

Gray Trust, The Gordon *192*

Great Britain Sasakawa Foundation, The *193*

Green Foundation, The Charles *193*

Green Foundation, Constance *194*

Green, J H F *194*

Green Memorial Fund, The Barry *194*

Greenaway Foundation, The Alan *194*

Greene & Co Charity Limited *195*

Greenwood Charitable Trust, The G B *195*

Greenwood Charitable Trust, Naomi & Jeffrey *195*

Greenwood Charity Trust, J R *195*

Gregson Trust, The John *195*

Greibach Charitable Trust, The *196*

Gresham Charitable Trust, The *196*

Greystoke Trust, The *196*

Grimsdale Charitable Trust *196*

Grocers' Charity *197*

Gross Charities Limited, M & R *197*

Grosshill Charitable Trust *197*

Grove Charitable Trust, The *197*

Grove Charitable Trust, Mary Isobel *197*

Groves Charitable Trust, The *197*

Growth Building Trust, The *198*

Grumett Foundation, The David and Marie *198*

Grut Charitable Trust, The *198*

Guardian Royal Exchange Charitable Trust, The *198*

Gulbenkian Foundation (Lisbon) United Kingdom Branch, Calouste *199*

Gunnell Charitable Trust, The *199*

Gunter Charitable Trust, The *199*

Gur Trust, The *199*

Gurney Foundation, The Samuel *200*

Gurunanak *200*

HACT (The Housing Association's Charitable Trust) *201*

HB Charitable Trust *201*

Haberdashers' Eleemosynary Charity *201*

Hacking & Sons Ltd Charitable Trust, C G *201*

Haddon Charitable Trust, William *202*

Haemophilia Society, The *202*

Haendler, The Nathan and Adolphe *202*

Halecat Charitable Trust, The *203*

Haley Charitable Trust, The Ethel *203*

Hamamelis Trust, The *204*

Hame Trust, The *205*

Hamilton Educational Trust, Eleanor *205*

Hamilton Trust, The *205*

Hamlyn Foundation, The Helen *205*

Hamlyn Foundation, The Paul *205*

Hammerson Foundation, The Sue *206*

Hammerson's Charitable Trust, Sue *206*

Handicapped Children's Aid Committee *207*

Hanley Trust (1987), The *207*

Hannay Memorial Charity, Kathleen *208*

Hanover Charitable Trust, The *208*

Harbinson Charitable Trust, Roderick *208*

Harbour Charitable Trust, The *208*

Harbour Foundation Ltd, The *208*

Hardy Trust, The Patsy *209*

Harford Charitable Trust *209*

Hargreaves Trust, The Kenneth *210*

Harmony Trust, The *210*

Harris Charitable Trust, The John *210*

Harris Charitable Trust, The Philip & Pauline *210*

Harrisons & Crosfield Charitable Fund *211*

Harvey Charitable Trust, Gordon *211*

Hattori Foundation, The *212*

Hawthorne Charitable Trust, The *212*

Hay Charitable Trust, Dora *213*

Haydan Charitable Trust, The *213*

Hayward Foundation, The *213*

Hayward Trust, The Charles *213*

Headley Trust, The *214*

Heath Charitable Trust *214*

Heath Charitable Trust, The Edward *214*

Heathcoat Trust *214*

Heber Percy Charitable Trust, The Mrs C S *215*

Heinz Company Limited Charitable Trust, The H J *215*

Held Settlement, The Gisela *215*

Help the Homeless *215*

Henhurst Charitable Trust, The *216*

Hennell Charitable Trust, Esther *216*

Heritage Lottery Fund *216*

Heseltine Charitable Trust, Michael *217*

Hewett/Driver Education Trust, The *217*

Hiam Charitable Trust, Sir Frederick *218*

Hicks Foundation, The Sir John *218*

Higgs and Hill plc Charitable Trust *218*

Higgs Charitable Trust, The *218*

Highcroft Charitable Trust *218*

Hilden Charitable Fund, The *219*

Hiley Trust, Joseph and Mary *219*

Hill Charitable Foundation, Herbert Charles *219*

Hill Trust, The Charles Littlewood *220*

Hillards Charitable Trust, Gay & Peter Hartley's *220*

Hillcote Trust, The *220*

Hinrichsen Foundation, The *221*

Hinton Charitable Trust, Mrs F E *221*

Hird Charitable Trust, The Thora *221*

Historical Research Trust, The *222*

Hobbs Trust Limited, The Betty *222*

Hobson Charitable Trust, The *222*

Hobson Charity Limited, The *222*

Hockerill Educational Foundation *223*

Hodge Charitable Trust, The Sir Julian *223*

Hodgson Charitable Trust, Kenneth *223*

Holford Trust Fund *224*

Holloway Charitable Trust, The *224*

Holly Hill Charitable Trust *224*

Holmes Charitable Trust, The Dorothy *224*

Holmes Foundation, Godfrey *224*

Holmleigh Trust, The *225*

Holt Charitable Trust, The Douglas *225*

Holt Charitable Trust, P H *225*

Holt Trust, The Edward *225*

Home Housing Trust *225*

Homelands Charitable Trust *225*

Homfray Charitable Trust, Mary *226*

Hood's Charitable Trust, Sir Harold *226*

Hoover Foundation, The *226*

Hopkins Charitable Foundation, The Sir Anthony *226*

Hopkinson Educational Trust, Robert Addy *227*

Horn Trust, The Cuthbert *227*

Hornby Charitable Trust, Miss D *227*

Hornby Charitable Trust, The Edward *227*

Hornby's Charitable Settlement, Mrs E G *228*

Houblon-Norman Fund *229*

Howarth Charity Trust, Clifford *229*

Hubert Charitable Trust, A *229*

Hughes Charitable Trust, The Geoffery C *230*

Hugonin Family Trust, The *230*

Hunt's Trust, William *231*

Hurst Will Trust, Arthur *231*

Hussey Trust, The *232*

Hutchinson Charitable Trust, E B *232*

Hyams Trust, The P Y N and B *232*

IB Charitable Trust, The *233*

IBM United Kingdom Trust *233*

IPE Charitable Trust, The *233*

Ibbetson Settlement, Harry *233*

Idlewild Trust, The *234*

Inchcape Charitable Trust Fund *234*

Inlight *235*

Inman Charity, The *235*

Innominate Trust, The *235*

International Arab Women's Council Charities Fund *236*

International Bar Association Educational Trust *236*

Inverforth Charitable Trust, The *236*

Ireland Fund of Great Britain, The *237*

Iris Trust, The *237*

JCA Charitable Foundation *238*

JCSCJ Charitable Trust, The *238*

JHL Trust, The *239*

JJ Charitable Trust, The *239*

JL Charity Trust, The *239*

JMK Charitable Trust *239*

JMR Charitable Trust, The *240*

Jacobs Charitable Trust, The J P *240*

Jacobs Charity, The Dorothy *240*

Jacobsen Foundation Limited *240*

Jacobson Charitable Trust, The Anne & Malcolm *241*

Jacobson Charitable Trust (No 2), The Ruth & Lionel *241*

James Charitable Trust, John *241*

James Trust, The *242*

Janelaw Trust, The *242*

Janes Charitable Trust, Lois & Robert *242*

Janes Memorial Trust, Peter *243*

Jansen Charitable Trust, Peter *243*

Jason Charitable Trust, The Jane *243*

Jeffreys Road Fund, Rees *243*

Jenour Foundation, The *244*

Jephcott Charitable Trust, The *244*

Jerusalem Trust *244*

Jesus Lane Trust, The *245*

Jewish Aged Needy Pension Society, The *245*

Jewish Childs' Day *245*

Joels Charitable Trust, The Harold *245*

Joels Charitable Trust, The Jacob & Lena *246*

Joels Charitable Trust, The Jonathan *246*

Joels Charitable Trust, The Nicholas *246*

Joels Charitable Trust, The Norman *246*

Johnson Charitable Settlement, Bridget Catherine *246*

Johnson Foundation, The Beth *247*

Juno Charity Trust, The *249*

Jurgens Charitable Trust, The Anton *249*

Jusaca Charitable Trust, The *249*

Kahn Charitable Trust, Bernard *250*

Kalms Foundation, The Stanley *250*

Karloff Charitable Foundation, The Boris *250*

Karten Charitable Trust, The Ian *250*

Kaufman Charitable Trust, The C S *251*

Kaye Charitable Trust, The Henry *251*

Keane Charitable Settlement, The *251*

Kejriwal Foundation *251*

Keller Charitable Trust, Samuel *251*

Kendall Leukaemia Fund, Kay *252*

Kendrew Charitable Settlement, The Florence Amelia *252*

Kennedy Charitable Trust, The Mathilda & Terence *252*

Kennel Club Charitable Trust, The *252*

Kenyon Charitable Trust, The Nancy *253*

Kermaville Ltd *253*

Keymer Trust, The Ronald and Mary *253*

Keyser Charitable Trust, C M *254*

Kiln Charitable Trust, Robert *254*

Kilverstone Wildlife Charitable Trust, The *254*

King Charitable Settlement, Philip *254*

Kings Medical Research Trust, The *255*

Kingsgrove Charitable Trust, The *255*

Kingsmill Charitable Trust *256*

Kingston Old People's Home Fund for Ileostomists, The *256*

Kinnison Charitable Trust, R O *256*

Kirkham Foundation, The Graham *257*

Kleinwort Benson Charitable Trust *257*

Kleinwort Charitable Trust, The Ernest *257*

Knott Family Trust, The James *258*

Kobler Trust, The *258*

Kornberg's 1969 Charitable Settlement, Mrs Bessie *258*

Kreitman Foundation *258*

Kroch Foundation, The Heinz & Anna *259*

Kweller Charitable Trust, The Harry *259*

Kyte Charitable Trust, The *259*

LGT Asset Management Charitable Trust *260*

LSA Charitable Trust *260*

Lacy Charity Trust, The Late Sir Pierce *260*

Laing Charitable Trust, The David *260*

Laing Foundation, The Christopher *260*

Laing Foundation, The Kirby *261*

Laing Foundation, The Martin *261*

Laing Foundation, The Maurice *261*

Laing Trust, Beatrice *261*

Laing Trust, The J W *261*

Laing's Charitable Trust *262*

Lambert Charitable Trust, The *262*

Landale Charitable Trust, The *263*

Landy Charitable Trust, Harry and Gertrude *263*

Lane Foundation, The Allen *263*

Langdale Trust *264*

Langley Charitable Trust, The *264*

Lankelly Foundation, The *264*

Lansdowne Charitable Trust, The *265*

Lanvern Foundation *265*

Laspen Trust *265*

Lass Charities Limited, Rachel and Jack *265*

Lauchentilly Charitable Foundation 1988, The *266*

Laufer Charitable Trust *266*

Lauffer Charitable Foundation, The R & D *266*

Laurence's Trust, Kathleen *266*

Lawley Foundation, The Edgar E *267*

Lawson-Beckman Charitable Trust *267*

Layton Charity Trust, The Julian *267*

Leach Fourteenth Trust, The *267*

League of the Helping Hand, The *268*

Leathersellers' Company Charitable Fund, The *268*

Lebus Charitable Trust, The *268*

Leche Trust, The *268*

Lee Charitable Trust, The Arnold *269*

Lee Foundation, The Edgar *269*

Leeside Charitable Trust *269*

Lehmann Charitable Trust, The *270*

Leigh Charitable Trust, Gerald *270*

Leigh Charitable Trust, Kennedy *270*

Leigh Foundation, The Morris *270*

Leigh Trust, The *270*

Leigh-Bramwell Trust 'E', P *270*

Leonard Trust, The Mark *271*

Leukaemia Research Fund *271*

Levein Family Charitable Trust, The *271*

Levens Charitable Trust, The Leslie *272*

Leverhulme Trade Charities Trust, The *272*

Leverhulme Trust, The *272*

Levy Charitable Foundation, Joseph *272*

Levy Charitable Trust, The Lawrence *273*

Lewis Charitable Trust, Henry *273*

Lewis Family Charitable Trust, The *273*

Lewis Family Charitable Trust *273*

Lewis Foundation, The Sir Edward *273*

Lewis Foundation, The John Spedan *274*

Lilley Memorial Trust, The Thomas *275*

Linbury Trust, The *275*

Lindale Educational Foundation, The *275*

Linder Foundation, The Enid *275*

Lindeth Charitable Trust, The *276*

Lingwood Charitable Trust, The *276*

Lipton Charitable Trust, The Ruth & Stuart *276*

Lister Charitable Trust, The *277*

Littler Foundation, The Emile *277*

Livesley 1992 Charitable Trust, Mrs C M *277*

Lloyd Charity, The S and D *278*

Lloyd-Everett Trust, The *278*

Lloyd's Charities Trust *278*

Lloyd's Patriotic Fund *279*

Locker Foundation, The *280*

London Law Trust *280*

Lord's Taverners, The *281*

Lottery Arts Fund for England, Scotland, Wales and Northern Ireland *281*

Lottery Sports Funds for England, Northern Ireland, Scotland and Wales *283*

Lovell Charitable Trust, P and M *284*

Lowndes Charitable Trust, The Vanessa *285*

Lucas Charitable Trust Limited, The Joseph *286*

Lunn-Rockliffe Charitable Trust, Paul *286*

Lunzer Charitable Trust, The Ruth & Jack *287*

Lyndhurst Settlement *287*

Lyndhurst Trust, The *287*

Lynn Foundation, The *288*

Lynwood Charitable Trust, The 288

Lyons Charitable Trust, The 288

Lyons Charitable Trust, Sir Jack 288

Lyster 1980 Charitable Trust, The Lionel 288

M D & S Charitable Trust, The 289

MDM Memorial Trust 289

MKR Charitable Trust 289

MVM Charitable Trust 289

MYA Charitable Trust 289

MacAndrew Trust, The E M 289

Macaulay Family Charitable Trust 290

Maccabi Foundation, The 290

McCamman Trust, The Eileen 290

McCarthy Foundation, The John 290

McCorquodale Charitable Trust, The 290

Macdonald-Buchanan Charitable Trust 291

McDougall Trust, The 291

Macfarlane Walker Trust 291

McKechnie Foundation, A N 292

McKenzie Trust, The Robert 292

MacKintosh Charitable Trust, Viscount 292

Mackintosh Foundation, The 292

McLaren Foundation 292

McLaren Memorial Trust, The Martin 293

McMorran Charitable Foundation, The Helen Isabella 293

McPhail Charitable Settlement, D D 293

MacPherson Charitable Settlement, G P S 293

MacRobert Trusts, The 294

Mahavir Trust 294

Major Charitable Trust, The 294

Man of the People Fund 295

Manifold Charitable Trust, The 295

Maranatha Christian Trust 296

Marchig Animal Welfare Trust 297

Margaret Foundation, The 297

Margulies Charitable Trust, The Stella and Alexander 297

Maritime Trust, The 297

Marks' Charitable Settlement, J M 298

Marks' Charitable Trust, Harry 298

Marks Charitable Trust, Michael 298

Marks Foundation, The Hilda and Samuel 298

Markus Charitable Foundation, The Erich 298

Marmor Charitable Trust, The Julie 299

Marsh Christian Trust, The 299

Marshall Charitable Trust, The 299

Marshall Charitable Trust, The Bob and Barbara 299

Marshall Charitable Trust, The Charlotte 300

Martin Charitable Trust, Mervyn 300

Marylebone Charitable Foundation 301

Mason Charitable Trust, The George 301

Matchan Fund Limited, The Leonard 301

Material World Charitable Foundation Limited, The 301

Matthews Wrightson Charity Trust 301

Mattock Charitable Trust, The W T 302

Maude 1988 Charitable Trust, M F T 302

Mauray Charitable Trust, The Violet 302

Max Charitable Trust, The Wendy 302

Maxwell Foundation, The Pamela and Jack 302

Maxwell Law Scholarship Trust, The Alexander 303

Mayfair Charities Limited 303

Maypride Ltd 303

Mays-Smith Charitable Trust, The Ivona 303

Meath, Charity of Mary Jane, Countess of 304

Medical Aid Trust 304

Mediterranean Archaeological Trust 304

Medlock Charitable Trust, The 304

Mellows Charitable Settlement, The Anthony and Elizabeth 305

Mental Health Foundation, The 305

Mercers' Charitable Foundation 306

Mercers' Company Educational Trust Fund, The 306

Merchant Taylors' Consolidated Charities for the Infirm 306

Mercury Phoenix Trust 307

Merton and George Woofindin Convalescent Trust, The Zachary 307

Messel & Co Charitable Trust, L 308

Micholls Deceased Charitable Trust Fund, Col Wilfred Horatio 309

Micklem Charitable Trust, The Gerald 309

Middlesex County Rugby Football Union Memorial Fund 309

Migraine Trust, The 310

Mijoda Charitable Trust, The 310

Millennium Commission 311

Millett Charitable Trust, The Alan and Janet 312

Millichope Foundation, The 312

Milton Mount Foundation 313

Milward Charity, The Edgar 313

Minge's Gift 314

Misener Charitable Trust, Laurence 314

Mishcon Charitable Trust, Victor 314

Miskin Charitable Trust, Mary 314

Missionary Friends Trust 314

Mitchell Trust 315

Modiano Charitable Trust 315

Montagu Family Charitable Trust, The 316

Montefiore Trust, The David 316

Monument Trust, The 316

Moody Charitable Trust, The 316

Moore Charitable Trust, The Horace 316

Moores Family Charitable Foundation, The Nigel 317

Moores Foundation, The Peter 318

Morel Charitable Trust, The 318

Morris Charitable Trust, Bernard 319

Morris Charitable Trust, The Douglas 320

Morris Charitable Trust, The Willie & Mabel 320

Morrison Charitable Foundation, The Peter 320

Morrison Charitable Trust, G M 320

Moshal Charitable Trust 321

Moulton Charitable Trust, The 321

Mount 'A' Charitable Trust 321

Mount 'B' Charitable Trust 321

Mount Everest Foundation, The 321

Mountbatten Memorial Trust, The 322

Mountbatten Trust, The Edwina 322

Moxon Charitable Trust, Gweneth 322

Muirhead Charitable Trust, The F H *322*
Multiple Sclerosis Society of Great Britain & Northern Ireland *322*
Multithon Trust, The *323*
Munro Charitable Trust, The *323*
Music for World Development *323*
Music Libraries Trust, The *323*
Music Therapy Charity, The *324*
NCL Charitable Trust *325*
NR Charitable Trust, The *325*
Naaman Trust, The *325*
Nagel Charitable Trust, The Willie *325*
Nakou Foundation, The Eleni *326*
Nash Charitable Trust, The Janet *326*
Natasha Trust, The *326*
Nathan Charitable Trust *326*
Nathan Charitable Trust, Peter *326*
National Animal Sanctuary's Support League *327*
National Art-Collections Fund *327*
National Kidney Research Fund Limited, The *328*
National Lottery Charities Board *328*
National Poetry Foundation, The *329*
National Waterways Restoration & Development Fund of the Inland Waterways Association, The *330*
Neave Trust, The Airey *330*
Nelson Memorial Trust, The Barbara *331*
Nemoral Ltd *331*
Nestle Rowntree York Community Fund, Employees of *331*
New Chasers Charitable Trust, The *332*
New Court Charitable Trust *332*
New Durlston Trust, The *332*
Newby Trust Ltd *332*
Newcastle's 1986 Charitable Trust, Duke of *333*
Newhope Trust, The *333*
Newitt Fund, Richard *333*
Newman's Charity, John *334*
Newstead Charity, The *334*
Newton Charitable Trust *334*
Nichol-Young Foundation *334*
Nidditch Foundation, The Laurie *335*
Nightingale Trust, The *335*
Noah Trust, The *335*
Norman Trust, The *337*

Northern Dairies Educational Trust *339*
Norwood Settlement *340*
Noswad Charity, The *341*
Noswal Charitable Trust, The *341*
Nuffield Auxiliary Fund, The Viscount *341*
Nuffield Foundation *342*
Nuffield Provincial Hospitals Trust *342*
Oak Trust, The *343*
Oakley Charitable Trust, The *343*
Oakmoor Trust, The *343*
Oasis Church Chadwell Heath Charitable Trust *343*
Ofenheim Charitable Trust, The *343*
Ogilvie Charities (Deed No 1) *344*
Ogle Trust, The *344*
Old Possums Practical Trust, The *344*
Oliver Trust, Kate Wilson *345*
Open Door Women's Trust *346*
Oppenheim Charitable Settlement, K A *346*
Oppenheimer Charitable Trust *346*
Oppenheimer Foundation, The Phillip *346*
Ormonde Foundation *347*
Ormsby Charitable Trust, The *347*
Orr Mackintosh Foundation Limited *347*
Orrin Charitable Trust *347*
Osborne Charitable Trust, The *347*
Ouseley Trust, The *347*
Owen Family Trust, The *348*
Owen Trust, Margaret *348*
Oxfam (United Kingdom and Ireland) *348*
Oxford Trust, The *349*
PAR Charitable Trust *349*
PB Charitable Trust *349*
PDC Trust, The *349*
PES Associates' Charitable Trust *350*
PF Charitable Trust *350*
PJD Charitable Trust *350*
PPP Healthcare Medical Trust Limited *350*
Packlington, The Gift of Thomas *350*
Paget Trust, The *351*
Paisner Charitable Trust, The *351*
Palmer Trust, The Gerald *352*
Panton Trust, The *352*
Parham Park Trust (1984), The *352*
Park Hill Trust, The *353*
Parkinson Agricultural Trust, The Frank *353*

Pascoe Charitable Trust, Alan *354*
Paterson Charitable Foundation, The Constance *354*
Paterson Charitable Trust, Arthur James *354*
Patrick Charitable Trust, The *354*
Paul Foundation, The *355*
Payne Charitable Trust, The *355*
Peacock Charitable Foundation, The Michael *356*
Peacock Charitable Trust, The *356*
Peake Charitable Trust, The Susanna *357*
Pearson Charity Trust, Hon Charles *357*
Pearson Foundation, The Frank *357*
Pearson plc Charitable Trust, The *357*
Pearson's 1987 Charity Trust, Rosanna *357*
Pedmore Trust *357*
Peel Medical Research Trust, The *358*
Peirce Memorial Trust, The Joe *358*
Pelech Charitable Trust, The *358*
Pelly Charitable Settlement, The Joanne *358*
Penny in the Pound Fund Charitable Trust *359*
Peppiatt Charitable Trust, The Brian *359*
Perry Charitable Trust, Miss Frances Lucille *359*
Pershore Nashdom & Elmore Trust Ltd, The *360*
Personal Assurance Charitable Trust *360*
Persula Foundation, The *360*
Peskin Charitable Trust, The Hazel and Leslie *360*
Pettit Charitable Trust *360*
Pewterers' Charity Trust *361*
Pfeffer Trust (1962), Anshel *361*
Phelps Charitable Trust, Brigadier and Mrs D V *361*
Phillips Charitable Foundation, Reginald M *361*
Phillips Family Charitable Trust, The *361*
Pickford Charitable Foundation, The David *362*
Pilgrim Trust, The *362*
Pilkington Charitable Trust, Cecil *363*
Pilkington Charity, The C F *363*
Pilkington Trust, The Austin and Hope *363*
Pilkington's Charitable Trust, Dr L H A *363*

Pilozzo Charitable Trust *364*
Plaut Charitable Trust Limited, G S *364*
Podde Trust *365*
Polden-Puckham Charitable Foundation, The *365*
Pollitzer Charitable Settlement, George and Esme *366*
Pollitzer's Charitable Settlement, J S F *366*
Porcupine Trust, The *366*
Porter Charitable Trust, John *366*
Porter Foundation *366*
Poulden Charitable Trust, The Frank and Dorothy *366*
Prendergast Charitable Trust, The Simone *368*
Prevezer Charitable Settlement, S B *368*
Primrose Trust, The *369*
Prince Foundation, The *369*
Prince's Trust (now includes King George's Jubilee Trust (1935) and the Queen's Silver Jubilee Trust (1977)), The *369*
Priory Foundation, The *369*
Prophit, Charity of James Maxwell Grant *370*
Proven Family Trust, The *370*
Pryor Charitable Trust, The John *370*
Psoriasis Association Research Fund (1968), The *371*
Puebla Charitable Trust Limited, The *371*
Pye's No 1 Charitable Settlement, Mr and Mrs J A *372*
Pyke Charity Trust *372*
Queen Anne Street Educational Trust Limited *373*
Quothquan Charitable Trust, The Second *373*
RED Trust, The *374*
REMEDI (Rehabilitation and Medical Research Trust) *374*
RVW Trust *374*
Rachel Charitable Trust *375*
Radcliffe's Trust, Dr *375*
Radley Charitable Trust *375*
Rainbow Charitable Trust *376*
Rainford Trust, The *376*
Randall Charitable Trust, The Joseph and Lena *376*
Rangoonwala Foundation, ZVM *376*
Rank Benevolent Trust, Joseph *377*
Rank Foundation, The *377*
Rank Xerox Trust, The *378*
Rapaport Charitable Trust, Fanny *378*
Rathbone Charitable Trust, The Eleanor *378*
Rathbone Charity, The Elizabeth *378*

Rav Chesed Trust, The *379*
Raven Charitable Trust *379*
Ravensdale Trust, The *379*
Rayne Foundation, The *379*
Rayne Trust, The *380*
Rayner Charitable Trust, The John *380*
Reader's Digest Trust, The *380*
Reckitt Charity, Sir James *381*
Red Arrows Trust, The *381*
Redfern Charitable Foundation, C A *381*
Reekie Trust, R A & V B *381*
Reeves Charitable Trust, The Christopher H R *382*
Reuter Foundation, The *382*
Rhododendron Trust, The *383*
Rich Charities, S & J *383*
Richard Charitable Trust, The Cliff *383*
Richards Charity, The Violet M *384*
Rickard Animals' Charity, Miss Maria Susan *385*
Rickard Cats' Charity, Miss Maria Susan *385*
Rickman Trust, Muriel Edith *385*
Riddell Charitable Trust, R G *385*
Riggs Charity, The *386*
Riley-Smith Charitable Trust, The F A *386*
Rind Foundation, The *386*
Ripple Effect Foundation, The *387*
Ritblat Charitable Trust No 1, The John *387*
Rivendell Trust, The *387*
River Trust, The *387*
Robertson Charitable Trust, The J W *388*
Robinson Charitable Trust, P R & T L *388*
Robyn Charitable Trust *389*
Rockwell UK Charitable Trust *389*
Rodewald's Charitable Settlement, Mr C A *389*
Roedean School Mission Fund *390*
Roland Grange Trust *390*
Rolfe Charitable Trust, The *390*
Roper Charitable Trust, The D G M *391*
Rosen Foundation, Cecil *392*
Rosenbaum Golden Trust, Teresa *392*
Rothschild Foundation, The *393*
Rothschild Group Charitable Trust, The J *393*
Roughley Charitable Trust, The *393*
Rowan Charitable Trust, The *393*
Rowntree Charitable Trust, The Joseph *394*

Rowntree Foundation, Joseph *394*
Royal Commission for the Exhibition of 1851 *395*
Royal Gardeners' Orphan Fund, The *395*
Royal Theatrical Fund, The *396*
Royal's Memorial Fund, Princess *396*
Royle Memorial Trust, Kirstin *397*
Rozel Trust, The *397*
Rubens Foundation, J B *397*
Rubens Highgate Trust, The Frank and Enid *397*
Rudabede *397*
Rudolf Charitable Trust, Carrie *398*
Rufford Foundation *398*
Rugby Football Union Charitable Fund, The *398*
Russell Charitable Trust, Frank *398*
Russell Charitable Trust, The Willy *398*
Russon Charitable Trust, Frank *398*
SEDOS Jubilee Charity Fund *399*
SEM Charitable Trust *399*
SMB Trust, The *400*
Sacher Charitable Trust, The Audrey *400*
Sacher Charitable Trust, The Michael *400*
Sadagora Trust, The Ruzin *400*
Saddlers Company Charitable Fund, The *401*
Sainsbury Animal Welfare Trust, Jean *401*
Sainsbury Charitable Fund, The Alan & Babette *402*
Sainsbury Charitable Fund Ltd, The *402*
St Christopher's Trust, The *402*
St George's Trust, The *403*
St John's Wood Trust, The *403*
St Jude's Trust *403*
St Luke's College Foundation *404*
Saint Sarkis Charity Trust *404*
Saintbury Trust, The *405*
Saints and Sinners Trust Limited, The *405*
Salamander Charitable Trust, The *405*
Salmon Charitable Settlement, Harold Joseph *405*
Salmon Charity, The Guy *405*
Salters Charities *405*
Sammermar Trust, The *406*
Samuel Charitable Trust, The Basil *406*
Samuel Charitable Trust, Coral *406*
Samuel Charitable Trust, M J *406*
Samuel Fund, The Camillla *406*

Sanders Charitable Settlement, G S *407*
Sanity *407*
Saranda Charitable Trust, The *407*
Sassoon Charitable Trust, The Late Aaron D *408*
Save & Prosper Educational Trust *408*
Save & Prosper Foundation *409*
Scarr-Hall Memorial Trust, The *409*
Schiff Charitable Trust, The Annie *409*
Schmidt-Bodner Charitable Trust, The *410*
Schroder Charity Trust *410*
Scopus Jewish Educational Trust *411*
Scott Bader Commonwealth Ltd, The *411*
Scott of Yews Trust, Sir Samuel *412*
Seahorse Charitable Trust, The *413*
Sears Foundation *413*
Second Ferndale Trust *414*
Securicor Charitable Trust, The *414*
Seedfield Trust, The *414*
Segal Charitable Trust *414*
Selig Charitable Trust, The *415*
Senna Foundation, The Ayrton *415*
Setterfield Trust, The *415*
Settlement Dated 31st March 1966 (Ref PT 865) *415*
Sewell Charitable Trust, The *416*
Shack Trust, The Cyril *416*
Shah Trust, The Dr N K *416*
Sharon Trust, The *416*
Shaw Foundation, The Linley *416*
Sheepdrove Trust, The *417*
Shepherd Conservation Foundation, The David *418*
Sherman Charitable Trust, The Archie *419*
Shimpling Trust Limited, The *419*
Shine Charitable Foundation, Barnett *419*
Shine No 1 Charitable Trust, The Barnett and Sylvia *419*
Shipwrights' Company Educational Trust, The *420*
Shuttlewood Clarke Foundation, The *421*
Shuttleworth Memorial Trust, Barbara A *421*
Sidbury Trust, The Second *421*
Sieff Charitable Trust, The David and Jennifer *421*
Sieff Charitable Trust, The Lily & Marcus *421*

Silman Charitable Trust, The Julius *421*
Simon Population Trust, The *422*
Simpson Foundation, The *422*
Simpson Settlement, Miss D B *422*
Sinclair Charitable Trust, The Huntly & Margery *423*
Singer Foundation *423*
Skinner Charitable Trust, Edward *424*
Skinners' Company Lady Neville Charity *424*
Slater Foundation Ltd, The *424*
Slaughter Charitable Trust, The Ernest William *425*
Slavin Charitable Foundation, The Josephine & Barry *425*
Sloane Street Trust, The *425*
Smallpeice Trust, The *425*
Smiley Charitable Trust, The Andrew *425*
Smiley's Second Charity Trust, Mrs *425*
Smith Charitable Settlement, The N *426*
Smith Charitable Trust, The *426*
Smith Charitable Trust, The Harold *426*
Smith (Estates Charities), Henry *426*
Smith Foundation, The Leslie *427*
Smith General Charitable Trust, The Stanley *427*
Sobell Foundation, The *428*
Society of Friends of the Torah, The *429*
Soddy Trust, The Frederick *429*
Solev Co Limited *429*
Solomon Family Charitable Trust, The *429*
Solomons Charitable Trust, David *430*
Somerfield Curtis Will Trust, The Dorothy *430*
Songdale Limited *430*
South Square Trust *430*
Southall Charitable Trust, Kenneth & Phyllis *431*
Southall Trust, W F *432*
Southdown Trust *432*
Spalding Trust *433*
Spencer Hart Charitable Trust, The *433*
Spencer Trust, The Jessie *433*
Spooner Charitable Trust, W W *434*
Sport Aid 88 Trust *434*
Sportsman's Aid Charity Ltd, The *434*
Stanhope-Palmer Charity *435*
Stanley Foundation Limited *435*
Stanley Residuary Trust, Bishop *435*

Stansfield Charitable Trust *435*
Staples Trust *435*
Starkie Bence Charitable Trust *436*
Steel Charitable Trust, The *436*
Stephenson Charitable Trust Fund *436*
Sternberg Charitable Foundation, The Sir Sigmund *436*
Stevens Foundation, The June *437*
Stewards' Charitable Trust, The *437*
Stewardship Trust Ripon, The *437*
Stewart Charitable Trust, George *437*
Stewart Charitable Trust, Mary Stephanie *437*
Stewart Trust, Sir Halley *437*
Still Waters Charitable Trust *438*
Stoate Charitable Trust, The Leonard Laity *438*
Stone Foundation, The *438*
Stonehouse Trust Ltd, Eric *438*
Storey Family Charitable Trust, The Samuel *439*
Stow Allen Trust, The *439*
Street Charitable Foundation, W O *440*
Streeter Charitable Settlement, David James *440*
Strict And Particular Baptist Trust Corporation, The *440*
Stroke Association, The *441*
Strudwick Charitable Trust, The Roy *441*
Sudborough Foundation, The *441*
Sugar Foundation, The Alan *441*
Summer's and I May's Charitable Settlement, The Late Misses (A N) *442*
Sumner's Trust Section 'A', Sir John *443*
Sumray Charitable Trust, The *443*
Sunley Charitable Foundation, The Bernard *443*
Susman Charitable Trust, The Ann *443*
Sussman Charitable Trust, Adrienne & Leslie *443*
Swan Mountain Trust *444*
Swan Trust *444*
Swann-Morton Foundation, The *444*
Sweett Charitable Trust, The Barbara *445*
Swindon Charitable Trust, The Walter *445*
Swinstead Charitable Trust, The *445*
Swire 1989 Charitable Trust, John *445*

Sykes Trust, The 445
Symons Charitable Trust, The Stella 446
Szeben Peto Foundation, The 446
TG No 1 Charitable Trust 447
TUUT Charitable Trust, The 448
Tait Charity, The Richard 448
Talbot House Trust, The 448
Talteg Ltd 448
Tangent Charitable Trust 448
Tankel Charitable Trust, Gerald 449
Tanner Charitable Settlement, The Joan 449
Tavener Charitable Trust, Mrs K M 449
Taverne Trust, The 449
Taylor Charitable Trust, The 449
Taylor Charitable Trust, A R 449
Taylor Charitable Trust, The B R 450
Tear Fund 450
Teman Trust, The 450
Tenovus – The Cancer Charity 451
Tesco Charity Trust 452
Tesler Foundation, The 452
Thames Wharf Charity, The 452
Thatcher Charitable Trust, The Margaret 452
Third Sector Trust, The 452
Tho Memorial Foundation, Loke Wan 452
Thompson Charitable Trust, The 453
Thompson Family Charitable Trust, The 453
Thomson Corporation Charitable Trust, The 453
Thomson Foundation, The Sue 454
Thorn Charitable Trust, The Sir Jules 454
Thornton Charitable Settlement, The Ruth 454
Thornton Foundation, The 455
Thornton Fund, The 455
Thornton-Smith Trust, The 455
Thorpe Charity Trust, The 455
3i Charitable Trust, The 455
Thriplow Charitable Trust 456
Tillett Trust, The 456
Tindle Family Charity, The 457
Tisbury Telegraph Trust, The 457
Toler Foundation, The 457
Tolkien Trust, The 458
Tollemache (Buckminster) Charitable Trust 458
Tomchei Torah Charitable Trust 458
Tompkins Foundation, The 458
Torchbearer Trust 458

Towry Law Charitable Trust, The 459
Toy Trust, The 459
Toyota (GB) Charitable Trust, The 459
Trans-Antarctic Association, The 460
Trenance Charitable Trust 460
Triodos Foundation 460
Troughton's Charity Trust, Mrs S H 461
Truemark Trust, The 461
Trust for the Homeless 462
Trust Fund for the Training of Handicapped Children in Arts and Crafts 462
Tryst Settlement, The 462
Tucker Charitable Settlement, The Roy 462
Tudor Rose Ltd 463
Tudor Trust, The 463
Tufton Charitable Trust, The 463
Tunstall Charitable Trust 463
Turkish Women's Philanthropic Association of England 463
Turner Charitable Trust, The Joseph and Hannah 464
Turner Charitable Trust, The R D 464
Tutton Charitable Trust, Miss S M 465
29th May 1961 Charity, The 465
Tyler's Charitable Trust, The Late Miss Eileen Margaret 465
Tyndale Memorial Trust Ltd 465
Tyndale Trust 466
Ullmann Trust, The 467
Ulverscroft Foundation, The 468
United Society for Christian Literature 468
United Society for the Propagation of the Gospel 468
Unitek Foundation 469
Upjohn Charitable Trust, The 469
Uxbridge Charitable Trust 469
Valentine Charitable Trust, The 470
Van Berchem Charitable Trust, The Alec 470
van Geest Foundation, The John and Lucille 470
Van Heemstra's Charitable Trust, Baroness 470
Van Leer Foundation UK Trust, Bernard 470
Van Neste Foundation, The 471
Van Norden's Charitable Foundation, Mrs Maud 471
Vandervell Foundation 471
Vardy Foundation, The 471

Variety Club Children's Charity Limited, The 471
Vendquot Ltd 472
Veronique Charitable Trust 472
Vincent Wildlife Trust, The 473
Vineyard Christian Fellowship of South West 473
Vinson Charity Trust, The 1969 473
Vision Charity 474
Vivdale Ltd 474
Vodafone Group Charitable Trust, The 474
Vogel Charitable Trust, The Nathan 474
Wade Foundation 475
Waghorn Charitable Trust, The Albert 475
Wainwright Charity, The Scurrah 475
Wakeham Trust, The 476
Wales Charities, The Prince of 477
Wales' Charities Trust, The Princess of 477
Walker 597 Trust, The 477
Wall Trust, Thomas 478
Wallis Charitable Trust, The Francis 479
War on Want 479
Warbeck Fund Limited 480
Warburg's Voluntary Settlement, Sir Siegmund 480
Warwick Trust, The 480
Waterhouse Charitable Trust, Mrs 480
Waters 1989 Charity Trust, The Roger 481
Watkinson Charity Trust, May 481
Watson Foundation, The Bertie 482
Weavers' Company Benevolent Fund, The 482
Webb Charitable Trust, The Denis George 483
Weinberg Foundation, The 483
Weinstein Foundation, The 484
Weinstock Fund, The 484
Weintrop Charity, The Alfred and Beatrice 484
Weir Foundation, The James 484
Welfare Charity Establishment 485
Wellcome Trust, The 485
Welton Foundation, The 485
Wesleyan Charitable Trust, The 485
West & Others, Charity of John 486
West London Synagogue Charitable Fund 486

Western Foils Charitable Trust *487*

Weston Bampfylde Trust, The *488*

Weston Foundation, Garfield *488*

Westward Trust, The *488*

Whesby Ltd *488*

Whetherly's Charitable Trust, The Hon Mrs R G A *489*

Whitaker Charitable Trust *489*

Whitbread 1988 Charitable Trust, The *489*

Whitbread Charitable Trust, Samuel *489*

Whitbread Charitable Trust, The Simon *489*

White Rose Children's Aid International Charity *489*

Whitecourt Charitable Trust, The *490*

Whitehall Charitable Foundation Limited *490*

Whitehead Charitable Trust, J E *490*

Whitehead's Charitable Trust, Sydney Dean *490*

Whitley Animal Protection Trust *491*

Whitley Trust, Sheila *491*

Whittington Charitable Trust, The *491*

Wicksteed Village Trust, The *491*

Wiggins Charity Trust, Cyril *491*

Wightwick Charitable Trust, The Gladys *492*

Wilde Charitable Trust, The Felicity *492*

Wilde Sapte Charitable Trust, The *492*

Will Charitable Trust, The *492*

Willan Charitable Trust, The *492*

Willcox Trust, The Ronald *492*

Williamson Trust *493*

Wills 1961 Charitable Trust, Mr Frederick *493*

Wills 1961 Charitable Trust, Major Michael Thomas *494*

Wills 1965 Charitable Trust, The H D H *494*

Wills Charitable Trust, Dame Violet *494*

Wilson Trust for Animal Welfare, The Kit *495*

Wimpey Charitable Trust, The George *495*

Wincott Foundation, The *496*

Wine Charitable Trust, The J L *496*

Winegarten Charitable Trust, Benjamin *496*

Wingate Foundation, The Harold Hyam *496*

Wingfield's Charitable Trust, Mrs *496*

Winstone Foundation, Hyman *497*

Wise Charitable Trust, The James *497*

Wiseman Memorial Fund Limited, The Max *497*

Wix Charitable Trust, Michael and Anna *497*

Wohl Charitable Foundation, The Maurice *498*

Wohl Charitable Trust, The Maurice *498*

Wolfe Family's Charitable Trust, The *498*

Wolff Charity Trust *498*

Wolfson Charitable Trust, The Aviezer *499*

Wolfson Charitable Trust, The Charles *499*

Wolfson Family Charitable Trust, The *499*

Wolfson Foundation, The *499*

Wood Charitable Foundation, The Louise *501*

Wood Charity, The Phyllis E *501*

Woodroffe Benton Foundation, The *502*

Woods Charitable Foundation, Geoffrey *502*

Woodward Charitable Trust, The *502*

Woolf Charitable Trust, The *502*

Woolmen's Company Charitable Trust, The *503*

Wootton Grange Charitable Trust, The *503*

Worms Charitable Trust, The Freda and Della *504*

Worshipful Company of Cutlers, The *504*

Worshipful Company of Engineers' Charitable Trust Fund, The *504*

Worshipful Company of Feltmakers of London Charitable Foundation, The *505*

Worshipful Company of Innholders General Charity Fund *505*

Worshipful Company of Shipwrights Charitable Fund, The *506*

Worshipful Company of Turners, The *506*

Worshipful Company of Weavers Textile Education Fund, The *506*

Wychdale Limited *507*

Wyre Animal Welfare *507*

Yablon Family Charity Company Limited, The *508*

Yapp Education and Research Trust, The *508*

Yapp Welfare Trust, The *508*

Yardy Charitable Trust, The Dennis Alan *509*

Youell Foundation Ltd, The *510*

Young Charitable Settlement, The John *510*

Young Explorers' Trust *511*

Zaiger Trust, The Elizabeth and Prince *512*

Zochonis Charitable Trust, The *512*

England

Full area

Allied Dunbar Staff Charity Fund *13*

Almshouse Association, The *14*

Army Benevolent Fund, The *22*

Arts Council of England, The *23*

Assheton-Smith Charitable Trust *25*

Astor Foundation, The *26*

Austin of Longbridge Will Trust, The Rt Hon Herbert, Baron *27*

Avon Trust, The *28*

Bacta Charitable Trust, The *30*

Beale Charitable Trust, David *38*

Bengough Trust, The *43*

Betton's Charity (Educational), Mr Thomas *46*

Blott Charitable Settlement, Robert Orpwood *55*

Brampton Trust, The *58*

Britland Charitable Trust, The *63*

Brookhouse's Will Trust, Mr John Charles *65*

Burton 1960 Charitable Settlement, Audrey & Stanley *70*

CLA Charitable Trust *74*

Catholic Education Service for England and Wales *86*

Church Urban Fund *95*

Cobb Charity *103*

Collier Charitable Trust, The *105*

Company of Chartered Surveyors Charitable Trust Fund, The *108*

Countryside Trust, The *115*

Coxen Trust Fund, Sir William *116*

David Trust, The Lesley *124*

Debtors' Relief Fund Charity *128*

Denby Charitable Foundation, The *130*

Doughty Charity Trust, The *136*

du Boulay Charitable Trust, The Anthony *138*

Edgar Foundation, The Gilbert and Eileen *145*

Esperanza Charitable Trust, The *153*

Fabry Trust, W F *157*

Fane Research Trust, The Edmund *159*

Fattorini Charitable Trust, James J *160*

Fleming Charitable Trust, The Ian *164*

Fletcher Charitable Trust, The Joyce *164*

Fortune Trust, The *167*

Frazer Charities Trust, The *171*

Frazer Trust, Joseph Strong *171*

General Nursing Council for England and Wales Trust, The *180*

Gibbins Trust, The *181*

Glyn Charitable Trust, The *186*

Graham Charitable Trust, Reginald *190*

Grand Charity (of Freemasons under the United Grand Lodge of England), The *190*

HACT (The Housing Association's Charitable Trust) *201*

Hartnett Charitable Trust, The *211*

Hind Trust, Lady *220*

Historic Churches Preservation Trust, The *221*

Holt Charitable Trust, P H *225*

Homfray Trust, The *226*

Hopkins Charitable Foundation, The Sir Anthony *226*

Howard Charitable Trust, John & Ruth *229*

Incorporated Church Building Society, The *234*

Joseph Charitable Trust, J E *248*

King Charitable Trust, The Lorna *254*

Latham Trust, The *266*

Leach Fourteenth Trust, The *267*

Lee Foundation, The Edgar *269*

Lewis Partnership, John *274*

Licensed Trade Charities Trust, The *274*

Linmardon Trust *276*

(Lloyds) TSB Foundation for England and Wales *279*

London Law Trust *280*

Loseley & Guildway Charitable Trust, The *281*

Lynall Foundation, The D G *287*

Mackintosh Foundation, The *292*

Marshall's Charity *300*

Milburn Charitable Trust, Frederick *310*

Milward Charity, The Edgar *313*

Moss Charitable Trust, Philip *321*

Music Sales Charitable Trust, The *324*

National Art-Collections Fund *327*

National Catholic Fund *327*

National Committee of The Women's World Day of Prayer for England, Wales

and Northern Ireland, The *327*

National Power Charitable Trust, The *330*

Natwest Staff Samaritan Fund *330*

Noel Buxton Trust, The *335*

Oasis Church Chadwell Heath Charitable Trust *343*

Patients' Aid Association Hospital and Medical Charities Trust *354*

Paul Charitable Trust, Margaret Jeanne *355*

Paul Charitable Trust, Pamela Milton *355*

Persula Foundation, The *360*

Pickford Charitable Foundation, The David *362*

Pitman Charitable Trust, The John *364*

Plaisterers' Company Charitable Trust, The *364*

Portrack Charitable Trust, The *366*

Pyke Charity Trust *372*

Rank Foundation, The *377*

Reckitt Charitable Trust, The Albert *381*

Rest-Harrow Trust, The *382*

Ridgmount Foundation, The *386*

Roberts Charitable Trust, F G *388*

Rookes Charitable Trust, C A *390*

Royal Botanical & Horticultural Society of Manchester and the Northern Counties, The *395*

Royal Society of St George Charitable Trust, The *396*

Sargeant's Charitable Trust, Mrs M E *407*

Scholes Charitable Trust, The R H *410*

SCOPE *410*

Scott Bader Commonwealth Ltd, The *411*

Scouloudi Foundation, The *413*

Shaw Foundation, The Linley *416*

Smallpeice Trust, The *425*

Snipe Charitable Trust *428*

Southdown Trust *432*

Stoate Charitable Trust, The Leonard Laity *438*

TSB Foundation for Northern Ireland *447*

Tanner Charitable Settlement, The Joan *449*

Tisbury Telegraph Trust, The *457*

Trades Union Congress Educational Trust *460*

Wales Charities, The Prince of *477*

Waley-Cohen Charitable Trust, Robert & Felicity *477*

Waterhouse Charitable Trust, Mrs *480*

Webber Trust Fund, Ethel *483*

Welby Trust, The Barbara *484*

Whitaker Charitable Trust *489*

Winham Foundation, The Francis *497*

Wolfe Family's Charitable Trust, The *498*

Woodhead Charitable Trust, Michael *501*

Worshipful Company of Glass Sellers' Charity Trust, The *505*

Yorkshire and Humberside Arts *510*

■ North East

Full region

Adamson Charitable Trust, The John and Florence *7*

Allied Dunbar Staff Charity Fund *13*

Almshouse Association, The *14*

Amory's Charitable Trust, Sir John and Lady *16*

Andrew Charitable Trust, The Prince *16*

Army Benevolent Fund, The *22*

Assheton-Smith Charitable Trust *25*

Bacta Charitable Trust, The *30*

Barbour Trust, The *33*

Barleycorn Trust, The *34*

Bowring (Charities Fund) Ltd, C T *57*

Brookhouse's Will Trust, Mr John Charles *65*

Brough Charitable Trust, Joseph *65*

CfBT Education Services *74*

CLA Charitable Trust *74*

Camelot Foundation, The *78*

Carnegie United Kingdom Trust, The *82*

Chownes Foundation, The *93*

Company of Chartered Surveyors Charitable Trust Fund, The *108*

Construction Industry Trust for Youth, The *110*

Continuation Charitable Trust, The *110*

Countryside Trust, The *115*

Curzon Charitable Trust, The Wallace *120*

Dashe Trust, The *124*

David Trust, The Lesley *124*

Delacour, Charity of Theresa Harriet Mary *129*

Denby Charitable Foundation, The *130*

Dicken Charitable Trust, The Albert *133*

Egerton of Tatton Will Trust, Lord *146*

Esperanza Charitable Trust, The *153*

Fattorini Charitable Trust, James J *160*

Fletcher Charitable Trust, The Joyce *164*

Four Winds Trust *168*

Franklin Trust, Jill *170*

Frazer Charities Trust, The *171*

Galinski Charitable Trust *177*

Garbacz Charitable Trust, The Bernard & Vera *178*

Gelston Charitable Trust, The *179*

Gibbins Trust, The *181*

Good Neighbours Trust, The *188*

Grant-Lawson Charitable Trust, Lady Virginia *192*

Great Britain Sasakawa Foundation, The *193*

Greenaway Foundation, The Sir Derek *194*

Harewood's Charitable Settlement, Lord *209*

Hartley Memorial Trust, The N & P *211*

Hedley Will Trust, Percy *215*

Historic Churches Preservation Trust, The *221*

Homfray Trust, The *226*

Hopkins Charitable Foundation, The Sir Anthony *226*

Howard Charitable Trust, John & Ruth *229*

Hudson Benevolent Trust, The Thomas *230*

King Charitable Trust, The Lorna *254*

Lacy Charity Trust, The Late Sir Pierce *260*

Laing Charitable Trust, The David *260*

Lankelly Foundation, The *264*

Leech Charity, The William *269*

Lewis Partnership, John *274*

Lloyd's Charities Trust *278*

(Lloyds) TSB Foundation for England and Wales *279*

London Law Trust *280*

Lynall Foundation, The D G *287*

Mackintosh Foundation, The *292*

Manning Trust, Leslie & Lilian *296*

Marshall's Charity *300*

Milward Charity, The Edgar *313*

Mountbatten Trust, The Edwina *322*

Natwest Staff Samaritan Fund *330*

Northern Arts *339*

PF Charitable Trust *350*

Penny in the Pound Fund Charitable Trust *359*

Pyke Charity Trust *372*

Reader's Digest Trust, The *380*

Rope Third Charitable Settlement, The Mrs *391*

Rothley Trust, The *392*

Rothschild Group Charitable Trust, The J *393*

Royal Botanical & Horticultural Society of Manchester and the Northern Counties, The *395*

Salters Charities *405*

Sargeant's Charitable Trust, Mrs M E *407*

Scott Charitable Will Trust, The Storrow *412*

Shaw Foundation, The Linley *416*

Shepherd Charitable Trust, The Patricia and Donald *417*

Smallpeice Trust, The *425*

Strangward Trust, The *439*

Sykes Trust, The Charles *445*

Symons Charitable Trust, The Stella *446*

Tanner Charitable Settlement, The Joan *449*

Thomson Foundation, The Sue *454*

Trades Union Congress Educational Trust *460*

Travis Charitable Trust, Constance *460*

Tyne & Wear Foundation *466*

Tyneside Leukaemia Research Association, The *466*

Webster Charitable Trust, William *483*

Welby Trust, The Barbara *484*

Wills 1961 Charitable Trust, Mr Frederick *493*

Wolfe Family's Charitable Trust, The *498*

Woodhead Charitable Trust, Michael *501*

Worshipful Company of Glass Sellers' Charity Trust, The *505*

Yardy Charitable Trust, The Dennis Alan *509*

Yorkshire Bank Charitable Trust, The *510*

Yorkshire Field Studies Trust *510*

Cleveland

Barbour Trust, The *33*

Bell Charitable Trust, John *41*

Camelot Foundation, The *78*

Cleveland Community Foundation *100*

Franklin Trust, Jill *170*

Hadrian Trust, The *202*

Hospital of God at Greatham, The *229*

Leech Charity, The William 269
Northern Arts 339
Travis Charitable Trust, Constance 460
Yorkshire Agricultural Society 509

Durham
Ballinger Charitable Trust, The 32
Barbour Trust, The 33
Bell Charitable Trust, John 41
Burn Charity Trust, The J H 70
Camelot Foundation, The 78
County Durham Foundation 115
Gelston Charitable Trust, The 179
Hadrian Trust, The 202
Hospital of God at Greatham, The 229
Knott Trust, Sir James 258
Leech Charity, The William 269
Northern Arts 339
Ravenscroft Foundation, The 379
Travis Charitable Trust, Constance 460
Yorkshire Agricultural Society 509

Hartlepool
Barbour Trust, The 33
Bell Charitable Trust, John 41
Camelot Foundation, The 78
Cleveland Community Foundation 100
Gelston Charitable Trust, The 179
Hadrian Trust, The 202
Knott Trust, Sir James 258
Leech Charity, The William 269
Northern Arts 339
Travis Charitable Trust, Constance 460
Yorkshire Agricultural Society 509

Middlesborough
Barbour Trust, The 33
Bell Charitable Trust, John 41
Bell's Charitable Trust, Lady Mary 42
Camelot Foundation, The 78
Cleveland Community Foundation 100
Franklin Trust, Jill 170
Gelston Charitable Trust, The 179
Leech Charity, The William 269
Northern Arts 339
Travis Charitable Trust, Constance 460
Yorkshire Agricultural Society 509

Northumberland
Ballinger Charitable Trust, The 32
Barbour Trust, The 33
Bell Charitable Trust, John 41
Burn Charity Trust, The J H 70
Camelot Foundation, The 78
Carr-Ellison Charitable Trust, The 83
Gelston Charitable Trust, The 179
Hadrian Trust, The 202
Hospital of God at Greatham, The 229
Joicey Trust, The 247
Knott Trust, Sir James 258
Leech Charity, The William 269
Mann Trustees Limited, R W 296
Milburn Charitable Trust, Frederick 310
Northern Arts 339
Northern Electric Employee Charity Association 339
Ravenscroft Foundation, The 379
Robinson Brothers (Ryders Green) Ltd, Charitable Trust 388
Rowbotham Charitable Trust, The Christopher 393
St Hilda's Trust 403
Smith (Haltwhistle & District) Charitable Trust, The 427
Travis Charitable Trust, Constance 460
Yorkshire Agricultural Society 509

Stockton-on-Tees
Barbour Trust, The 33
Bell Charitable Trust, John 41
Camelot Foundation, The 78
Cleveland Community Foundation 100
Franklin Trust, Jill 170
Gelston Charitable Trust, The 179
Hadrian Trust, The 202
Leech Charity, The William 269
Northern Arts 339
Travis Charitable Trust, Constance 460
Yorkshire Agricultural Society 509

Tyne & Wear
Ballinger Charitable Trust, The 32
Barbour Trust, The 33
Bell Charitable Trust, John 41
Burn Charity Trust, The J H 70
Camelot Foundation, The 78
Carr-Ellison Charitable Trust, The 83
Chapman Foundation 88

Clarke Charitable Settlement, The 99
Franklin Trust, Jill 170
Gelston Charitable Trust, The 179
Gibson Trust, The R F F 182
Hadrian Trust, The 202
Hodgson Charitable Trust, Bill & May 223
Hospital of God at Greatham, The 229
Joicey Trust, The 247
Knott Trust, Sir James 258
Leech Charity, The William 269
Mann Trustees Limited, R W 296
Metro FM Pop Fund 308
Milburn Charitable Trust, Frederick 310
Millfield House Foundation 312
Northern Arts 339
Patients' Aid Association Hospital and Medical Charities Trust 354
Ravenscroft Foundation, The 379
Rowbotham Charitable Trust, The Christopher 393
SO Charitable Trust 400
St Hilda's Trust 403
Smith & Mount Trust, The Mrs 426
Travis Charitable Trust, Constance 460
Tyneside Charitable Trust 466
Yorkshire Agricultural Society 509

■ **North West**
Full region
Allied Dunbar Staff Charity Fund 13
Almshouse Association, The 14
Andrew Charitable Trust, The Prince 16
Army Benevolent Fund, The 22
Assheton-Smith Charitable Trust 25
Bacta Charitable Trust, The 30
Bowring (Charities Fund) Ltd, C T 57
Bridges Foundation, The Harold 60
Brookhouse's Will Trust, Mr John Charles 65
CfBT Education Services 74
CLA Charitable Trust 74
Camelot Foundation, The 78
Carnegie United Kingdom Trust, The 82
Chownes Foundation, The 93
Company of Chartered Surveyors Charitable Trust Fund, The 108
Countryside Trust, The 115

Dashe Trust, The *124*
David Trust, The Lesley *124*
Denby Charitable Foundation, The *130*
Dock Charitable Fund, Otherwise Mersey Docks and Harbour Company Charitable Fund *135*
Elkes Charity Fund, The Wilfred & Elsie *147*
Esperanza Charitable Trust, The *153*
Eventhall Family Charitable Trust, The *155*
Fattorini Charitable Trust, James J *160*
Ferguson Benevolent Fund Limited *161*
Fletcher Charitable Trust, The Joyce *164*
Frazer Charities Trust, The *171*
Galinski Charitable Trust *177*
Gelston Charitable Trust, The *179*
General Charity Fund, The *180*
Gibbins Trust, The *181*
Good Neighbours Trust, The *188*
Granada Foundation, The *190*
Grant-Lawson Charitable Trust, Lady Virginia *192*
Great Britain Sasakawa Foundation, The *193*
Greenaway Foundation, The Sir Derek *194*
Harewood's Charitable Settlement, Lord *209*
Hartley Memorial Trust, The N & P *211*
Historic Churches Preservation Trust, The *221*
Homfray Trust, The *226*
Hopkins Charitable Foundation, The Sir Anthony *226*
Hudson Benevolent Trust, The Thomas *230*
King Charitable Trust, The Lorna *254*
Lacy Charity Trust, The Late Sir Pierce *260*
Laing Charitable Trust, The David *260*
Lancaster's Trust, Bryan *263*
Lankelly Foundation, The *264*
Lewis Partnership, John *274*
Lloyd's Charities Trust *278*
(Lloyds) TSB Foundation for England and Wales *279*
London Law Trust *280*
Lynall Foundation, The D G *287*
Mackintosh Foundation, The *292*
Marriage's Charitable Trust, Miss G M *299*
Marshall's Charity *300*
Milward Charity, The Edgar *313*

Natwest Staff Samaritan Fund *330*
Oldham Foundation *345*
PF Charitable Trust *350*
Penny in the Pound Fund Charitable Trust *359*
Pye Christian Trust, The *371*
Pyke Charity Trust *372*
Rayner Charitable Trust, The John *380*
Reader's Digest Trust, The *380*
Rope Third Charitable Settlement, The Mrs *391*
Rothschild Group Charitable Trust, The J *393*
Royal Botanical & Horticultural Society of Manchester and the Northern Counties, The *395*
Salters Charities *405*
Sargeant's Charitable Trust, Mrs M E *407*
Scott Charitable Will Trust, The Storrow *412*
Shaw Foundation, The Linley *416*
Shepherd Charitable Trust, The Patricia and Donald *417*
Smallpeice Trust, The *425*
Strangward Trust, The *439*
Sykes Trust, The Charles *445*
Symons Charitable Trust, The Stella *446*
Tanner Charitable Settlement, The Joan *449*
Thomson Foundation, The Sue *454*
Trades Union Congress Educational Trust *460*
Travis Charitable Trust, Constance *460*
Welby Trust, The Barbara *484*
Westminster Foundation, The *487*
Wills 1961 Charitable Trust, Mr Frederick *493*
Wolfe Family's Charitable Trust, The *498*
Woodhead Charitable Trust, Michael *501*
Worshipful Company of Glass Sellers' Charity Trust, The *505*
Yardy Charitable Trust, The Dennis Alan *509*
Yorkshire Bank Charitable Trust, The *510*

Cheshire

Birtwistle Memorial Trust, The G E *50*
Bloom Foundation, Abraham Algy *54*
Camelot Foundation, The *78*
Chrimes Family Charitable Trust, The *93*

Clarke Charitable Settlement, The *99*
Egerton of Tatton Will Trust, Lord *146*
Ferguson Benevolent Fund Limited *161*
Four Winds Trust *168*
Gelston Charitable Trust, The *179*
Granada Foundation, The *190*
Humphreys Charitable Settlement, J A M *231*
JDM Charitable Trust *239*
Johnson Foundation, The *246*
Leverhulme's Charitable Trust, Lord *272*
Lowe Trust, Mrs D G *285*
Moores Foundation, John *318*
North West Arts Board *337*
North West Cancer Research Fund *338*
Patients' Aid Association Hospital and Medical Charities Trust *354*
Pennycress Trust, The *359*
Rowbotham Charitable Trust, The Christopher *393*
Sykes Trust, The Charles *445*
Thwaite Charitable Trust, The Daniel *456*
Wedge, The *483*

Cumbria

Camelot Foundation, The *78*
Cornerstone Charitable Trust *114*
Dock Charitable Fund, Otherwise Mersey Docks and Harbour Company Charitable Fund *135*
Egerton of Tatton Will Trust, Lord *146*
Fisher Foundation, The Sir John *163*
Four Winds Trust *168*
Gelston Charitable Trust, The *179*
Gilpin Trust, The John *184*
Granada Foundation, The *190*
North West Cancer Research Fund *338*
Northern Arts *339*
Provincial Trust for Kendal, The *370*
Rowbotham Charitable Trust, The Christopher *393*
Scott Charitable Trust, The Francis C *412*
Skelton Bounty, The *423*
Salter Trust Ltd *424*
Solway Sound Charitable Trust *430*
Sykes Trust, The Charles *445*
Thwaite Charitable Trust, The Daniel *456*
Whiteley Trust, Norman *490*

Greater Manchester
Amelan Charitable Trust, The
Harold *15*
Barnabas Charitable Trust *34*
Bloom Foundation, Abraham
Algy *54*
Busby Charities Fund, Sir Matt
71
Camelot Foundation, The *78*
Chronicle Cinderella Home
Fund No 1, The *95*
Community Trust for Greater
Manchester, The *108*
Coutts Charitable Trust, The
116
Dock Charitable Fund,
Otherwise Mersey Docks
and Harbour Company
Charitable Fund *135*
Egerton of Tatton Will Trust,
Lord *146*
Ferguson Benevolent Fund
Limited *161*
Four Winds Trust *168*
Franklin Trust, Jill *170*
Gelston Charitable Trust, The
179
Granada Foundation, The *190*
Johnson Charitable Settlement,
The N B *246*
Joseph Charitable Trust, J E
248
Laski Memorial Charitable
Trust, Nathan *265*
Manchester and Salford
Medical Charities Fund *295*
Manchester Guardian Society
Charitable Trust, The *295*
Mole Charitable Trust *315*
North West Arts Board *337*
Rowbotham Charitable Trust,
The Christopher *393*
Skelton Bounty, The *423*
Sykes Trust, The Charles *445*
Thwaite Charitable Trust, The
Daniel *456*
Walton Charitable Trust, The
479

Isle of Man
Camelot Foundation, The *78*
Coutts Charitable Trust, The
116
Dock Charitable Fund,
Otherwise Mersey Docks
and Harbour Company
Charitable Fund *135*
Egerton of Tatton Will Trust,
Lord *146*
Four Winds Trust *168*
Gelston Charitable Trust, The
179
North West Cancer Research
Fund *338*
Sykes Trust, The Charles *445*

Knowsley
Brotherton Trust, The Charles
65
Camelot Foundation, The *78*
Chrimes Family Charitable
Trust, The *93*
Dock Charitable Fund,
Otherwise Mersey Docks
and Harbour Company
Charitable Fund *135*
Egerton of Tatton Will Trust,
Lord *146*
Ford of Britain Trust *166*
Four Winds Trust *168*
Franklin Trust, Jill *170*
Gelston Charitable Trust, The
179
Granada Foundation, The *190*
Johnson Foundation, The *246*
Johnson Group Cleaners
Charity *247*
Moores Foundation, John *318*
North West Arts Board *337*
North West Cancer Research
Fund *338*
Skelton Bounty, The *423*
Sykes Trust, The Charles *445*
Thwaite Charitable Trust, The
Daniel *456*
Wedge, The *483*
Wilson Bequest Fund, The John
495
Woolton Charitable Trust, The
503

Lancashire
Bloom Foundation, Abraham
Algy *54*
Camelot Foundation, The *78*
Charity for Change *89*
Dock Charitable Fund,
Otherwise Mersey Docks
and Harbour Company
Charitable Fund *135*
Egerton of Tatton Will Trust,
Lord *146*
Ferguson Benevolent Fund
Limited *161*
Four Winds Trust *168*
Franklin Trust, Jill *170*
Gelston Charitable Trust, The
179
Granada Foundation, The *190*
Harris Charity, The *211*
JDM Charitable Trust *239*
Moores Foundation, John *318*
North West Arts Board *337*
North West Cancer Research
Fund *338*
Rowbotham Charitable Trust,
The Christopher *393*
Scott Charitable Trust, The
Francis C *412*
Skelton Bounty, The *423*
Sykes Trust, The Charles *445*
Thwaite Charitable Trust, The
Daniel *456*

Waterhouse Charitable Trust,
Mrs *480*
Wedge, The *483*

Liverpool
Barnabas Charitable Trust *34*
Brotherton Trust, The Charles
65
Camelot Foundation, The *78*
Chrimes Family Charitable
Trust, The *93*
Clarke Charitable Settlement,
The *99*
Dock Charitable Fund,
Otherwise Mersey Docks
and Harbour Company
Charitable Fund *135*
Egerton of Tatton Will Trust,
Lord *146*
Ford of Britain Trust *166*
Four Winds Trust *168*
Franklin Trust, Jill *170*
Gelston Charitable Trust, The
179
Granada Foundation, The *190*
Growth Building Trust, The
198
JDM Charitable Trust *239*
Johnson Foundation, The *246*
Johnson Group Cleaners
Charity *247*
Laspen Trust *265*
Moores Foundation, John *318*
North West Arts Board *337*
North West Cancer Research
Fund *338*
Shifrin Charitable Trust, The
Maurice and Hilda *419*
Skelton Bounty, The *423*
Sykes Trust, The Charles *445*
Thwaite Charitable Trust, The
Daniel *456*
Wedge, The *483*
Woolton Charitable Trust, The
503

Merseyside
Aveling Bounty, Charles and
Edith *27*
Brotherton Trust, The Charles
65
Camelot Foundation, The *78*
Chrimes Family Charitable
Trust, The *93*
Cozens-Hardy Trust, The Lord
117
Dock Charitable Fund,
Otherwise Mersey Docks
and Harbour Company
Charitable Fund *135*
Egerton of Tatton Will Trust,
Lord *146*
Ferguson Benevolent Fund
Limited *161*
Ford of Britain Trust *166*
Four Winds Trust *168*
Franklin Trust, Jill *170*

Gelston Charitable Trust, The
179
Gilpin Trust, The John *184*
Granada Foundation, The *190*
Holt Charitable Trust, P H *225*
Humphreys Charitable
Settlement, J A M *231*
JDM Charitable Trust *239*
Johnson Foundation, The *246*
Johnson Group Cleaners
Charity *247*
Laspen Trust *265*
Liverpool Child Welfare
Association Incorporated
277
Moores Family Charity
Foundation, The *317*
Moores Foundation, John *318*
North West Arts Board *337*
North West Cancer Research
Fund *338*
Shifrin Charitable Trust, The
Maurice and Hilda *419*
Shone Memorial Trust, J A *420*
Skelton Bounty, The *423*
Sykes Trust, The Charles *445*
Thwaite Charitable Trust, The
Daniel *456*
Tillotson Charitable Trust, G L
457
Ward Blenkinsop Trust, The
480
Wedge, The *483*
Woolton Charitable Trust, The
503

Sefton

Camelot Foundation, The *78*
Chrimes Family Charitable
Trust, The *93*
Dock Charitable Fund,
Otherwise Mersey Docks
and Harbour Company
Charitable Fund *135*
Egerton of Tatton Will Trust,
Lord *146*
Ford of Britain Trust *166*
Four Winds Trust *168*
Franklin Trust, Jill *170*
Gelston Charitable Trust, The
179
Granada Foundation, The *190*
JDM Charitable Trust *239*
Johnson Foundation, The *246*
Johnson Group Cleaners
Charity *247*
Moores Foundation, John *318*
North West Arts Board *337*
North West Cancer Research
Fund *338*
Shifrin Charitable Trust, The
Maurice and Hilda *419*
Skelton Bounty, The *423*
Sykes Trust, The Charles *445*
Thwaite Charitable Trust, The
Daniel *456*

Wedge, The *483*
Woolton Charitable Trust, The
503

St Helens

Camelot Foundation, The *78*
Chrimes Family Charitable
Trust, The *93*
Dock Charitable Fund,
Otherwise Mersey Docks
and Harbour Company
Charitable Fund *135*
Egerton of Tatton Will Trust,
Lord *146*
Ford of Britain Trust *166*
Four Winds Trust *168*
Franklin Trust, Jill *170*
Gelston Charitable Trust, The
179
Granada Foundation, The *190*
JDM Charitable Trust *239*
Moores Foundation, John *318*
North West Arts Board *337*
North West Cancer Research
Fund *338*
Rainford Trust, The *376*
Shifrin Charitable Trust, The
Maurice and Hilda *419*
Skelton Bounty, The *423*
Sykes Trust, The Charles *445*
Thwaite Charitable Trust, The
Daniel *456*
Wedge, The *483*
Woolton Charitable Trust, The
503

Wirral

Brotherton Trust, The Charles
65
Camelot Foundation, The *78*
Chrimes Family Charitable
Trust, The *93*
Dock Charitable Fund,
Otherwise Mersey Docks
and Harbour Company
Charitable Fund *135*
Egerton of Tatton Will Trust,
Lord *146*
Ford of Britain Trust *166*
Four Winds Trust *168*
Franklin Trust, Jill *170*
Gelston Charitable Trust, The
179
Granada Foundation, The *190*
JDM Charitable Trust *239*
Johnson Foundation, The *246*
Johnson Group Cleaners
Charity *247*
Laspen Trust *265*
Moores Foundation, John *318*
North West Arts Board *337*
North West Cancer Research
Fund *338*
Shifrin Charitable Trust, The
Maurice and Hilda *419*
Sykes Trust, The Charles *445*

Thwaite Charitable Trust, The
Daniel *456*
Tillotson Charitable Trust, G L
457
Wedge, The *483*
Woolton Charitable Trust, The
503

....

■ East Midlands

Full region

Allied Dunbar Staff Charity
Fund *13*
Almshouse Association, The *14*
Andrew Charitable Trust, The
Prince *16*
Army Benevolent Fund, The *22*
Assheton-Smith Charitable
Trust *25*
Bacta Charitable Trust, The *30*
Barleycorn Trust, The *34*
Bowring (Charities Fund) Ltd,
C T *57*
Brookhouse's Will Trust, Mr
John Charles *65*
CfBT Education Services *74*
CLA Charitable Trust *74*
Cadbury Charitable Trust,
William Adlington *75*
Camelot Foundation, The *78*
Carnegie United Kingdom
Trust, The *82*
Chownes Foundation, The *93*
Clipsham Charitable
Settlement, R E *101*
Company of Chartered
Surveyors Charitable Trust
Fund, The *108*
Countryside Trust, The *115*
Dashe Trust, The *124*
David Trust, The Lesley *124*
Denby Charitable Foundation,
The *130*
Egerton of Tatton Will Trust,
Lord *146*
Elkes Charity Fund, The Wilfred
& Elsie *147*
Esperanza Charitable Trust, The
153
Fattorini Charitable Trust,
James J *160*
Fletcher Charitable Trust, The
Joyce *164*
Four Winds Trust *168*
Frazer Charities Trust, The *171*
Galinski Charitable Trust *177*
Gelston Charitable Trust, The
179
Gibbins Trust, The *181*
Good Neighbours Trust, The
188
Grant-Lawson Charitable Trust,
Lady Virginia *192*
Great Britain Sasakawa
Foundation, The *193*
Greenaway Foundation, The Sir
Derek *194*

Hartley Memorial Trust, The N & P *211*

Historic Churches Preservation Trust, The *221*

Homfray Trust, The *226*

Hopkins Charitable Foundation, The Sir Anthony *226*

Hornton Trust, The *228*

Howard Charitable Trust, John & Ruth *229*

Hudson Benevolent Trust, The Thomas *230*

Ingles Charitable Trust, The *234*

King Charitable Trust, The Lorna *254*

Lacy Charity Trust, The Late Sir Pierce *260*

Laing Charitable Trust, The David *260*

Lankelly Foundation, The *264*

Lewis Partnership, John *274*

Lloyd's Charities Trust *278*

(Lloyds) TSB Foundation for England and Wales *279*

London Law Trust *280*

Lynall Foundation, The D G *287*

Mackintosh Foundation, The *292*

Marriage's Charitable Trust, Miss G M *299*

Marshall's Charity *300*

Milward Charity, The Edgar *313*

Natwest Staff Samaritan Fund *330*

PF Charitable Trust *350*

Paget Trust, The *351*

Patients' Aid Association Hospital and Medical Charities Trust *354*

Patrick Charitable Trust, The *354*

Penny in the Pound Fund Charitable Trust *359*

Pyke Charity Trust *372*

Reader's Digest Trust, The *380*

Rope Third Charitable Settlement, The Mrs *391*

Rothschild Group Charitable Trust, The J *393*

Royal Botanical & Horticultural Society of Manchester and the Northern Counties, The *395*

Salters Charities *405*

Sargeant's Charitable Trust, Mrs M E *407*

Schuster Charitable Trust, The *410*

Shaw Foundation, The Linley *416*

Smallpeice Trust, The *425*

Strangward Trust, The *439*

Strauss Charitable Trust *440*

Symons Charitable Trust, The Stella *446*

Tanner Charitable Settlement, The Joan *449*

Thomson Foundation, The Sue *454*

Trades Union Congress Educational Trust *460*

Wander Charitable Fund, The Dr Albert *479*

Warren Foundation, The John *480*

Welby Trust, The Barbara *484*

Westminster Foundation, The *487*

Wills 1961 Charitable Trust, Mr Frederick *493*

Wolfe Family's Charitable Trust, The *498*

Woodhead Charitable Trust, Michael *501*

Worshipful Company of Glass Sellers' Charity Trust, The *505*

Yardy Charitable Trust, The Dennis Alan *509*

Yorkshire Bank Charitable Trust, The *510*

Derbyshire

Barnabas Charitable Trust *34*

Bottom Charitable Trust, Harry *56*

Burton Breweries Charitable Trust, The *70*

Chetwode Foundation, The *91*

Clarke Charitable Settlement, The *99*

East Midlands Arts Board Ltd *143*

Everard Foundation, The *155*

Hatton Charitable Trust, The Howard *212*

Keeling Charitable Trust, The Petronella *251*

North West Arts Board *337*

Sheldon Trust, The *417*

Sykes Charitable Trust, The Hugh & Ruby *445*

Sykes Trust, The Charles *445*

Travis Charitable Trust, Constance *460*

Woodroffe Benton Foundation, The *502*

Leicestershire

Chetwode Foundation, The *91*

Corah Foundation Fund, J Reginald *112*

East Midlands Arts Board Ltd *143*

Everard Foundation, The *155*

Hickinbotham Charitable Trust *218*

Invermark Charity *236*

Keeling Charitable Trust, The Petronella *251*

Paget Trust, The *351*

Riddleston Charity of Leicester, The Harry James *385*

Sheldon Trust, The *417*

Shipman Charitable Trust, Thomas Stanley *420*

Stathern Chapel Close Trust, The *436*

Travis Charitable Trust, Constance *460*

Lincolnshire

Cottingham Charitable Trust, Mrs Diana Mary *114*

Eastern Arts Board *143*

Everard Foundation, The *155*

Halkes Settlement, John Robert *204*

Keeling Charitable Trust, The Petronella *251*

Sandars Charitable Trust, The J E *407*

Sykes Trust, The Charles *445*

Travis Charitable Trust, Constance *460*

Wander Charitable Fund, The Dr Albert *479*

Wright Deceased Trust, John William *506*

Northamptonshire

Balney Charitable Trust, The *32*

Barratt Charitable Trust, The Elaine *36*

Cripps Foundation *118*

East Midlands Arts Board Ltd *143*

Elkington Charitable Trust, The Maud *147*

Everard Foundation, The *155*

Fitzwilliam Charitable Trust, The Earl *164*

Greenaway Foundation, The Sir Derek *194*

Haddon Charitable Trust, William *202*

Horne Foundation, The *228*

Ibbett Trust, The *233*

Keeling Charitable Trust, The Petronella *251*

Luke Trust, The *286*

Sheldon Trust, The *417*

Strangward Trust, The *439*

Timson Family Charitable Trust *457*

Travis Charitable Trust, Constance *460*

Wyvill Charitable Trust, The *507*

Nottinghamshire

Adams Charitable Trust, Kate *6*

Boots Charitable Trust *56*

Chetwode Foundation, The *91*

Coutts Charitable Trust, The *116*

Derbyshire Trust, J N *130*
Dunn Charitable Trust, The
  Harry *140*
Earwicker Trust *142*
East Midlands Arts Board Ltd
  143
Eastwood Foundation, Sir John
  143
Everard Foundation, The *155*
Farr Charitable Trust, The
  Thomas *159*
Gray Trust, The *192*
Keeling Charitable Trust, The
  Petronella *251*
Linmardon Trust *276*
Paget Trust, The *351*
Sheldon Trust, The *417*
Sykes Trust, The Charles *445*
Thoresby Charitable Trust *454*
Travis Charitable Trust,
  Constance *460*
Wander Charitable Fund, The
  Dr Albert *479*

■ **West Midlands**

Full region
Allied Dunbar Staff Charity
  Fund *13*
Almshouse Association, The *14*
Andrew Charitable Trust, The
  Prince *16*
Army Benevolent Fund, The *22*
Assheton-Smith Charitable
  Trust *25*
Avon Trust, The *28*
Bacta Charitable Trust, The *30*
Barleycorn Trust, The *34*
Beattie Charitable Trust, The
  James *39*
Blakemore Foundation, The *53*
Bowring (Charities Fund) Ltd,
  C T *57*
Brocton Trust, The *64*
Brookhouse's Will Trust, Mr
  John Charles *65*
CfBT Education Services *74*
CLA Charitable Trust *74*
Cadbury Charitable Trust
  (Incorporated), Edward *75*
Cadbury Charitable Trust,
  Richard *75*
Cadbury Charitable Trust,
  William Adlington *75*
Cadbury Trust (1928), The
  Edward & Dorothy *76*
Camelot Foundation, The *78*
Carnegie United Kingdom
  Trust, The *82*
Chownes Foundation, The *93*
Company of Chartered
  Surveyors Charitable Trust
  Fund, The *108*
Countryside Trust, The *115*
Dashe Trust, The *124*
David Trust, The Lesley *124*

Denby Charitable Foundation,
  The *130*
Dumbell Charitable Trust, The
  P B *139*
Dunn Trust, The W E *140*
Egerton of Tatton Will Trust,
  Lord *146*
Elkes Charity Fund, The Wilfred
  & Elsie *147*
Esperanza Charitable Trust, The
  153
Fattorini Charitable Trust,
  James J *160*
Fletcher Charitable Trust, The
  Joyce *164*
Four Winds Trust *168*
Frazer Charities Trust, The *171*
Galinski Charitable Trust *177*
Gelston Charitable Trust, The
  179
Gibbins Trust, The *181*
Good Neighbours Trust, The
  188
Graham Charity, The Mrs D M
  190
Grant-Lawson Charitable Trust,
  Lady Virginia *192*
Great Britain Sasakawa
  Foundation, The *193*
Greenaway Foundation, The Sir
  Derek *194*
Hannay Charitable Trust, The
  Lennox *208*
Hartley Memorial Trust, The N
  & P *211*
Historic Churches Preservation
  Trust, The *221*
Homfray Trust, The *226*
Hopkins Charitable Foundation,
  The Sir Anthony *226*
Hornton Trust, The *228*
Howard Charitable Trust, John
  & Ruth *229*
Hudson Benevolent Trust, The
  Thomas *230*
Ingles Charitable Trust, The
  234
Kenrick Charitable Trust, Hugh
  253
King Charitable Trust, The
  Lorna *254*
Lacy Charity Trust, The Late Sir
  Pierce *260*
Laing Charitable Trust, The
  David *260*
Lankelly Foundation, The *264*
Lewis Partnership, John *274*
Lloyd's Charities Trust *278*
(Lloyds) TSB Foundation for
  England and Wales *279*
London Law Trust *280*
Lower Hall Charitable Trust
  285
Lynall Foundation, The D G
  287
Mackintosh Foundation, The
  292

Marriage's Charitable Trust,
  Miss G M *299*
Marshall's Charity *300*
Midland Group Training
  Services Ltd *310*
Milward Charity, The Edgar
  313
Missionary Friends Trust *314*
Natwest Staff Samaritan Fund
  330
PF Charitable Trust *350*
Parivar Trust, The *353*
Patients' Aid Association
  Hospital and Medical
  Charities Trust *354*
Patrick Charitable Trust, The
  354
Pedmore Sporting Club Trust
  Fund *357*
Penny in the Pound Fund
  Charitable Trust *359*
Peugeot Talbot Motor
  Company plc Charity Trust
  361
Pyke Charity Trust *372*
Ratcliff Foundation, The *378*
Reader's Digest Trust, The *380*
Rockcliffe Charitable Trust *389*
Rocket Club Benevolent Fund,
  The *389*
Rope Third Charitable
  Settlement, The Mrs *391*
Rothschild Group Charitable
  Trust, The J *393*
Royal Botanical & Horticultural
  Society of Manchester and
  the Northern Counties, The
  395
Salters Charities *405*
Schuster Charitable Trust, The
  410
Shaw Foundation, The Linley
  416
Sheldon Trust, The *417*
Smallpeice Trust, The *425*
Stokes Trust, F C *438*
Strangward Trust, The *439*
Strauss Charitable Trust *440*
Symons Charitable Trust, The
  Stella *446*
Tanner Charitable Settlement,
  The Joan *449*
Trades Union Congress
  Educational Trust *460*
Travis Charitable Trust,
  Constance *460*
Turner Trust, G J W *464*
29th May 1961 Charity, The
  465
Welby Trust, The Barbara *484*
West Midlands Regional Arts
  Board *486*
Westminster Foundation, The
  487
Wills 1961 Charitable Trust, Mr
  Frederick *493*
Wolfe Family's Charitable
  Trust, The *498*

Woodhead Charitable Trust,
Michael *501*
Woodlands Trust *501*
Worshipful Company of Glass
Sellers' Charity Trust, The
505
Wragge & Co Charitable Trust,
The *506*
Yardy Charitable Trust, The
Dennis Alan *509*
Yorkshire Bank Charitable
Trust, The *510*

Hereford & Worcester
Barrie Charitable Trust, The
Misses *36*
Bulmer Charitable Trust, Becket
68
Bulmer Charitable Trust, The
Howard *68*
Chance Trust, Sir Hugh *87*
Churchill Christian Fellowship
Trust *95*
Corbett's Charity, Thomas *112*
Davenport's Charity Trust,
Baron *124*
Dumbreck Charity *139*
Eveson Charitable Trust, The
155
French Foundation, The Betty
172
Grimley Charity, The *196*
Haines Charitable Trust, The
Alfred *203*
Payne Trust, The Harry *356*
Richards Charity, The Clive *384*
Sargeant's Charitable Trust,
Mrs M E *407*
Summerfield Charitable Trust,
The *442*
Wylde Memorial Charity, The
Anthony and Gwendoline
507

Shropshire
Fletcher Trust, Roy *165*
Haines Charitable Trust, The
Alfred *203*
JDM Charitable Trust *239*
Lower Hall Charitable Trust
285
North West Cancer Research
Fund *338*
Payne Trust, The Harry *356*
Sargeant's Charitable Trust,
Mrs M E *407*
Stanley Residuary Trust, Bishop
435
Walker Trust, The *477*
Westcroft Trust *486*

Staffordshire
Brotherton Trust, The Charles
65
Burton Breweries Charitable
Trust, The *70*

Clarke Charitable Settlement,
The *99*
Corbett's Charity, Thomas *112*
Davenport's Charity Trust,
Baron *124*
Haines Charitable Trust, The
Alfred *203*
Harding Trust, The *209*
Humphreys Charitable
Settlement, J A M *231*
JDM Charitable Trust *239*
Payne Trust, The Harry *356*
Ravenscroft Foundation, The
379
Sargeant's Charitable Trust,
Mrs M E *407*
Strasser Foundation, The *439*

Warwickshire
Brotherton Trust, The Charles
65
Davenport's Charity Trust,
Baron *124*
Digby Charitable Trust, Simon
133
Dumbreck Charity *139*
Haines Charitable Trust, The
Alfred *203*
Hudson Charitable Trust, The
230
Midland Group Training
Services Ltd *310*
Norton Foundation, The *340*
Payne Trust, The Harry *356*
Rest-Harrow Trust, The *382*
Rokeby Charitable Trust *390*
Rookes Charitable Trust, C A
390
Sargeant's Charitable Trust,
Mrs M E *407*
Seccombe Charitable Trust,
Leslie and Doris *414*
Sparkes Charitable Trust, The
Eric F *433*

West Midlands
Barnabas Charitable Trust *34*
Bewley Charitable Trust, The
46
Brotherton Trust, The Charles
65
Cole Charitable Trust, The *105*
Collins Charity, The George
Henry *106*
Coutts Charitable Trust, The
116
Dana Charitable Settlement,
The *123*
Digbeth Trust Ltd, The *133*
Dumbreck Charity *139*
Eveson Charitable Trust, The
155
Franklin Trust, Jill *170*
Grimley Charity, The *196*
Haines Charitable Trust, The
Alfred *203*

Hudson Charitable Trust, The
230
Leadbeater Trust, The Alfred
268
Lower Hall Charitable Trust
285
Measures Charity, The James
Frederick and Ethel Anne
303
Norton Foundation, The *340*
Payne Trust, The Harry *356*
Robinson Brothers (Ryders
Green) Ltd, Charitable Trust
388
Sargeant's Charitable Trust,
Mrs M E *407*
Sayer Charity, Henry James
409
Sparkhill Trust, The *433*
Turner Trust, The Douglas *464*
Workman Trust, The *503*
Yardley Great Trust *508*

■ Eastern
Full region
Allied Dunbar Staff Charity
Fund *13*
Almshouse Association, The *14*
Andrew Charitable Trust, The
Prince *16*
Army Benevolent Fund, The *22*
Assheton-Smith Charitable
Trust *25*
Bacta Charitable Trust, The *30*
Barleycorn Trust, The *34*
Bowring (Charities Fund) Ltd,
C T *57*
Brookhouse's Will Trust, Mr
John Charles *65*
Buxton Trust, Denis *72*
CfBT Education Services *74*
CLA Charitable Trust *74*
Camelot Foundation, The *78*
Carnegie United Kingdom
Trust, The *82*
Clipsham Charitable
Settlement, R E *101*
Company of Chartered
Surveyors Charitable Trust
Fund, The *108*
Countryside Trust, The *115*
Curzon Charitable Trust, The
Wallace *120*
Dashe Trust, The *124*
David Trust, The Lesley *124*
Denby Charitable Foundation,
The *130*
Egerton of Tatton Will Trust,
Lord *146*
Esperanza Charitable Trust, The
153
Fattorini Charitable Trust,
James J *160*
Four Winds Trust *168*
Frazer Charities Trust, The *171*
Galinski Charitable Trust *177*

Gelston Charitable Trust, The
179

Gibbins Trust, The *181*

Good Neighbours Trust, The
188

Grant-Lawson Charitable Trust,
Lady Virginia *192*

Great Britain Sasakawa
Foundation, The *193*

Greenaway Foundation, The Sir
Derek *194*

Hannay Charitable Trust, The
Lennox *208*

Haymills Charitable Trust *213*

Historic Churches Preservation
Trust, The *221*

Hopkins Charitable Foundation,
The Sir Anthony *226*

Ingles Charitable Trust, The
234

King Charitable Trust, The
Lorna *254*

Lacy Charity Trust, The Late Sir
Pierce *260*

Laing Charitable Trust, The
David *260*

Lankelly Foundation, The *264*

Lewis Partnership, John *274*

Lloyd's Charities Trust *278*

(Lloyds) TSB Foundation for
England and Wales *279*

London Law Trust *280*

Low & Bonar Charitable Fund,
The *284*

Lynall Foundation, The D G
287

Mackintosh Foundation, The
292

Marriage's Charitable Trust,
Miss G M *299*

Marshall's Charity *300*

Milward Charity, The Edgar
313

Natwest Staff Samaritan Fund
330

PF Charitable Trust *350*

Pyke Charity Trust *372*

Reader's Digest Trust, The *380*

Rockcliffe Charitable Trust *389*

Rothschild Group Charitable
Trust, The J *393*

Salters Charities *405*

Sargeant's Charitable Trust,
Mrs M E *407*

Schuster Charitable Trust, The
410

Seagram Distillers Charitable
Trust *413*

Shaw Foundation, The Linley
416

Smallpeice Trust, The *425*

Smith & Mount Trust, The Mrs
426

Strangward Trust, The *439*

Strauss Charitable Trust *440*

Symons Charitable Trust, The
Stella *446*

Tankel Charitable Trust, Alfred
449

Tanner Charitable Settlement,
The Joan *449*

Trades Union Congress
Educational Trust *460*

Travis Charitable Trust,
Constance *460*

Wander Charitable Fund, The
Dr Albert *479*

Welby Trust, The Barbara *484*

Wills 1961 Charitable Trust, Mr
Frederick *493*

Wolfe Family's Charitable
Trust, The *498*

Woodhead Charitable Trust,
Michael *501*

Worshipful Company of Glass
Sellers' Charity Trust, The
505

Yardy Charitable Trust, The
Dennis Alan *509*

Yorkshire Bank Charitable
Trust, The *510*

Bedfordshire

Alexander Charitable Trust,
The *10*

Balney Charitable Trust, The
32

Carlton Television Trust *81*

Eastern Arts Board *143*

Gale Charitable Trust, Horace
and Marjorie *177*

Gale Charitable Trust, R G *177*

Hudson Benevolent Trust, The
Thomas *230*

Ibbett Trust, The *233*

Keeling Charitable Trust, The
Petronella *251*

Luke Trust, The *286*

Neighbourly Charitable Trust,
The *331*

Pyke Charity Trust *372*

Sell Charitable Trust, Leslie *415*

Warren Foundation, The John
480

Cambridgeshire

Cole Charitable Trust, The *105*

Eastern Arts Board *143*

Fitzwilliam Charitable Trust,
The Earl *164*

Hudson Benevolent Trust, The
Thomas *230*

Jarrold Trust Ltd, John *243*

Keeling Charitable Trust, The
Petronella *251*

Kingston Religious Trust Fund,
The *256*

Pyke Charity Trust *372*

Strangward Trust, The *439*

Warren Foundation, The John
480

Essex (not London Boroughs)

Aldwyns Trust, The *10*

Benham Charitable Trust,
Hervey *43*

Buxton Trust, Denis *72*

Carlton Television Trust *81*

Courtauld Trust, The Augustine
116

Curriers Company Charitable
Fund *119*

Denne Charitable Trust *130*

Eastern Arts Board *143*

Essex Heritage Trust *153*

Essex Provincial Charity Fund
154

Essex Radio Helping Hands
Trust, The *154*

Ford of Britain Trust *166*

Fowler Memorial Trust, The
169

French Charitable Trust,
Charles S *171*

Glasspool Trust, R L *184*

Hornsey Parochial Charities
(Educational and Vocational
Foundation), The *228*

Hudson Benevolent Trust, The
Thomas *230*

Jarrold Trust Ltd, John *243*

Jones Settlement, Edward Cecil
248

London Taxi Drivers' Fund for
Underprivileged Children,
The *280*

Meridian Broadcasting
Charitable Trust *307*

Oasis Church Chadwell Heath
Charitable Trust *343*

Ogilvie Charities (Deed No 2)
344

Pyke Charity Trust *372*

Rayleigh's Charitable Trust,
Lord *379*

Rosca Trust *391*

Sherwood Charitable Trust,
Colonel J D *419*

Smith Memorial Trust, The
Albert & Florence *427*

Hertfordshire (not London Boroughs)

Carlton Television Trust *81*

Dacorum Community Trust *121*

Eastern Arts Board *143*

Glasspool Trust, R L *184*

Hertfordshire Community
Trust, The *217*

Hertfordshire Society for the
Blind, The *217*

Hudson Benevolent Trust, The
Thomas *230*

Jones Settlement, Edward Cecil
248

Living and Waking Naturally
278

London Taxi Drivers' Fund for Underprivileged Children, The *280*
Pyke Charity Trust *372*
Riddon Trust, The *386*
Sell Charitable Trust, Leslie *415*
Stanley Residuary Trust, Bishop *435*
Wander Charitable Fund, The Dr Albert *479*
Woodlands Trust *501*

Norfolk

Adnams Charity, The *7*
Alper Charitable Trust, The *15*
Aquarius Charitable Foundation, The *19*
Bassham Charitable Trust, The Paul *37*
Buxton Trust, Denis *72*
Colman Charitable Trust, The Timothy *107*
Cozens-Hardy Trust, The Lord *117*
Eastern Arts Board *143*
French Charitable Trust, Charles S *171*
Gardner Charitable Trust, R & J *178*
Goodman Trust, The *189*
Hill House Trust *219*
Hudson Benevolent Trust, The Thomas *230*
Jarrold Trust Ltd, John *243*
Keeling Charitable Trust, The Petronella *251*
Kingston Religious Trust Fund, The *256*
MacKintosh Charitable Trust, Viscount *292*
Nichol-Young Foundation *334*
Norfolk and Suffolk Voluntary Health Benevolent Fund, The *336*
Norfolk Churches Trust Ltd *336*
Norman, The Educational Foundation of Alderman John *337*
Norwich Church of England Young Men's Society *340*
Penny in the Pound Fund Charitable Trust *359*
Pennycress Trust, The *359*
Pyke Charity Trust *372*
Rackham Charitable Trust, The Mr & Mrs Philip *375*
Rae Charity, H J *375*
Van Berchem Charitable Trust, The Alec *470*
Wood Charity, The Phyllis E *501*

Suffolk

Adnams Charity, The *7*
Alper Charitable Trust, The *15*
Aquarius Charitable Foundation, The *19*
Burton Charitable Trust, The Geoffrey *71*
Buxton Trust, Denis *72*
Colyer-Fergusson Charitable Trust, The *107*
Curriers Company Charitable Fund *119*
Early's Charitable Settlement, Richard *142*
Eastern Arts Board *143*
Elmchurch Trust, The *148*
Gardner Charitable Trust, R & J *178*
Hill House Trust *219*
Hudson Benevolent Trust, The Thomas *230*
Jarrold Trust Ltd, John *243*
Jones Settlement, Edward Cecil *248*
Moncrieff Charity, D C *315*
Nichol-Young Foundation *334*
Norfolk and Suffolk Voluntary Health Benevolent Fund, The *336*
Ogilvie Charities (Deed No 2) *344*
Paul Charitable Trust, The Late Barbara May *355*
Paul's Charitable Trust, R J *355*
Penny in the Pound Fund Charitable Trust *359*
Pyke Charity Trust *372*
Rackham Charitable Trust, The Mr & Mrs Philip *375*
Rae Charity, H J *375*
Rope Third Charitable Settlement, The Mrs *391*
Scarfe Charitable Trust, The *409*
Tranmer Charitable Trust, Annie *460*
Van Berchem Charitable Trust, The Alec *470*
Vinten Trust, The William and Ellen *474*
Williams Charitable Trust, Alfred *493*
Wood Charity, The Phyllis E *501*

....

■ Yorks & Humberside

Full region

Allied Dunbar Staff Charity Fund *13*
Almshouse Association, The *14*
Andrew Charitable Trust, The Prince *16*
Army Benevolent Fund, The *22*
Assheton-Smith Charitable Trust *25*

Bacta Charitable Trust, The *30*
Barleycorn Trust, The *34*
Bottom Charitable Trust, Harry *56*
Bowring (Charities Fund) Ltd, C T *57*
Brookhouse's Will Trust, Mr John Charles *65*
Burton 1960 Charitable Settlement, Audrey & Stanley *70*
CfBT Education Services *74*
CLA Charitable Trust *74*
Camelot Foundation, The *78*
Carnegie United Kingdom Trust, The *82*
Company of Chartered Surveyors Charitable Trust Fund, The *108*
Countryside Trust, The *115*
Dashe Trust, The *124*
David Trust, The Lesley *124*
Denby Charitable Foundation, The *130*
Eaton Charitable Trust, J C J *143*
Egerton of Tatton Will Trust, Lord *146*
Esperanza Charitable Trust, The *153*
Fattorini Charitable Trust, James J *160*
Fletcher Charitable Trust, The Joyce *164*
Four Winds Trust *168*
Frazer Charities Trust, The *171*
Galinski Charitable Trust *177*
Gelston Charitable Trust, The *179*
Gibbins Trust, The *181*
Good Neighbours Trust, The *188*
Grant-Lawson Charitable Trust, Lady Virginia *192*
Great Britain Sasakawa Foundation, The *193*
Greenaway Foundation, The Sir Derek *194*
Harewood's Charitable Settlement, Lord *209*
Historic Churches Preservation Trust, The *221*
Homfray Trust, The *226*
Hopkins Charitable Foundation, The Sir Anthony *226*
Hudson Benevolent Trust, The Thomas *230*
Ingles Charitable Trust, The *234*
Keeling Charitable Trust, The Petronella *251*
King Charitable Trust, The Lorna *254*
Lacy Charity Trust, The Late Sir Pierce *260*
Laing Charitable Trust, The David *260*
Lankelly Foundation, The *264*

Lewis Partnership, John *274*
Lloyd's Charities Trust *278*
(Lloyds) TSB Foundation for England and Wales *279*
London Law Trust *280*
Low & Bonar Charitable Fund, The *284*
Lynall Foundation, The D G *287*
Mackintosh Foundation, The *292*
Marriage's Charitable Trust, Miss G M *299*
Marshall's Charity *300*
Milward Charity, The Edgar *313*
N D Educational Trust *325*
Natwest Staff Samaritan Fund *330*
Normanby Charitable Trust *337*
Oldham Foundation *345*
PF Charitable Trust *350*
Paristamen Foundation, The *352*
Pyke Charity Trust *372*
Reader's Digest Trust, The *380*
Rothschild Group Charitable Trust, The J *393*
Royal Botanical & Horticultural Society of Manchester and the Northern Counties, The *395*
Salters Charities *405*
Sargeant's Charitable Trust, Mrs M E *407*
Shaw Foundation, The Linley *416*
Smallpeice Trust, The *425*
Strangward Trust, The *439*
Sykes Trust, The Charles *445*
Symons Charitable Trust, The Stella *446*
Tanner Charitable Settlement, The Joan *449*
Thackray General Charitable Trust, The P & L *452*
Trades Union Congress Educational Trust *460*
Travis Charitable Trust, Constance *460*
Welby Trust, The Barbara *484*
Wills 1961 Charitable Trust, Mr Frederick *493*
Wolfe Family's Charitable Trust, The *498*
Woodhead Charitable Trust, Michael *501*
Worshipful Company of Glass Sellers' Charity Trust, The *505*
Yardy Charitable Trust, The Dennis Alan *509*
Yorkshire and Humberside Arts *510*

Yorkshire Bank Charitable Trust, The *510*
Yorkshire Field Studies Trust *510*

East Riding of Yorkshire

Alec-Smith Charitable Trust, R A *10*
Brotherton Trust, The Charles *65*
Cattle Trust, The Joseph and Annie *86*
Cottingham Charitable Trust, Mrs Diana Mary *114*
Coulthurst Trust, The *115*
Halifax Charitable Trust, The *204*
Hartley Memorial Trust, The N & P *211*
Hull & East Riding Charitable Trust, The *230*
Martin Trust, The Sir George *300*
Moore Foundation, The George A *316*
Pratt Charitable Trust, The W L *367*
Pyke Charity Trust *372*
Shepherd Charitable Trust, The Sylvia and Colin *418*
Yorkshire Agricultural Society *509*

Kingston upon Hull

Alec-Smith Charitable Trust, R A *10*
Cattle Trust, The Joseph and Annie *86*
Hartley Memorial Trust, The N & P *211*
Hull & East Riding Charitable Trust, The *230*
Nunburnholme Trust, The Incorporated Trustees of the *342*
Pyke Charity Trust *372*
Smith Trust, The Sydney *428*
Yorkshire Agricultural Society *509*

North Lincolnshire

Cottingham Charitable Trust, Mrs Diana Mary *114*
Eastern Arts Board *143*
Hartley Memorial Trust, The N & P *211*
Pyke Charity Trust *372*
Warren Foundation, The John *480*
Yorkshire Agricultural Society *509*

North East Lincolnshire

Cottingham Charitable Trust, Mrs Diana Mary *114*
Eastern Arts Board *143*
Hartley Memorial Trust, The N & P *211*
Pyke Charity Trust *372*
Warren Foundation, The John *480*
Yorkshire Agricultural Society *509*

North Yorkshire

Barbour Trust, The *33*
Bell's Charitable Trust, Lady Mary *42*
Brotherton Trust, The Charles *65*
Butler's Trust, Lucilla *72*
Coulthurst Trust, The *115*
Emmandjay Charitable Trust *150*
Fitzwilliam Charitable Trust, The Earl *164*
Hartley Memorial Trust, The N & P *211*
Jacobson Charitable Trust, The Yvette and Hermione *241*
Martin Trust, The Sir George *300*
Metro FM Pop Fund *308*
Moore Foundation, The George A *316*
Pratt Charitable Trust, The W L *367*
Pyke Charity Trust *372*
Rothley Trust, The *392*
Shepherd Charitable Trust, The Sylvia and Colin *418*
Shepherd Family Charitable Trust, The Sir Peter *418*
Smith Trust, Metcalfe *427*
Yorkshire Agricultural Society *509*

South Yorkshire

Coote Old People's Charity Fund, The Marjorie *112*
Coulthurst Trust, The *115*
Dixon Trust Fund, Henry *135*
Emmandjay Charitable Trust *150*
Fitzwilliam Charitable Trust, The Earl *164*
Freshgate Trust Foundation, The *172*
Graves Charitable Trust, J G *192*
Hartley Memorial Trust, The N & P *211*
Hawley Residuary Fund, Harry Fieldsend *212*
Living and Waking Naturally *278*
Martin Trust, The Sir George *300*

Neill Charitable Settlement, J H
331
Pryor Charity, The Ronald &
Kathleen 371
Pyke Charity Trust 372
Shepherd Charitable Trust, The
Sylvia and Colin 418
Smith Trust, Metcalfe 427
South Yorkshire Community
Foundation 431
Sykes Charitable Trust, The
Hugh & Ruby 445
Victoria & Johnson Memorial
Trust, Queen 472
Winstone Foundation, Hyman
497
Yorkshire Agricultural Society
509

York

Brotherton Trust, The Charles
65
Collinson Charitable Trust, The
Norman 106
Coulthurst Trust, The 115
Gray Charitable Trust, R B 192
Hartley Memorial Trust, The N
& P 211
Martin Trust, The Sir George
300
Moore Foundation, The
George A 316
Nestle Rowntree York
Community Fund,
Employees of 331
Pratt Charitable Trust, The W L
367
Pyke Charity Trust 372
Rowntree Charitable Trust, The
Joseph 394
Shepherd Charitable Trust, The
Sylvia and Colin 418
Shepherd Family Charitable
Trust, The Sir Peter 418
Terry Charitable Trust, Noel
Goddard 451
York Common Good Trust 509
Yorkshire Agricultural Society
509

West Yorkshire

Brooke Benevolent Fund,
William 65
Brotherton Trust, The Charles
65
Coulthurst Trust, The 115
Dugdale Charity, The Henry
Percy 138
Emmandjay Charitable Trust
150
Fitzwilliam Charitable Trust,
The Earl 164
Gray Charitable Trust, R B 192
Growth Building Trust, The
198
Hartley Memorial Trust, The N
& P 211

Martin Trust, The Sir George
300
Moore Foundation, The
George A 316
Penny in the Pound Fund
Charitable Trust 359
Pye Christian Trust, The 371
Pyke Charity Trust 372
Rowntree Charitable Trust, The
Joseph 394
Shepherd Charitable Trust, The
Sylvia and Colin 418
Smith Trust, Metcalfe 427
Woodhead Charitable Trust,
Michael 501
Woodhouse Charitable Trust,
Edwin 501
Yorkshire Agricultural Society.
509

■ South East

Full region

Allied Dunbar Staff Charity
Fund 13
Almshouse Association, The 14
Andrew Charitable Trust, The
Prince 16
Army Benevolent Fund, The 22
Assheton-Smith Charitable
Trust 25
Aylesfield Foundation, The 28
Bacta Charitable Trust, The 30
Barleycorn Trust, The 34
Belmont Trust, The 42
Bentall Charity Trust, Rowan
44
Bowring (Charities Fund) Ltd,
C T 57
Brookhouse's Will Trust, Mr
John Charles 65
CfBT Education Services 74
CLA Charitable Trust 74
Camelot Foundation, The 78
Carnegie United Kingdom
Trust, The 82
Clipsham Charitable
Settlement, R E 101
Coates Charitable Trust, The
John 103
Company of Chartered
Surveyors Charitable Trust
Fund, The 108
Countryside Trust, The 115
Dashe Trust, The 124
David Trust, The Lesley 124
Denby Charitable Foundation,
The 130
Egerton of Tatton Will Trust,
Lord 146
Esperanza Charitable Trust, The
153
Fattorini Charitable Trust,
James J 160
Fortune Trust, The 167
Four Winds Trust 168
Frazer Charities Trust, The 171

Galinski Charitable Trust 177
Gelston Charitable Trust, The
179
Gibbins Trust, The 181
Good Neighbours Trust, The
188
Grant-Lawson Charitable Trust,
Lady Virginia 192
Great Britain Sasakawa
Foundation, The 193
Greenaway Foundation, The Sir
Derek 194
Hall Charitable Trust, E F &
M G 204
Hannay Charitable Trust, The
Lennox 208
Historic Churches Preservation
Trust, The 221
Hopkins Charitable Foundation,
The Sir Anthony 226
Howard Charitable Trust, John
& Ruth 229
Ingles Charitable Trust, The
234
King Charitable Trust, The
Lorna 254
Lacy Charity Trust, The Late Sir
Pierce 260
Laing Charitable Trust, The
David 260
Lankelly Foundation, The 264
Lawson Charitable Trust,
Raymond and Blanche 267
Lewis Partnership, John 274
Lloyd's Charities Trust 278
(Lloyds) TSB Foundation for
England and Wales 279
London Law Trust 280
Longley Trust 280
Low & Bonar Charitable Fund,
The 284
Lynall Foundation, The D G
287
Mackintosh Foundation, The
292
Marriage's Charitable Trust,
Miss G M 299
Marshall's Charity 300
Natwest Staff Samaritan Fund
330
Norfolk's Family Charitable
Trust, Lavinia 336
PF Charitable Trust 350
Prince Foundation, The 369
Pyke Charity Trust 372
QAS Charitable Trust 373
Reader's Digest Trust, The 380
Ridgmount Foundation, The
386
Rockcliffe Charitable Trust 389
Rothschild Group Charitable
Trust, The J 393
Salters Charities 405
Sargeant's Charitable Trust,
Mrs M E 407
Schuster Charitable Trust, The
410

Seagram Distillers Charitable
Trust *413*
Shaw Foundation, The Linley
416
Smallpeice Trust, The *425*
Southon Charitable Trust, The
432
Strangward Trust, The *439*
Strauss Charitable Trust *440*
Symons Charitable Trust, The
Stella *446*
Tankel Charitable Trust, Alfred
449
Tanner Charitable Settlement,
The Joan *449*
Trades Union Congress
Educational Trust *460*
Travis Charitable Trust,
Constance *460*
Wander Charitable Fund, The
Dr Albert *479*
Welby Trust, The Barbara *484*
Wills 1961 Charitable Trust, Mr
Frederick *493*
Wolfe Family's Charitable
Trust, The *498*
Woodhead Charitable Trust,
Michael *501*
Worshipful Company of Glass
Sellers' Charity Trust, The
505
Wyford Charitable Trust, The
507
Yardy Charitable Trust, The
Dennis Alan *509*

Berkshire
Bayne Benefaction *38*
Berkshire Community Trust *45*
Blagrave Charitable Trust, The
Herbert and Peter *52*
Buckinghamshire Masonic
Centenary Fund *67*
Carlton Television Trust *81*
Cave Foundation, The Wilfred
and Constance *86*
Dixon Charitable Trust, F E *134*
Earley Charity, The *142*
Gibbins Trust, The *181*
Glasspool Trust, R L *184*
Grant Foundation, The
Raymond *191*
Hyde Charitable Trust *232*
Johnson Wax Limited
Charitable Trust *247*
Longley Trust *280*
Meridian Broadcasting
Charitable Trust *307*
Milward Charity, The Edgar
313
Pyke Charity Trust *372*
Samuel Charitable Trust, Peter
406
Southern Arts *432*

Buckinghamshire
Balney Charitable Trust, The
32
Bayne Benefaction *38*
Buckinghamshire Historic
Churches Trust *67*
Buckinghamshire Masonic
Centenary Fund *67*
Carlton Television Trust *81*
Curtis Charitable Trust, The
Thomas *120*
Gibbins Trust, The *181*
Glasspool Trust, R L *184*
Gold Hill Church Trust *186*
Grant Foundation, The
Raymond *191*
Longley Trust *280*
Milton Keynes Community
Trust Ltd, The *312*
Milward Charity, The Edgar
313
Powell Foundation, The *367*
Pyke Charity Trust *372*
Sell Charitable Trust, Leslie *415*
Southern Arts *432*
Wander Charitable Fund, The
Dr Albert *479*

East Sussex
Askew Charitable Trust, The
Ian *25*
Askew Trust, The Dorothy *25*
Assheton-Smith Charitable
Trust *25*
Brighton & Hove Charitable
Youth Trust *60*
Carlton Television Trust *81*
Charities in Need *89*
Chownes Foundation, The *93*
Curriers Company Charitable
Fund *119*
Denne Charitable Trust *130*
Gibbins Trust, The *181*
Glynde Place Charitable Trust
(1974), The *186*
Hale Trust, The *203*
Lawson Charitable Trust,
Raymond and Blanche *267*
Lilley Benevolent Trust *275*
Longley Trust *280*
MacKintosh Charitable Trust,
Viscount *292*
Mayhew Charitable Trust,
Anthony *303*
Meridian Broadcasting
Charitable Trust *307*
Milward Charity, The Edgar
313
Murphy-Neumann Charity
Company Limited *323*
Pyke Charity Trust *372*
Robinson Trust No 3, The J C
388
Robinson Trust 4, The J C *388*
Sailors' and Soldiers' Home
Fund, and Leonard Lionel

Bloomfield's Charity, The
401
Smith Trust Fund, The Griffith
427
South East Arts Board *430*
Southover Manor General
Education Trust Ltd *433*

Hampshire
Aylesfield Foundation, The *28*
Belmont Trust, The *42*
Blagrave Charitable Trust, The
Herbert and Peter *52*
Bonhomie United Charity
Society *56*
Campbell Charitable
Foundation, The Ellis *79*
Carlton Television Trust *81*
Challice Trust, The *87*
Cranbury Foundation, The *117*
Dibden Allotments Charity *132*
Elvetham Charitable Trust, The
149
Ford of Britain Trust *166*
Four Lanes Trust, The *168*
Gibbins Trust, The *181*
Glasspool Trust, R L *184*
Grant-Lawson Charitable Trust,
Lady Virginia *192*
Haywood Charitable Trust *214*
Hyde Charitable Trust *232*
Johnson Wax Limited
Charitable Trust *247*
Knightly Charitable Trust, The
David *257*
Linmardon Trust *276*
Longley Trust *280*
Meridian Broadcasting
Charitable Trust *307*
Milward Charity, The Edgar
313
Morphy Memorial Fund, Arthur
319
Northcott Charity Trust, The
338
Pyke Charity Trust *372*
Robbins Trust, The Cheshire
387
Samuel Charitable Trust, Peter
406
Southern Arts *432*
Stephenson (Decd), Will Trust
of Edgar John Henry *436*
Vec Acorn Trust, The *472*

Isle of Wight
Belmont Trust, The *42*
Ford of Britain Trust *166*
Gibbins Trust, The *181*
Longley Trust *280*
Meridian Broadcasting
Charitable Trust *307*
Milward Charity, The Edgar
313
Pyke Charity Trust *372*
Southern Arts *432*

Kent (not London Boroughs)

Astor of Hever Trust, The 26
Betteshanger Charitable Trust 46
Birchwood Trust, The 49
Brickkiln Trust, The 59
Carlton Television Trust 81
Cole Charitable Trust, The 105
Colyer-Fergusson Charitable Trust, The 107
D'Avigdor Goldsmid Charitable Trust, The Sarah 125
Denne Charitable Trust 130
Doubleday Trust, The Garth 136
Friends of Kent Churches 173
Gibbins Trust, The 181
Glasspool Trust, R L 184
Greenaway Foundation, The Sir Derek 194
Hale Trust, The 203
Hyde Charitable Trust 232
Jessel Charitable Trust, The Sir Charles 244
Lawson Charitable Trust, Raymond and Blanche 267
London Taxi Drivers' Fund for Underprivileged Children, The 280
Longley Trust 280
MacKintosh Charitable Trust, Viscount 292
Meridian Broadcasting Charitable Trust 307
Milward Charity, The Edgar 313
Pyke Charity Trust 372
Sailors' and Soldiers' Home Fund, and Leonard Lionel Bloomfield's Charity, The 401
Smith & Mount Trust, The Mrs 426
South East Arts Board 430
Swale Charity Trust 443
Tory Family Foundation, The 459

Oxfordshire

Astor's Charitable Trust, The Hon M L 26
Ballard Charitable Trust, The Stanton 32
Bayne Benefaction 38
Bishopsdown Trust, The 51
Brunner Third Charitable Trust, Sir Felix 66
Buckinghamshire Masonic Centenary Fund 67
Bull Charitable Trust, Henry Robert 68
CHK Charities Limited 74
Carlton Television Trust 81
Cooper Charitable Trust, The 111

Dawson Educational Foundation, Thomas 126
Early's Charitable Settlement, Richard 142
Gibbins Trust, The 181
Grant Foundation, The Raymond 191
Longley Trust 280
Meridian Broadcasting Charitable Trust 307
Milward Charity, The Edgar 313
Pyke Charity Trust 372
Simon's Charity 422
Southern Arts 432
Waley-Cohen Charitable Trust, Robert & Felicity 477

Surrey (not London Boroughs)

Beckwith-Smith's Charitable Settlement, Mrs 40
Birtwistle Memorial Trust, The G E 50
Carlton Television Trust 81
Challice Trust, The 87
Curriers Company Charitable Fund 119
Gibbins Trust, The 181
Glasspool Trust, R L 184
Grundy Foundation, The Stanley 198
Hale Trust, The 203
Hyde Charitable Trust 232
Johnson Wax Limited Charitable Trust 247
Lambourne Memorial Trust, The Emma 262
Lavender Trust, The 267
Leonard Trust, The Erica 270
London Taxi Drivers' Fund for Underprivileged Children, The 280
Longley Trust 280
Meridian Broadcasting Charitable Trust 307
Milward Charity, The Edgar 313
Morphy Memorial Fund, Arthur 319
Pyke Charity Trust 372
Roberts Charitable Trust, F G 388
Smith & Mount Trust, The Mrs 426
South East Arts Board 430
Wagstaff Charitable Trust, Bob 475
Wates Charitable Trust, John 481

West Sussex

Abel Charitable Trust 5
Aldwyns Trust, The 10
Askew Charitable Trust, The Ian 25
Askew Trust, The Dorothy 25

Assheton-Smith Charitable Trust 25
Beckwith-Smith's Charitable Settlement, Mrs 40
Belmont Trust, The 42
Brighton & Hove Charitable Youth Trust 60
Carlton Television Trust 81
Challice Trust, The 87
Charities in Need 89
Chownes Foundation, The 93
Curriers Company Charitable Fund 119
Curzon Charitable Trust, The Wallace 120
Denne Charitable Trust 130
Friarsgate Trust 172
Gibbins Trust, The 181
Glynde Place Charitable Trust (1974), The 186
Hale Trust, The 203
Hyde Charitable Trust 232
Innes Memorial Fund 235
Lilley Benevolent Trust 275
Longley Trust 280
MacKintosh Charitable Trust, Viscount 292
Mayhew Charitable Trust, Anthony 303
Meridian Broadcasting Charitable Trust 307
Milward Charity, The Edgar 313
Morphy Memorial Fund, Arthur 319
Murphy-Neumann Charity Company Limited 323
Norfolk's Family Charitable Trust, Lavinia 336
Older's School Charity, William 345
Pyke Charity Trust 372
Ravenscroft Foundation, The 379
Robinson Trust No 3, The J C 388
Rotary Club of Worthing's Community Service Fund 392
Shippam Trust, Bassil 420
South East Arts Board 430
Southover Manor General Education Trust Ltd 433

■ South West & Channel Islands

Full region

Allied Dunbar Staff Charity Fund 13
Almshouse Association, The 14
Andrew Charitable Trust, The Prince 16
Army Benevolent Fund, The 22
Assheton-Smith Charitable Trust 25
Bacta Charitable Trust, The 30

Barleycorn Trust, The *34*

Bowring (Charities Fund) Ltd, C T *57*

Brookhouse's Will Trust, Mr John Charles *65*

CfBT Education Services *74*

CLA Charitable Trust *74*

Camelot Foundation, The *78*

Carnegie United Kingdom Trust, The *82*

Coates Charitable Trust, The John *103*

Company of Chartered Surveyors Charitable Trust Fund, The *108*

Cornwall Benevolent Fund, The Duke of *114*

Curzon Charitable Trust, The Wallace *120*

Dashe Trust, The *124*

David Trust, The Lesley *124*

Denby Charitable Foundation, The *130*

du Boulay Charitable Trust, The Anthony *138*

Egerton of Tatton Will Trust, Lord *146*

Esperanza Charitable Trust, The *153*

Fattorini Charitable Trust, James J *160*

Ferguson Benevolent Fund Limited *161*

Fletcher Charitable Trust, The Joyce *164*

Four Winds Trust *168*

Frazer Charities Trust, The *171*

Galinski Charitable Trust *177*

Gelston Charitable Trust, The *179*

Gibbins Trust, The *181*

Good Neighbours Trust, The *188*

Great Britain Sasakawa Foundation, The *193*

Greenaway Foundation, The Sir Derek *194*

Hannay Charitable Trust, The Lennox *208*

Historic Churches Preservation Trust, The *221*

Hopkins Charitable Foundation, The Sir Anthony *226*

Howard Charitable Trust, John & Ruth *229*

King Charitable Trust, The Lorna *254*

Lacy Charity Trust, The Late Sir Pierce *260*

Laing Charitable Trust, The David *260*

Lankelly Foundation, The *264*

Leach Fourteenth Trust, The *267*

Lewis Partnership, John *274*

Lloyd's Charities Trust *278*

London Law Trust *280*

Low & Bonar Charitable Fund, The *284*

Lynall Foundation, The D G *287*

Mackintosh Foundation, The *292*

Marriage's Charitable Trust, Miss G M *299*

Marshall's Charity *300*

Milward Charity, The Edgar *313*

Natwest Staff Samaritan Fund *330*

Oldham Foundation *345*

PF Charitable Trust *350*

Prestwich Charitable Trust, The Douglas P *368*

Prince Foundation, The *369*

Reader's Digest Trust, The *380*

Ripley's Charitable Trust, Pat *386*

Rockcliffe Charitable Trust *389*

Rothschild Group Charitable Trust, The J *393*

Salters Charities *405*

Sargeant's Charitable Trust, Mrs M E *407*

Schuster Charitable Trust, The *410*

Shaw Foundation, The Linley *416*

Smallpeice Trust, The *425*

Southon Charitable Trust, The *432*

Strangward Trust, The *439*

Strauss Charitable Trust *440*

Studd Charitable Trust *441*

Symons Charitable Trust, The Stella *446*

Tankel Charitable Trust, Alfred *449*

Tanner Charitable Settlement, The Joan *449*

Travis Charitable Trust, Constance *460*

Verdon-Smith Family Charitable Settlement, The *472*

Wakefield Trust, The *476*

Welby Trust, The Barbara *484*

Wills 1961 Charitable Trust, Mr Frederick *493*

Wills Will Trust 1965, Dame Violet *494*

Wolfe Family's Charitable Trust, The *498*

Woodhead Charitable Trust, Michael *501*

Worshipful Company of Glass Sellers' Charity Trust, The *505*

Yardy Charitable Trust, The Dennis Alan *509*

Bath & North East Somerset

Boyd Charitable Trust, The Viscountess *57*

Britton Charitable Trust, The J & M *63*

Bugden Charitable Trust, The Rosemary *67*

Countryside Trust, The *115*

Coutts Charitable Trust, The *116*

GWR Community Trust *176*

Grant-Lawson Charitable Trust, Lady Virginia *192*

Harris Charitable Settlement, R J *210*

Lalonde Trust *262*

Leach Fourteenth Trust, The *267*

(Lloyds) TSB Foundation for England and Wales *279*

Needham Cooper Charitable Trust, The *331*

Norman Family Charitable Trust, The *337*

Pyke Charity Trust *372*

South West Arts *431*

Summer's and I May's Charitable Settlement, The Late Misses (A N) *442*

Trades Union Congress Educational Trust *460*

Bristol

Armstrong Trust, The *21*

Boyd Charitable Trust, The Viscountess *57*

Britton Charitable Trust, The J & M *63*

Bugden Charitable Trust, The Rosemary *67*

Countryside Trust, The *115*

Coutts Charitable Trust, The *116*

Davies Charitable Foundation, Richard *124*

GWR Community Trust *176*

Grant-Lawson Charitable Trust, Lady Virginia *192*

Greater Bristol Foundation *193*

Harris Charitable Settlement, R J *210*

James (No 2) Charitable Foundation, The Dawn *242*

Lalonde Trust *262*

(Lloyds) TSB Foundation for England and Wales *279*

Needham Cooper Charitable Trust, The *331*

Pyke Charity Trust *372*

Robinson Trust No 3, The J C *388*

Scobell Charitable Trust, The *410*

South West Arts *431*

Summer's and I May's
Charitable Settlement, The
Late Misses (A N) *442*
Trades Union Congress
Educational Trust *460*
Wall Charitable Trust, The *478*

Channel Islands (Jersey & Guernsey)
Ferguson Benevolent Fund
Limited *161*
Grant-Lawson Charitable Trust,
Lady Virginia *192*
Pyke Charity Trust *372*

Cornwall
BCH 1971 Charitable Trust *29*
Blanchminster Trust, The *54*
Boyd Charitable Trust, The
Viscountess *57*
Clinton's Charitable Trust, Lord
100
Cornwell Charitable Trust, The
114
Countryside Trust, The *115*
Davis Charitable Trust, Wilfrid
Bruce *126*
Elmgrant Trust *149*
Grant-Lawson Charitable Trust,
Lady Virginia *192*
Hudson Charitable Trust, The
230
(Lloyds) TSB Foundation for
England and Wales *279*
Norman Family Charitable
Trust, The *337*
Pole 1973 Charitable Trust, The
Sir Richard Carew *365*
Pole Charitable Trust, Carew
365
Pyke Charity Trust *372*
Rayner Trust, Elizabeth *380*
South West Arts *431*
Summer's and I May's
Charitable Settlement, The
Late Misses (A N) *442*
Trades Union Congress
Educational Trust *460*

Devon
BCH 1971 Charitable Trust *29*
Boyd Charitable Trust, The
Viscountess *57*
Clinton's Charitable Trust, Lord
100
Cornerstone Charitable Trust
114
Countryside Trust, The *115*
Devon Association for the
Blind *131*
Elmgrant Trust *149*
Fogwell's Charity, Sarah Wood
166
Gahan's Charitable Foundation,
Mrs D H *176*
Gilley Charitable Trust, The L &
R *183*

Grant-Lawson Charitable Trust,
Lady Virginia *192*
Hudson Charitable Trust, The
230
Lalonde Trust *262*
Lesley Lesley and Mutter Trust
271
(Lloyds) TSB Foundation for
England and Wales *279*
Norman Family Charitable
Trust, The *337*
Northcott Devon Foundation
338
Pike Charity Settlement *362*
Pike Woodlands Trust, Claude
& Margaret *362*
Pole 1973 Charitable Trust, The
Sir Richard Carew *365*
Pole Charitable Trust, Carew
365
Pyke Charity Trust *372*
Rayner Trust, Elizabeth *380*
South West Arts *431*
Sparkes Charitable Trust, The
Eric F *433*
Summer's and I May's
Charitable Settlement, The
Late Misses (A N) *442*
Trades Union Congress
Educational Trust *460*
Webber Trust Fund, Ethel *483*

Dorset
Britton Charitable Trust, The J
& M *63*
Clinton's Charitable Trust, Lord
100
Countryside Trust, The *115*
Digby Charitable Trust, Simon
133
Grant-Lawson Charitable Trust,
Lady Virginia *192*
Harris Charitable Settlement,
R J *210*
Knightly Charitable Trust, The
David *257*
(Lloyds) TSB Foundation for
England and Wales *279*
Meridian Broadcasting
Charitable Trust *307*
Pyke Charity Trust *372*
Robbins Trust, The Cheshire
387
South West Arts *431*
Southern Arts *432*
Stephenson (Decd), Will Trust
of Edgar John Henry *436*
Summer's and I May's
Charitable Settlement, The
Late Misses (A N) *442*
Trades Union Congress
Educational Trust *460*

Gloucestershire
Armstrong Trust, The *21*
Britton Charitable Trust, The J
& M *63*

Bugden Charitable Trust, The
Rosemary *67*
Bull Charitable Trust, Henry
Robert *68*
CHK Charities Limited *74*
Countryside Trust, The *115*
Grant-Lawson Charitable Trust,
Lady Virginia *192*
Harris Charitable Settlement,
R J *210*
Irving Charitable Trust, The
Charles *237*
Langtree Trust, The *264*
(Lloyds) TSB Foundation for
England and Wales *279*
Needham Cooper Charitable
Trust, The *331*
Notgrove Trust, The *341*
Penny in the Pound Fund
Charitable Trust *359*
Pyke Charity Trust *372*
Ravenscroft Foundation, The
379
Rest-Harrow Trust, The *382*
Ross Charitable Trust, The *392*
Sedbury Trust, The *414*
South West Arts *431*
Stevens Foundation, The June
437
Summerfield Charitable Trust,
The *442*
Summer's and I May's
Charitable Settlement, The
Late Misses (A N) *442*
Trades Union Congress
Educational Trust *460*

Isles of Scilly
Boyd Charitable Trust, The
Viscountess *57*
Clinton's Charitable Trust, Lord
100
Countryside Trust, The *115*
Grant-Lawson Charitable Trust,
Lady Virginia *192*
Leach Fourteenth Trust, The
267
(Lloyds) TSB Foundation for
England and Wales *279*
Pyke Charity Trust *372*

North West Somerset
Britton Charitable Trust, The J
& M *63*
Bugden Charitable Trust, The
Rosemary *67*
Countryside Trust, The *115*
Grant-Lawson Charitable Trust,
Lady Virginia *192*
Harris Charitable Settlement,
R J *210*
Lalonde Trust *262*
(Lloyds) TSB Foundation for
England and Wales *279*
Needham Cooper Charitable
Trust, The *331*

Norman Family Charitable
Trust, The *337*
Pyke Charity Trust *372*
South West Arts *431*
Summer's and I May's
Charitable Settlement, The
Late Misses (A N) *442*
Trades Union Congress
Educational Trust *460*

Somerset
Britton Charitable Trust, The J
& M *63*
Bugden Charitable Trust, The
Rosemary *67*
Countryside Trust, The *115*
Gilley Charitable Trust, The L &
R *183*
Grant-Lawson Charitable Trust,
Lady Virginia *192*
Harris Charitable Settlement,
R J *210*
Lalonde Trust *262*
(Lloyds) TSB Foundation for
England and Wales *279*
Needham Cooper Charitable
Trust, The *331*
Norman Family Charitable
Trust, The *337*
Pyke Charity Trust *372*
South West Arts *431*
Summer's and I May's
Charitable Settlement, The
Late Misses (A N) *442*
Trades Union Congress
Educational Trust *460*

South Gloucestershire
Britton Charitable Trust, The J
& M *63*
Countryside Trust, The *115*
Early's Charitable Settlement,
Richard *142*
Grant-Lawson Charitable Trust,
Lady Virginia *192*
Harris Charitable Settlement,
R J *210*
Lalonde Trust *262*
(Lloyds) TSB Foundation for
England and Wales *279*
Needham Cooper Charitable
Trust, The *331*
Pyke Charity Trust *372*
Robinson Trust No 3, The J C
388
South West Arts *431*
Summer's and I May's
Charitable Settlement, The
Late Misses (A N) *442*
Trades Union Congress
Educational Trust *460*

Wiltshire
Blagrave Charitable Trust, The
Herbert and Peter *52*
Britton Charitable Trust, The J
& M *63*

Cave Foundation, The Wilfred
and Constance *86*
Countryside Trust, The *115*
GWR Community Trust *176*
Gale Charitable Trust, A W *176*
Grant-Lawson Charitable Trust,
Lady Virginia *192*
Harris Charitable Settlement,
R J *210*
Haymills Charitable Trust *213*
Knightly Charitable Trust, The
David *257*
Leach Fourteenth Trust, The
267
(Lloyds) TSB Foundation for
England and Wales *279*
Margadale Charitable Trust,
Lord *297*
Meridian Broadcasting
Charitable Trust *307*
Needham Cooper Charitable
Trust, The *331*
Pyke Charity Trust *372*
Sarum St Michael Educational
Charity, The *408*
Southern Arts *432*
Summer's and I May's
Charitable Settlement, The
Late Misses (A N) *442*
Trades Union Congress
Educational Trust *460*
Wiltshire Community
Foundation *495*

■ London
Full region
Abel Charitable Trust *5*
Aldwyns Trust, The *10*
Alexandra Trust *11*
Allied Dunbar Staff Charity
Fund *13*
Almshouse Association, The *14*
Andrew Charitable Trust, The
Prince *16*
Army Benevolent Fund, The *22*
Assembled Church of Christ
Trust, The *25*
Assheton-Smith Charitable
Trust *25*
Bacta Charitable Trust, The *30*
Barleycorn Trust, The *34*
Bengough Trust, The *43*
Bowring (Charities Fund) Ltd,
C T *57*
Brookhouse's Will Trust, Mr
John Charles *65*
Buxton Trust, Denis *72*
CfBT Education Services *74*
CLA Charitable Trust *74*
Cadogan Charity, The *77*
Camelot Foundation, The *78*
Carlton Television Trust *81*
Carnegie United Kingdom
Trust, The *82*
Cass's Foundation, Sir John *85*

Charity Fund of the Worshipful
Company of Paviors *89*
Charterhouse Charitable Trust,
The *90*
Chownes Foundation, The *93*
City and Metropolitan Welfare
Charity, The *96*
Clipsham Charitable
Settlement, R E *101*
Coates Charitable Trust, The
John *103*
Company of Chartered
Surveyors Charitable Trust
Fund, The *108*
Company of Tobacco Pipe
Makers and Tobacco
Blenders Benevolent Fund
109
Construction Industry Trust for
Youth, The *110*
Coutts Charitable Trust, The
116
Cripplegate Foundation *118*
Curriers Company Charitable
Fund *119*
Curzon Charitable Trust, The
Wallace *120*
Dashe Trust, The *124*
David Trust, The Lesley *124*
Delmar Charitable Trust *129*
Denby Charitable Foundation,
The *130*
Deutsch Charitable Trust, The
Andre *131*
Egerton of Tatton Will Trust,
Lord *146*
Esperanza Charitable Trust, The
153
Fattorini Charitable Trust,
James J *160*
Fishmongers' Company's
Charitable Trust *163*
Fogel Charitable Trust, The
Gerald *165*
Four Winds Trust *168*
Frazer Charities Trust, The *171*
Fulham Cross Christian Mission
175
Galinski Charitable Trust *177*
Garbacz Charitable Trust, The
Bernard & Vera *178*
Gelston Charitable Trust, The
179
Gibbins Trust, The *181*
Glasspool Trust, R L *184*
Glynde Place Charitable Trust
(1974), The *186*
Good Neighbours Trust, The
188
Grant-Lawson Charitable Trust,
Lady Virginia *192*
Great Britain Sasakawa
Foundation, The *193*
Greenaway Foundation, The Sir
Derek *194*
Hannay Charitable Trust, The
Lennox *208*

Haslemere Estates Charitable
Trust *212*
Heritage of London Trust, The
216
Historic Churches Preservation
Trust, The *221*
Hopkins Charitable Foundation,
The Sir Anthony *226*
Howard Charitable Trust, John
& Ruth *229*
Ingles Charitable Trust, The
234
Jacobson Charitable Trust, The
Yvette and Hermione *241*
Joseph Charitable Trust, J E
248
Keeling Charitable Trust, The
Petronella *251*
Kendall's Charity, William *252*
King Charitable Trust, The
Lorna *254*
King's Fund, The *255*
Lacy Charity Trust, The Late Sir
Pierce *260*
Laing Charitable Trust, The
David *260*
Lester Trust Fund, The *271*
Lewis Partnership, John *274*
Liffe Benefit *274*
Lloyd's Charities Trust *278*
(Lloyds) TSB Foundation for
England and Wales *279*
London Arts Board *280*
London Law Trust *280*
London Taxi Drivers' Fund for
Underprivileged Children,
The *280*
Low & Bonar Charitable Fund,
The *284*
Lowenthal Charitable Trust,
The L and C *285*
Lynall Foundation, The D G
287
Lyon's Charity, John *288*
Mackintosh Foundation, The
292
Marriage's Charitable Trust,
Miss G M *299*
Marshall's Charity *300*
Melchett Children's Trust, The
Violet *305*
Metropolitan Police Combined
Benevolent Fund *308*
Milward Charity, The Edgar
313
Moore Stephens Charitable
Foundation, The *317*
Napier Charitable Trust, The
Gordon *326*
Natwest Staff Samaritan Fund
330
Newman Foundation, The
Frances and Augustus *334*
Ogilvie Charities (Deed No 2)
344
Oliver Charitable Foundation,
The *345*
PF Charitable Trust *350*

Plaisterers' Company Charitable
Trust, The *364*
Prestwich Charitable Trust, The
Douglas P *368*
Pyke Charity Trust *372*
Reader's Digest Trust, The *380*
Reeve's Foundation *382*
Ridgmount Foundation, The
386
Rockcliffe Charitable Trust *389*
Rogers Charitable Settlement,
The Richard *390*
Rope Third Charitable
Settlement, The Mrs *391*
Rothschild Group Charitable
Trust, The J *393*
Royal Victoria Hall Foundation,
The *396*
S Group Charitable Trust *399*
Saint Edmund King and Martyr
Trust *402*
Salters Charities *405*
Sargeant's Charitable Trust,
Mrs M E *407*
Schuster Charitable Trust, The
410
Seagram Distillers Charitable
Trust *413*
Shine No 2 Charitable Trust,
The Barnett and Sylvia *420*
Smallpeice Trust, The *425*
Smith & Mount Trust, The Mrs
426
Southon Charitable Trust, The
432
Strangward Trust, The *439*
Strauss Charitable Trust *440*
Sulgrave Charitable Trust *442*
Sussman Charitable Trust,
Adrienne & Leslie *443*
Symons Charitable Trust, The
Stella *446*
Tankel Charitable Trust, Alfred
449
Tanner Charitable Settlement,
The Joan *449*
Trades Union Congress
Educational Trust *460*
Travis Charitable Trust,
Constance *460*
Turner Charitable Settlement,
The Sir Mark and Lady *464*
Waley-Cohen Charitable Trust,
Robert & Felicity *477*
Wander Charitable Fund, The
Dr Albert *479*
Wates Charitable Trust, John
481
Wates Foundation, The *481*
Welby Trust, The Barbara *484*
Whitaker Charitable Trust *489*
Wills 1961 Charitable Trust, Mr
Frederick *493*
Wolfe Family's Charitable
Trust, The *498*
Woodhead Charitable Trust,
Michael *501*

Worshipful Company of
Builders Merchants *504*
Worshipful Company of
Founders Charities, The *505*
Worshipful Company of Glass
Sellers' Charity Trust, The
505
Worshipful Company of
Launderers Benevolent Trust
Fund, The *505*
Worshipful Company of
Needlemakers' Charitable
Fund *505*
Wyford Charitable Trust, The
507
Yardy Charitable Trust, The
Dennis Alan *509*

Northern Ireland

Full area
Allied Dunbar Staff Charity Fund *13*
Army Benevolent Fund, The *22*
Assheton-Smith Charitable Trust *25*
Astor Foundation, The *26*
Bengough Trust, The *43*
Blackburn Trust, The *51*
Britland Charitable Trust, The *63*
Brookhouse's Will Trust, Mr John Charles *65*
Buxton Trust, Denis *72*
Cadbury Charitable Trust, William Adlington *75*
Cobb Charity *103*
Company of Chartered Surveyors Charitable Trust Fund, The *108*
Construction Industry Trust for Youth, The *110*
David Trust, The Lesley *124*
Denby Charitable Foundation, The *130*
Enkalon Foundation *151*
Esperanza Charitable Trust, The *153*
Fattorini Charitable Trust, James J *160*
Fleming Charitable Trust, The Ian *164*
Four Winds Trust *168*
Grant-Lawson Charitable Trust, Lady Virginia *192*
HACT (The Housing Association's Charitable Trust) *201*
Hopkins Charitable Foundation, The Sir Anthony *226*
Hudson Benevolent Trust, The Thomas *230*
Ireland Funds, The *237*
Lankelly Foundation, The *264*
Lee Foundation, The Edgar *269*
London Law Trust *280*
Mackintosh Foundation, The *292*
Milward Charity, The Edgar *313*
Mitchell Trust, Esme *315*
Moores Foundation, John *318*
National Art-Collections Fund *327*
National Committee of The Women's World Day of Prayer for England, Wales and Northern Ireland, The *327*
Northern Ireland Voluntary Trust *339*
Persula Foundation, The *360*
Pyke Charity Trust *372*
Rank Foundation, The *377*

Ridgmount Foundation, The *386*
Rope Third Charitable Settlement, The Mrs *391*
Rowntree Charitable Trust, The Joseph *394*
Scotbelge Charitable Trust, The *411*
Scott Bader Commonwealth Ltd, The *411*
Smallpeice Trust, The *425*
Southdown Trust *432*
Sykes Trust, The Charles *445*
Tanner Charitable Settlement, The Joan *449*
Tisbury Telegraph Trust, The *457*
Ultach Trust *467*
Wates Foundation, The *481*
Whitaker Charitable Trust *489*
Wolfe Family's Charitable Trust, The *498*
Women Caring Trust, The *500*

Antrim
Allied Dunbar Staff Charity Fund *13*
Andrew Charitable Trust, The Prince *16*
Army Benevolent Fund, The *22*
Assheton-Smith Charitable Trust *25*
Blackburn Trust, The *51*
Brookhouse's Will Trust, Mr John Charles *65*
Buxton Trust, Denis *72*
CfBT Education Services *74*
Camelot Foundation, The *78*
Campbell Charitable Foundation, The Ellis *79*
Carnegie United Kingdom Trust, The *82*
Company of Chartered Surveyors Charitable Trust Fund, The *108*
Construction Industry Trust for Youth, The *110*
Curzon Charitable Trust, The Wallace *120*
David Trust, The Lesley *124*
Egerton of Tatton Will Trust, Lord *146*
Fattorini Charitable Trust, James J *160*
Ford of Britain Trust *166*
Four Winds Trust *168*
Gelston Charitable Trust, The *179*
Grant-Lawson Charitable Trust, Lady Virginia *192*
Great Britain Sasakawa Foundation, The *193*
Hopkins Charitable Foundation, The Sir Anthony *226*
Ireland Funds, The *237*
Lacy Charity Trust, The Late Sir Pierce *260*

Laspen Trust *265*
Lloyd's Charities Trust *278*
London Law Trust *280*
Mackintosh Foundation, The *292*
Mitchell Trust, Esme *315*
PF Charitable Trust *350*
Penny in the Pound Fund Charitable Trust *359*
Pyke Charity Trust *372*
Reader's Digest Trust, The *380*
Rowntree Charitable Trust, The Joseph *394*
Strangward Trust, The *439*
Sykes Trust, The Charles *445*
Tanner Charitable Settlement, The Joan *449*
Wates Foundation, The *481*
Whitaker Charitable Trust *489*
Wills 1961 Charitable Trust, Mr Frederick *493*
Women Caring Trust, The *500*
Yardy Charitable Trust, The Dennis Alan *509*
Yorkshire Field Studies Trust *510*

Armagh
Andrew Charitable Trust, The Prince *16*
Army Benevolent Fund, The *22*
Assheton-Smith Charitable Trust *25*
Blackburn Trust, The *51*
Brookhouse's Will Trust, Mr John Charles *65*
CfBT Education Services *74*
Camelot Foundation, The *78*
Carnegie United Kingdom Trust, The *82*
Company of Chartered Surveyors Charitable Trust Fund, The *108*
Construction Industry Trust for Youth, The *110*
David Trust, The Lesley *124*
Egerton of Tatton Will Trust, Lord *146*
Fattorini Charitable Trust, James J *160*
Ford of Britain Trust *166*
Four Winds Trust *168*
Grant-Lawson Charitable Trust, Lady Virginia *192*
Great Britain Sasakawa Foundation, The *193*
Hopkins Charitable Foundation, The Sir Anthony *226*
Ireland Funds, The *237*
Lacy Charity Trust, The Late Sir Pierce *260*
Laspen Trust *265*
London Law Trust *280*
Mackintosh Foundation, The *292*
Mitchell Trust, Esme *315*
Pyke Charity Trust *372*

Reader's Digest Trust, The *380*
Rowntree Charitable Trust, The
Joseph *394*
Strangward Trust, The *439*
Sykes Trust, The Charles *445*
Tanner Charitable Settlement,
The Joan *449*
Wates Foundation, The *481*
Whitaker Charitable Trust *489*
Wills 1961 Charitable Trust, Mr
Frederick *493*
Women Caring Trust, The *500*
Yardy Charitable Trust, The
Dennis Alan *509*

Down
Andrew Charitable Trust, The
Prince *16*
Army Benevolent Fund, The *22*
Assheton-Smith Charitable
Trust *25*
Blackburn Trust, The *51*
Brookhouse's Will Trust, Mr
John Charles *65*
CfBT Education Services *74*
Camelot Foundation, The *78*
Carnegie United Kingdom
Trust, The *82*
Company of Chartered
Surveyors Charitable Trust
Fund, The *108*
Construction Industry Trust for
Youth, The *110*
David Trust, The Lesley *124*
Egerton of Tatton Will Trust,
Lord *146*
Fattorini Charitable Trust,
James J *160*
Ford of Britain Trust *166*
Four Winds Trust *168*
Grant-Lawson Charitable Trust,
Lady Virginia *192*
Great Britain Sasakawa
Foundation, The *193*
Hopkins Charitable Foundation,
The Sir Anthony *226*
Ireland Funds, The *237*
Lacy Charity Trust, The Late Sir
Pierce *260*
Laspen Trust *265*
London Law Trust *280*
Mackintosh Foundation, The
292
Mitchell Trust, Esme *315*
Penny in the Pound Fund
Charitable Trust *359*
Pyke Charity Trust *372*
Reader's Digest Trust, The *380*
Rowntree Charitable Trust, The
Joseph *394*
Strangward Trust, The *439*
Sykes Trust, The Charles *445*
Tanner Charitable Settlement,
The Joan *449*
Wates Foundation, The *481*
Whitaker Charitable Trust *489*

Wills 1961 Charitable Trust, Mr
Frederick *493*
Women Caring Trust, The *500*
Yardy Charitable Trust, The
Dennis Alan *509*

Fermanagh
Andrew Charitable Trust, The
Prince *16*
Army Benevolent Fund, The *22*
Assheton-Smith Charitable
Trust *25*
Blackburn Trust, The *51*
Brookhouse's Will Trust, Mr
John Charles *65*
CfBT Education Services *74*
Camelot Foundation, The *78*
Carnegie United Kingdom
Trust, The *82*
Company of Chartered
Surveyors Charitable Trust
Fund, The *108*
Construction Industry Trust for
Youth, The *110*
David Trust, The Lesley *124*
Egerton of Tatton Will Trust,
Lord *146*
Fattorini Charitable Trust,
James J *160*
Four Winds Trust *168*
Grant-Lawson Charitable Trust,
Lady Virginia *192*
Great Britain Sasakawa
Foundation, The *193*
Hopkins Charitable Foundation,
The Sir Anthony *226*
Ireland Funds, The *237*
Lacy Charity Trust, The Late Sir
Pierce *260*
Laspen Trust *265*
London Law Trust *280*
Mackintosh Foundation, The
292
Mitchell Trust, Esme *315*
Pyke Charity Trust *372*
Reader's Digest Trust, The *380*
Rowntree Charitable Trust, The
Joseph *394*
Strangward Trust, The *439*
Sykes Trust, The Charles *445*
Tanner Charitable Settlement,
The Joan *449*
Wates Foundation, The *481*
Whitaker Charitable Trust *489*
Wills 1961 Charitable Trust, Mr
Frederick *493*
Women Caring Trust, The *500*
Yardy Charitable Trust, The
Dennis Alan *509*

Londonderry
Andrew Charitable Trust, The
Prince *16*
Army Benevolent Fund, The *22*
Assheton-Smith Charitable
Trust *25*
Blackburn Trust, The *51*

Brookhouse's Will Trust, Mr
John Charles *65*
CfBT Education Services *74*
Camelot Foundation, The *78*
Carnegie United Kingdom
Trust, The *82*
Company of Chartered
Surveyors Charitable Trust
Fund, The *108*
Construction Industry Trust for
Youth, The *110*
David Trust, The Lesley *124*
Egerton of Tatton Will Trust,
Lord *146*
Fattorini Charitable Trust,
James J *160*
Four Winds Trust *168*
Grant-Lawson Charitable Trust,
Lady Virginia *192*
Great Britain Sasakawa
Foundation, The *193*
Hopkins Charitable Foundation,
The Sir Anthony *226*
Ireland Funds, The *237*
Lacy Charity Trust, The Late Sir
Pierce *260*
Laspen Trust *265*
London Law Trust *280*
Mackintosh Foundation, The
292
Mitchell Trust, Esme *315*
Pyke Charity Trust *372*
Reader's Digest Trust, The *380*
Rowntree Charitable Trust, The
Joseph *394*
Strangward Trust, The *439*
Sykes Trust, The Charles *445*
Tanner Charitable Settlement,
The Joan *449*
Wates Foundation, The *481*
Whitaker Charitable Trust *489*
Wills 1961 Charitable Trust, Mr
Frederick *493*
Women Caring Trust, The *500*
Yardy Charitable Trust, The
Dennis Alan *509*

Tyrone
Andrew Charitable Trust, The
Prince *16*
Army Benevolent Fund, The *22*
Assheton-Smith Charitable
Trust *25*
Blackburn Trust, The *51*
Brookhouse's Will Trust, Mr
John Charles *65*
CfBT Education Services *74*
Camelot Foundation, The *78*
Carnegie United Kingdom
Trust, The *82*
Company of Chartered
Surveyors Charitable Trust
Fund, The *108*
Construction Industry Trust for
Youth, The *110*
David Trust, The Lesley *124*

Egerton of Tatton Will Trust,
Lord *146*
Fattorini Charitable Trust,
James J *160*
Four Winds Trust *168*
Grant-Lawson Charitable Trust,
Lady Virginia *192*
Great Britain Sasakawa
Foundation, The *193*
Hopkins Charitable Foundation,
The Sir Anthony *226*
Ireland Funds, The *237*
Lacy Charity Trust, The Late Sir
Pierce *260*
Laspen Trust *265*
London Law Trust *280*
Mackintosh Foundation, The
292
Mitchell Trust, Esme *315*
Pyke Charity Trust *372*
Reader's Digest Trust, The *380*
Rowntree Charitable Trust, The
Joseph *394*
Strangward Trust, The *439*
Sykes Trust, The Charles *445*
Tanner Charitable Settlement,
The Joan *449*
Wates Foundation, The *481*
Whitaker Charitable Trust *489*
Wills 1961 Charitable Trust, Mr
Frederick *493*
Women Caring Trust, The *500*
Yardy Charitable Trust, The
Dennis Alan *509*

Scotland

Full area
Allied Dunbar Staff Charity
Fund *13*
Army Benevolent Fund, The *22*
Assheton-Smith Charitable
Trust *25*
Astor Foundation, The *26*
Bacta Charitable Trust, The *30*
Bengough Trust, The *43*
Bourne-May Charitable Trust,
The *57*
Britland Charitable Trust, The
63
Brookhouse's Will Trust, Mr
John Charles *65*
Cadbury Charitable Trust,
William Adlington *75*
Carnegie Trust for the
Universities of Scotland *82*
Cobb Charity *103*
Company of Chartered
Surveyors Charitable Trust
Fund, The *108*
David Trust, The Lesley *124*
Denby Charitable Foundation,
The *130*
Esperanza Charitable Trust, The
153
Fattorini Charitable Trust,
James J *160*
Fleming Charitable Trust, The
Ian *164*
Four Winds Trust *168*
Fraser Charitable Trust, The
Gordon *170*
Frazer Charities Trust, The *171*
Gamma Trust *177*
Gannochy Trust, The *177*
Glyn Charitable Trust, The *186*
Gough Charitable Trust, The
189
Grant-Lawson Charitable Trust,
Lady Virginia *192*
HACT (The Housing
Association's Charitable
Trust) *201*
Harbinson Charitable Trust *208*
Harbinson Charitable Trust,
Roderick *208*
Hillhouse Trust, M V *220*
Hopkins Charitable Foundation,
The Sir Anthony *226*
Hudson Benevolent Trust, The
Thomas *230*
Lankelly Foundation, The *264*
Lee Foundation, The Edgar
269
Leggat Charitable Trust,
Duncan *269*
Lewis Partnership, John *274*
Liebes Charitable Trust, The
Martha Bud *274*
London Law Trust *280*
Lynall Foundation, The D G
287

Mackintosh Foundation, The
292
Mickel Fund *309*
Miller Bequest, Hugh and Mary
311
Milward Charity, The Edgar
313
National Art-Collections Fund
327
Natwest Staff Samaritan Fund
330
Noel Buxton Trust, The *335*
Paul Charitable Trust, Margaret
Jeanne *355*
Paul Charitable Trust, Pamela
Milton *355*
Persula Foundation, The *360*
Perth's Charitable Trust, The
Earl of *360*
Portrack Charitable Trust, The
366
Pyke Charity Trust *372*
Rank Foundation, The *377*
Reckitt Charitable Trust, The
Albert *381*
Riddon Trust, The *386*
Rockcliffe Charitable Trust *389*
Rope Third Charitable
Settlement, The Mrs *391*
Scott Bader Commonwealth
Ltd, The *411*
Shepherd Charitable Trust, The
Patricia and Donald *417*
Smallpeice Trust, The *425*
Southdown Trust *432*
Sykes Trust, The Charles *445*
TSB Foundation for Scotland
447
Tanner Charitable Settlement,
The Joan *449*
Templeton Goodwill Trust *451*
Tenovus – Scotland *451*
Tisbury Telegraph Trust, The
457
Trades Union Congress
Educational Trust *460*
Wallace Charity Trust, The A F
478
Watson's Trust, John *482*
Whitaker Charitable Trust *489*
Wilson Bequest Fund, The John
495
Wolfe Family's Charitable
Trust, The *498*
Wolfson (Scotland) Trust, The
Edith & Isaac *500*
Woodhead Charitable Trust,
Michael *501*

■ North Scotland
Full region
Allied Dunbar Staff Charity
Fund *13*
Andrew Charitable Trust, The
Prince *16*
Army Benevolent Fund, The *22*

Assheton-Smith Charitable Trust 25

Bacta Charitable Trust, The 30

Barleycorn Trust, The 34

Brookhouse's Will Trust, Mr John Charles 65

Buxton Trust, Denis 72

CfBT Education Services 74

Camelot Foundation, The 78

Carnegie Trust for the Universities of Scotland 82

Carnegie United Kingdom Trust, The 82

Company of Chartered Surveyors Charitable Trust Fund, The 108

Construction Industry Trust for Youth, The 110

Dashe Trust, The 124

David Trust, The Lesley 124

Egerton of Tatton Will Trust, Lord 146

Esperanza Charitable Trust, The 153

Fattorini Charitable Trust, James J 160

Four Winds Trust 168

Franklin Trust, Jill 170

Fraser Charitable Trust, The Gordon 170

Frazer Charities Trust, The 171

Gamma Trust 177

Gelston Charitable Trust, The 179

Grant-Lawson Charitable Trust, Lady Virginia 192

Great Britain Sasakawa Foundation, The 193

Greenaway Foundation, The Sir Derek 194

Hillhouse Trust, M V 220

Hopkins Charitable Foundation, The Sir Anthony 226

Knott Trust, Sir James 258

Lacy Charity Trust, The Late Sir Pierce 260

Lloyd's Charities Trust 278

London Law Trust 280

Lynall Foundation, The D G 287

Mackintosh Foundation, The 292

Mickel Fund 309

Milward Charity, The Edgar 313

Natwest Staff Samaritan Fund 330

Northcott Devon Foundation 338

PF Charitable Trust 350

Pyke Charity Trust 372

Reader's Digest Trust, The 380

Riddon Trust, The 386

Rockcliffe Charitable Trust 389

Rothschild Group Charitable Trust, The J 393

Royal Gardeners' Orphan Fund, The 395

Schuster Charitable Trust, The 410

Scotbelge Charitable Trust, The 411

Shaw Foundation, The Linley 416

Shepherd Charitable Trust, The Patricia and Donald 417

Smallpeice Trust, The 425

Strangward Trust, The 439

Sykes Trust, The Charles 445

Symons Charitable Trust, The Stella 446

TSB Foundation for Scotland 447

Tanner Charitable Settlement, The Joan 449

Tenovus – Scotland 451

Trades Union Congress Educational Trust 460

Weir Foundation, The James 484

Whitaker Charitable Trust 489

Wills 1961 Charitable Trust, Mr Frederick 493

Wolfe Family's Charitable Trust, The 498

Woodhead Charitable Trust, Michael 501

Worshipful Company of Glass Sellers' Charity Trust, The 505

Yardy Charitable Trust, The Dennis Alan 509

Yorkshire Field Studies Trust 510

Grampian

David Trust, The Lesley 124

Gladstone Charitable Trust, The E W 184

North British Hotel Trust 337

Penny in the Pound Fund Charitable Trust 359

Pyke Charity Trust 372

Rothschild Group Charitable Trust, The J 393

Seagram Distillers Charitable Trust 413

Wallace Charity Trust, The A F 478

Worshipful Company of Glass Sellers' Charity Trust, The 505

Highland

Buxton Trust, Denis 72

David Trust, The Lesley 124

Garnett's 1973 Charitable Trust, Mrs A M 178

Mackintosh Foundation, The 292

North British Hotel Trust 337

Pyke Charity Trust 372

Rothschild Group Charitable Trust, The J 393

Seagram Distillers Charitable Trust 413

Wallace Charity Trust, The A F 478

Worshipful Company of Glass Sellers' Charity Trust, The 505

Orkney

David Trust, The Lesley 124

Pyke Charity Trust 372

Rothschild Group Charitable Trust, The J 393

Seagram Distillers Charitable Trust 413

Worshipful Company of Glass Sellers' Charity Trust, The 505

Shetland

David Trust, The Lesley 124

Pyke Charity Trust 372

Rothschild Group Charitable Trust, The J 393

Seagram Distillers Charitable Trust 413

Worshipful Company of Glass Sellers' Charity Trust, The 505

Western Isles

Buxton Trust, Denis 72

David Trust, The Lesley 124

Mackintosh Foundation, The 292

Margadale Charitable Trust, Lord 297

Marriage's Charitable Trust, Miss G M 299

Pyke Charity Trust 372

Rothschild Group Charitable Trust, The J 393

Seagram Distillers Charitable Trust 413

Worshipful Company of Glass Sellers' Charity Trust, The 505

■ South Scotland

Full region

Allied Dunbar Staff Charity Fund 13

Andrew Charitable Trust, The Prince 16

Army Benevolent Fund, The 22

Assheton-Smith Charitable Trust 25

Bacta Charitable Trust, The 30

Barleycorn Trust, The 34

Brookhouse's Will Trust, Mr John Charles 65

CfBT Education Services 74

Camelot Foundation, The 78

Carnegie Trust for the Universities of Scotland 82

Carnegie United Kingdom Trust, The *82*

Company of Chartered Surveyors Charitable Trust Fund, The *108*

Construction Industry Trust for Youth, The *110*

Dashe Trust, The *124*

David Trust, The Lesley *124*

Egerton of Tatton Will Trust, Lord *146*

Esperanza Charitable Trust, The *153*

Fattorini Charitable Trust, James J *160*

Four Winds Trust *168*

Franklin Trust, Jill *170*

Fraser Charitable Trust, The Gordon *170*

Frazer Charities Trust, The *171*

Gamma Trust *177*

Gelston Charitable Trust, The *179*

Grant-Lawson Charitable Trust, Lady Virginia *192*

Great Britain Sasakawa Foundation, The *193*

Greenaway Foundation, The Sir Derek *194*

Hillhouse Trust, M V *220*

Hopkins Charitable Foundation, The Sir Anthony *226*

Knott Trust, Sir James *258*

Lacy Charity Trust, The Late Sir Pierce *260*

London Law Trust *280*

Lynall Foundation, The D G *287*

Mackintosh Foundation, The *292*

Mickel Fund *309*

Milward Charity, The Edgar *313*

Natwest Staff Samaritan Fund *330*

Northcott Devon Foundation *338*

PF Charitable Trust *350*

Pyke Charity Trust *372*

Reader's Digest Trust, The *380*

Riddon Trust, The *386*

Rockcliffe Charitable Trust *389*

Rothschild Group Charitable Trust, The J *393*

Royal Gardeners' Orphan Fund, The *395*

Scotbelge Charitable Trust, The *411*

Shaw Foundation, The Linley *416*

Shepherd Charitable Trust, The Patricia and Donald *417*

Smallpeice Trust, The *425*

Strangward Trust, The *439*

Sykes Trust, The Charles *445*

Symons Charitable Trust, The Stella *446*

TSB Foundation for Scotland *447*

Tanner Charitable Settlement, The Joan *449*

Templeton Goodwill Trust *451*

Tenovus – Scotland *451*

Trades Union Congress Educational Trust *460*

Weir Foundation, The James *484*

Whitaker Charitable Trust *489*

Wills 1961 Charitable Trust, Mr Frederick *493*

Wolfe Family's Charitable Trust, The *498*

Woodhead Charitable Trust, Michael *501*

Worshipful Company of Glass Sellers' Charity Trust, The *505*

Yardy Charitable Trust, The Dennis Alan *509*

Yorkshire Field Studies Trust *510*

Borders

David Trust, The Lesley *124*

Melville Trust for Care and Cure of Cancer *305*

Mickel Fund *309*

Pyke Charity Trust *372*

Rothschild Group Charitable Trust, The J *393*

Seagram Distillers Charitable Trust *413*

Worshipful Company of Glass Sellers' Charity Trust, The *505*

Central

David Trust, The Lesley *124*

Mickel Fund *309*

North British Hotel Trust *337*

Penny in the Pound Fund Charitable Trust *359*

Pyke Charity Trust *372*

Rothschild Group Charitable Trust, The J *393*

Seagram Distillers Charitable Trust *413*

Wood Bequest Fund, James *500*

Worshipful Company of Glass Sellers' Charity Trust, The *505*

Dumfries & Galloway

David Trust, The Lesley *124*

Mickel Fund *309*

North British Hotel Trust *337*

Penny in the Pound Fund Charitable Trust *359*

Pyke Charity Trust *372*

Rothschild Group Charitable Trust, The J *393*

Seagram Distillers Charitable Trust *413*

Worshipful Company of Glass Sellers' Charity Trust, The *505*

Fife

Melville Trust for Care and Cure of Cancer *305*

Mickel Fund *309*

Penny in the Pound Fund Charitable Trust *359*

Pyke Charity Trust *372*

Rothschild Group Charitable Trust, The J *393*

Seagram Distillers Charitable Trust *413*

Worshipful Company of Glass Sellers' Charity Trust, The *505*

Lothian

Buccleuch Place Trust *67*

David Trust, The Lesley *124*

Massey Charitable Trust, The Nancie *301*

Melville Trust for Care and Cure of Cancer *305*

Mickel Fund *309*

North British Hotel Trust *337*

Penny in the Pound Fund Charitable Trust *359*

Pyke Charity Trust *372*

Rothschild Group Charitable Trust, The J *393*

Seagram Distillers Charitable Trust *413*

Worshipful Company of Glass Sellers' Charity Trust, The *505*

Strathclyde

Bellahouston Bequest Fund *42*

Chrimes Family Charitable Trust, The *93*

David Trust, The Lesley *124*

Merchants House of Glasgow *307*

Mickel Fund *309*

Morrison Bequest Fund, Thomas Wharrie *320*

North British Hotel Trust *337*

Penny in the Pound Fund Charitable Trust *359*

Pyke Charity Trust *372*

Rothschild Group Charitable Trust, The J *393*

Seagram Distillers Charitable Trust *413*

Weir Foundation, The James *484*

Worshipful Company of Glass Sellers' Charity Trust, The *505*

Tayside

Campbell Charitable Foundation, The Ellis *79*

David Trust, The Lesley *124*

Hill Memorial Trust, L E *219*

Low & Bonar Charitable Fund, The *284*

Mickel Fund *309*

North British Hotel Trust *337*

Pyke Charity Trust *372*

Rothschild Group Charitable Trust, The J *393*

Seagram Distillers Charitable Trust *413*

Worshipful Company of Glass Sellers' Charity Trust, The *505*

Wales

Full area

Allied Dunbar Staff Charity Fund *13*

Almshouse Association, The *14*

Arts Council of Wales, The *23*

Assheton-Smith Charitable Trust *25*

Astor Foundation, The *26*

Austin of Longbridge Will Trust, The Rt Hon Herbert, Baron *27*

Bacta Charitable Trust, The *30*

Bengough Trust, The *43*

Betton's Charity (Educational), Mr Thomas *46*

Blott Charitable Settlement, Robert Orpwood *55*

Britland Charitable Trust, The *63*

Brookhouse's Will Trust, Mr John Charles *65*

CLA Charitable Trust *74*

Cadbury Charitable Trust, William Adlington *75*

Catholic Education Service for England and Wales *86*

Cobb Charity *103*

Company of Chartered Surveyors Charitable Trust Fund, The *108*

David Trust, The Lesley *124*

Davies Charity, The Gwendoline and Margaret *125*

Debtors' Relief Fund Charity *128*

Denby Charitable Foundation, The *130*

Dinam Charity *134*

Esperanza Charitable Trust, The *153*

Fattorini Charitable Trust, James J *160*

Fleming Charitable Trust, The Ian *164*

Four Winds Trust *168*

Frazer Charities Trust, The *171*

Frazer Trust, Joseph Strong *171*

General Nursing Council for England and Wales Trust, The *180*

Gibbins Trust, The *181*

Glyn Charitable Trust, The *186*

Grand Charity (of Freemasons under the United Grand Lodge of England), The *190*

Grant-Lawson Charitable Trust, Lady Virginia *192*

Griffiths Trust, The E E and D M *196*

Gwent County Council Welsh Church Fund *200*

Gwynedd County Council Welsh Church Fund *200*

HACT (The Housing Association's Charitable Trust) *201*

Hind Trust, Lady *220*

Historic Churches Preservation Trust, The *221*

Hopkins Charitable Foundation, The Sir Anthony *226*

Howard Charitable Trust, John & Ruth *229*

Hudson Benevolent Trust, The Thomas *230*

Hudson Charitable Trust, The *230*

Humphreys Charitable Settlement, J A M *231*

Incorporated Church Building Society, The *234*

James Foundation, The Catherine and Lady Grace *241*

James Foundation, John & Rhys Thomas *242*

Jones Trust, Cemlyn *248*

Lankelly Foundation, The *264*

Lee Foundation, The Edgar *269*

Licensed Trade Charities Trust, The *274*

(Lloyds) TSB Foundation for England and Wales *279*

London Law Trust *280*

Lynall Foundation, The D G *287*

Mackintosh Foundation, The *292*

Marshall's Charity *300*

Milward Charity, The Edgar *313*

Morgan Foundation, The Mr & Mrs J T *319*

Moss Charitable Trust, Philip *321*

National Art-Collections Fund *327*

National Catholic Fund *327*

National Committee of The Women's World Day of Prayer for England, Wales and Northern Ireland, The *327*

National Power Charitable Trust, The *330*

Natwest Staff Samaritan Fund *330*

Noel Buxton Trust, The *335*

Oakdale Trust, The *343*

Paul Charitable Trust, Margaret Jeanne *355*

Paul Charitable Trust, Pamela Milton *355*

Persula Foundation, The *360*

Prince's Trust - BRO, The *369*

Pyke Charity Trust *372*

Rank Foundation, The *377*

Reckitt Charitable Trust, The Albert *381*

Rope Third Charitable Settlement, The Mrs *391*
SCOPE *410*
Scott Bader Commonwealth Ltd, The *411*
Smallpeice Trust, The *425*
Sobell Welsh People's Charitable Association, Michael *429*
Southdown Trust *432*
Stoate Charitable Trust, The Leonard Laity *438*
Sykes Trust, The Charles *445*
Tanner Charitable Settlement, The Joan *449*
Tisbury Telegraph Trust, The *457*
Trades Union Congress Educational Trust *460*
Whitaker Charitable Trust *489*
Wolfe Family's Charitable Trust, The *498*
Woodhead Charitable Trust, Michael *501*

■ North Wales

Full region

Allied Dunbar Staff Charity Fund *13*
Almshouse Association, The *14*
Andrew Charitable Trust, The Prince *16*
Army Benevolent Fund, The *22*
Arts Council of Wales, The *23*
Assheton-Smith Charitable Trust *25*
Bacta Charitable Trust, The *30*
Barleycorn Trust, The *34*
Brookhouse's Will Trust, Mr John Charles *65*
CfBT Education Services *74*
CLA Charitable Trust *74*
Camelot Foundation, The *78*
Carnegie United Kingdom Trust, The *82*
Chrimes Family Charitable Trust, The *93*
Company of Chartered Surveyors Charitable Trust Fund, The *108*
Cripplegate Foundation *118*
Curzon Charitable Trust, The Wallace *120*
Dashe Trust, The *124*
David Trust, The Lesley *124*
Davies Charity, The Gwendoline and Margaret *125*
Egerton of Tatton Will Trust, Lord *146*
Esperanza Charitable Trust, The *153*
Fattorini Charitable Trust, James J *160*
Four Winds Trust *168*
Frazer Charities Trust, The *171*

Gelston Charitable Trust, The *179*
Gibbins Trust, The *181*
Grant-Lawson Charitable Trust, Lady Virginia *192*
Great Britain Sasakawa Foundation, The *193*
Greenaway Foundation, The Sir Derek *194*
Griffiths Trust, The E E and D M *196*
Historic Churches Preservation Trust, The *221*
Hopkins Charitable Foundation, The Sir Anthony *226*
Humphreys Charitable Settlement, J A M *231*
Lacy Charity Trust, The Late Sir Pierce *260*
Laspen Trust *265*
Lloyd's Charities Trust *278*
(Lloyds) TSB Foundation for England and Wales *279*
London Law Trust *280*
Mackintosh Foundation, The *292*
Marshall's Charity *300*
Milward Charity, The Edgar *313*
Natwest Staff Samaritan Fund *330*
North West Cancer Research Fund *338*
Oakdale Trust, The *343*
PF Charitable Trust *350*
Penny in the Pound Fund Charitable Trust *359*
Prince's Trust - BRO, The *369*
Pyke Charity Trust *372*
RT Trust, The *374*
Reader's Digest Trust, The *380*
Rothley Trust, The *392*
Rothschild Group Charitable Trust, The J *393*
Royal Gardeners' Orphan Fund, The *395*
Salters Charities *405*
Shaw Foundation, The Linley *416*
Smallpeice Trust, The *425*
Strangward Trust, The *439*
Symons Charitable Trust, The Stella *446*
Tanner Charitable Settlement, The Joan *449*
Trades Union Congress Educational Trust *460*
Whitaker Charitable Trust *489*
Wills 1961 Charitable Trust, Mr Frederick *493*
Wolfe Family's Charitable Trust, The *498*
Woodhead Charitable Trust, Michael *501*
Yardy Charitable Trust, The Dennis Alan *509*

Gwynedd

Assheton-Smith Charitable Trust *25*
CLA Charitable Trust *74*
Flintshire Welsh Church Fund *165*
Griffiths Trust, The E E and D M *196*
Gwynedd County Council Welsh Church Fund *200*
Lloyd Foundation, The Charles *278*
Oakdale Trust, The *343*
Pen-Y-Clip Charitable Trust *359*
Rothschild Group Charitable Trust, The J *393*
Sykes Trust, The Charles *445*

Clwyd

Assheton-Smith Charitable Trust *25*
CLA Charitable Trust *74*
Gladstone Charitable Trust, The E W *184*
Griffiths Trust, The E E and D M *196*
JDM Charitable Trust *239*
Lloyd Foundation, The Charles *278*
Oakdale Trust, The *343*
Rothschild Group Charitable Trust, The J *393*
Sykes Trust, The Charles *445*

■ South Wales

Full region

Almshouse Association, The *14*
Andrew Charitable Trust, The Prince *16*
Army Benevolent Fund, The *22*
Arts Council of Wales, The *23*
Assheton-Smith Charitable Trust *25*
Bacta Charitable Trust, The *30*
Brookhouse's Will Trust, Mr John Charles *65*
CfBT Education Services *74*
CLA Charitable Trust *74*
Camelot Foundation, The *78*
Cardiff & Swansea Methodist District Charitable Trust Fund *80*
Carnegie United Kingdom Trust, The *82*
Company of Chartered Surveyors Charitable Trust Fund, The *108*
Cripplegate Foundation *118*
Dashe Trust, The *124*
David Trust, The Lesley *124*
Davies Charity, The Gwendoline and Margaret *125*
Egerton of Tatton Will Trust, Lord *146*

South Wales

Esperanza Charitable Trust, The
153
Fattorini Charitable Trust,
James J 160
Four Winds Trust 168
Frazer Charities Trust, The 171
Gelston Charitable Trust, The
179
Gibbins Trust, The 181
Grant-Lawson Charitable Trust,
Lady Virginia 192
Great Britain Sasakawa
Foundation, The 193
Greenaway Foundation, The Sir
Derek 194
Griffiths Trust, The E E and
D M 196
Historic Churches Preservation
Trust, The 221
Hopkins Charitable Foundation,
The Sir Anthony 226
Lacy Charity Trust, The Late Sir
Pierce 260
Lloyd's Charities Trust 278
(Lloyds) TSB Foundation for
England and Wales 279
Lynall Foundation, The D G
287
Mackintosh Foundation, The
292
Marshall's Charity 300
Milward Charity, The Edgar
313
Natwest Staff Samaritan Fund
330
Oakdale Trust, The 343
PF Charitable Trust 350
Prince's Trust - BRO, The 369
Pyke Charity Trust 372
Reader's Digest Trust, The 380
Rothley Trust, The 392
Rothschild Group Charitable
Trust, The J 393
Royal Gardeners' Orphan Fund,
The 395
Smallpeice Trust, The 425
Sobell Welsh People's
Charitable Association,
Michael 429
Stoate Charitable Trust, The
Leonard Laity 438
Strangward Trust, The 439
Symons Charitable Trust, The
Stella 446
Tanner Charitable Settlement,
The Joan 449
Trades Union Congress
Educational Trust 460
Whitaker Charitable Trust 489
Wills 1961 Charitable Trust, Mr
Frederick 493
Wolfe Family's Charitable
Trust, The 498
Woodhead Charitable Trust,
Michael 501

Worshipful Company of Glass
Sellers' Charity Trust, The
505
Yardy Charitable Trust, The
Dennis Alan 509

Powys
Flintshire Welsh Church Fund
165
Garthgwynion Charities 179
Griffiths Trust, The E E and
D M 196
Hudson Charitable Trust, The
230
Lloyd Foundation, The Charles
278
North West Cancer Research
Fund 338
Powys Welsh Church Fund 367
Rothschild Group Charitable
Trust, The J 393
Worshipful Company of Glass
Sellers' Charity Trust, The
505

Dyfed
CLA Charitable Trust 74
Carmarthenshire Welsh Church
Fund 81
Flintshire Welsh Church Fund
165
Griffiths Trust, The E E and
D M 196
Hudson Charitable Trust, The
230
Lloyd Foundation, The Charles
278
Rothschild Group Charitable
Trust, The J 393

Mid Glamorgan
CLA Charitable Trust 74
Flintshire Welsh Church Fund
165
Ford of Britain Trust 166
Griffiths Trust, The E E and
D M 196
Hudson Charitable Trust, The
230
Rothschild Group Charitable
Trust, The J 393

West Glamorgan
CLA Charitable Trust 74
Flintshire Welsh Church Fund
165
Ford of Britain Trust 166
Griffiths Trust, The E E and
D M 196
Hudson Charitable Trust, The
230
Lloyd Foundation, The Charles
278
Rothschild Group Charitable
Trust, The J 393
West Glamorgan Welsh Church
Fund, The 486

South Glamorgan
CLA Charitable Trust 74
Flintshire Welsh Church Fund
165
Ford of Britain Trust 166
Griffiths Trust, The E E and
D M 196
Hudson Charitable Trust, The
230
Rothschild Group Charitable
Trust, The J 393

Gwent
CLA Charitable Trust 74
Flintshire Welsh Church Fund
165
Griffiths Trust, The E E and
D M 196
Gwent County Council Welsh
Church Fund 200
Hudson Charitable Trust, The
230
Penny in the Pound Fund
Charitable Trust 359
Rothschild Group Charitable
Trust, The J 393

Overseas

AB Charitable Trust 3
AB Charitable Trust, The 3
AIIT (The Ancient India and Iran Trust) 3
AW Charitable Trust 4
Abrahams 2nd Charitable Foundation, The Henry and Grete 5
Aga Khan Foundation (UK) 7
Agricola Trust, The 8
Aid to the Church in Need (United Kingdom) 8
Ajahma Charitable Trust, The 9
Alchemy Foundation, The 9
Aleh Charitable Foundation, The 10
All Saints Educational Trust 12
Allachy Trust, The 12
Allied Domecq Trust 13
Allied Dunbar Charitable Trust Limited, The 13
Allied Dunbar Staff Charity Fund 13
Almond Trust, The 14
Ammco Trust, The 15
Anglo Hong Kong Trust, The 17
Anglo-Arab Aid Ltd 17
Anglo-Catholic Ordination Candidates Fund, The 18
Anglo-German Foundation for the Study of Industrial Society 18
Animal Defence Trust, The 18
Anne's Charities, The Princess 18
Anstruther Memorial Trust, The Fagus 19
Aquarian Healing Trust 19
Archer Trust, The 20
Arkleton Trust, The 21
Army Benevolent Fund, The 22
Ashby Charitable Trust, The 23
Ashden Charitable Trust, The 24
Astor Foundation, The 26
Avenue Charitable Trust, The 27
BP Conservation Programme 29
Bachad Fellowship – Friends of Bnei Akiva 30
Bagri Foundation 30
Bailey Charitable Trust, Veta 30
Bain Memorial Trust Fund, Dr James and Dr Bozena 30
Baker Trust, The C Alma 31
Balint Charitable Trust, Paul 31
Ballinger Charitable Trust, The 32
Bancroft (No 2) Charitable Trust and Jenepher Gillett Trust, William P 32

Barbour Paton Charitable Trust 33
Baring Foundation, The 34
Barleycorn Trust, The 34
Baronets Trust, The 35
Bartholomew Christian Trust 36
Bassham Charitable Trust, The Paul 37
Batchworth Trust, The 37
Beacon Trust 38
Bear Mordechai Ltd 39
Beaverbrook Foundation, The 39
Beckwith Charitable Trust, The John 40
Beecham 1981 Charitable Trust, R J 40
Behrens Charitable Trust, E M 40
Beit Trust, The 40
Bell's Charitable Trust, Lady Mary 42
Benesco Charity Limited 43
Berris Charitable Trust 45
Berthoud Charitable Trust, Patrick 45
Bestway Foundation, The 46
BibleLands 47
Biggs Charity, The Elizabeth Emily 48
Birtwistle Memorial Trust, The G E 50
Black Charitable Trust, Edna 51
Black Charitable Trust, Peter 51
Black Charitable Trust, Sydney 51
Blond Charitable Trust, Neville & Elaine 54
Bloom Foundation, Abraham Algy 54
Body Charitable Trust, Bernard Richard 55
Body Shop Foundation, The 55
Bornstein Charitable Trust, M & S 56
Bourne Foundation, The Anthony 57
Bourne-May Charitable Trust, The 57
Bowland Charitable Trust, The 57
Bramble Charitable Trust 58
Brand Trust, The 59
British Council for Prevention of Blindness 61
British Diabetic Association, The 61
British Dietetic Association General and Education Trust Fund, The 61
British Friends of Chinuch Atzmai Trust, The 62
British Institute of Archaeology at Ankara 62

British Schools and Universities Foundation (Inc) 62
Britland Charitable Trust, The 63
Brocklebank Charitable Trust, Charles 64
Brown Charitable Settlement, Mrs E E 65
Brownless Charitable Trust, R S 66
Burden Trust, The 69
Burns Charity, The Dorothy 70
Burton 1960 Charitable Settlement, Audrey & Stanley 70
Burton Charitable Trust, R M 71
Butler Charitable Trust, The A S 71
Buxton Trust, Denis 72
CAF (Charities Aid Foundation) 73
CAFOD (Catholic Fund for Overseas Development) 73
CB Charitable Trust, The 73
CfBT Education Services 74
Cadbury Charitable Trust (Incorporated), Edward 75
Cadbury Charitable Trust, William Adlington 75
Cadbury Charity, C James 76
Cadbury Trust (1928), The Edward & Dorothy 76
Cadman Charitable Trust, The Beatrice A V 77
Cairns Charitable Trust, The 78
Cancer Relief Macmillan Fund 79
Candap Trust, The 80
Canning Trust, The 80
Caplin Foundation, The Fay and Robert 80
Carmarthenshire Welsh Church Fund 81
Carpenter Charitable Trust 82
Carter Charitable Trust, The Leslie Mary 83
Cassel Educational Trust (Overseas Research Grants), Sir Ernest 84
Catholic Foreign Missions 86
Cazalet Charitable Trust, The Raymond 87
Cen Foundation, The Hyman 87
Charitable Fund Administered by The Russia Company 89
Charity Know How Fund 89
Charity Projects 90
Chesters Settlement for Methodist Church Purposes, Mr H G 91
Chickadee Trust, The 91
Childs Charitable Trust, The 92
Childwick Trust, The 93
Christabella Charitable Trust 93
Christendom Trust, The 94

Christian Aid 94
Christian Renewal Trust, The 94
Christian Vision 94
Christmas Cracker Trust 95
Ciba Fellowship Trust, The 95
Civil Service Benevolent Fund, The 97
Clark Charitable Trust 98
Clark 1965 Charitable Trust, Stephen 98
Cleopatra Trust 99
Clover Trust 102
Coates Charitable Trust, The John 103
Cockenzie Charitable Trust, The 103
Cohen and William Leech Foundation, Sebag 103
Cohen Charitable Trust, The Andrew 104
Cohen Charitable Trust, The Vivienne and Samuel 104
Cohen's Charitable Settlement, The Hon L H L 105
Collier Charitable Trust, The 105
Colman Charitable Fund Ltd, The E Alec 106
Colt Foundation, The 107
Commonwealth Relations Trust 108
Conrad Charitable Trust, Neville and Carole 109
Conservation Foundation, The 110
Continuation Charitable Trust, The 110
Cooper Charitable Trust 111
Coote Animal Charity Fund, The Marjorie 111
Coote Charitable Trust, Nicholas 111
Copperfield Trust, David 112
Corfield Charitable Settlement, The Holbeche 113
Corman Charitable Trust, Ruth and Charles 113
Cornerstone Charitable Trust 114
Cotton Trust, The 114
Cruse Trust, The 119
Curzon Charitable Trust, The Wallace 120
DCW Trust 121
DLM Charitable Trust, The 121
Daiwa Anglo-Japanese Foundation, The 122
Dashe Trust, The 124
Datnow Limited 124
David Trust, The Lesley 124
Davies Charities Limited, J 125
de Freitas Charitable Trust, The Helen and Geoffrey 126
De Groot Charitable Trust, Zena and Ralph 127
De La Rue Charitable Trust 127

De Rothschild 1981 Charitable Trust, The Edmund 127
De Rothschild 1980 Charitable Trust, The Leopold 127
De Vere Hunt Charitable Trust, The 128
De Yong Charitable Trust, The Emma 128
De Yong's Charitable Trust 1984, Nicholas 128
Dean Refugee Trust Fund, The Miriam 128
Delafield Charitable Trust, The William 129
Delius Trust, The 129
Desmond Charitable Trust, The Richard 131
Deutsch Charitable Trust, The H & M 131
Devonshire's Charitable Trust, The Duke of 131
Diamond Charitable Trust, The Alan & Sheila 132
Direct Response 134
Double 'O' Charity Ltd 136
Doughty Charity Trust, The 136
Drummond Trust, The 138
du Boulay Charitable Trust, The Anthony 138
Dulverton Trust, The 139
Dumbreck Charity 139
Early's Charitable Settlement, Richard 142
Earwicker Trust 142
Edgar Foundation, The Gilbert and Eileen 145
Ellerman Foundation, The John 148
Ellis 1985 Charitable Trust, Edith M 148
Elshore Limited 149
Elton John Aids Foundation, The 149
Emanuel Charitable Settlement, Ralph and Muriel 150
Emmaus Christian Foundation 150
Epigoni Trust 152
Ericson Trust 152
Essefian Charitable Trust, The Mihran 153
Eton Action 154
European Cultural Foundation (UK Committee) 154
Evershed Trust, The Norman 155
Falkner Charitable Trust, The Daniel 158
Famos Foundation Trust 158
Farmer's Trust, Samuel William 159
Farthing Trust, The 159
Federation of Jewish Relief Organisations 160
Feed the Minds 160
Fencewood Trust, The 161
Fenton Trust, The A M 161

Ferguson Benevolent Fund Limited 161
Ferraris Charitable Trust, The 162
Firdale Christian Trust, The 162
Fleisher Deceased, The Will of Sydney 164
Follett Trust, The 166
Foreman 1980 Charitable Trust, The Russell and Mary 167
Foreman Foundation, The Carl & Eve 167
Fox Memorial Trust 169
Frampton Charitable Trust, The David 169
Frankel Memorial Charitable Trust, The Isaac & Freda 169
Franklin Trust, Jill 170
Fraser Charitable Trust, The Gordon 170
Frays Charitable Trust, The 171
Friends of Biala Ltd 172
Friends of Wiznitz Limited 173
Frome Christian Fellowship 174
Frost Foundation, The Patrick 174
Fund for Human Need 175
GABO Trust for Sculpture Conservation 175
GW Trust, The 176
Galinski Charitable Trust 177
Garbacz Charitable Trust, The Bernard & Vera 178
Garrod Memorial Charitable Trust, The John and Daisy 179
Gatsby Charitable Foundation, The 179
Gelston Charitable Trust, The 179
Gem Charitable Trust 179
Gibson Charitable Trust, The Simon 182
Gibson's Charity Trust, The Hon H M T 182
Gibson's Charity Trust, The Hon P N 183
Gilchrist Educational Trust 183
Glencore Foundation for Education and Welfare 185
Global Care 185
Gluck Charitable Trust, Avraham Yitzchak 185
Gold Hill Church Trust 186
Goldberg Charitable Trust, The Lewis 186
Goldberg Charity Trust, The Isaac 187
Goodman Trust, The S & F 189
Gradel Foundation, The 189
Grahame Charitable Foundation, The 190
Grant Charitable Trust, The 191
Green Foundation, The Charles 193

Greenaway Foundation, The Sir Derek *194*
Greene & Co Charity Limited *195*
Greenwood Charitable Trust, Naomi & Jeffrey *195*
Griffiths Trust, The E E and D M *196*
Gross Charities Limited, M & R *197*
Grosshill Charitable Trust *197*
Grove Charitable Trust, The *197*
Groves Charitable Trust, The *197*
Growth Building Trust, The *198*
Guardian Foundation, The *198*
Gulbenkian Foundation (Lisbon) United Kingdom Branch, Calouste *199*
HB Charitable Trust *201*
Hacking & Sons Ltd Charitable Trust, C G *201*
Haddon Charitable Trust, William *202*
Haendler, The Nathan and Adolphe *202*
Haines Charitable Trust, The Alfred *203*
Hamlyn Foundation, The Paul *205*
Handicapped Children's Aid Committee *207*
Hanley Trust (1987), The *207*
Hannay Memorial Charity, Kathleen *208*
Harbinson Charitable Trust, Roderick *208*
Harbour Foundation Ltd, The *208*
Harford Charitable Trust *209*
Hattori Foundation, The *212*
Hay Charitable Trust, Dora *213*
Headley Trust, The *214*
Heath Charitable Trust *214*
Heath Charitable Trust, The Edward *214*
Heber Percy Charitable Trust, The Mrs C S *215*
Heinz Company Limited Charitable Trust, The H J *215*
Henhurst Charitable Trust, The *216*
Highcroft Charitable Trust *218*
Hilden Charitable Fund, The *219*
Hiley Trust, Joseph and Mary *219*
Hillcote Trust, The *220*
Hodgson Charitable Trust, Kenneth *223*
Holford Trust Fund *224*
Holt Charitable Trust, P H *225*
Homeless International *225*
Hood's Charitable Trust, Sir Harold *226*

Humanitarian Trust, The *230*
Hussey for Africans, Charity of Rebecca *231*
Hussey Trust, The *232*
IPE Charitable Trust, The *233*
Inchcape Charitable Trust Fund *234*
International Arab Women's Council Charities Fund *236*
International Bar Association Educational Trust *236*
Ireland Fund of Great Britain, The *237*
Ireland Funds, The *237*
JCA Charitable Foundation *238*
JCSCJ Charitable Trust, The *238*
JJ Charitable Trust, The *239*
JMK Charitable Trust *239*
JNF Charitable Trust *240*
Jacobs Charitable Trust, The J P *240*
Jacobson Charitable Trust (No 2), The Ruth & Lionel *241*
James Trust, The *242*
Jarrold Trust Ltd, John *243*
Jephcott Charitable Trust, The *244*
Jerusalem Trust *244*
Jesus Lane Trust, The *245*
Jewish Childs' Day *245*
Jewish Philanthropic Association for Israel and the Middle East, The *245*
Joseph Charitable Trust, J E *248*
Jubilee Outreach Yorkshire *248*
Jurgens Charitable Trust, The Anton *249*
Jusaca Charitable Trust, The *249*
Kalms Foundation, The Stanley *250*
Karimjee Trust, The Momamedali *250*
Keane Charitable Settlement, The *251*
Keeling Charitable Trust, The Petronella *251*
Kejriwal Foundation *251*
Keswick Foundation Ltd *253*
Keymer Trust, The Ronald and Mary *253*
Kilverstone Wildlife Charitable Trust, The *254*
Kingsgrove Charitable Trust, The *255*
Kleinwort Charitable Trust, The Ernest *257*
Kobler Trust, The *258*
Kornberg's 1969 Charitable Settlement, Mrs Bessie *258*
Kreitman Foundation *258*
Kroch Foundation, The Heinz & Anna *259*
Kulika Charitable Trust, The *259*

Kyte Charitable Trust, The *259*
Lacy Charity Trust, The Late Sir Pierce *260*
Laing Foundation, The Kirby *261*
Laing Foundation, The Maurice *261*
Laing Trust, Beatrice *261*
Laing Trust, The J W *261*
Lambert Charitable Trust, The *262*
Lane Foundation, The Allen *263*
Langdale Trust *264*
Langley Charitable Trust, The *264*
Laspen Trust *265*
Latham Trust, The *266*
Lauchentilly Charitable Foundation 1988, The *266*
Lauffer Charitable Foundation, The R & D *266*
Leach Fourteenth Trust, The *267*
Lebus Charitable Trust, The *268*
Leche Trust, The *268*
Lee Foundation, The Edgar *269*
Leigh Charitable Trust, Kennedy *270*
Lewin Charitable Trust, The Robert and Rena *273*
Lewis Family Charitable Trust *273*
Lewis Partnership, John *274*
Linder Foundation, The Enid *275*
Lindeth Charitable Trust, The *276*
Lingwood Charitable Trust, The *276*
Lipton Charitable Trust, The Ruth & Stuart *276*
Listeners, The *276*
Lloyd's Charities Trust *278*
Loseley & Guildway Charitable Trust, The *281*
Lowndes Charitable Trust, The Vanessa *285*
Lunn-Rockliffe Charitable Trust, Paul *286*
Lyndhurst Settlement *287*
Lyndhurst Trust, The *287*
Lyons Charitable Trust, Sir Jack *288*
MKR Charitable Trust *289*
MYA Charitable Trust *289*
Macaulay Family Charitable Trust *290*
McDougall Trust, The *291*
Mackintosh Foundation, The *292*
Marchday Charitable Fund, The *296*
Marchig Animal Welfare Trust *297*

Marriage's Charitable Trust, Miss G M *299*
Marr-Munning Trust *299*
Marshall Charitable Trust, The *299*
Martin Charitable Trust, Mervyn *300*
Mauray Charitable Trust, The Violet *302*
Mayfair Charities Limited *303*
Measures Charity, The James Frederick and Ethel Anne *303*
Medical Aid Trust *304*
Mediterranean Archaeological Trust *304*
Migraine Trust, The *310*
Mijoda Charitable Trust, The *310*
Millichope Foundation, The *312*
Milward Charity, The Edgar *313*
Missionary Friends Trust *314*
Mitchell Trust *315*
Montefiore Trust, The David *316*
Moores Family Charitable Foundation, The Nigel *317*
Morel Charitable Trust, The *318*
Morris Charitable Trust, The Douglas *320*
Mount 'A' Charitable Trust *321*
Mount 'B' Charitable Trust *321*
Mount Everest Foundation, The *321*
Mountbatten Memorial Trust, The *322*
Mountbatten Trust, The Edwina *322*
Music for World Development *323*
Muslim Hands *324*
NAM Charitable Trust *325*
NR Charitable Trust, The *325*
Nakou Foundation, The Eleni *326*
Nathan Charitable Trust *326*
Nathan Charitable Trust, Peter *326*
National Lottery Charities Board *328*
Nestle Rowntree York Community Fund, Employees of *331*
New Durlston Trust, The *332*
Newby Trust Ltd *332*
Newman Charitable Trust, Mr and Mrs F E F *334*
Noel Buxton Trust, The *335*
Normanby Charitable Trust *337*
Northern Dairies Educational Trust *339*
Norwich Church of England Young Men's Society *340*
Oakdale Trust, The *343*

Oasis Church Chadwell Heath Charitable Trust *343*
Ogle Trust, The *344*
Old Possums Practical Trust, The *344*
Oldham Foundation *345*
Ormsby Charitable Trust, The *347*
Osborne Charitable Trust, The *347*
Owen Family Trust, The *348*
Oxfam (United Kingdom and Ireland) *348*
PAR Charitable Trust *349*
PDC Trust, The *349*
Paget Trust, The *351*
Panton Trust, The *352*
Paristamen Foundation, The *352*
Parivar Trust, The *353*
Payne Trust, The Harry *356*
Pedmore Trust *357*
Peppiatt Charitable Trust, The Brian *359*
Personal Assurance Charitable Trust *360*
Pettit Charitable Trust *360*
Pickford Charitable Foundation, The David *362*
Pilkington Trust, The Austin and Hope *363*
Pilkington's Charitable Trust, Dr L H A *363*
Pitman Charitable Trust, The John *364*
Polden-Puckham Charitable Foundation, The *365*
Porter Foundation *366*
Portrack Charitable Trust, The *366*
Pratt Charitable Trust, The W L *367*
Prendergast Charitable Trust, The Simone *368*
Prevezer Charitable Settlement, S B *368*
Provincial Trust for Kendal, The *370*
Pryor Charitable Trust, The John *370*
Puebla Charitable Trust Limited, The *371*
Pye Christian Trust, The *371*
Rachel Charitable Trust *375*
Radley Charitable Trust *375*
Rainbow Charitable Trust *376*
Randall Charitable Trust, The Joseph and Lena *376*
Rav Chesed Trust, The *379*
Ravenscroft Foundation, The *379*
Rest-Harrow Trust, The *382*
Reuter Foundation, The *382*
Rhodes Trust – Public Purposes Fund, The *383*
Rhododendron Trust, The *383*
Richard Charitable Trust, The Cliff *383*

Riggs Charity, The *386*
Riley-Smith Charitable Trust, The F A *386*
Ritblat Charitable Trust No 1, The John *387*
Rivendell Trust, The *387*
Robbins Trust, The Cheshire *387*
Robertson Charitable Trust, The J W *388*
Robinson Brothers (Ryders Green) Ltd, Charitable Trust *388*
Rolfe Charitable Trust, The *390*
Rotary Club of Worthing's Community Service Fund *392*
Rowan Charitable Trust, The *393*
Rowntree Charitable Trust, The Joseph *394*
Royal Commission for the Exhibition of 1851 *395*
Rufford Foundation *398*
SEM Charitable Trust *399*
SMB Trust, The *400*
Sadagora Trust, The Ruzin *400*
Said Foundation, The Karim Rida *401*
Sainsbury Animal Welfare Trust, Jean *401*
St Christopher's Trust, The *402*
St Francis Leprosy Guild *402*
St George's Trust, The *403*
St Luke's College Foundation *404*
Saint Sarkis Charity Trust *404*
Sargeant's Charitable Trust, Mrs M E *407*
Sassoon Charitable Trust, The Late Aaron D *408*
Schuster Charitable Trust, The *410*
Scott Bader Commonwealth Ltd, The *411*
Scott of Yews Trust, Sir Samuel *412*
Seahorse Charitable Trust, The *413*
Securicor Charitable Trust, The *414*
Seedfield Trust, The *414*
Senna Foundation, The Ayrton *415*
Seva Trust, Rampaba Sadhu *415*
Sharon Trust, The *416*
Sheepdrove Trust, The *417*
Shepherd Conservation Foundation, The David *418*
Sherman Cardiff Charitable Foundation, The Archie *418*
Sherman Charitable Trust, The Archie *419*
Simon Population Trust, The *422*
Simon's Charity *422*
Simpson Foundation, The *422*

Slavin Charitable Foundation, The Josephine & Barry *425*

Smith (UK) Horticultural Trust, Stanley *428*

Society of Friends of the Torah, The *429*

Soddy Trust, The Frederick *429*

Spalding Trust *433*

Sport Aid 88 Trust *434*

Spurrell Charitable Trust *435*

Stansfield Charitable Trust *435*

Staples Trust *435*

Stewart Charitable Trust, George *437*

Stewart Trust, Sir Halley *437*

Still Waters Charitable Trust *438*

Stonehouse Trust Ltd, Eric *438*

Stow Allen Trust, The *439*

Strathspey Charitable Trust, The *440*

Summer's and I May's Charitable Settlement, The Late Misses (A N) *442*

Sunley Charitable Foundation, The Bernard *443*

Sussman Charitable Trust, Adrienne & Leslie *443*

Swansea and Brecon Diocesan Board of Finance Ltd *444*

Swaziland Charitable Trust *444*

Swinstead Charitable Trust, The *445*

Sykes Trust, The Charles *445*

Sylvanus Charitable Trust, The *446*

Symons Charitable Trust, The Stella *446*

TSB Foundation for the Channel Islands *447*

TUUT Charitable Trust, The *448*

Tait Charity, The Richard *448*

Tanner Charitable Settlement, The Joan *449*

Taylor Trust, C B & H H *450*

Third Sector Trust, The *452*

Thornton Charitable Settlement, The Ruth *454*

Thorpe Charity Trust, The *455*

Tindall's Charitable Trust, Mrs R P *457*

Tisbury Telegraph Trust, The *457*

Tomchei Torah Charitable Trust *458*

Torchbearer Trust *458*

Tory Family Foundation, The *459*

Toy Trust, The *459*

Trades Union Congress Educational Trust *460*

Trans-Antarctic Association, The *460*

Travis Charitable Trust, Constance *460*

Trenance Charitable Trust *460*

Triodos Foundation *460*

Trust for the Homeless *462*

Tryst Settlement, The *462*

Tudor Trust, The *463*

Tunstall Charitable Trust *463*

Turkish Women's Philanthropic Association of England *463*

Turner Charitable Trust, The Joseph and Hannah *464*

Turner Trust, The Douglas *464*

Tyndale Trust *466*

United Kingdom Friends for Further Education in Israel *468*

United Society for Christian Literature *468*

United Society for the Propagation of the Gospel *468*

Unitek Foundation *469*

Uxbridge Charitable Trust *469*

Van Berchem Charitable Trust, The Alec *470*

Van Leer Foundation UK Trust, Bernard *470*

Van Neste Foundation, The *471*

Vineyard Christian Fellowship of South West *473*

Vinson Charity Trust, The 1969 *473*

Vivdale Ltd *474*

Waghorn Charitable Trust, The Albert *475*

Wagstaff Charitable Trust, Bob *475*

Walker 597 Trust, The *477*

Wallington Missionary Mart & Auctions *478*

War on Want *479*

Wates Foundation, The *481*

Watson Foundation, The Bertie *482*

Webb Charitable Trust, The Denis George *483*

Welby Trust, The Barbara *484*

Wellcome Trust, The *485*

Welton Foundation, The *485*

Westcroft Trust *486*

Western Foils Charitable Trust *487*

Whitaker Charitable Trust *489*

White Rose Children's Aid International Charity *489*

Whitecourt Charitable Trust, The *490*

Whitehead Charitable Trust, J E *490*

Whitley Animal Protection Trust *491*

Williams Trust, James *493*

Wills 1962 Charitable Trust, P J H *494*

Wills 1965 Charitable Trust, The H D H *494*

Wincott Foundation, The *496*

Wingate Foundation, The Harold Hyam *496*

Winstone Foundation, Hyman *497*

Wohl Charitable Foundation, The Maurice *498*

Wohl Charitable Trust, The Maurice *498*

Wolff Charity Trust *498*

Wolfson Charitable Trust, The Charles *499*

Wolfson Family Charitable Trust, The *499*

Wolfson Foundation, The *499*

Woodlands Trust *501*

Worshipful Company of Cutlers, The *504*

Worshipful Company of Engineers' Charitable Trust Fund, The *504*

Worshipful Company of Feltmakers of London Charitable Foundation, The *505*

Wychdale Limited *507*

Wyford Charitable Trust, The *507*

Wyre Animal Welfare *507*

Yardy Charitable Trust, The Dennis Alan *509*

Young Charitable Settlement, The John *510*

Youth Appeal for Eastern Europe *511*

Trusts by field of interest and type of beneficiary

The green pages contain two separate listings.

Categorisation of fields of interest and types of beneficiary This lists all the headings used in the *DGMT* to categorise fields of interest and types of beneficiary. It is based on the Charity Commission classification and so groups similar types of activity together.

Trusts by field of interest and type of beneficiary
This lists the trusts appearing in the *DGMT* under the fields of interest and types of beneficiary for which they have expressed a funding preference.

Fields of interest and type of beneficiary

Social care & development

■ Community facilities 125
Art galleries & cultural centres 86
Community centres & village halls 122
Libraries & museums 227
Parks 248
Playgrounds 250
Recreation grounds 259
Sports centres 289
Theatres & opera houses 296

■ Community services 129
Adoption & fostering services 64
Care in the community 103
Clubs 117
Community transport 133
Counselling (social issues) 146
Crime prevention schemes 148
Day centres 154
Emergency care, refugees, famine 168
Holidays & outings 204
Income support & maintenance 215
Meals provision 229
Playschemes 251

■ Campaigning (social issues) 99
Community issues 128
Development proposals 155
Gay & lesbian rights 180
International rights of the individual 222
Penal reform 249
Racial equality, discrimination, relations 258
Transport proposals 300
Unborn children's rights 301

■ Advocacy (social issues) 75
Equal opportunities 175
Individual rights 217

■ Advice & information (social issues) 68
Advice centres 71
Law centres 226

Accomodation & housing

■ Residential facilities & services 270
Advice & information (housing) 67
Almshouses 79
Emergency & short-term housing 167
Holiday accommodation 204
Hostels 212
Housing associations 213
Residential facilities 269
Respite 273
Sheltered accommodation 283

Page references refer to the list of trusts that begins on page 59

Arts, culture & recreation

■ Arts & arts facilities 88
Architecture 86
Combined arts 119
Crafts 147
Dance & ballet 153
Film, video, multimedia, broadcasting 178
Fine art 178
Literature 228
Music 238
Opera 245
Residences 269
Theatre 296
Visual arts 308

■ Community arts & recreation 119
Arts activities 87
Arts education 91
Dance groups 153
Opera companies, opera groups 246
Orchestras 247
Theatrical companies, theatre groups 297

■ Cultural heritage (of national & historical importance) 150
Cultural activity 148
English literature 171

Education & training

■ Schools & colleges 279
Business schools 95
Church schools 116
Independent schools 216
Junior schools 224
Language schools 226
Postgraduate education 252
Pre-school education 253
Primary schools 254
Secondary schools 283
Special schools 287
Tertiary & higher education 294

■ Education & training 163
Cultural & religious teaching 149
English as a second or foreign language – TESL & TEFL 171
Literacy 228
Professional, specialist training 257
Special needs education 287
Textiles & upholstery 295
Training for community development 298
Training for personal development 299
Training for work 300
Vocational training 308

■ Costs of study 141
Bursaries & fees 95
Fellowships 178
Scholarships 278

■ Academic subjects, sciences & research 59
Archaeology 86
Engineering 170
Medicine 235
Physics 249
Research institutes 268
Science & technology 282
Specialist research 288

Conservation & environment

■ Conservation 135
Church buildings 115
Fauna 177
Flora 180
Historic buildings 203
Lakes 225
Landscapes 225
Memorials & monuments 235
Nature reserves 239
Waterways 309

■ Animal facilities & services 82
Animal homes 84
Animal welfare 85
Bird sanctuaries 93
Cats – catteries & other facilities for cats 106
Dogs – kennels & other facilities for dogs 162
Horses – stables & other facilities for horses 208
Wildlife parks 310
Wildlife sanctuaries 311
Zoos 315

■ Environment & animal sciences 171
Agriculture 79
Animal breeding 81
Botany 94
Ecology 162
Horticulture 208
Natural history 239
Organic food production 247
Ornithology & zoology 248

■ Conservation & campaigning 138
Endangered species 170
Environmental issues 174
Heritage 202
Nuclear energy, nuclear power 240
Renewable energy, renewable power 268
Transport & alternative transport 300

Health

■ Health care 192
Acute health care 63
Aftercare 78
Alternative health care 80
Counselling (health) 145
Dentistry 155
Family planning clinic 177
First aid 179
Hospice at home 208
Nursing service 241
Primary health care 253
Respite care, care for carers 275
Support, self help groups 291
Well woman clinics 310

■ Health facilities & buildings 197
Ambulances & mobile units 81
Convalescent homes 140
Hospices 210
Hospitals 211
Medical centres 230
Nursing homes 240
Rehabilitation centres 261

■ Medical studies & research 230
Cancer research 101
MS research 237
Ophthalmology 247

■ Campaigning (health) 95
Health education 196
Health issues 201
Health promotion 201

■ Advocacy (health) 72
Health related volunteer schemes 202

Religion

■ Advancement of religion 65
Christian outreach 113
Missionaries, evangelicals 236

■ Religious buildings 263
Cemeteries & burial grounds 107
Churches 116
Mosques 237
Religious ancillary buildings 262
Synagogues 294
Temples, gurdwaras 294

■ Religious umbrella bodies 265
Catholic bodies 106
Diocesan boards 156

Infrastructure support & development

■ Infrastructure & technical support 217
Building services 94
Financial services 178
Information technology & computers 217
Legal services 226
Management services 228
Personnel & human resource services 249
Publishing & printing 258
Recruitment services 260

■ Infrastructure development 220
Community businesses 122
Community development 124
Economic regeneration schemes 163
Job creation 223
Small enterprises 285
Support to voluntary & community organisations 292
Support to volunteers 293
Tourism 298

■ Professional bodies 255
Health professional bodies 201
Social care professional bodies 285

■ Charity or voluntary umbrella bodies 107
Council for Voluntary Service (CVS) 145
Rural Community Council (RCC) 278
Volunteer bureaux 309

General charitable purposes 181

The trusts listed under this heading have indicated that they are willing to consider funding applications from charities and good causes of all sorts. No preferences have been expressed for any specific type of project or work, nor for a specific area of activity. However, users should check whether any beneficiary or beneficial area priorities have been identified.

Beneficiaries

■ Beneficiaries by age

Children 110
Young adults 311
Older people 242

....

■ Beneficiaries by professional & economic group

Actors & entertainment professionals 63
Chemists 110
Clergy 117
Ex-service & service people 176
Medical professionals, nurses & doctors 230
Musicians 239
Retired 276
Scientists 283
Seafarers & fishermen 283
Sportsmen & women 290
Students 290
Teachers & governesses 294
Textile workers & designers 295
Unemployed 301
Volunteers 309
Writers & poets 311

....

■ Beneficiaries by family situation

In care, fostered & adopted 215
Parents & children 248
One parent families 245
Widows & widowers 310

....

■ Beneficiaries by religion & culture

Baptists 93
Buddhists & Jainists 94
Christians 114
Church of England 116
Ethnic minority groups 175
Evangelists 175
Jews 223
Methodists 236
Muslims 239
Quakers 258
Roman Catholics 277
Unitarians 301

■ Beneficiaries by disease & medical condition

Alzheimer's disease 81
Arthritis & rheumatism 87
Asthma 92
Autism 93
Blood disorders & haemophilia 94
Cancers 102
Cerebral palsy 107
Crohn's disease 148
Cystic fibrosis 153
Diabetes 156
Dietary – special dietary needs 156
Epilepsy 175
Friedrichs ataxia 180
Head & other injuries 192
Hearing loss 202
Heart disease 202
HIV & AIDS 204
Kidney disease 225
Leprosy 226
Mental illness 235
Motor neurone disease 237
Multiple sclerosis 238
Muscular dystrophy 238
Paediatric diseases 248
Parkinson's disease 248
Polio 252
Psoriasis 258
Sight loss 285
Stroke 290
Substance misuse 291
Terminally ill 294
Tropical diseases 301
Tuberculosis 301

....

■ Beneficiaries by social circumstances

At risk groups 92
Carers 105
Disabled people (physical, sensory, learning impairments) 156
Disadvantaged by poverty 157
Disaster victims 161
Ex-offenders & those at risk of offending 175
Gays & lesbians 181
Homeless 206
Immigrants 214
Refugees 260
Rural areas – living in 277
Socially isolated 286
Travellers 301
Urban areas – living in 301
Victims of abuse 303

Continued overleaf

Beneficiaries continued

Victims of crime *303*
Victims of domestic violence *304*
Victims of famine *305*
Victims of man-made or natural disasters *306*
Victims of war *306*

Trusts by field of interest and type of beneficiary

■ **Abuse**
see Victims of abuse

■ **Academic prizes**
see Costs of study

■ **Academic subjects, sciences & research**
see also Archaeology, Engineering, Medicine, Physics, Research institutes, Science & technology, Specialist research

Funding priority

AB Charitable Trust, The *3*
AIIT (The Ancient India and Iran Trust) *3*
Achiezer Association Limited *6*
Aga Khan Foundation (UK) *7*
Airflow Community Ltd, The *9*
Alcohol Education and Research Council *9*
Aleh Charitable Foundation, The *10*
Alexander Charitable Trust, The *10*
Alexander Charitable Trust, Mrs K L *11*
Alliance Family Foundation Limited *13*
Allsop Charitable Trust, Pat *14*
Appelbe Trust, Ambrose & Ann *19*
Armourers' & Brasiers' Gauntlet Trust, The *21*
Ashton Foundation, The Norman C *24*
Astor of Hever Trust, The *26*
Baker Trust, The C Alma *31*
Ball Charitable Trust, The Bruce *31*
Bear Mordechai Ltd *39*
Bestway Foundation, The *46*
Biological Trust, The *49*
Black Foundation, The Bertie *51*
Blank Donations Ltd, The David *54*
Bottom Charitable Trust, Harry *56*
Bridgeman TRA Foundation, The Dick *60*
British Schools and Universities Foundation (Inc) *62*
British Sugar Foundation *63*
Brotherton Trust, The Charles *65*
Cadbury Schweppes Foundation, The *76*
Canine Supporters Charity, The *80*
Carnegie Trust for the Universities of Scotland *82*

Carron Charitable Trust, The *83*
Carter Trust, The Frederick William *84*
Cen Foundation, The Hyman *87*
Chippindale Foundation, Sam *93*
Christendom Trust, The *94*
Ciba Fellowship Trust, The *95*
Clark Charitable Trust *98*
Clark Charitable Trust, J Anthony *98*
Coates Charitable Settlement, The *102*
Cohen Charitable Trust, The Vivienne and Samuel *104*
Company of Tobacco Pipe Makers and Tobacco Blenders Benevolent Fund *109*
Crescent Trust, The *117*
Curry Charitable Trust, Dennis *119*
Daily Telegraph Charitable Trust *122*
Daiwa Anglo-Japanese Foundation, The *122*
Dandeen Charitable Trust *123*
Davy Foundation, The J *126*
De La Rue Charitable Trust *127*
Denton Charitable Trust, The *130*
Deutsch Charitable Trust, The Andre *131*
Deutsch Charitable Trust, The H & M *131*
Diamond Industry Educational Charity, The *132*
Djanogly Foundation, The *135*
Dulverton Trust, The *139*
Edinburgh Trust, No 2 Account *145*
Education Services *145*
Elephant Jobs Charity *146*
Ellis 1985 Charitable Trust, Edith M *148*
European Cultural Foundation (UK Committee) *154*
Fairbairn Charitable Trust, The Esmee *157*
Fairway Trust, The *158*
Famos Foundation Trust *158*
Follett Trust, The *166*
Foyle Trust, Charles Henry *169*
Franklin Bequest, The Rosalind *169*
Franklin Deceased's New Second Charity, Sydney E *170*
Gatsby Charitable Foundation, The *179*
General Nursing Council for England and Wales Trust, The *180*
Gibbs Charitable Trusts, The *181*

Gilchrist Educational Trust *183*
Girdlers' Company Charitable Trust, The *184*
Goodman Charitable Foundation, The Everard and Mina *188*
Goodman Trust, The *189*
Grahame Charitable Foundation, The *190*
Greenwood Charitable Trust, The G B *195*
Gross Charities Limited, M & R *197*
Grosshill Charitable Trust *197*
Gwent County Council Welsh Church Fund *200*
Hamilton Educational Trust, Eleanor *205*
Harbour Foundation Ltd, The *208*
Hargreaves Trust, The Kenneth *210*
Heinz Company Limited Charitable Trust, The H J *215*
Held Settlement, The Gisela *215*
Highcroft Charitable Trust *218*
Hitachi Charitable Trust, The *222*
Hoover Foundation, The *226*
Hopkinson Educational Trust, Robert Addy *227*
Horne Foundation, The *228*
Houblon-Norman Fund *229*
IBM United Kingdom Trust *233*
IPE Charitable Trust, The *233*
JCA Charitable Foundation *238*
James Foundation, The Catherine and Lady Grace *241*
Jeffreys Road Fund, Rees *243*
Jewish Philanthropic Association for Israel and the Middle East, The *245*
Jones Trust, Cemlyn *248*
Kahn Charitable Trust, Bernard *250*
Karten Charitable Trust, The Ian *250*
Kiln Charitable Trust, Robert *254*
Kobler Trust, The *258*
Kreitman Foundation *258*
Kulika Charitable Trust, The *259*
Kweller Charitable Trust, The Harry *259*
Landy Charitable Trust, Harry and Gertrude *263*
Lanvern Foundation *265*
Laski Memorial Charitable Trust, Nathan *265*
Lauffer Charitable Foundation, The R & D *266*
Lee Foundation, The Edgar *269*

Leigh-Bramwell Trust 'E', P *270*
Lester Trust Fund, The *271*
Leverhulme Trust, The *272*
Lucas Charitable Trust Limited, The Joseph *286*
Lunzer Charitable Trust, The Ruth & Jack *287*
Lyons Charitable Trust, Sir Jack *288*
Maccabi Foundation, The *290*
McDougall Trust, The *291*
McKenzie Trust, The Robert *292*
MacRobert Trusts, The *294*
Marks Foundation, The Hilda and Samuel *298*
Marmor Charitable Trust, The Julie *299*
Marshall Charitable Trust, The Charlotte *300*
Martin Trust, The Sir George *300*
Mayfair Charities Limited *303*
Medlock Charitable Trust, The *304*
Mellows Charitable Settlement, The Anthony and Elizabeth *305*
Mental Health Foundation, The *305*
Millett Charitable Trust, The Alan and Janet *312*
Modiano Charitable Trust *315*
Moore Charitable Trust, The Horace *316*
Moores Foundation, The Peter *318*
Morgan Foundation, The Mr & Mrs J T *319*
Muslim Hands *324*
Neave Trust, The Airey *330*
New Durlston Trust, The *332*
Newman Charitable Trust, Mr and Mrs F E F *334*
Noah Trust, The *335*
Northern Dairies Educational Trust *339*
Northern Electric Employee Charity Association *339*
Nuffield Foundation *342*
Old Possums Practical Trust, The *344*
Oxford Trust, The *349*
PPP Healthcare Medical Trust Limited *350*
Peel Medical Research Trust, The *358*
Pelech Charitable Trust, The *358*
Phillips Charitable Foundation, Reginald M *361*
QAS Charitable Trust *373*
Rainbow Charitable Trust *376*
Rayne Foundation, The *379*
Richard III and Yorkist History Trust *384*
Robbins Trust, The Cheshire *387*

Royal Botanical & Horticultural Society of Manchester and the Northern Counties, The *395*
Royal Commission for the Exhibition of 1851 *395*
Rozel Trust, The *397*
Said Foundation, The Karim Rida *401*
St John's Wood Trust, The *403*
St Jude's Trust *403*
Save & Prosper Foundation *409*
Scarr-Hall Memorial Trust, The *409*
Seva Trust, Rampaba Sadhu *415*
Shah Trust, The Dr N K *416*
Sherman Charitable Trust, The Archie *419*
Shine No 2 Charitable Trust, The Barnett and Sylvia *420*
Sidbury Trust, The Second *421*
Salter Trust Ltd *424*
Society of Friends of the Torah, The *429*
South Square Trust *430*
Southall Charitable Trust, Kenneth & Phyllis *431*
Southall Trust, W F *432*
Spalding Trust *433*
Spoore, Merry & Rixman Foundation, The *434*
Stanley Foundation Limited *435*
Stathern Chapel Close Trust, The *436*
Stewart Charitable Trust, Mary Stephanie *437*
Street Charitable Foundation, W O *440*
TSB Foundation for the Channel Islands *447*
Tesco Charity Trust *452*
Tesler Foundation, The *452*
Third Sector Trust, The *452*
Thompson Memorial Fund, The Edwin John *453*
Thriplow Charitable Trust *456*
Timson Family Charitable Trust *457*
Tyndale Trust *466*
United Kingdom Friends for Further Education in Israel *468*
Weinstock Fund, The *484*
Wellcome Trust, The *485*
Westcroft Trust *486*
White Rose Children's Aid International Charity *489*
Wincott Foundation, The *496*
Wohl Charitable Foundation, The Maurice *498*
Wohl Charitable Trust, The Maurice *498*
Wolff Charity Trust *498*
Wolfson Family Charitable Trust, The *499*

Wolfson Foundation, The *499*
Wolverhampton Rotary Club Charitable Trust *500*
Woods Charitable Foundation, Geoffrey *502*
Worms Charitable Trust, The Freda and Della *504*
Worshipful Company of Engineers' Charitable Trust Fund, The *504*
Worshipful Company of Needlemakers' Charitable Fund *505*
Zaiger Trust, The Elizabeth and Prince *512*

Will consider
AHJ Charitable Trust, The *3*
Acacia Charitable Trust *6*
All Saints Educational Trust *12*
Allied Domecq Trust *13*
Anderson Trust, Andrew *16*
Angler's Inn Trust *17*
Anglo Hong Kong Trust, The *17*
Anglo-German Foundation for the Study of Industrial Society *18*
Aquarian Healing Trust *19*
Aquinas Trust *20*
Askew Charitable Trust, The Ian *25*
Assembled Church of Christ Trust, The *25*
Assheton-Smith Charitable Trust *25*
Asthma Allergy and Inflammation Research Trust *25*
Astor's 1969 Charity, The Hon M L *26*
BBC Children in Need Appeal, The *29*
BUPA Foundation, The *29*
Bachad Fellowship – Friends of Bnei Akiva *30*
Barnby's Foundation, Lord *35*
Barnes Workhouse Fund *35*
Barnsbury Charitable Trust *35*
Barton Trust, Eleanor *37*
Bateman Charitable Trust, Lady Margaret *37*
Bealey Foundation, The *38*
Beckwith Charitable Trust, The Peter *40*
Beckwith-Smith's Charitable Settlement, Mrs *40*
Bergqvist Charitable Trust *44*
Biological Trust, The *49*
Blagrave Charitable Trust, The Herbert and Peter *52*
Blakey Charitable Trust, The Celia and Conrad *53*
Blanchminster Trust, The *54*
Boltons Trust, The *55*
Borthwick Memorial Trust, The Oliver *56*

Bowland Charitable Trust, The *57*
British Dietetic Association General and Education Trust Fund, The *61*
British Friends of Chinuch Atzmai Trust, The *62*
British Schools and Universities Foundation (Inc) *62*
Brook Charitable Settlement, R E *64*
Brookhouse's Will Trust, Mr John Charles *65*
Brotherton Trust, The Charles *65*
Burden Trust, The *69*
Burn Charity Trust, The J H *70*
Burns Charity, The Dorothy *70*
Burry Charitable Trust, The *70*
Burton Charitable Trust, The Geoffrey *71*
Butler's Trust, Lord *71*
Butler's Trust, Lucilla *72*
CfBT Education Services *74*
Campden Charities, The *79*
Cardiff & Swansea Methodist District Charitable Trust Fund *80*
Carlton Television Trust *81*
Carnegie Trust for the Universities of Scotland *82*
Cassel Educational Trust (Mountbatten Memorial Grants to Commonwealth Students), The Sir Ernest *84*
Cass's Foundation, Sir John *85*
Castang Charitable Trust, H and M *85*
Charity Projects *90*
Christian Aid *94*
Cinderford Charitable Trust, The *96*
Closehelm Ltd *101*
Clutterbuck Charitable Trust, Robert *102*
Coates Charitable Trust 1969, Lance *103*
Cohen Charity Trust, Lucy *104*
Cohen Foundation, The John S *104*
Condon Family Trust *109*
Cope Charitable Trust, Alfred *112*
Cymerman Trust Limited, Itzchok Meyer *120*
Davies Charity, The Gwendoline and Margaret *125*
De Avenley Foundation, The *126*
De Rothschild 1981 Charitable Trust, The Edmund *127*
De Yong Charitable Trust, The Emma *128*
Denton Charitable Trust, The *130*
Desmond Charitable Trust, The Richard *131*

Dicken Charitable Trust, The Albert *133*
Dinam Charity *134*
Doughty Charity Trust, The *136*
Dove-Bowerman Trust *137*
D'Oyly Carte Charitable Trust, The *137*
Drapers' Charitable Fund *137*
Drayton Trust, The *138*
Dunn Charitable Trust, The Harry *140*
Earmark Trust, The *142*
Ebb and Flow Charitable Trust *144*
Edgar Trust, The Gilbert *145*
Eling Trust *147*
Ellinson Foundation Limited *148*
Elshore Limited *149*
Eranda Foundation, The *152*
Family Trust, The *158*
Farmers' Company Charitable Fund, The *159*
Federation of Jewish Relief Organisations *160*
Fletcher Trust, Roy *165*
Foreman Foundation, The Carl & Eve *167*
Foyle Trust, Charles Henry *169*
Frazer Charities Trust, The *171*
Fry Charitable Trust, Maurice *174*
Garthgwynion Charities *179*
Gibson's Charity Trust, The Hon Mr & Mrs Clive *182*
Gilchrist Educational Trust *183*
Gillett Charitable Trust, J A *183*
Gill's Charitable Trust, Mrs M M *184*
Gold Hill Church Trust *186*
Goldberg Charitable Trust, The Lewis *186*
Goodman Trust, The S & F *189*
Gradel Foundation, The *189*
Great Britain Sasakawa Foundation, The *193*
Green Foundation, Constance *194*
Grut Charitable Trust, The *198*
Gulbenkian Foundation (Lisbon) United Kingdom Branch, Calouste *199*
HB Charitable Trust *201*
Hacking & Sons Ltd Charitable Trust, C G *201*
Hampton Fuel Allotment Charity *207*
Harding's Charity, William *209*
Harvey Charitable Trust, Gordon *211*
Hawthorne Charitable Trust, The *212*
Heinz Company Limited Charitable Trust, The H J *215*

Hewett/Driver Education Trust, The *217*

Hillards Charitable Trust, Gay & Peter Hartley's *220*

Hodge Foundation, The Jane *223*

Holford Trust Fund *224*

Hoover Foundation, The *226*

Hopkinson Educational Trust, Robert Addy *227*

Horn Trust, The Cuthbert *227*

Hornby Charitable Trust, Miss D *227*

Hornton Trust, The *228*

Hughes Charitable Trust, The Geoffery C *230*

Humanitarian Trust, The *230*

Hussey for Africans, Charity of Rebecca *231*

Hyde Park Place Estate Charity, The *232*

Inman Charity, The *235*

Johnson Foundation, The *246*

KC Charitable Trust, The *250*

Kalms Foundation, The Stanley *250*

Keyes Trust, The Ursula *253*

Kingsgrove Charitable Trust, The *255*

Kinnison Charitable Trust, R O *256*

Kleinwort Charitable Trust, The Ernest *257*

Knott Trust, Sir James *258*

Laspen Trust *265*

Lavender Trust, The *267*

Lawley Foundation, The Edgar E *267*

Leach Fourteenth Trust, The *267*

Lee Foundation, The Edgar *269*

Levy Charitable Foundation, Joseph *272*

Lewis Foundation, The John Spedan *274*

Liffe Benefit *274*

Lingwood Charitable Trust, The *276*

Lloyd Charity, The S and D *278*

Lloyd's Charities Trust *278*

Localtrent Ltd *279*

Low & Bonar Charitable Fund, The *284*

Lynwood Charitable Trust, The *288*

Lyons Charitable Trust, The *288*

MDM Memorial Trust *289*

MacAndrew Trust, The E M *289*

McKechnie Foundation, A N *292*

McLaren Foundation *292*

McLaren Memorial Trust, The Martin *293*

Margadale Charitable Trust, Lord *297*

Marks Charitable Trust, Michael *298*

Markus Charitable Foundation, The Erich *298*

Marr-Munning Trust *299*

Matchan Fund Limited, The Leonard *301*

Material World Charitable Foundation Limited, The *301*

Mattock Charitable Trust, The W T *302*

Maxwell Law Scholarship Trust, The Alexander *303*

Measures Charity, The James Frederick and Ethel Anne *303*

Mercers' Company Educational Trust Fund, The *306*

Millichope Foundation, The *312*

Montefiore Trust, The David *316*

Morel Charitable Trust, The *318*

Morgan Crucible Company plc Charitable Trust, The *319*

Morris Charitable Trust, The Willie & Mabel *320*

Moulton Charitable Trust, The *321*

Music Sales Charitable Trust, The *324*

Naaman Trust, The *325*

National Lottery Charities Board *328*

New Court Charitable Trust *332*

Newcastle's 1986 Charitable Trust, Duke of *333*

Newcomen Collett Foundation *333*

Newstead Charity, The *334*

Nidditch Foundation, The Laurie *335*

Norfolk's Family Charitable Trust, Lavinia *336*

Northcott Charity Trust, The *338*

Northern Electric Employee Charity Association *339*

Owen Family Trust, The *348*

Owen Trust, Margaret *348*

PDC Trust, The *349*

PJD Charitable Trust *350*

Palmer Trust, The Gerald *352*

Paristamen Foundation, The *352*

Pascoe Charitable Trust, Alan *354*

Paul Charitable Trust, The Late Barbara May *355*

Paul Charitable Trust, Margaret Jeanne *355*

Paul Charitable Trust, Pamela Milton *355*

Paul Foundation, The *355*

Paul's Charitable Trust, R J *355*

Payne Charitable Trust, The *355*

Perry Charitable Trust, Miss Frances Lucille *359*

Pershore Nashdom & Elmore Trust Ltd, The *360*

Peskin Charitable Trust, The Hazel and Leslie *360*

Pitt Trust, Headley *364*

Porter Foundation *366*

Powys Welsh Church Fund *367*

Puebla Charitable Trust Limited, The *371*

Queen Anne Street Educational Trust Limited *373*

RT Trust, The *374*

Rackham Charitable Trust, The Mr & Mrs Philip *375*

Radley Charitable Trust *375*

Rae Charity, H J *375*

Rainford Trust, The *376*

Rav Chesed Trust, The *379*

Reekie Trust, R A & V B *381*

Rest-Harrow Trust, The *382*

Reuter Foundation, The *382*

Richards Charity, The Clive *384*

Richards Charity, The Violet M *384*

Richmond Parish Lands Charity *384*

Rivendell Trust, The *387*

Robyn Charitable Trust *389*

Rodewald's Charitable Settlement, Mr C A *389*

Rogers Charitable Settlement, The Richard *390*

Rolfe Charitable Trust, The *390*

Rosen Foundation, Cecil *392*

S Group Charitable Trust *399*

Said Foundation, The Karim Rida *401*

Salters Charities *405*

Samuel Charitable Trust, M J *406*

Save & Prosper Educational Trust *408*

Scopus Jewish Educational Trust *411*

Sheepdrove Trust, The *417*

Shifrin Charitable Trust, The Maurice and Hilda *419*

Silvester Charitable Gift Trust *422*

Simon's Charity *422*

Solomons Charitable Trust, David *430*

Somerfield Curtis Will Trust, The Dorothy *430*

Sumner's Trust Section 'A', Sir John *443*

Swann-Morton Foundation, The *444*

Symons Charitable Trust, The Stella *446*

TSB Foundation for Scotland *447*

Tait Charity, The Richard *448*

Taylor Charitable Trust, The B R *450*
Terry Charitable Trust, Noel Goddard *451*
Thompson Charitable Trust, The *453*
Thorpe Charity Trust, The *455*
van Geest Foundation, The John and Lucille *470*
Van Leer Foundation UK Trust, Bernard *470*
Van Norden's Charitable Foundation, Mrs Maud *471*
Vineyard Christian Fellowship of South West *473*
Vinson Charity Trust, The 1969 *473*
Vogel Charitable Trust, The Nathan *474*
Wakefield Trust, The *476*
Walker Trust, The *477*
Wander Charitable Fund, The Dr Albert *479*
Ward Blenkinsop Trust, The *480*
Watson's Trust, John *482*
Welby Trust, The Barbara *484*
Whetherly's Charitable Trust, The Hon Mrs R G A *489*
Whitehead Charitable Trust, J E *490*
Whittington Charitable Trust, The *491*
Wiggins Charity Trust, Cyril *491*
Wilde Charitable Trust, The Felicity *492*
Wingate Foundation, The Harold Hyam *496*
Winstone Foundation, Hyman *497*
Woburn 1986 Charitable Trust *498*
Woodhouse Charitable Trust, Edwin *501*
Worshipful Company of Founders Charities, The *505*
Wychdale Limited *507*
Yapp Education and Research Trust, The *508*
Youell Foundation Ltd, The *510*

■ **Actors & entertainment professionals**
Funding priority
Karloff Charitable Foundation, The Boris *250*
Royal Theatrical Fund, The *396*
Snipe Charitable Trust *428*

....
■ **Acute health care**
see also **Health care**
Funding priority
Birmingham Amenities and Welfare Trust, The *49*
Bottom Charitable Trust, Harry *56*
Cancer Relief Macmillan Fund *79*
Cooper Charitable Trust *111*
Davis Charitable Trust, Wilfrid Bruce *126*
Elton John Aids Foundation, The *149*
Fogel Charitable Trust, The Gerald *165*
Garnett's 1973 Charitable Trust, Mrs A M *178*
Grant Foundation, The Raymond *191*
Heath Charitable Trust *214*
Heritage of London Trust, The *216*
Lawson Charitable Trust, Raymond and Blanche *267*
Lloyd's Charities Trust *278*
Loseley & Guildway Charitable Trust, The *281*
Manning Trust, Leslie & Lilian *296*
Mercury Phoenix Trust *307*
Multiple Sclerosis Society of Great Britain & Northern Ireland *322*
Royal Theatrical Fund, The *396*
SMB Trust, The *400*
Stonehouse Trust Ltd, Eric *438*
Strangward Trust, The *439*
Tisbury Telegraph Trust, The *457*

Will consider
Allen Trust, Mrs M H *13*
Ammco Trust, The *15*
Army Benevolent Fund, The *22*
Ashby Charitable Trust, The *23*
Astor Foundation, The *26*
Bancroft Trust, The *33*
Barbour Trust, The *33*
Beckwith Charitable Settlement, The Heather *39*
Beit Trust, The *40*
Berris Charitable Trust *45*
BibleLands *47*
Birtwistle Memorial Trust, The G E *50*
Bourne-May Charitable Trust, The *57*
British Dietetic Association General and Education Trust Fund, The *61*
Britton Charitable Trust, The J & M *63*
Buckinghamshire Masonic Centenary Fund *67*
Butlin Charity Trust, Bill *72*

Clinton's Charitable Trust, Lord *100*
Commonwealth Relations Trust *108*
Community Trust for Greater Manchester, The *108*
Coxen Trust Fund, Sir William *116*
Curzon Charitable Trust, The Wallace *120*
Dahl Foundation, The Roald *122*
Denne Charitable Trust *130*
Digby Charitable Trust, Simon *133*
Dorus Trust *136*
Earley Charity, The *142*
Edgar Foundation, The Gilbert and Eileen *145*
Edgar Trust, The Gilbert *145*
Elkes Charity Fund, The Wilfred & Elsie *147*
Emmandjay Charitable Trust *150*
Emmaus Christian Foundation *150*
Epigoni Trust *152*
Eveson Charitable Trust, The *155*
Follett Trust, The *166*
Foreman Foundation, The Carl & Eve *167*
Fortune Trust, The *167*
Gardner Charitable Trust, R & J *178*
Gibbins Trust, The *181*
Golding Fund, The Sir John *187*
Gray Charitable Trust, R B *192*
Great Britain Sasakawa Foundation, The *193*
Greater Bristol Foundation *193*
Greenaway Foundation, The Alan *194*
Greenaway Foundation, The Sir Derek *194*
Grocers' Charity *197*
Grundy Foundation, The Stanley *198*
Hawley Residuary Fund, Harry Fieldsend *212*
Haywood Charitable Trust *214*
Humanitarian Trust, The *230*
Innes Memorial Fund *235*
JDM Charitable Trust *239*
JHL Trust, The *239*
JMK Charitable Trust *239*
Laing Charitable Trust, The David *260*
Leach Fourteenth Trust, The *267*
Leadbeater Trust, The Alfred *268*
Lee Foundation, The Edgar *269*
Leech Charity, The William *269*
Linford Charitable Trust, The Fred *276*

Linmardon Trust *276*
Lloyd Charity, The S and D *278*
London Law Trust *280*
Lowenthal Charitable Trust,
The L and C *285*
Lynall Foundation, The D G
287
Mackintosh Foundation, The
292
Metropolitan Hospital-Sunday
Fund, The *308*
Milward Charity, The Edgar
313
Moore Foundation, The
George A *316*
Multithon Trust, The *323*
Music for World Development
323
Natwest Staff Samaritan Fund
330
New Court Charitable Trust
332
Newby Trust Ltd *332*
North British Hotel Trust *337*
Penny in the Pound Fund
Charitable Trust *359*
Pratt Charitable Trust, The W L
367
Rowbotham Charitable Trust,
The Christopher *393*
Royal's Memorial Fund,
Princess *396*
Shelroy Charitable Trust, The
417
South Square Trust *430*
Sportsman's Aid Charity Ltd,
The *434*
Sussman Charitable Trust,
Adrienne & Leslie *443*
TSB Foundation for Northern
Ireland *447*
Thompson Charitable Trust,
The *453*
Travis Charitable Trust,
Constance *460*
Turner Trust, The Douglas *464*
Van Neste Foundation, The
471
Webber Trust Fund, Ethel *483*
Weir Foundation, The James
484
Wylde Memorial Charity, The
Anthony and Gwendoline
507

■ Addiction

see Substance misuse

■ Adoption &
fostering services

see also Community
services

Funding priority

Access 4 Trust *6*
Anstey Charitable Settlement,
J C W *18*
Christmas Cracker Trust *95*
Clipsham Charitable
Settlement, R E *101*
Harford Charitable Trust *209*
Hudson Benevolent Trust, The
Thomas *230*
SMB Trust, The *400*
TSB Foundation for Scotland
447
Wates Foundation, The *481*

Will consider

Archer Trust, The *20*
Astor Foundation, The *26*
Berkshire Community Trust *45*
Blackburn Trust, The *51*
Blakenham's Charity Trust,
Lady *53*
Boots Charitable Trust *56*
Bowland Charitable Trust, The
57
Brough Charitable Trust,
Joseph *65*
CLA Charitable Trust *74*
Cadbury Charitable Trust
(Incorporated), Edward *75*
Chiddick Charitable Trust *92*
Chrimes Family Charitable
Trust, The *93*
Commonwealth Relations Trust
108
Community Trust for Greater
Manchester, The *108*
County Durham Foundation
115
Coutts Charitable Trust, The
116
Curriers Company Charitable
Fund *119*
Curzon Charitable Trust, The
Wallace *120*
Derbyshire Trust, J N *130*
Digby Charitable Trust, Simon
133
Direct Response *134*
Dumbreck Charity *139*
Earwicker Trust *142*
Edgar Foundation, The Gilbert
and Eileen *145*
Elkes Charity Fund, The Wilfred
& Elsie *147*
Emmaus Christian Foundation
150
Ferguson Benevolent Fund
Limited *161*
Fletcher Trust, Roy *165*
Follett Trust, The *166*
Gelston Charitable Trust, The
179

Grosshill Charitable Trust *197*
Hertfordshire Community
Trust, The *217*
Ingles Charitable Trust, The
234
Inverforth Charitable Trust, The
236
Iris Trust, The *237*
Isle of Dogs Community
Foundation *238*
JDM Charitable Trust *239*
Jarrold Trust Ltd, John *243*
Johnson Foundation, The *246*
Kroch Foundation, The Heinz &
Anna *259*
Kyte Charitable Trust, The *259*
Laing Foundation, The
Christopher *260*
Lankelly Foundation, The *264*
Leech Charity, The William *269*
Lewis Partnership, John *274*
(Lloyds) TSB Foundation for
England and Wales *279*
Lynall Foundation, The D G
287
Marchday Charitable Fund, The
296
Milburn Charitable Trust,
Frederick *310*
Moores Foundation, John *318*
Multithon Trust, The *323*
NR Charitable Trust, The *325*
National Power Charitable
Trust, The *330*
New Court Charitable Trust
332
Norfolk's Family Charitable
Trust, Lavinia *336*
Norman Family Charitable
Trust, The *337*
Oakdale Trust, The *343*
Parivar Trust, The *353*
Payne Trust, The Harry *356*
Pye Christian Trust, The *371*
Pyke Charity Trust *372*
Rayner Charitable Trust, The
John *380*
Robinson Brothers (Ryders
Green) Ltd, Charitable Trust
388
Rope Third Charitable
Settlement, The Mrs *391*
Rothley Trust, The *392*
St Christopher's Trust, The *402*
Schuster Charitable Trust, The
410
Shepherd Family Charitable
Trust, The Sir Peter *418*
South Square Trust *430*
Sparkhill Trust, The *433*
Stevens Foundation, The June
437
Tisbury Telegraph Trust, The
457
Towler Charity Trust, The Fred
459
Travis Charitable Trust,
Constance *460*

Tyne & Wear Foundation *466*

Upjohn Charitable Trust, The *469*

Wander Charitable Fund, The Dr Albert *479*

Wesleyan Charitable Trust, The *485*

■ Advancement of religion

see also Christian outreach, Missionaries, evangelicals

Funding priority

AB Charitable Trust, The *3*

Acacia Charitable Trust *6*

Achiezer Association Limited *6*

Aid to the Church in Need (United Kingdom) *8*

Alglen Ltd *11*

Alliance Family Foundation Limited *13*

Almond Trust, The *14*

Aston Charities Trust Ltd *25*

Astor of Hever Trust, The *26*

Bateman Charitable Trust, Lady Margaret *37*

Beacon Trust *38*

Bear Mordechai Ltd *39*

Beauland Ltd *39*

Bellahouston Bequest Fund *42*

Belljoe Tzedoko Ltd *42*

BibleLands *47*

Bisgood Trust, The *50*

Bisgood's Charitable Trust, Miss Jeanne *50*

Black Charitable Trust, The Cyril W *51*

Black Charitable Trust, Sydney *51*

Black Foundation, The Bertie *51*

Blank Donations Ltd, The David *54*

Bottom Charitable Trust, Harry *56*

Brand Charitable Trust *58*

Britland Charitable Trust, The *63*

Brushmill Ltd *66*

Buckingham Trust *67*

Carmichael-Montgomery Charitable Trust, The *81*

Catholic Foreign Missions *86*

Cen Foundation, The Hyman *87*

Chesters Settlement for Methodist Church Purposes, Mr H G *91*

Chownes Foundation, The *93*

Christendom Trust, The *94*

Church Urban Fund *95*

Clark Charitable Trust *98*

Cockenzie Charitable Trust, The *103*

Cohen and William Leech Foundation, Sebag *103*

Cohen Charity Trust, Lucy *104*

Cope Charitable Trust, Alfred *112*

Cymerman Trust Limited, Itzchok Meyer *120*

Dandeen Charitable Trust *123*

Delmar Charitable Trust *129*

Dibdin Foundation, Thomas Peter *132*

Drummond Trust, The *138*

Dulverton Trust, The *139*

Earmark Trust, The *142*

Ecclesiastical Music Trust, The *144*

Education Services *145*

Elanore Ltd *146*

Eling Trust *147*

Ellis 1985 Charitable Trust, Edith M *148*

Elshore Limited *149*

Fairway Trust, The *158*

Famos Foundation Trust *158*

Federation of Jewish Relief Organisations *160*

Ferguson Benevolent Fund Limited *161*

Firdale Christian Trust, The *162*

Franklin Deceased's New Second Charity, Sydney E *170*

Gelston Charitable Trust, The *179*

Gibbs Charitable Trusts, The *181*

Gillett Charitable Trust, J A *183*

Goodman Charitable Foundation, The Everard and Mina *188*

Goodman Trust, The *189*

Gough Charitable Trust, The *189*

Grahame Charitable Foundation, The *190*

Griffiths Trust, The E E and D M *196*

Gross Charities Limited, M & R *197*

Grosshill Charitable Trust *197*

Grove Charitable Trust, The *197*

Growth Building Trust, The *198*

Haines Charitable Trust, The Alfred *203*

Highcroft Charitable Trust *218*

IPE Charitable Trust, The *233*

James Foundation, The Catherine and Lady Grace *241*

James Foundation, John & Rhys Thomas *242*

Jesus Lane Trust, The *245*

Jones Trust, Cemlyn *248*

Joseph Charitable Trust, J E *248*

Jubilee Outreach Yorkshire *248*

Kahn Charitable Trust, *250*

Kalms Foundation, The Stanley *250*

Kingston Religious Trust Fund, The *256*

Lacy Charity Trust, The Late Sir Pierce *260*

Laing Trust, Beatrice *261*

Lancaster's Trust, Bryan *263*

Layton Charity Trust, The Julian *267*

Leigh-Bramwell Trust 'E', P *270*

Lester Trust Fund, The *271*

Localtrent Ltd *279*

Lucas Charitable Trust Limited, The Joseph *286*

Lynwood Charitable Trust, The *288*

McLaren Memorial Trust, The Martin *293*

Marks Foundation, The Hilda and Samuel *298*

Missionary Friends Trust *314*

Morgan Foundation, The Mr & Mrs J T *319*

National Catholic Fund *327*

Nemoral Ltd *331*

New Durlston Trust, The *332*

Newman Charitable Trust, Mr and Mrs F E F *334*

Nidditch Foundation, The Laurie *335*

Norton Foundation, The *340*

Palmer Trust, The Gerald *352*

Pedmore Trust *357*

Pickford Charitable Foundation, The David *362*

Podde Trust *365*

Rae Charity, H J *375*

Richards Charity, The Clive *384*

Rope Third Charitable Settlement, The Mrs *391*

St Jude's Trust *403*

Saint Sarkis Charity Trust *404*

Seva Trust, Rampaba Sadhu *415*

Sewell Charitable Trust, The *416*

Shah Trust, The Dr N K *416*

Sheepdrove Trust, The *417*

Somerfield Curtis Will Trust, The Dorothy *430*

Sylvanus Charitable Trust, The *446*

Talteg Ltd *448*

Thornton Fund, The *455*

Thorpe Charity Trust, The *455*

Trenance Charitable Trust *460*

Truemark Trust, The *461*

Woods Charitable Foundation, Geoffrey *502*

Woolf Charitable Trust, The *502*

Worshipful Company of Needlemakers' Charitable Fund *505*

Wright Deceased Trust, John William *506*

Youell Foundation Ltd, The *510*

Zaiger Trust, The Elizabeth and Prince *512*

Will consider

AHJ Charitable Trust, The *3*

Airflow Community Ltd, The *9*

Aleh Charitable Foundation, The *10*

Angler's Inn Trust *17*

Appelbe Trust, Ambrose & Ann *19*

Appleton Trust, The *19*

Aquinas Trust *20*

Askew Charitable Trust, The Ian *25*

Astor Foundation, The *26*

Astor's 1969 Charity, The Hon M L *26*

Barnby's Foundation, Lord *35*

Barnsbury Charitable Trust *35*

Barton Trust, Eleanor *37*

Bealey Foundation, The *38*

Beattie Charitable Trust, The James *39*

Beckwith Charitable Trust, The Peter *40*

Beckwith-Smith's Charitable Settlement, Mrs *40*

Bergqvist Charitable Trust *44*

Blagrave Charitable Trust, The Herbert and Peter *52*

Blakey Charitable Trust, The Celia and Conrad *53*

Boltons Trust, The *55*

Borthwick Memorial Trust, The Oliver *56*

Bowland Charitable Trust, The *57*

British Sugar Foundation *63*

Brook Charitable Settlement, R E *64*

Brookhouse's Will Trust, Mr John Charles *65*

Burn Charity Trust, The J H *70*

Burns Charity, The Dorothy *70*

Burry Charitable Trust, The *70*

Burton Charitable Trust, The Geoffrey *71*

Butler's Trust, Lord *71*

Butler's Trust, Lucilla *72*

Cadbury Schweppes Foundation, The *76*

Cadbury Trust (1928), The Edward & Dorothy *76*

Carron Charitable Trust, The *83*

Castang Charitable Trust, H and M *85*

Catto Charitable Settlement, The Thomas Sivewright *86*

Charity Projects *90*

Cinderford Charitable Trust, The *96*

Clark Charitable Trust, J Anthony *98*

Clutterbuck Charitable Trust, Robert *102*

Coates Charitable Settlement, The *102*

Coates Charitable Trust 1969, Lance *103*

Cohen Charitable Trust, The Vivienne and Samuel *104*

Company of Tobacco Pipe Makers and Tobacco Blenders Benevolent Fund *109*

Condon Family Trust *109*

Crescent Trust, The *117*

Curry Charitable Trust, Dennis *119*

Daily Telegraph Charitable Trust *122*

David Trust, The Lesley *124*

Davy Foundation, The J *126*

De Avenley Foundation, The *126*

De La Rue Charitable Trust *127*

De Rothschild 1981 Charitable Trust, The Edmund *127*

De Yong Charitable Trust, The Emma *128*

Denby Charitable Foundation, The *130*

Denton Charitable Trust, The *130*

Desmond Charitable Trust, The Richard *131*

Deutsch Charitable Trust, The Andre *131*

Deutsch Charitable Trust, The H & M *131*

Dibs Charitable Trust, The *133*

Dinam Charity *134*

Djanogly Foundation, The *135*

D'Oyly Carte Charitable Trust, The *137*

Drayton Trust, The *138*

Dunn Charitable Trust, The Harry *140*

Edinburgh Trust, No 2 Account *145*

Foreman Foundation, The Carl & Eve *167*

Foyle Trust, Charles Henry *169*

Franklin Bequest, The Rosalind *169*

Fry Charitable Trust, Maurice *174*

Garthgwynion Charities *179*

Gibson's Charity Trust, The Hon Mr & Mrs Clive *182*

Gill's Charitable Trust, Mrs M M *184*

Girdlers' Company Charitable Trust, The *184*

Gladstone Charitable Trust, The E W *184*

Goldberg Charitable Trust, The Lewis *186*

Gradel Foundation, The *189*

Green Foundation, Constance *194*

Greenaway Foundation, The Sir Derek *194*

Grut Charitable Trust, The *198*

HB Charitable Trust *201*

Hacking & Sons Ltd Charitable Trust, C G *201*

Hamilton Educational Trust, Eleanor *205*

Harbour Foundation Ltd, The *208*

Harvey Charitable Trust, Gordon *211*

Hawthorne Charitable Trust, The *212*

Held Settlement, The Gisela *215*

Hillards Charitable Trust, Gay & Peter Hartley's *220*

Hodge Foundation, The Jane *223*

Hoover Foundation, The *226*

Horn Trust, The Cuthbert *227*

Hornton Trust, The *228*

Hughes Charitable Trust, The Geoffery C *230*

Hurst Will Trust, Arthur *231*

Inman Charity, The *235*

JCSCJ Charitable Trust, The *238*

Jacobs Charitable Trust, The J P *240*

Jarrold Trust Ltd, John *243*

KC Charitable Trust, The *250*

Karten Charitable Trust, The Ian *250*

Keyes Trust, The Ursula *253*

Kinnison Charitable Trust, R O *256*

Kleinwort Charitable Trust, The Ernest *257*

Kobler Trust, The *258*

Kreitman Foundation *258*

Kulika Charitable Trust, The *259*

Kweller Charitable Trust, The Harry *259*

Laing Foundation, The Christopher *260*

Landy Charitable Trust, Harry and Gertrude *263*

Lanvern Foundation *265*

Laski Memorial Charitable Trust, Nathan *265*

Lauffer Charitable Foundation, The R & D *266*

Lawley Foundation, The Edgar E *267*

Leach Fourteenth Trust, The *267*

Levy Charitable Foundation, Joseph *272*

Liffe Benefit *274*

Lunzer Charitable Trust, The Ruth & Jack *287*

Lyons Charitable Trust, The
288
MDM Memorial Trust 289
MacAndrew Trust, The E M
289
Maccabi Foundation, The 290
McKechnie Foundation, A N
292
McKenzie Trust, The Robert
292
MacKintosh Charitable Trust,
Viscount 292
McLaren Foundation 292
Margadale Charitable Trust,
Lord 297
Marks Charitable Trust,
Michael 298
Markus Charitable Foundation,
The Erich 298
Marr-Munning Trust 299
Martin Trust, The Sir George
300
Material World Charitable
Foundation Limited, The
301
Mattock Charitable Trust, The
W T 302
Medlock Charitable Trust, The
304
Mellows Charitable Settlement,
The Anthony and Elizabeth
305
Millett Charitable Trust, The
Alan and Janet 312
Millichope Foundation, The
312
Modiano Charitable Trust 315
Montefiore Trust, The David
316
Moore Charitable Trust, The
Horace 316
Moore Stephens Charitable
Foundation, The 317
Morel Charitable Trust, The
318
Morgan Crucible Company plc
Charitable Trust, The 319
Morris Charitable Trust, The
Willie & Mabel 320
Moulton Charitable Trust, The
321
Music Sales Charitable Trust,
The 324
Newcastle's 1986 Charitable
Trust, Duke of 333
Newstead Charity, The 334
Norfolk's Family Charitable
Trust, Lavinia 336
Northcott Charity Trust, The
338
Northern Arts 339
Northern Electric Employee
Charity Association 339
Old Possums Practical Trust,
The 344
Oppenheimer Charitable Trust
346
Owen Trust, Margaret 348

PDC Trust, The 349
PJD Charitable Trust 350
Pascoe Charitable Trust, Alan
354
Paul Charitable Trust, The Late
Barbara May 355
Paul Charitable Trust, Margaret
Jeanne 355
Paul Charitable Trust, Pamela
Milton 355
Paul Foundation, The 355
Paul's Charitable Trust, R J 355
Pelech Charitable Trust, The
358
Peppiatt Charitable Trust, The
Brian 359
Perry Charitable Trust, Miss
Frances Lucille 359
Peskin Charitable Trust, The
Hazel and Leslie 360
Phillips Charitable Foundation,
Reginald M 361
Powys Welsh Church Fund 367
QAS Charitable Trust 373
RT Trust, The 374
Rackham Charitable Trust, The
Mr & Mrs Philip 375
Radley Charitable Trust 375
Rav Chesed Trust, The 379
Reekie Trust, R A & V B 381
Riggs Charity, The 386
Rivendell Trust, The 387
Rodewald's Charitable
Settlement, Mr C A 389
Rogers Charitable Settlement,
The Richard 390
Rolfe Charitable Trust, The 390
Rosen Foundation, Cecil 392
Salamander Charitable Trust,
The 405
Salters Charities 405
Saunderson Foundation, The
408
Save & Prosper Foundation
409
Scarr-Hall Memorial Trust, The
409
Sharon Trust, The 416
Shelroy Charitable Trust, The
417
Sherman Charitable Trust, The
Archie 419
Shifrin Charitable Trust, The
Maurice and Hilda 419
Sidbury Trust, The Second 421
Silvester Charitable Gift Trust
422
Sobell Welsh People's
Charitable Association,
Michael 429
Solomons Charitable Trust,
David 430
Stanley Foundation Limited
435
Stewart Charitable Trust, Mary
Stephanie 437
Taylor Charitable Trust, A R
449

Taylor Charitable Trust, The B R
450
Templeton Goodwill Trust 451
Terry Charitable Trust, Noel
Goddard 451
Tesco Charity Trust 452
Tesler Foundation, The 452
3i Charitable Trust, The 455
van Geest Foundation, The
John and Lucille 470
Van Neste Foundation, The
471
Van Norden's Charitable
Foundation, Mrs Maud 471
Vincent Trust Fund, Eric W 473
Vinson Charity Trust, The 1969
473
Vivdale Ltd 474
Wakefield Trust, The 476
Wander Charitable Fund, The
Dr Albert 479
Ward Blenkinsop Trust, The
480
Weinstock Fund, The 484
Welby Trust, The Barbara 484
Whetherly's Charitable Trust,
The Hon Mrs R G A 489
Whitehead Charitable Trust, J E
490
Whittington Charitable Trust,
The 491
Wilde Charitable Trust, The
Felicity 492
Wills 1961 Charitable Trust,
Major Michael Thomas 494
Woburn 1986 Charitable Trust
498
Wohl Charitable Foundation,
The Maurice 498
Wohl Charitable Trust, The
Maurice 498
Wolfson Family Charitable
Trust, The 499
Worms Charitable Trust, The
Freda and Della 504

....

■ Advice & information (housing)

see also **Residential facilities & services**

Funding priority

Barbour Trust, The 33
City Parochial Foundation 96
County Durham Foundation
115
HACT (The Housing
Association's Charitable
Trust) 201
Hyde Charitable Trust 232
Kroch Foundation, The Heinz &
Anna 259
Moores Foundation, John 318
Paristamen Foundation, The
352

Will consider

Abbey National Charitable Trust *4*

Ashden Charitable Trust, The *24*

Berkshire Community Trust *45*

Boots Charitable Trust *56*

Cadbury Trust (1928), The Edward & Dorothy *76*

Chase Charity, The *91*

Clark 1965 Charitable Trust, Stephen *98*

Clifford Charity Oxford, The *100*

Coutts Charitable Trust, The *116*

David Trust, The Lesley *124*

de Freitas Charitable Trust, The Helen and Geoffrey *126*

Digby Charitable Trust, Simon *133*

Direct Response *134*

Ebb and Flow Charitable Trust *144*

Elkes Charity Fund, The Wilfred & Elsie *147*

Follett Trust, The *166*

Gibbins Trust, The *181*

Help the Homeless *215*

Hertfordshire Community Trust, The *217*

Isle of Dogs Community Foundation *238*

Johnson Foundation, The *246*

Laing Trust, Beatrice *261*

Laing's Charitable Trust *262*

Lane Foundation, The Allen *263*

Leech Charity, The William *269*

Marchday Charitable Fund, The *296*

Milton Keynes Community Trust Ltd, The *312*

NR Charitable Trust, The *325*

Needham Cooper Charitable Trust, The *331*

New Court Charitable Trust *332*

Noah Trust, The *335*

Norfolk's Family Charitable Trust, Lavinia *336*

Payne Trust, The Harry *356*

Rest-Harrow Trust, The *382*

Rothley Trust, The *392*

Rowntree Foundation, Joseph *394*

Scott Bader Commonwealth Ltd, The *411*

Smith & Mount Trust, The Mrs *426*

Summerfield Charitable Trust, The *442*

TSB Foundation for Northern Ireland *447*

Tisbury Telegraph Trust, The *457*

Travis Charitable Trust, Constance *460*

Wesleyan Charitable Trust, The *485*

Winstone Foundation, Hyman *497*

Woodlands Trust *501*

....

■ Advice & information (social issues)

see also Advice centres, Law centres

Funding priority

Allied Dunbar Charitable Trust Limited, The *13*

Anderson Trust, Andrew *16*

Berkshire Community Trust *45*

City Parochial Foundation *96*

Community Trust for Greater Manchester, The *108*

Condon Family Trust *109*

Fairbairn Charitable Trust, The Esmee *157*

Franklin Trust, Jill *170*

Green Foundation, Constance *194*

Hacking & Sons Ltd Charitable Trust, C G *201*

Jones Trust, Cemlyn *248*

Lester Trust Fund, The *271*

Millfield House Foundation *312*

Moores Foundation, John *318*

National Power Charitable Trust, The *330*

Northcott Devon Foundation *338*

Pitman Charitable Trust, The John *364*

Smith Foundation, The Leslie *427*

Wates Foundation, The *481*

West Midlands Regional Arts Board *486*

Westminster Amalgamated Charity *487*

Will consider

AHJ Charitable Trust, The *3*

Abbey National Charitable Trust *4*

Achiezer Association Limited *6*

Aga Khan Foundation (UK) *7*

Airflow Community Ltd, The *9*

Ajahma Charitable Trust, The *9*

Aleh Charitable Foundation, The *10*

Allachy Trust, The *12*

Angler's Inn Trust *17*

Appelbe Trust, Ambrose & Ann *19*

Aquinas Trust *20*

Askew Charitable Trust, The Ian *25*

Assembled Church of Christ Trust, The *25*

Assheton-Smith Charitable Trust *25*

Astor Foundation, The *26*

Astor of Hever Trust, The *26*

Astor's 1969 Charity, The Hon M L *26*

Austin of Longbridge Will Trust, The Rt Hon Herbert, Baron *27*

BBC Children in Need Appeal, The *29*

Barbour Trust, The *33*

Baring Foundation, The *34*

Barnabas Charitable Trust *34*

Barnby's Foundation, Lord *35*

Barnsbury Charitable Trust *35*

Barton Trust, Eleanor *37*

Bateman Charitable Trust, Lady Margaret *37*

Bealey Foundation, The *38*

Beckwith Charitable Trust, The Peter *40*

Beckwith-Smith's Charitable Settlement, Mrs *40*

Bergqvist Charitable Trust *44*

Bilton Charity, The Percy *48*

Black Foundation, The Bertie *51*

Blagrave Charitable Trust, The Herbert and Peter *52*

Blakenham's Charity Trust, Lady *53*

Blakey Charitable Trust, The Celia and Conrad *53*

Blank Donations Ltd, The David *54*

Boltons Trust, The *55*

Borthwick Memorial Trust, The Oliver *56*

Bottom Charitable Trust, Harry *56*

Bowland Charitable Trust, The *57*

British Sugar Foundation *63*

Brook Charitable Settlement, R E *64*

Brookhouse's Will Trust, Mr John Charles *65*

Brough Charitable Trust, Joseph *65*

Buckinghamshire Masonic Centenary Fund *67*

Burn Charity Trust, The J H *70*

Burns Charity, The Dorothy *70*

Burry Charitable Trust, The *70*

Burton Charitable Trust, The Geoffrey *71*

Butler's Trust, Lord *71*

Butler's Trust, Lucilla *72*

Buxton Trust, Denis *72*

Cadbury Schweppes Foundation, The *76*

Campden Charities, The *79*

Cardiff & Swansea Methodist District Charitable Trust Fund *80*

Carron Charitable Trust, The
83
Castang Charitable Trust, H
and M 85
Charity Projects 90
Chase Charity, The 91
Chiddick Charitable Trust 92
Chippindale Foundation, Sam
93
Christian Aid 94
Church Urban Fund 95
Cinderford Charitable Trust,
The 96
Clark Charitable Trust, J
Anthony 98
Closehelm Ltd 101
Clutterbuck Charitable Trust,
Robert 102
Coates Charitable Settlement,
The 102
Coates Charitable Trust 1969,
Lance 103
Cohen Charitable Trust, The
Vivienne and Samuel 104
Cohen Charity Trust, Lucy 104
Cole Charitable Trust, The 105
Company of Tobacco Pipe
Makers and Tobacco
Blenders Benevolent Fund
109
Cope Charitable Trust, Alfred
112
Cotton Trust, The 114
Crescent Trust, The 117
Cripplegate Foundation 118
Curry Charitable Trust, Dennis
119
Cymerman Trust Limited,
Itzchok Meyer 120
Daily Telegraph Charitable
Trust 122
Dandeen Charitable Trust 123
Davy Foundation, The J 126
De Avenley Foundation, The
126
De La Rue Charitable Trust
127
De Rothschild 1981 Charitable
Trust, The Edmund 127
De Yong Charitable Trust, The
Emma 128
Denton Charitable Trust, The
130
Derbyshire Trust, J N 130
Desmond Charitable Trust, The
Richard 131
Deutsch Charitable Trust, The
Andre 131
Deutsch Charitable Trust, The
H & M 131
Dibden Allotments Charity 132
Dicken Charitable Trust, The
Albert 133
Dinam Charity 134
Djanogly Foundation, The 135
Doughty Charity Trust, The
136

D'Oyly Carte Charitable Trust,
The 137
Drayton Trust, The 138
Dulverton Trust, The 139
Dunn Charitable Trust, The
Harry 140
Earmark Trust, The 142
Ebb and Flow Charitable Trust
144
Edinburgh Trust, No 2 Account
145
Eling Trust 147
Elshore Limited 149
Elvetham Charitable Trust, The
149
Family Trust, The 158
Famos Foundation Trust 158
Federation of Jewish Relief
Organisations 160
Ford of Britain Trust 166
Foreman Foundation, The Carl
& Eve 167
Four Lanes Trust, The 168
Foyle Trust, Charles Henry 169
Franklin Bequest, The Rosalind
169
Franklin Deceased's New
Second Charity, Sydney E
170
Friarsgate Trust 172
Frome Christian Fellowship
174
Fry Charitable Trust, Maurice
174
Galinski Charitable Trust 177
Garthgwynion Charities 179
Gibson's Charity Trust, The Hon
Mr & Mrs Clive 182
Gillett Charitable Trust, J A
183
Gill's Charitable Trust, Mrs M M
184
Girdlers' Company Charitable
Trust, The 184
Glynde Place Charitable Trust
(1974), The 186
Gold Hill Church Trust 186
Goldberg Charitable Trust, The
Lewis 186
Goldsmiths' Company's
Charities, The 188
Goodman Charitable
Foundation, The Everard
and Mina 188
Goodman Trust, The 189
Goodman Trust, The S & F 189
Gradel Foundation, The 189
Graves Charitable Trust, J G
192
Gross Charities Limited, M & R
197
Grosshill Charitable Trust 197
Grut Charitable Trust, The 198
Gulbenkian Foundation
(Lisbon) United Kingdom
Branch, Calouste 199
Gwent County Council Welsh
Church Fund 200

HB Charitable Trust 201
Haines Charitable Trust, The
Alfred 203
Hamilton Educational Trust,
Eleanor 205
Hampstead Wells and
Campden Trust 206
Harbour Foundation Ltd, The
208
Harvey Charitable Trust,
Gordon 211
Hawthorne Charitable Trust,
The 212
Heinz Company Limited
Charitable Trust, The H J
215
Held Settlement, The Gisela
215
Hertfordshire Community
Trust, The 217
Hillards Charitable Trust, Gay &
Peter Hartley's 220
Hitachi Charitable Trust, The
222
Holford Trust Fund 224
Hoover Foundation, The 226
Horn Trust, The Cuthbert 227
Hornby Charitable Trust, Miss
D 227
Hornton Trust, The 228
Hughes Charitable Trust, The
Geoffery C 230
Hyde Park Place Estate Charity,
The 232
IPE Charitable Trust, The 233
Inman Charity, The 235
Irving Charitable Trust, The
Charles 237
JCSCJ Charitable Trust, The
238
James Foundation, The
Catherine and Lady Grace
241
Jarrold Trust Ltd, John 243
Johnson Foundation, The Beth
247
KC Charitable Trust, The 250
Karten Charitable Trust, The
Ian 250
Keyes Trust, The Ursula 253
Kingsgrove Charitable Trust,
The 255
Kinnison Charitable Trust, R O
256
Kleinwort Charitable Trust, The
Ernest 257
Kobler Trust, The 258
Kreitman Foundation 258
Kulika Charitable Trust, The
259
Kweller Charitable Trust, The
Harry 259
Lancaster's Trust, Bryan 263
Landy Charitable Trust, Harry
and Gertrude 263
Lane Foundation, The Allen
263

Langley Charitable Trust, The 264

Lankelly Foundation, The 264

Lanvern Foundation 265

Laski Memorial Charitable Trust, Nathan 265

Laspen Trust 265

Lauffer Charitable Foundation, The R & D 266

Lavender Trust, The 267

Lawley Foundation, The Edgar E 267

Leigh-Bramwell Trust 'E', P 270

Levy Charitable Foundation, Joseph 272

Lewis Family Charitable Trust, The 273

Lewis Partnership, John 274

Liffe Benefit 274

Lingwood Charitable Trust, The 276

(Lloyds) TSB Foundation for England and Wales 279

Localtrent Ltd 279

Lucas Charitable Trust Limited, The Joseph 286

Lunzer Charitable Trust, The Ruth & Jack 287

Lynwood Charitable Trust, The 288

Lyons Charitable Trust, The 288

Lyons Charitable Trust, Sir Jack 288

MDM Memorial Trust 289

MacAndrew Trust, The E M 289

Maccabi Foundation, The 290

McKechnie Foundation, A N 292

McKenzie Trust, The Robert 292

McLaren Foundation 292

McLaren Memorial Trust, The Martin 293

MacRobert Trusts, The 294

Margadale Charitable Trust, Lord 297

Marks Charitable Trust, Michael 298

Markus Charitable Foundation, The Erich 298

Marriage's Charitable Trust, Miss G M 299

Marr-Munning Trust 299

Marshall Charitable Trust, The Charlotte 300

Martin Trust, The Sir George 300

Matchan Fund Limited, The Leonard 301

Material World Charitable Foundation Limited, The 301

Mattock Charitable Trust, The W T 302

Mayfair Charities Limited 303

Medlock Charitable Trust, The 304

Mellows Charitable Settlement, The Anthony and Elizabeth 305

Mental Health Foundation, The 305

Mid Moss Charitable Trust, The 309

Millett Charitable Trust, The Alan and Janet 312

Millichope Foundation, The 312

Modiano Charitable Trust 315

Montefiore Trust, The David 316

Moore Charitable Trust, The Horace 316

Morel Charitable Trust, The 318

Morgan Crucible Company plc Charitable Trust, The 319

Morris Charitable Trust, The Willie & Mabel 320

Moulton Charitable Trust, The 321

Music Sales Charitable Trust, The 324

National Lottery Charities Board 328

Newcastle Children's Mission & Institute 333

Newcastle's 1986 Charitable Trust, Duke of 333

Newman Charitable Trust, Mr and Mrs F E F 334

Newstead Charity, The 334

Northcott Charity Trust, The 338

Northern Dairies Educational Trust 339

Northern Electric Employee Charity Association 339

Northern Ireland Voluntary Trust 339

Old Possums Practical Trust, The 344

Oppenheimer Charitable Trust 346

Owen Trust, Margaret 348

PDC Trust, The 349

PJD Charitable Trust 350

Palmer Trust, The Gerald 352

Paristamen Foundation, The 352

Park Hill Trust, The 353

Pascoe Charitable Trust, Alan 354

Paul Charitable Trust, The Late Barbara May 355

Paul Charitable Trust, Margaret Jeanne 355

Paul Charitable Trust, Pamela Milton 355

Paul Foundation, The 355

Paul's Charitable Trust, R J 355

Payne Charitable Trust, The 355

Pelech Charitable Trust, The 358

Perry Charitable Trust, Miss Frances Lucille 359

Pershore Nashdom & Elmore Trust Ltd, The 360

Personal Assurance Charitable Trust 360

Peskin Charitable Trust, The Hazel and Leslie 360

Phillips Charitable Foundation, Reginald M 361

Pilkington Charitable Trust, Cecil 363

Pitt Trust, Headley 364

Porter Foundation 366

Powys Welsh Church Fund 367

Puebla Charitable Trust Limited, The 371

QAS Charitable Trust 373

Quothquan Charitable Trust, The Second 373

RT Trust, The 374

Rackham Charitable Trust, The Mr & Mrs Philip 375

Radley Charitable Trust 375

Rae Charity, H J 375

Rainford Trust, The 376

Rav Chesed Trust, The 379

Reekie Trust, R A & V B 381

Rest-Harrow Trust, The 382

Reuter Foundation, The 382

Richards Charity, The Clive 384

Richmond Parish Lands Charity 384

Rivendell Trust, The 387

Robbins Trust, The Cheshire 387

Rodewald's Charitable Settlement, Mr C A 389

Rogers Charitable Settlement, The Richard 390

Rokeby Charitable Trust 390

Rolfe Charitable Trust, The 390

Rosen Foundation, Cecil 392

Rothley Trust, The 392

Rowan Charitable Trust, The 393

S Group Charitable Trust 399

St Jude's Trust 403

Salters Charities 405

Samuel Charitable Trust, M J 406

Save & Prosper Foundation 409

Scarr-Hall Memorial Trust, The 409

Scott Charitable Trust, The Francis C 412

Seva Trust, Rampaba Sadhu 415

Sherman Charitable Trust, The Archie 419

Shifrin Charitable Trust, The Maurice and Hilda 419

Shine No 2 Charitable Trust, The Barnett and Sylvia 420

Shuttlewood Clarke Foundation, The *421*
Sidbury Trust, The Second *421*
Silvester Charitable Gift Trust *422*
Simon's Charity *422*
Skinners' Company Lady Neville Charity *424*
Salter Trust Ltd *424*
Society of Friends of the Torah, The *429*
Solomons Charitable Trust, David *430*
Somerfield Curtis Will Trust, The Dorothy *430*
Stanley Foundation Limited *435*
Stewart Charitable Trust, Mary Stephanie *437*
Street Charitable Foundation, W O *440*
Sumner's Trust Section 'A', Sir John *443*
Symons Charitable Trust, The Stella *446*
TSB Foundation for Scotland *447*
TSB Foundation for the Channel Islands *447*
Taylor Charitable Trust, The B R *450*
Terry Charitable Trust, Noel Goddard *451*
Tesco Charity Trust *452*
Tesler Foundation, The *452*
3i Charitable Trust, The *455*
Tyne & Wear Foundation *466*
Unitek Foundation *469*
van Geest Foundation, The John and Lucille *470*
Van Norden's Charitable Foundation, Mrs Maud *471*
Vineyard Christian Fellowship of South West *473*
Vinson Charity Trust, The 1969 *473*
Vogel Charitable Trust, The Nathan *474*
Wagstaff Charitable Trust, Bob *475*
Wakefield Trust, The *476*
Wakeham Trust, The *476*
Ward Blenkinsop Trust, The *480*
Weinstock Fund, The *484*
Whetherly's Charitable Trust, The Hon Mrs R G A *489*
Whitehead Charitable Trust, J E *490*
Whittington Charitable Trust, The *491*
Wiggins Charity Trust, Cyril *491*
Wilde Charitable Trust, The Felicity *492*
Wills 1961 Charitable Trust, Major Michael Thomas *494*

Wiltshire Community Foundation *495*
Winstone Foundation, Hyman *497*
Woburn 1986 Charitable Trust *498*
Wohl Charitable Foundation, The Maurice *498*
Wohl Charitable Trust, The Maurice *498*
Wolff Charity Trust *498*
Wolfson Family Charitable Trust, The *499*
Woodhouse Charitable Trust, Edwin *501*
Woods Charitable Foundation, Geoffrey *502*
Worms Charitable Trust, The Freda and Della *504*
Worshipful Company of Needlemakers' Charitable Fund *505*
Wychdale Limited *507*
Wylde Memorial Charity, The Anthony and Gwendoline *507*
Youell Foundation Ltd, The *510*
Zaiger Trust, The Elizabeth and Prince *512*

....

■ Advice centres

see also Advice & information (social issues)

Funding priority

Alexandra Trust *11*
Berkshire Community Trust *45*
Challice Trust, The *87*
County Durham Foundation *115*
HACT (The Housing Association's Charitable Trust) *201*
Humphreys Charitable Settlement, J A M *231*
Isle of Dogs Community Foundation *238*
Kroch Foundation, The Heinz & Anna *259*
Lancaster's Trust, Bryan *263*
Swan Mountain Trust *444*
Wilde Sapte Charitable Trust, The *492*

Will consider

Abel Charitable Trust *5*
Ammco Trust, The *15*
Anstey Charitable Settlement, J C W *18*
Archer Trust, The *20*
Astor Foundation, The *26*
Barbour Trust, The *33*
Blanchminster Trust, The *54*
Boots Charitable Trust *56*
Bridge Trust, The *60*

Buckinghamshire Masonic Centenary Fund *67*
Cadbury Charitable Trust (Incorporated), Edward *75*
Cadbury Trust (1928), The Edward & Dorothy *76*
Camelot Foundation, The *78*
Carnegie Dunfermline Trust *82*
Catto Charitable Settlement, The Thomas Sivewright *86*
Challice Trust, The *87*
Clark 1965 Charitable Trust, Stephen *98*
Clifford Charity Oxford, The *100*
Coutts Charitable Trust, The *116*
Curriers Company Charitable Fund *119*
David Trust, The Lesley *124*
Davies Charity, The Gwendoline and Margaret *125*
de Freitas Charitable Trust, The Helen and Geoffrey *126*
Debtors' Relief Fund Charity *128*
Dibs Charitable Trust, The *133*
Digby Charitable Trust, Simon *133*
Dumbreck Charity *139*
Edgar Foundation, The Gilbert and Eileen *145*
Edgar Trust, The Gilbert *145*
Emmandjay Charitable Trust *150*
Ferguson Benevolent Fund Limited *161*
Fletcher Trust, Roy *165*
Four Lanes Trust, The *168*
Gelston Charitable Trust, The *179*
Gibbins Trust, The *181*
Great Britain Sasakawa Foundation, The *193*
Hamlyn Foundation, The Paul *205*
Harford Charitable Trust *209*
Heath Charitable Trust *214*
Hudson Benevolent Trust, The Thomas *230*
Hyde Charitable Trust *232*
Ireland Funds, The *237*
Iris Trust, The *237*
Isle of Dogs Community Foundation *238*
Johnson Group Cleaners Charity *247*
King Charitable Settlement, Philip *254*
Knott Trust, Sir James *258*
Kroch Foundation, The Heinz & Anna *259*
Lancaster's Trust, Bryan *263*
Lankelly Foundation, The *264*
Lawson Charitable Trust, Raymond and Blanche *267*
Leech Charity, The William *269*

Lloyd's Charities Trust *278*
Low & Bonar Charitable Fund, The *284*
Lyndhurst Settlement *287*
MacKintosh Charitable Trust, Viscount *292*
Marchday Charitable Fund, The *296*
Mental Health Foundation, The *305*
Milton Keynes Community Trust Ltd, The *312*
Minet Trust, The Peter *313*
Music for World Development *323*
NR Charitable Trust, The *325*
Needham Cooper Charitable Trust, The *331*
New Court Charitable Trust *332*
Newby Trust Ltd *332*
Noah Trust, The *335*
Norman Family Charitable Trust, The *337*
Patients' Aid Association Hospital and Medical Charities Trust *354*
Payne Trust, The Harry *356*
Persula Foundation, The *360*
Powell Foundation, The *367*
Pyke Charity Trust *372*
Rayner Charitable Trust, The John *380*
Rest-Harrow Trust, The *382*
Rope Third Charitable Settlement, The Mrs *391*
Rothley Trust, The *392*
Sainsbury Charitable Fund Ltd, The *402*
Seagram Distillers Charitable Trust *413*
Sheldon Trust, The *417*
Shepherd Charitable Trust, The Sylvia and Colin *418*
Skelton Bounty, The *423*
South Yorkshire Community Foundation *431*
Summerfield Charitable Trust, The *442*
Swan Mountain Trust *444*
Sykes Trust, The Charles *445*
TSB Foundation for Northern Ireland *447*
Tear Fund *450*
Tisbury Telegraph Trust, The *457*
Travis Charitable Trust, Constance *460*
Truemark Trust, The *461*
Tudor Trust, The *463*
Wade & Others, The Charity of Thomas *475*
Wakefield (Tower Hill, Trinity Square) Trust *476*
Wesleyan Charitable Trust, The *485*
Wilde Sapte Charitable Trust, The *492*

Wills 1961 Charitable Trust, Mr Frederick *493*
Wiltshire Community Foundation *495*
Wylde Memorial Charity, The Anthony and Gwendoline *507*
Yorkshire Bank Charitable Trust, The *510*

....

■ Advocacy (health)

see also Health related volunteer schemes

Funding priority
Aga Khan Foundation (UK) *7*
Alexander Charitable Trust, Mrs K L *11*
Allied Dunbar Charitable Trust Limited, The *13*
Aquinas Trust *20*
Astor of Hever Trust, The *26*
Avins Trustees, The John *28*
Baring Foundation, The *34*
Bealey Foundation, The *38*
Beauland Ltd *39*
Beckwith-Smith's Charitable Settlement, Mrs *40*
Birmingham District Nursing Charitable Trust *49*
Blakey Charitable Trust, The Celia and Conrad *53*
Boltons Trust, The *55*
British Sugar Foundation *63*
Brook Charitable Settlement, R E *64*
Burns Charity, The Dorothy *70*
Carron Charitable Trust, The *83*
Carter Trust, The Frederick William *84*
Cinderford Charitable Trust, The *96*
City Parochial Foundation *96*
Clark Charitable Trust, J Anthony *98*
Cohen Charitable Trust, The Vivienne and Samuel *104*
Condon Family Trust *109*
Crawford Children's Charity, Michael *117*
Crescent Trust, The *117*
Delmar Charitable Trust *129* ●
Djanogly Foundation, The *135*
D'Oyly Carte Charitable Trust, The *137*
Dunn Charitable Trust, The Harry *140*
Elvetham Charitable Trust, The *149*
Franklin Trust, Jill *170*
Fry Charitable Trust, Maurice *174*
Gibson's Charity Trust, The Hon Mr & Mrs Clive *182*
Girdlers' Company Charitable Trust, The *184*

Goodman Charitable Foundation, The Everard and Mina *188*
Goodman Trust, The *189*
Gradel Foundation, The *189*
Green Foundation, Constance *194*
Greenwood Charitable Trust, The G B *195*
Hitachi Charitable Trust, The *222*
IPE Charitable Trust, The *233*
Jones Trust, Cemlyn *248*
Keyes Trust, The Ursula *253*
Kobler Trust, The *258*
Landy Charitable Trust, Harry and Gertrude *263*
Lanvern Foundation *265*
Lauffer Charitable Foundation, The R & D *266*
Levy Charitable Foundation, Joseph *272*
Liffe Benefit *274*
Lucas Charitable Trust Limited, The Joseph *286*
MacAndrew Trust, The E M *289*
MacRobert Trusts, The *294*
Medlock Charitable Trust, The *304*
Mental Health Foundation, The *305*
Millichope Foundation, The *312*
Moore Charitable Trust, The Horace *316*
Moulton Charitable Trust, The *321*
Newstead Charity, The *334*
Northcott Devon Foundation *338*
Northern Dairies Educational Trust *339*
Northern Electric Employee Charity Association *339*
Oppenheimer Charitable Trust *346*
Palmer Trust, The Gerald *352*
Pascoe Charitable Trust, Alan *354*
Paul Foundation, The *355*
Peskin Charitable Trust, The Hazel and Leslie *360*
Pick Charitable Trust, The George and Jessie *362*
QAS Charitable Trust *373*
Reekie Trust, R A & V B *381*
Robbins Trust, The Cheshire *387*
Rowntree Charitable Trust, The Joseph *394*
Sherman Charitable Trust, The Archie *419*
Shifrin Charitable Trust, The Maurice and Hilda *419*
Taylor Charitable Trust, The B R *450*
Trust for London *461*

Valentine Charitable Trust, The
470

Wesleyan Charitable Trust, The
485

Westminster Amalgamated
Charity 487

Whittington Charitable Trust,
The 491

Wilde Charitable Trust, The
Felicity 492

Wohl Charitable Foundation,
The Maurice 498

Wohl Charitable Trust, The
Maurice 498

Wolfson Family Charitable
Trust, The 499

Woodcote Trust, The 501

Woolf Charitable Trust, The
502

Will consider

AHJ Charitable Trust, The 3

Achiezer Association Limited 6

Airflow Community Ltd, The 9

Aleh Charitable Foundation,
The 10

Alliance Family Foundation
Limited 13

Allsop Charitable Trust, Pat 14

Anderson Trust, Andrew 16

Angler's Inn Trust 17

Appelbe Trust, Ambrose & Ann
19

Askew Charitable Trust, The
Ian 25

Assembled Church of Christ
Trust, The 25

Assheton-Smith Charitable
Trust 25

Asthma Allergy and
Inflammation Research Trust
25

Astor Foundation, The 26

Astor's 1969 Charity, The Hon
M L 26

BBC Children in Need Appeal,
The 29

BUPA Foundation, The 29

Barbour Trust, The 33

Barnby's Foundation, Lord 35

Barnsbury Charitable Trust 35

Bateman Charitable Trust, Lady
Margaret 37

Beckwith Charitable
Settlement, The Heather 39

Beckwith Charitable Trust, The
Peter 40

Bergqvist Charitable Trust 44

Black Foundation, The Bertie
51

Blagrave Charitable Trust, The
Herbert and Peter 52

Blakenham's Charity Trust,
Lady 53

Blank Donations Ltd, The David
54

Borthwick Memorial Trust, The
Oliver 56

Bottom Charitable Trust, Harry
56

Bowland Charitable Trust, The
57

Brookhouse's Will Trust, Mr
John Charles 65

Burn Charity Trust, The J H 70

Burry Charitable Trust, The 70

Burton Charitable Trust, The
Geoffrey 71

Butler's Trust, Lord 71

Butler's Trust, Lucilla 72

Cadbury Schweppes
Foundation, The 76

Cardiff & Swansea Methodist
District Charitable Trust
Fund 80

Castang Charitable Trust, H
and M 85

Charity Projects 90

Chase Charity, The 91

Christian Aid 94

Closehelm Ltd 101

Clutterbuck Charitable Trust,
Robert 102

Coates Charitable Settlement,
The 102

Coates Charitable Trust 1969,
Lance 103

Cohen Charity Trust, Lucy 104

Community Trust for Greater
Manchester, The 108

Company of Tobacco Pipe
Makers and Tobacco
Blenders Benevolent Fund
109

Cope Charitable Trust, Alfred
112

Cotton Trust, The 114

County Durham Foundation
115

Curry Charitable Trust, Dennis
119

Cymerman Trust Limited,
Itzchok Meyer 120

Daily Telegraph Charitable
Trust 122

Dandeen Charitable Trust 123

Davy Foundation, The J 126

De Avenley Foundation, The
126

De La Rue Charitable Trust
127

De Rothschild 1981 Charitable
Trust, The Edmund 127

De Yong Charitable Trust, The
Emma 128

Denton Charitable Trust, The
130

Derbyshire Trust, J N 130

Desmond Charitable Trust, The
Richard 131

Deutsch Charitable Trust, The
Andre 131

Deutsch Charitable Trust, The
H & M 131

Dicken Charitable Trust, The
Albert 133

Dinam Charity 134

Doughty Charity Trust, The
136

Drayton Trust, The 138

Earmark Trust, The 142

Edinburgh Trust, No 2 Account
145

Eling Trust 147

Elshore Limited 149

Emmandjay Charitable Trust
150

Esperanza Charitable Trust, The
153

Family Trust, The 158

Famos Foundation Trust 158

Federation of Jewish Relief
Organisations 160

Fishmongers' Company's
Charitable Trust 163

Follett Trust, The 166

Foreman Foundation, The Carl
& Eve 167

Foyle Trust, Charles Henry 169

Franklin Bequest, The Rosalind
169

Franklin Deceased's New
Second Charity, Sydney E
170

Frome Christian Fellowship
174

Garthgwynion Charities 179

Gillett Charitable Trust, J A
183

Gill's Charitable Trust, Mrs M M
184

Gold Hill Church Trust 186

Goldberg Charitable Trust, The
Lewis 186

Goldsmiths' Company's
Charities, The 188

Goodman Trust, The S & F 189

Greenaway Foundation, The Sir
Derek 194

Grocers' Charity 197

Gross Charities Limited, M & R
197

Grosshill Charitable Trust 197

Grut Charitable Trust, The 198

HB Charitable Trust 201

Hacking & Sons Ltd Charitable
Trust, C G 201

Hamilton Educational Trust,
Eleanor 205

Harbour Foundation Ltd, The
208

Hargreaves Trust, The Kenneth
210

Harvey Charitable Trust,
Gordon 211

Hawley Residuary Fund, Harry
Fieldsend 212

Hawthorne Charitable Trust,
The 212

Heinz Company Limited
Charitable Trust, The H J
215

Held Settlement, The Gisela 215

Hertfordshire Community Trust, The 217

Higgs Charitable Trust, The 218

Hillards Charitable Trust, Gay & Peter Hartley's 220

Holford Trust Fund 224

Hoover Foundation, The 226

Horn Trust, The Cuthbert 227

Hornby Charitable Trust, Miss D 227

Hornton Trust, The 228

Hughes Charitable Trust, The Geoffery C 230

Inman Charity, The 235

Irving Charitable Trust, The Charles 237

JCSCJ Charitable Trust, The 238

James Foundation, The Catherine and Lady Grace 241

Johnson Foundation, The 246

Jubilee Outreach Yorkshire 248

KC Charitable Trust, The 250

Karten Charitable Trust, The Ian 250

Kingsgrove Charitable Trust, The 255

Kinnison Charitable Trust, R O 256

Kleinwort Charitable Trust, The Ernest 257

Kreitman Foundation 258

Kulika Charitable Trust, The 259

Kweller Charitable Trust, The Harry 259

Lambourne Memorial Trust, The Emma 262

Langley Charitable Trust, The 264

Lankelly Foundation, The 264

Laski Memorial Charitable Trust, Nathan 265

Laspen Trust 265

Lavender Trust, The 267

Lawley Foundation, The Edgar E 267

Leach Fourteenth Trust, The 267

Leigh-Bramwell Trust 'E', P 270

Lewis Family Charitable Trust, The 273

Lingwood Charitable Trust, The 276

Livesley 1992 Charitable Trust, Mrs C M 277

(Lloyds) TSB Foundation for England and Wales 279

Localtrent Ltd 279

Lunzer Charitable Trust, The Ruth & Jack 287

Lynwood Charitable Trust, The 288

Lyons Charitable Trust, The 288

Lyons Charitable Trust, Sir Jack 288

MDM Memorial Trust 289

McKechnie Foundation, A N 292

McKenzie Trust, The Robert 292

McLaren Foundation 292

McLaren Memorial Trust, The Martin 293

Margadale Charitable Trust, Lord 297

Marks Charitable Trust, Michael 298

Marks Foundation, The Hilda and Samuel 298

Markus Charitable Foundation, The Erich 298

Marriage's Charitable Trust, Miss G M 299

Marr-Munning Trust 299

Marshall Charitable Trust, The Charlotte 300

Martin Trust, The Sir George 300

Matchan Fund Limited, The Leonard 301

Material World Charitable Foundation Limited, The 301

Mattock Charitable Trust, The W T 302

Mayfair Charities Limited 303

Medical Aid Trust 304

Mellows Charitable Settlement, The Anthony and Elizabeth 305

Millett Charitable Trust, The Alan and Janet 312

Modiano Charitable Trust 315

Montefiore Trust, The David 316

Moore Stephens Charitable Foundation, The 317

Moores Foundation, John 318

Morel Charitable Trust, The 318

Morgan Crucible Company plc Charitable Trust, The 319

Morris Charitable Trust, The Willie & Mabel 320

Music Sales Charitable Trust, The 324

Muslim Hands 324

National Lottery Charities Board 328

National Power Charitable Trust, The 330

Newcastle's 1986 Charitable Trust, Duke of 333

Newman Charitable Trust, Mr and Mrs F E F 334

Noah Trust, The 335

North West Arts Board 337

Northcott Charity Trust, The 338

Northern Ireland Voluntary Trust 339

Nuffield Foundation 342

Old Possums Practical Trust, The 344

Owen Trust, Margaret 348

PDC Trust, The 349

PJD Charitable Trust 350

Paget Trust, The 351

Paristamen Foundation, The 352

Paul Charitable Trust, The Late Barbara May 355

Paul Charitable Trust, Margaret Jeanne 355

Paul Charitable Trust, Pamela Milton 355

Paul's Charitable Trust, R J 355

Payne Charitable Trust, The 355

Pelech Charitable Trust, The 358

Perry Charitable Trust, Miss Frances Lucille 359

Pershore Nashdom & Elmore Trust Ltd, The 360

Phillips Charitable Foundation, Reginald M 361

Pilkington Charitable Trust, Cecil 363

Pitt Trust, Headley 364

Porter Foundation 366

Powys Welsh Church Fund 367

Puebla Charitable Trust Limited, The 371

Quothquan Charitable Trust, The Second 373

RT Trust, The 374

Rackham Charitable Trust, The Mr & Mrs Philip 375

Radley Charitable Trust 375

Rae Charity, H J 375

Rainford Trust, The 376

Rav Chesed Trust, The 379

Rayne Foundation, The 379

Reuter Foundation, The 382

Richards Charity, The Clive 384

Richards Charity, The Violet M 384

Richmond Parish Lands Charity 384

Rivendell Trust, The 387

Rodewald's Charitable Settlement, Mr C A 389

Rogers Charitable Settlement, The Richard 390

Rokeby Charitable Trust 390

Rolfe Charitable Trust, The 390

Rosen Foundation, Cecil 392

Rozel Trust, The 397

St Jude's Trust 403

Salters Charities 405

Samuel Charitable Trust, M J 406

Save & Prosper Foundation 409

Scarr-Hall Memorial Trust, The 409

Seva Trust, Rampaba Sadhu *415*

Sidbury Trust, The Second *421*

Silvester Charitable Gift Trust *422*

Skelton Bounty, The *423*

Salter Trust Ltd *424*

Society of Friends of the Torah, The *429*

Solomons Charitable Trust, David *430*

Somerfield Curtis Will Trust, The Dorothy *430*

Stanley Foundation Limited *435*

Stewart Charitable Trust, Mary Stephanie *437*

Street Charitable Foundation, W O *440*

Sumner's Trust Section 'A', Sir John *443*

Swann-Morton Foundation, The *444*

Symons Charitable Trust, The Stella *446*

TSB Foundation for Northern Ireland *447*

TSB Foundation for Scotland *447*

TSB Foundation for the Channel Islands *447*

Terry Charitable Trust, Noel Goddard *451*

Tesco Charity Trust *452*

Tesler Foundation, The *452*

Thompson Charitable Trust, The *453*

Tyne & Wear Foundation *466*

van Geest Foundation, The John and Lucille *470*

Van Norden's Charitable Foundation, Mrs Maud *471*

Vineyard Christian Fellowship of South West *473*

Vinson Charity Trust, The 1969 *473*

Vogel Charitable Trust, The Nathan *474*

Wakefield Trust, The *476*

Wander Charitable Fund, The Dr Albert *479*

Ward Blenkinsop Trust, The *480*

Weinstock Fund, The *484*

Whetherly's Charitable Trust, The Hon Mrs R G A *489*

White Rose Children's Aid International Charity *489*

Whitehead Charitable Trust, J E *490*

Wiggins Charity Trust, Cyril *491*

Wills 1961 Charitable Trust, Major Michael Thomas *494*

Wiltshire Community Foundation *495*

Winstone Foundation, Hyman *497*

Woburn 1986 Charitable Trust *498*

Wolff Charity Trust *498*

Woods Charitable Foundation, Geoffrey *502*

Worms Charitable Trust, The Freda and Della *504*

Worshipful Company of Needlemakers' Charitable Fund *505*

Wychdale Limited *507*

Youell Foundation Ltd, The *510*

Zaiger Trust, The Elizabeth and Prince *512*

....

■ Advocacy (social issues)

see also Equal opportunities, Individual rights

Funding priority

Allied Dunbar Charitable Trust Limited, The *13*

Anderson Trust, Andrew *16*

Baring Foundation, The *34*

City Parochial Foundation *96*

Commonwealth Relations Trust *108*

Condon Family Trust *109*

Fairbairn Charitable Trust, The Esmee *157*

Franklin Trust, Jill *170*

Green Foundation, Constance *194*

Hacking & Sons Ltd Charitable Trust, C G *201*

Jones Trust, Cemlyn *248*

Lester Trust Fund, The *271*

Mental Health Foundation, The *305*

Millfield House Foundation *312*

Northcott Devon Foundation *338*

Rodewald's Charitable Settlement, Mr C A *389*

Rowan Charitable Trust, The *393*

War on Want *479*

West Midlands Regional Arts Board *486*

Westcroft Trust *486*

Westminster Amalgamated Charity *487*

Will consider

AHJ Charitable Trust, The *3*

Achiezer Association Limited *6*

Aga Khan Foundation (UK) *7*

Airflow Community Ltd, The *9*

Ajahma Charitable Trust, The *9*

Aleh Charitable Foundation, The *10*

Allachy Trust, The *12*

Angler's Inn Trust *17*

Appelbe Trust, Ambrose & Ann *19*

Aquinas Trust *20*

Askew Charitable Trust, The Ian *25*

Assembled Church of Christ Trust, The *25*

Astor of Hever Trust, The *26*

Astor's 1969 Charity, The Hon M L *26*

Austin of Longbridge Will Trust, The Rt Hon Herbert, Baron *27*

BBC Children in Need Appeal, The *29*

Barnabas Charitable Trust *34*

Barnby's Foundation, Lord *35*

Barnsbury Charitable Trust *35*

Barton Trust, Eleanor *37*

Bateman Charitable Trust, Lady Margaret *37*

Bealey Foundation, The *38*

Beckwith Charitable Trust, The Peter *40*

Beckwith-Smith's Charitable Settlement, Mrs *40*

Bergqvist Charitable Trust *44*

Bilton Charity, The Percy *48*

Black Foundation, The Bertie *51*

Blagrave Charitable Trust, The Herbert and Peter *52*

Blakenham's Charity Trust, Lady *53*

Blakey Charitable Trust, The Celia and Conrad *53*

Blank Donations Ltd, The David *54*

Boltons Trust, The *55*

Borthwick Memorial Trust, The Oliver *56*

Bottom Charitable Trust, Harry *56*

Bowland Charitable Trust, The *57*

British Sugar Foundation *63*

Brook Charitable Settlement, R E *64*

Brookhouse's Will Trust, Mr John Charles *65*

Brough Charitable Trust, Joseph *65*

Burn Charity Trust, The J H *70*

Burns Charity, The Dorothy *70*

Burry Charitable Trust, The *70*

Burton Charitable Trust, The Geoffrey *71*

Butler's Trust, Lord *71*

Butler's Trust, Lucilla *72*

Buxton Trust, Denis *72*

Cardiff & Swansea Methodist District Charitable Trust Fund *80*

Carron Charitable Trust, The *83*

Castang Charitable Trust, H and M 85
Charity Projects 90
Chippindale Foundation, Sam 93
Christian Aid 94
Christmas Cracker Trust 95
Church Urban Fund 95
Cinderford Charitable Trust, The 96
Clark Charitable Trust, J Anthony 98
Closehelm Ltd 101
Clutterbuck Charitable Trust, Robert 102
Coates Charitable Settlement, The 102
Coates Charitable Trust 1969, Lance 103
Cohen Charitable Trust, The Vivienne and Samuel 104
Cohen Charity Trust, Lucy 104
Community Trust for Greater Manchester, The 108
Company of Tobacco Pipe Makers and Tobacco Blenders Benevolent Fund 109
Cope Charitable Trust, Alfred 112
Cotton Trust, The 114
Crescent Trust, The 117
Curry Charitable Trust, Dennis 119
Cymerman Trust Limited, Itzchok Meyer 120
Daily Telegraph Charitable Trust 122
Dandeen Charitable Trust 123
Davy Foundation, The J 126
De Avenley Foundation, The 126
De La Rue Charitable Trust 127
De Rothschild 1981 Charitable Trust, The Edmund 127
De Yong Charitable Trust, The Emma 128
Denton Charitable Trust, The 130
Derbyshire Trust, J N 130
Desmond Charitable Trust, The Richard 131
Deutsch Charitable Trust, The Andre 131
Deutsch Charitable Trust, The H & M 131
Dibden Allotments Charity 132
Dicken Charitable Trust, The Albert 133
Dinam Charity 134
Djanogly Foundation, The 135
Doughty Charity Trust, The 136
D'Oyly Carte Charitable Trust, The 137
Drayton Trust, The 138
Dulverton Trust, The 139

Dunn Charitable Trust, The Harry 140
Earmark Trust, The 142
Ebb and Flow Charitable Trust 144
Edinburgh Trust, No 2 Account 145
Eling Trust 147
Elshore Limited 149
Elvetham Charitable Trust, The 149
Family Trust, The 158
Famos Foundation Trust 158
Federation of Jewish Relief Organisations 160
Ford of Britain Trust 166
Foreman Foundation, The Carl & Eve 167
Foyle Trust, Charles Henry 169
Franklin Bequest, The Rosalind 169
Franklin Deceased's New Second Charity, Sydney E 170
Friarsgate Trust 172
Frome Christian Fellowship 174
Fry Charitable Trust, Maurice 174
Galinski Charitable Trust 177
Garthgwynion Charities 179
Gibson's Charity Trust, The Hon Mr & Mrs Clive 182
Gillett Charitable Trust, J A 183
Gill's Charitable Trust, Mrs M M 184
Girdlers' Company Charitable Trust, The 184
Glynde Place Charitable Trust (1974), The 186
Gold Hill Church Trust 186
Goldberg Charitable Trust, The Lewis 186
Goodman Charitable Foundation, The Everard and Mina 188
Goodman Trust, The 189
Goodman Trust, The S & F 189
Gradel Foundation, The 189
Gross Charities Limited, M & R 197
Grosshill Charitable Trust 197
Grut Charitable Trust, The 198
Gulbenkian Foundation (Lisbon) United Kingdom Branch, Calouste 199
Gwent County Council Welsh Church Fund 200
HB Charitable Trust 201
Hamilton Educational Trust, Eleanor 205
Hampstead Wells and Campden Trust 206
Harbour Foundation Ltd, The 208
Harvey Charitable Trust, Gordon 211

Hawthorne Charitable Trust, The 212
Heinz Company Limited Charitable Trust, The H J 215
Held Settlement, The Gisela 215
Hertfordshire Community Trust, The 217
Hillards Charitable Trust, Gay & Peter Hartley's 220
Hitachi Charitable Trust, The 222
Holford Trust Fund 224
Hoover Foundation, The 226
Horn Trust, The Cuthbert 227
Hornby Charitable Trust, Miss D 227
Hornton Trust, The 228
Hughes Charitable Trust, The Geoffery C 230
IPE Charitable Trust, The 233
Inman Charity, The 235
Irving Charitable Trust, The Charles 237
Isle of Dogs Community Foundation 238
James Foundation, The Catherine and Lady Grace 241
Johnson Foundation, The Beth 247
KC Charitable Trust, The 250
Karten Charitable Trust, The Ian 250
Keyes Trust, The Ursula 253
Kingsgrove Charitable Trust, The 255
Kinnison Charitable Trust, R O 256
Kleinwort Charitable Trust, The Ernest 257
Kobler Trust, The 258
Kreitman Foundation 258
Kulika Charitable Trust, The 259
Kweller Charitable Trust, The Harry 259
Laing Foundation, The Christopher 260
Landy Charitable Trust, Harry and Gertrude 263
Langley Charitable Trust, The 264
Lankelly Foundation, The 264
Lanvern Foundation 265
Laski Memorial Charitable Trust, Nathan 265
Lauffer Charitable Foundation, The R & D 266
Lavender Trust, The 267
Lawley Foundation, The Edgar E 267
Leigh-Bramwell Trust 'E', P 270
Levy Charitable Foundation, Joseph 272
Lewis Family Charitable Trust, The 273

Liffe Benefit *274*
Lingwood Charitable Trust, The *276*
(Lloyds) TSB Foundation for England and Wales *279*
Localtrent Ltd *279*
Lucas Charitable Trust Limited, The Joseph *286*
Lunzer Charitable Trust, The Ruth & Jack *287*
Lynwood Charitable Trust, The *288*
Lyons Charitable Trust, The *288*
Lyons Charitable Trust, Sir Jack *288*
MDM Memorial Trust *289*
MacAndrew Trust, The E M *289*
Maccabi Foundation, The *290*
McKechnie Foundation, A N *292*
McKenzie Trust, The Robert *292*
McLaren Foundation *292*
McLaren Memorial Trust, The Martin *293*
MacRobert Trusts, The *294*
Margadale Charitable Trust, Lord *297*
Marks Charitable Trust, Michael *298*
Markus Charitable Foundation, The Erich *298*
Marriage's Charitable Trust, Miss G M *299*
Marr-Munning Trust *299*
Marshall Charitable Trust, The Charlotte *300*
Martin Trust, The Sir George *300*
Matchan Fund Limited, The Leonard *301*
Material World Charitable Foundation Limited, The *301*
Mattock Charitable Trust, The W T *302*
Mayfair Charities Limited *303*
Medlock Charitable Trust, The *304*
Mellows Charitable Settlement, The Anthony and Elizabeth *305*
Mid Moss Charitable Trust, The *309*
Millett Charitable Trust, The Alan and Janet *312*
Millichope Foundation, The *312*
Modiano Charitable Trust *315*
Montefiore Trust, The David *316*
Moore Charitable Trust, The Horace *316*
Moores Foundation, John *318*
Morel Charitable Trust, The *318*

Morgan Crucible Company plc Charitable Trust, The *319*
Morris Charitable Trust, The Willie & Mabel *320*
Moulton Charitable Trust, The *321*
Music Sales Charitable Trust, The *324*
National Lottery Charities Board *328*
National Power Charitable Trust, The *330*
Newcastle Children's Mission & Institute *333*
Newcastle's 1986 Charitable Trust, Duke of *333*
Newman Charitable Trust, Mr and Mrs F E F *334*
Newstead Charity, The *334*
Norman Trust, The *337*
Northcott Charity Trust, The *338*
Northern Arts *339*
Northern Dairies Educational Trust *339*
Northern Electric Employee Charity Association *339*
Northern Ireland Voluntary Trust *339*
Old Possums Practical Trust, The *344*
Oppenheimer Charitable Trust *346*
Owen Trust, Margaret *348*
PDC Trust, The *349*
PJD Charitable Trust *350*
Palmer Trust, The Gerald *352*
Paristamen Foundation, The *352*
Pascoe Charitable Trust, Alan *354*
Paul Charitable Trust, The Late Barbara May *355*
Paul Charitable Trust, Margaret Jeanne *355*
Paul Charitable Trust, Pamela Milton *355*
Paul Foundation, The *355*
Paul's Charitable Trust, R J *355*
Payne Charitable Trust, The *355*
Pelech Charitable Trust, The *358*
Perry Charitable Trust, Miss Frances Lucille *359*
Pershore Nashdom & Elmore Trust Ltd, The *360*
Peskin Charitable Trust, The Hazel and Leslie *360*
Phillips Charitable Foundation, Reginald M *361*
Pilkington Charitable Trust, Cecil *363*
Pitt Trust, Headley *364*
Powell Foundation, The *367*
Powys Welsh Church Fund *367*
Puebla Charitable Trust Limited, The *371*

QAS Charitable Trust *373*
Quothquan Charitable Trust, The Second *373*
RT Trust, The *374*
Rackham Charitable Trust, The Mr & Mrs Philip *375*
Radley Charitable Trust *375*
Rae Charity, H J *375*
Rav Chesed Trust, The *379*
Reekie Trust, R A & V B *381*
Reuter Foundation, The *382*
Richards Charity, The Clive *384*
Richmond Parish Lands Charity *384*
Rivendell Trust, The *387*
Robbins Trust, The Cheshire *387*
Rogers Charitable Settlement, The Richard *390*
Rolfe Charitable Trust, The *390*
Rosen Foundation, Cecil *392*
S Group Charitable Trust *399*
St Jude's Trust *403*
Samuel Charitable Trust, M J *406*
Save & Prosper Foundation *409*
Scarr-Hall Memorial Trust, The *409*
Scott Charitable Trust, The Francis C *412*
Seva Trust, Rampaba Sadhu *415*
Sherman Charitable Trust, The Archie *419*
Shifrin Charitable Trust, The Maurice and Hilda *419*
Shine No 2 Charitable Trust, The Barnett and Sylvia *420*
Shuttlewood Clarke Foundation, The *421*
Sidbury Trust, The Second *421*
Silvester Charitable Gift Trust *422*
Simon's Charity *422*
Singer Foundation *423*
Salter Trust Ltd *424*
Society of Friends of the Torah, The *429*
Solomons Charitable Trust, David *430*
Somerfield Curtis Will Trust, The Dorothy *430*
Stanley Foundation Limited *435*
Stewart Charitable Trust, Mary Stephanie *437*
Street Charitable Foundation, W O *440*
Symons Charitable Trust, The Stella *446*
TSB Foundation for Northern Ireland *447*
TSB Foundation for Scotland *447*
TSB Foundation for the Channel Islands *447*

Taylor Charitable Trust, The B R 450

Terry Charitable Trust, Noel Goddard 451

Tesco Charity Trust 452

Tesler Foundation, The 452

Tyne & Wear Foundation 466

Unitek Foundation 469

van Geest Foundation, The John and Lucille 470

Van Norden's Charitable Foundation, Mrs Maud 471

Vineyard Christian Fellowship of South West 473

Vinson Charity Trust, The 1969 473

Vogel Charitable Trust, The Nathan 474

Wakefield Trust, The 476

Ward Blenkinsop Trust, The 480

Wates Foundation, The 481

Weinstock Fund, The 484

Whetherly's Charitable Trust, The Hon Mrs R G A 489

Whitehead Charitable Trust, J E 490

Whittington Charitable Trust, The 491

Wiggins Charity Trust, Cyril 491

Wilde Charitable Trust, The Felicity 492

Wiltshire Community Foundation 495

Woburn 1986 Charitable Trust 498

Wohl Charitable Foundation, The Maurice 498

Wohl Charitable Trust, The Maurice 498

Wolff Charity Trust 498

Wolfson Family Charitable Trust, The 499

Woods Charitable Foundation, Geoffrey 502

Worms Charitable Trust, The Freda and Della 504

Worshipful Company of Needlemakers' Charitable Fund 505

Wychdale Limited 507

Youell Foundation Ltd, The 510

Zaiger Trust, The Elizabeth and Prince 512

■ After school care

see Community services

■ Aftercare

see also Health care

Funding priority

Community Trust for Greater Manchester, The 108

Cooper Charitable Trust 111

Davis Charitable Trust, Wilfrid Bruce 126

Heath Charitable Trust 214

Heritage of London Trust, The 216

Kroch Foundation, The Heinz & Anna 259

Lloyd's Charities Trust 278

Loseley & Guildway Charitable Trust, The 281

Manning Trust, Leslie & Lilian 296

Mental Health Foundation, The 305

Merton and George Woofindin Convalescent Trust, The Zachary 307

Royal Theatrical Fund, The 396

Strangward Trust, The 439

Will consider

Allen Trust, Mrs M H 13

Andrew Convalescent Trust, The Frederick 17

Archer Trust, The 20

Army Benevolent Fund, The 22

Astor Foundation, The 26

Avon Trust, The 28

Bancroft Trust, The 33

Barbour Trust, The 33

Beckwith Charitable Settlement, The Heather 39

Beit Trust, The 40

Berkshire Community Trust 45

Berris Charitable Trust 45

BibleLands 47

Birmingham Amenities and Welfare Trust, The 49

Birtwistle Memorial Trust, The G E 50

Bottom Charitable Trust, Harry 56

Bourne-May Charitable Trust, The 57

British Dietetic Association General and Education Trust Fund, The 61

Britton Charitable Trust, The J & M 63

Butlin Charity Trust, Bill 72

Campden Charities, The 79

Cancer Relief Macmillan Fund 79

Cathedral Nursing Society Charitable Trust 85

Clinton's Charitable Trust, Lord 100

Commonwealth Relations Trust 108

Coxen Trust Fund, Sir William 116

Denne Charitable Trust 130

Digby Charitable Trust, Simon 133

Dorus Trust 136

Earley Charity, The 142

Edgar Foundation, The Gilbert and Eileen 145

Edgar Trust, The Gilbert 145

Elkes Charity Fund, The Wilfred & Elsie 147

Emmandjay Charitable Trust 150

Emmaus Christian Foundation 150

Epigoni Trust 152

Fogel Charitable Trust, The Gerald 165

Follett Trust, The 166

Foreman Foundation, The Carl & Eve 167

Fortune Trust, The 167

Gardner Charitable Trust, R & J 178

Gibbins Trust, The 181

Goldsmiths' Company's Charities, The 188

Grant Foundation, The Raymond 191

Gray Charitable Trust, R B 192

Great Britain Sasakawa Foundation, The 193

Greenaway Foundation, The Alan 194

Greenaway Foundation, The Sir Derek 194

Grocers' Charity 197

Hawley Residuary Fund, Harry Fieldsend 212

Humanitarian Trust, The 230

Innes Memorial Fund 235

Isle of Dogs Community Foundation 238

JDM Charitable Trust 239

Laing Charitable Trust, The David 260

Lawson Charitable Trust, Raymond and Blanche 267

Leach Fourteenth Trust, The 267

Leadbeater Trust, The Alfred 268

Leech Charity, The William 269

Lloyd Charity, The S and D 278

London Law Trust 280

Lynall Foundation, The D G 287

MacKintosh Charitable Trust, Viscount 292

Mackintosh Foundation, The 292

Marchday Charitable Fund, The 296

Metropolitan Hospital-Sunday Fund, The 308

Moore Foundation, The George A 316

Morris Charitable Trust, The Douglas 320

National Waterways
Restoration & Development
Fund of the Inland
Waterways Association, The
330
Natwest Staff Samaritan Fund
330
Needham Cooper Charitable
Trust, The *331*
New Court Charitable Trust
332
Newby Trust Ltd *332*
North British Hotel Trust *337*
Penny in the Pound Fund
Charitable Trust *359*
Pratt Charitable Trust, The W L
367
Rowbotham Charitable Trust,
The Christopher *393*
Sheldon Trust, The *417*
Shelroy Charitable Trust, The
417
Simon's Charity *422*
South Square Trust *430*
Stonehouse Trust Ltd, Eric *438*
Sussman Charitable Trust,
Adrienne & Leslie *443*
TSB Foundation for Northern
Ireland *447*
Thackray General Charitable
Trust, The P & L *452*
Thompson Charitable Trust,
The *453*
Travis Charitable Trust,
Constance *460*
Wakefield (Tower Hill, Trinity
Square) Trust *476*
Whitaker Charitable Trust *489*
Woodlands Trust *501*
Wylde Memorial Charity, The
Anthony and Gwendoline
507

■ **Agriculture**

see also **Environment &
animal sciences**

Funding priority
Bachad Fellowship – Friends of
Bnei Akiva *30*
Baker Trust, The C Alma *31*
Bull Charitable Trust, Henry
Robert *68*
Coates Charitable Trust 1969,
Lance *103*
Farmers' Company Charitable
Fund, The *159*
Homeless International *225*
Kulika Charitable Trust, The
259
LSA Charitable Trust *260*
MacRobert Trusts, The *294*
Nickerson Charitable
Foundation, The Joseph
335
Oldacre Foundation, The John
345

Paget Trust, The *351*
Parkinson Agricultural Trust,
The Frank *353*
Pilkington Charitable Trust,
Cecil *363*
Rolfe Charitable Trust, The *390*
Yorkshire Agricultural Society
509

Will consider
Allied Domecq Trust *13*
Ashley Foundation, The Laura
24
Astor Foundation, The *26*
Avenal *27*
Butler Charitable Trust, The A S
71
CLA Charitable Trust *74*
Chippindale Foundation, Sam
93
Clutterbuck Charitable Trust,
Robert *102*
Company of Chartered
Surveyors Charitable Trust
Fund, The *108*
Countryside Trust, The *115*
Digby Charitable Trust, Simon
133
Direct Response *134*
Eaton Charitable Trust, J C J
143
Education Services *145*
Glynde Place Charitable Trust
(1974), The *186*
Great Britain Sasakawa
Foundation, The *193*
Greenaway Foundation, The Sir
Derek *194*
Horn Trust, The Cuthbert *227*
Isle of Dogs Community
Foundation *238*
Laing Charitable Trust, The
David *260*
Living and Waking Naturally
278
Lloyd's Charities Trust *278*
Mattock Charitable Trust, The
W T *302*
NR Charitable Trust, The *325*
Needham Cooper Charitable
Trust, The *331*
Notgrove Trust, The *341*
Owen Family Trust, The *348*
Peppiatt Charitable Trust, The
Brian *359*
Pye Christian Trust, The *371*
Pyke Charity Trust *372*
Royal Botanical & Horticultural
Society of Manchester and
the Northern Counties, The
395
Shaw Foundation, The Linley
416
Staples Trust *435*
Summerfield Charitable Trust,
The *442*

Sumner's Trust Section 'A', Sir
John *443*
Tear Fund *450*
Woodlands Trust *501*
Woolmen's Company
Charitable Trust, The *503*

■ **AIDS**
see **HIV & AIDS**

■ **Alcohol
dependency**
see **Substance misuse**

■ **Almshouses**
see also **Residential facilities
& services**

Funding priority
Berkshire Community Trust *45*
Borthwick Memorial Trust, The
Oliver *56*
Chase Charity, The *91*
Corbett's Charity, Thomas *112*
Davenport's Charity Trust,
Baron *124*
Fishmongers' Company's
Charitable Trust *163*
Harding's Charity, William *209*
Hyde Charitable Trust *232*
King Charitable Trust, The
Lorna *254*

Will consider
Almshouse Association, The *14*
Amory Charitable Trust,
Viscount *16*
Anstey Charitable Settlement,
J C W *18*
Aquarius Charitable
Foundation, The *19*
Archer Trust, The *20*
Army Benevolent Fund, The *22*
Astor Foundation, The *26*
Avenal *27*
Balney Charitable Trust, The
32
Barbour Trust, The *33*
Barratt Charitable Trust, The
Elaine *36*
Beit Trust, The *40*
Bengough Trust, The *43*
Bilton Charity, The Percy *48*
Brotherton Trust, The Charles
65
Brough Charitable Trust,
Joseph *65*
Burdall Charity, H M *69*
Burden Trust, The *69*
Cadbury Trust (1928), The
Edward & Dorothy *76*
Campden Charities, The *79*
Challice Trust, The *87*

Charity Projects 90
Chiddick Charitable Trust 92
Company of Chartered
    Surveyors Charitable Trust
    Fund, The 108
County Durham Foundation
    115
Coutts Charitable Trust, The
    116
Curriers Company Charitable
    Fund 119
David Trust, The Lesley 124
de Freitas Charitable Trust, The
    Helen and Geoffrey 126
Derbyshire Trust, J N 130
Dibs Charitable Trust, The 133
Digby Charitable Trust, Simon
    133
Elkes Charity Fund, The Wilfred
    & Elsie 147
Emmandjay Charitable Trust
    150
Emmaus Christian Foundation
    150
Eventhall Family Charitable
    Trust, The 155
Follett Trust, The 166
Gibbins Trust, The 181
Greenaway Foundation, The
    Alan 194
HACT (The Housing
    Association's Charitable
    Trust) 201
Harford Charitable Trust 209
Harvey Charitable Trust,
    Gordon 211
Held Settlement, The Gisela
    215
Hudson Benevolent Trust, The
    Thomas 230
Isle of Dogs Community
    Foundation 238
Laing Charitable Trust, The
    David 260
Laing Foundation, The
    Christopher 260
Lancaster's Trust, Bryan 263
Lankelly Foundation, The 264
Lawson Charitable Trust,
    Raymond and Blanche 267
Leech Charity, The William 269
Lewis Partnership, John 274
Lyons Charitable Trust, The
    288
Mackintosh Foundation, The
    292
Manning Trust, Leslie & Lilian
    296
Margaret Foundation, The 297
Marriage's Charitable Trust,
    Miss G M 299
Merchant Taylors' Consolidated
    Charities for the Infirm 306
Milburn Charitable Trust,
    Frederick 310
Moore Foundation, The
    George A 316

Morphy Memorial Fund, Arthur
    319
Natwest Staff Samaritan Fund
    330
New Court Charitable Trust
    332
Newby Trust Ltd 332
Norman Family Charitable
    Trust, The 337
North British Hotel Trust 337
Northern Ireland Voluntary
    Trust 339
PF Charitable Trust 350
Paterson Charitable
    Foundation, The Constance
    354
Paterson Charitable Trust,
    Arthur James 354
Pratt Charitable Trust, The W L
    367
Ripley's Charitable Trust, Pat
    386
Saint Edmund King and Martyr
    Trust 402
Sparkhill Trust, The 433
Stonehouse Trust Ltd, Eric 438
Summerfield Charitable Trust,
    The 442
Sussman Charitable Trust,
    Adrienne & Leslie 443
Sykes Trust, The Charles 445
Travis Charitable Trust,
    Constance 460
Victoria & Johnson Memorial
    Trust, Queen 472
Wander Charitable Fund, The
    Dr Albert 479
Wesleyan Charitable Trust, The
    485
Whitehall Charitable
    Foundation Limited 490
Woburn 1986 Charitable Trust
    498
Wyford Charitable Trust, The
    507

....

■ Alternative health care

see also Health care

Funding priority
Eaton Charitable Trust, J C J
    143
Harbinson Charitable Trust,
    Roderick 208
Jessel Charitable Trust, The Sir
    Charles 244
Kroch Foundation, The Heinz &
    Anna 259
Mental Health Foundation, The
    305
Royal Theatrical Fund, The 396
Van Berchem Charitable Trust,
    The Alec 470

Will consider
Ammco Trust, The 15
Army Benevolent Fund, The 22
Astor Foundation, The 26
Bancroft Trust, The 33
Berkshire Community Trust 45
BibleLands 47
Birtwistle Memorial Trust, The
    G E 50
Bottom Charitable Trust, Harry
    56
Britton Charitable Trust, The J
    & M 63
Brooke Benevolent Fund,
    William 65
Camelot Foundation, The 78
Commonwealth Relations Trust
    108
Cripplegate Foundation 118
Curzon Charitable Trust, The
    Wallace 120
Dean Refugee Trust Fund, The
    Miriam 128
Denne Charitable Trust 130
Digby Charitable Trust, Simon
    133
Early's Charitable Settlement,
    Richard 142
Edgar Foundation, The Gilbert
    and Eileen 145
Fishmongers' Company's
    Charitable Trust 163
Follett Trust, The 166
Foreman Foundation, The Carl
    & Eve 167
Gibbins Trust, The 181
Grant Foundation, The
    Raymond 191
Great Britain Sasakawa
    Foundation, The 193
Grocers' Charity 197
Hawley Residuary Fund, Harry
    Fieldsend 212
Innes Memorial Fund 235
Isle of Dogs Community
    Foundation 238
Lawson Charitable Trust,
    Raymond and Blanche 267
Leadbeater Trust, The Alfred
    268
Leech Charity, The William 269
(Lloyds) TSB Foundation for
    England and Wales 279
MacKintosh Charitable Trust,
    Viscount 292
Marchday Charitable Fund, The
    296
Needham Cooper Charitable
    Trust, The 331
Penny in the Pound Fund
    Charitable Trust 359
Schuster Charitable Trust, The
    410
South Square Trust 430
Summerfield Charitable Trust,
    The 442
Thompson Charitable Trust,
    The 453

Tisbury Telegraph Trust, The
457
Truemark Trust, The 461
Van Leer Foundation UK Trust,
Bernard 470
Wylde Memorial Charity, The
Anthony and Gwendoline
507

■ Alzheimer's disease
Funding priority
Elkes Charity Fund, The Wilfred
& Elsie 147
Emmandjay Charitable Trust
150
Ferguson Benevolent Fund
Limited 161
Lloyd Charity, The S and D 278
Owen Family Trust, The 348
Paget Trust, The 351
Pye Christian Trust, The 371
Rest-Harrow Trust, The 382
St Christopher's Trust, The 402
Shepherd Charitable Trust, The
Sylvia and Colin 418
Southon Charitable Trust, The
432
Woodroffe Benton Foundation,
The 502

■ Ambulances & mobile units
see also Health facilities &
buildings
Funding priority
Garnett's 1973 Charitable
Trust, Mrs A M 178
Humphreys Charitable
Settlement, J A M 231
Needham Cooper Charitable
Trust, The 331

Will consider
Army Benevolent Fund, The 22
Astor Foundation, The 26
Bancroft Trust, The 33
Barbour Trust, The 33
Berkshire Community Trust 45
Britton Charitable Trust, The J
& M 63
Brotherton Trust, The Charles
65
Bullough Tompson Settlement,
The 68
Challice Trust, The 87
Corbett's Charity, Thomas 112
Coutts Charitable Trust, The
116
Dean Refugee Trust Fund, The
Miriam 128
Derbyshire Trust, J N 130
Digby Charitable Trust, Simon
133
Direct Response 134

Dorus Trust 136
Dumbreck Charity 139
Elkes Charity Fund, The Wilfred
& Elsie 147
Epigoni Trust 152
Fishmongers' Company's
Charitable Trust 163
Fogel Charitable Trust, The
Gerald 165
Franklin Deceased's New
Second Charity, Sydney E
170
Glynde Place Charitable Trust
(1974), The 186
Goldsmiths' Company's
Charities, The 188
Good Neighbours Trust, The
188
Grant Foundation, The
Raymond 191
Greenaway Foundation, The Sir
Derek 194
Hannay Memorial Charity,
Kathleen 208
Harvey Charitable Trust,
Gordon 211
Humanitarian Trust, The 230
Inman Charity, The 235
Isle of Dogs Community
Foundation 238
Laing Charitable Trust, The
David 260
Lawson Charitable Trust,
Raymond and Blanche 267
Lee Foundation, The Edgar
269
Leech Charity, The William 269
London Law Trust 280
Lowe Trust, Mrs D G 285
Luke Trust, The 286
Lynall Foundation, The D G
287
MacKintosh Charitable Trust,
Viscount 292
Mellows Charitable Settlement,
The Anthony and Elizabeth
305
Middlesex County Rugby
Football Union Memorial
Fund 309
Milburn Charitable Trust,
Frederick 310
Milward Charity, The Edgar
313
Minet Trust, The Peter 313
Mountbatten Trust, The
Edwina 322
Natwest Staff Samaritan Fund
330
Norman Family Charitable
Trust, The 337
Owen Family Trust, The 348
Parivar Trust, The 353
Paul's Charitable Trust, R J 355
Provincial Trust for Kendal, The
370
Pyke Charity Trust 372

Ravenscroft Foundation, The
379
Rookes Charitable Trust, C A
390
Rothley Trust, The 392
SMB Trust, The 400
Schuster Charitable Trust, The
410
Shelroy Charitable Trust, The
417
Stoate Charitable Trust, The
Leonard Laity 438
Stonehouse Trust Ltd, Eric 438
Sussman Charitable Trust,
Adrienne & Leslie 443
Sykes Trust, The Charles 445
Thompson Charitable Trust,
The 453
Travis Charitable Trust,
Constance 460

■ Animal breeding
see also Environment &
animal sciences
Funding priority
Farmers' Company Charitable
Fund, The 159
Homeless International 225

Will consider
Arbib Foundation 20
Ashley Foundation, The Laura
24
Astor Foundation, The 26
Butler Charitable Trust, The A S
71
Chippindale Foundation, Sam
93
Clutterbuck Charitable Trust,
Robert 102
Coates Charitable Trust 1969,
Lance 103
Community Trust for Greater
Manchester, The 108
Digby Charitable Trust, Simon
133
Greenaway Foundation, The Sir
Derek 194
Horn Trust, The Cuthbert 227
Isle of Dogs Community
Foundation 238
MacRobert Trusts, The 294
Mattock Charitable Trust, The
W T 302
Oldacre Foundation, The John
345
Woolmen's Company
Charitable Trust, The 503
Yorkshire Agricultural Society
509

■ Animal conservation
see Endangered species

■ Animal facilities & services

see also Animal homes, Animal welfare, Bird sanctuaries, Cats – catteries & other facilities for cats, Dogs – kennels & other facilities for dogs, Horses – stables & other facilities for horses, Wildlife parks, Wildlife sanctuaries, Zoos

Funding priority

Alexander Charitable Trust, Mrs K L *11*
Astor's 1969 Charity, The Hon M L *26*
Bourne-May Charitable Trust, The *57*
Burton Charitable Trust, The Geoffrey *71*
Canine Supporters Charity, The *80*
Clark Charitable Trust, J Anthony *98*
Clutterbuck Charitable Trust, Robert *102*
De Rothschild 1981 Charitable Trust, The Edmund *127*
Dulverton Trust, The *139*
Egerton of Tatton Will Trust, Lord *146*
Elvetham Charitable Trust, The *149*
Evans Memorial Trust, The Alan *155*
Fairbairn Charitable Trust, The Esmee *157*
Foreman 1980 Charitable Trust, The Russell and Mary *167*
Fry Charitable Trust, Maurice *174*
Hamamelis Trust, The *204*
Hawthorne Charitable Trust, The *212*
Heath Charitable Trust *214*
Hitachi Charitable Trust, The *222*
Marks Charitable Trust, Michael *298*
Material World Charitable Foundation Limited, The *301*
Measures Charity, The James Frederick and Ethel Anne *303*
Paget Trust, The *351*
Panton Trust, The *352*
Persula Foundation, The *360*
Sainsbury Animal Welfare Trust, Jean *401*
Samuel Charitable Trust, M J *406*
Scarfe Charitable Trust, The *409*
Southall Charitable Trust, Kenneth & Phyllis *431*
Sykes Trust, The Charles *445*

Sylvanus Charitable Trust, The *446*
Tyler's Charitable Trust, The Late Miss Eileen Margaret *465*
Van Norden's Charitable Foundation, Mrs Maud *471*
Woolmen's Company Charitable Trust, The *503*
Worshipful Company of Shipwrights Charitable Fund, The *506*

Will consider

AHJ Charitable Trust, The *3*
Achiezer Association Limited *6*
Airflow Community Ltd, The *9*
Aleh Charitable Foundation, The *10*
Anderson Trust, Andrew *16*
Angler's Inn Trust *17*
Appelbe Trust, Ambrose & Ann *19*
Aquarius Charitable Foundation, The *19*
Aquinas Trust *20*
Askew Charitable Trust, The Ian *25*
Assembled Church of Christ Trust, The *25*
Astor Foundation, The *26*
Astor of Hever Trust, The *26*
Astor's Charitable Trust, The Hon M L *26*
Barnsbury Charitable Trust *35*
Barton Trust, Eleanor *37*
Bateman Charitable Trust, Lady Margaret *37*
Bealey Foundation, The *38*
Beattie Charitable Trust, The James *39*
Beckwith Charitable Trust, The Peter *40*
Behrens Charitable Trust, E M *40*
Bergqvist Charitable Trust *44*
Black Foundation, The Bertie *51*
Blagrave Charitable Trust, The Herbert and Peter *52*
Blakenham's Charity Trust, Lady *53*
Blakey Charitable Trust, The Celia and Conrad *53*
Blank Donations Ltd, The David *54*
Boltons Trust, The *55*
Bonham-Carter Charitable Trust, The Charlotte *55*
Borthwick Memorial Trust, The Oliver *56*
Bottom Charitable Trust, Harry *56*
Bowland Charitable Trust, The *57*
British Sugar Foundation *63*

Brook Charitable Settlement, R E *64*
Brookhouse's Will Trust, Mr John Charles *65*
Burn Charity Trust, The J H *70*
Burns Charity, The Dorothy *70*
Burry Charitable Trust, The *70*
Butler's Trust, Lord *71*
Butler's Trust, Lucilla *72*
Cadbury Schweppes Foundation, The *76*
Cardiff & Swansea Methodist District Charitable Trust Fund *80*
Carter Charitable Trust, The Leslie Mary *83*
Castang Charitable Trust, H and M *85*
Catto Charitable Settlement, The Thomas Sivewright *86*
Charity Projects *90*
Childtime Trust, The *92*
Chippindale Foundation, Sam *93*
Christian Aid *94*
Cinderford Charitable Trust, The *96*
Closehelm Ltd *101*
Coates Charitable Settlement, The *102*
Coates Charitable Trust 1969, Lance *103*
Cohen Charitable Trust, The Vivienne and Samuel *104*
Cohen Charity Trust, Lucy *104*
Cohen Foundation, The John S *104*
Company of Tobacco Pipe Makers and Tobacco Blenders Benevolent Fund *109*
Condon Family Trust *109*
Conservation Foundation, The *110*
Cope Charitable Trust, Alfred *112*
Corden Trust, Cyril *113*
Crescent Trust, The *117*
Curry Charitable Trust, Dennis *119*
Cymerman Trust Limited, Itzchok Meyer *120*
Daily Telegraph Charitable Trust *122*
Dandeen Charitable Trust *123*
David Trust, The Lesley *124*
Davy Foundation, The J *126*
De Avenley Foundation, The *126*
De La Rue Charitable Trust *127*
De Yong Charitable Trust, The Emma *128*
Denton Charitable Trust, The *130*
Desmond Charitable Trust, The Richard *131*

Deutsch Charitable Trust, The Andre *131*

Deutsch Charitable Trust, The H & M *131*

Dicken Charitable Trust, The Albert *133*

Djanogly Foundation, The *135*

Doughty Charity Trust, The *136*

D'Oyly Carte Charitable Trust, The *137*

Drayton Trust, The *138*

Dumbreck Charity *139*

Dunn Charitable Trust, The Harry *140*

Earmark Trust, The *142*

Edinburgh Trust, No 2 Account *145*

Eling Trust *147*

Elkes Charity Fund, The Wilfred & Elsie *147*

Elshore Limited *149*

Family Trust, The *158*

Famos Foundation Trust *158*

Foreman Foundation, The Carl & Eve *167*

Foyle Trust, Charles Henry *169*

Franklin Bequest, The Rosalind *169*

Franklin Deceased's New Second Charity, Sydney E *170*

Garthgwynion Charities *179*

Gibson's Charity Trust, The Hon Mr & Mrs Clive *182*

Gillett Charitable Trust, J A *183*

Gill's Charitable Trust, Mrs M M *184*

Girdlers' Company Charitable Trust, The *184*

Gold Hill Church Trust *186*

Goldberg Charitable Trust, The Lewis *186*

Goodman Charitable Foundation, The Everard and Mina *188*

Goodman Trust, The *189*

Gradel Foundation, The *189*

Green Foundation, Constance *194*

Greenaway Foundation, The Sir Derek *194*

Gross Charities Limited, M & R *197*

Grosshill Charitable Trust *197*

Grundy Foundation, The Stanley *198*

Grut Charitable Trust, The *198*

HB Charitable Trust *201*

Hacking & Sons Ltd Charitable Trust, C G *201*

Hamilton Educational Trust, Eleanor *205*

Harbour Foundation Ltd, The *208*

Hargreaves Trust, The Kenneth *210*

Harvey Charitable Trust, Gordon *211*

Heinz Company Limited Charitable Trust, The H J *215*

Held Settlement, The Gisela *215*

Henhurst Charitable Trust, The *216*

Hillards Charitable Trust, Gay & Peter Hartley's *220*

Holford Trust Fund *224*

Hoover Foundation, The *226*

Horn Trust, The Cuthbert *227*

Hornby Charitable Trust, Miss D *227*

Hornton Trust, The *228*

Hudson Benevolent Trust, The Thomas *230*

Hughes Charitable Trust, The Geoffery C *230*

IBM United Kingdom Trust *233*

IPE Charitable Trust, The *233*

Inman Charity, The *235*

James Foundation, The Catherine and Lady Grace *241*

Jones Trust, Cemlyn *248*

KC Charitable Trust, The *250*

Karten Charitable Trust, The Ian *250*

Keyes Trust, The Ursula *253*

Kingsgrove Charitable Trust, The *255*

Kinnison Charitable Trust, R O *256*

Kleinwort Charitable Trust, The Ernest *257*

Kobler Trust, The *258*

Kreitman Foundation *258*

Kulika Charitable Trust, The *259*

Kweller Charitable Trust, The Harry *259*

Landy Charitable Trust, Harry and Gertrude *263*

Lankelly Foundation, The *264*

Lanvern Foundation *265*

Laski Memorial Charitable Trust, Nathan *265*

Laspen Trust *265*

Lauffer Charitable Foundation, The R & D *266*

Lavender Trust, The *267*

Lawley Foundation, The Edgar E *267*

Lee Foundation, The Edgar *269*

Leigh-Bramwell Trust 'E', P *270*

Levy Charitable Foundation, Joseph *272*

Lingwood Charitable Trust, The *276*

Livesley 1992 Charitable Trust, Mrs C M *277*

Localtrent Ltd *279*

Lowe Trust, Mrs D G *285*

Lucas Charitable Trust Limited, The Joseph *286*

Lunzer Charitable Trust, The Ruth & Jack *287*

Lynwood Charitable Trust, The *288*

Lyons Charitable Trust, The *288*

MacAndrew Trust, The E M *289*

McKechnie Foundation, A N *292*

McKenzie Trust, The Robert *292*

McLaren Foundation *292*

McLaren Memorial Trust, The Martin *293*

MacRobert Trusts, The *294*

Marchday Charitable Fund, The *296*

Marchig Animal Welfare Trust *297*

Margadale Charitable Trust, Lord *297*

Markus Charitable Foundation, The Erich *298*

Marr-Munning Trust *299*

Marshall Charitable Trust, The Charlotte *300*

Martin Trust, The Sir George *300*

Mattock Charitable Trust, The W T *302*

Mayfair Charities Limited *303*

Medlock Charitable Trust, The *304*

Mellows Charitable Settlement, The Anthony and Elizabeth *305*

Millett Charitable Trust, The Alan and Janet *312*

Millichope Foundation, The *312*

Modiano Charitable Trust *315*

Montefiore Trust, The David *316*

Moore Charitable Trust, The Horace *316*

Moore Stephens Charitable Foundation, The *317*

Morel Charitable Trust, The *318*

Morris Charitable Trust, The Willie & Mabel *320*

Moulton Charitable Trust, The *321*

Music Sales Charitable Trust, The *324*

Newcastle's 1986 Charitable Trust, Duke of *333*

Newman Charitable Trust, Mr and Mrs F E F *334*

Newstead Charity, The *334*

Norfolk's Family Charitable Trust, Lavinia *336*

Northcott Charity Trust, The *338*

Northern Dairies Educational Trust *339*

Northern Electric Employee Charity Association *339*

Northern Ireland Voluntary Trust *339*

Old Possums Practical Trust, The *344*

Oppenheimer Charitable Trust *346*

Owen Trust, Margaret *348*

PDC Trust, The *349*

PJD Charitable Trust *350*

Palmer Trust, The Gerald *352*

Park Hill Trust, The *353*

Pascoe Charitable Trust, Alan *354*

Paul Charitable Trust, The Late Barbara May *355*

Paul Charitable Trust, Margaret Jeanne *355*

Paul Charitable Trust, Pamela Milton *355*

Paul Foundation, The *355*

Paul's Charitable Trust, R J *355*

Payne Charitable Trust, The *355*

Pelech Charitable Trust, The *358*

Pershore Nashdom & Elmore Trust Ltd, The *360*

Peskin Charitable Trust, The Hazel and Leslie *360*

Phillips Charitable Foundation, Reginald M *361*

Pitt Trust, Headley *364*

Powys Welsh Church Fund *367*

Puebla Charitable Trust Limited, The *371*

QAS Charitable Trust *373*

RT Trust, The *374*

Rackham Charitable Trust, The Mr & Mrs Philip *375*

Radley Charitable Trust *375*

Rae Charity, H J *375*

Rainford Trust, The *376*

Rav Chesed Trust, The *379*

Reekie Trust, R A & V B *381*

Richards Charity, The Clive *384*

Riley-Smith Charitable Trust, The F A *386*

Rivendell Trust, The *387*

Robbins Trust, The Cheshire *387*

Rodewald's Charitable Settlement, Mr C A *389*

Rogers Charitable Settlement, The Richard *390*

Rolfe Charitable Trust, The *390*

Rosen Foundation, Cecil *392*

Rowan Charitable Trust, The *393*

St Jude's Trust *403*

Salters Charities *405*

Save & Prosper Foundation *409*

Scarr-Hall Memorial Trust, The *409*

Seva Trust, Rampaba Sadhu *415*

Sheepdrove Trust, The *417*

Shepherd Conservation Foundation, The David *418*

Sherman Charitable Trust, The Archie *419*

Shifrin Charitable Trust, The Maurice and Hilda *419*

Sidbury Trust, The Second *421*

Silvester Charitable Gift Trust *422*

Skinners' Company Lady Neville Charity *424*

Sobell Welsh People's Charitable Association, Michael *429*

Society of Friends of the Torah, The *429*

Solomons Charitable Trust, David *430*

Somerfield Curtis Will Trust, The Dorothy *430*

Stanley Foundation Limited *435*

Stevens Foundation, The June *437*

Stewart Charitable Trust, Mary Stephanie *437*

Sussman Charitable Trust, Adrienne & Leslie *443*

Swann-Morton Foundation, The *444*

Symons Charitable Trust, The Stella *446*

Taylor Charitable Trust, The B R *450*

Terry Charitable Trust, Noel Goddard *451*

Tesco Charity Trust *452*

Tesler Foundation, The *452*

Turner Trust, The Douglas *464*

Valentine Charitable Trust, The *470*

van Geest Foundation, The John and Lucille *470*

Vincent Trust Fund, Eric W *473*

Vineyard Christian Fellowship of South West *473*

Vinson Charity Trust, The 1969 *473*

Vogel Charitable Trust, The Nathan *474*

Wakefield Trust, The *476*

Ward Blenkinsop Trust, The *480*

Weinstock Fund, The *484*

Welby Trust, The Barbara *484*

Whetherly's Charitable Trust, The Hon Mrs R G A *489*

Whitehead Charitable Trust, J E *490*

Whitley Animal Protection Trust *491*

Whittington Charitable Trust, The *491*

Wiggins Charity Trust, Cyril *491*

Wilde Charitable Trust, The Felicity *492*

Wills 1961 Charitable Trust, Major Michael Thomas *494*

Wilson Trust for Animal Welfare, The Kit *495*

Winstone Foundation, Hyman *497*

Woburn 1986 Charitable Trust *498*

Wohl Charitable Foundation, The Maurice *498*

Wohl Charitable Trust, The Maurice *498*

Wolff Charity Trust *498*

Wolfson Family Charitable Trust, The *499*

Woods Charitable Foundation, Geoffrey *502*

Worms Charitable Trust, The Freda and Della *504*

Worshipful Company of Needlemakers' Charitable Fund *505*

Wychdale Limited *507*

Wylde Memorial Charity, The Anthony and Gwendoline *507*

Youell Foundation Ltd, The *510*

....

■ Animal homes

see also **Animal facilities & services**

Funding priority

Friends of the Animals *173*

Green Memorial Fund, The Barry *194*

Heath Charitable Trust *214*

King Charitable Trust, The Lorna *254*

Marchig Animal Welfare Trust *297*

Perry Charitable Trust, Miss Frances Lucille *359*

Sainsbury Animal Welfare Trust, Jean *401*

Zaiger Trust, The Elizabeth and Prince *512*

Will consider

Animal Defence Trust, The *18*

Astor Foundation, The *26*

Avenal *27*

Barnby's Foundation, Lord *35*

Body Charitable Trust, Bernard Richard *55*

Brotherton Trust, The Charles *65*

Butler Charitable Trust, The A S *71*

Carron Charitable Trust, The *83*

Community Trust for Greater Manchester, The *108*

Coote Animal Charity Fund,
The Marjorie *111*
Corden Trust, Cyril *113*
Digby Charitable Trust, Simon
133
Dinam Charity *134*
Dumbreck Charity *139*
Education Services *145*
Elkes Charity Fund, The Wilfred
& Elsie *147*
Evetts & Robert Luff Animal
Welfare Trust, Beryl *156*
Fattorini Charitable Trust,
James J *160*
Ford of Britain Trust *166*
Garnett Charitable Trust, The
178
Great Britain Sasakawa
Foundation, The *193*
Greenaway Foundation, The Sir
Derek *194*
Lee Foundation, The Edgar
269
Lowe Trust, Mrs D G *285*
MacKintosh Charitable Trust,
Viscount *292*
Marriage's Charitable Trust,
Miss G M *299*
Mitchell Trust *315*
Nathan Charitable Trust, Peter
326
Needham Cooper Charitable
Trust, The *331*
Norman Family Charitable
Trust, The *337*
Oakdale Trust, The *343*
Peppiatt Charitable Trust, The
Brian *359*
Richard Charitable Trust, The
Cliff *383*
South Square Trust *430*
Stevens Foundation, The June
437
Sumner's Trust Section 'A', Sir
John *443*
Vincent Wildlife Trust, The *473*
Walker 597 Trust, The *477*
Wyford Charitable Trust, The
507
Wylde Memorial Charity, The
Anthony and Gwendoline
507
Wyre Animal Welfare *507*

■ Animal Sciences

see Environment & animal
sciences

■ Animal services

see Animal facilities &
services

■ Animal welfare

see also **Animal facilities &
services**

Funding priority

Animal Defence Trust, The *18*
Body Charitable Trust, Bernard
Richard *55*
Coote Animal Charity Fund,
The Marjorie *111*
Corden Trust, Cyril *113*
Dinam Charity *134*
Education Services *145*
Evetts & Robert Luff Animal
Welfare Trust, Beryl *156*
Friends of the Animals *173*
Garnett Charitable Trust, The
178
Green Memorial Fund, The
Barry *194*
Grundy Foundation, The
Stanley *198*
Heath Charitable Trust *214*
Jessel Charitable Trust, The Sir
Charles *244*
King Charitable Trust, The
Lorna *254*
McLaren Foundation *292*
Marchig Animal Welfare Trust
297
Margadale Charitable Trust,
Lord *297*
Mitchell Trust *315*
Paget Trust, The *351*
Perry Charitable Trust, Miss
Frances Lucille *359*
Sainsbury Animal Welfare
Trust, Jean *401*
Vincent Wildlife Trust, The *473*
Walker 597 Trust, The *477*
Wicksteed Village Trust, The
491
Wilson Trust for Animal
Welfare, The Kit *495*
Wyre Animal Welfare *507*
Zaiger Trust, The Elizabeth and
Prince *512*

Will consider

Ammco Trust, The *15*
Arbib Foundation *20*
Astor Foundation, The *26*
Avenal *27*
Barbour Trust, The *33*
Barnby's Foundation, Lord *35*
Broadley Charitable Trust, The
64
Brotherton Trust, The Charles
65
Butler Charitable Trust, The A S
71
Carron Charitable Trust, The
83
Community Trust for Greater
Manchester, The *108*
Digby Charitable Trust, Simon
133
Dumbreck Charity *139*

Eaton Charitable Trust, J C J
143
Elkes Charity Fund, The Wilfred
& Elsie *147*
Fattorini Charitable Trust,
James J *160*
Ford of Britain Trust *166*
Great Britain Sasakawa
Foundation, The *193*
Greenaway Foundation, The Sir
Derek *194*
Laing Charitable Trust, The
David *260*
Laing Foundation, The Maurice
261
Lawson Charitable Trust,
Raymond and Blanche *267*
Lee Foundation, The Edgar
269
Leech Charity, The William *269*
Lloyd's Charities Trust *278*
Loseley & Guildway Charitable
Trust, The *281*
Lowe Trust, Mrs D G *285*
MacKintosh Charitable Trust,
Viscount *292*
Nathan Charitable Trust, Peter
326
Needham Cooper Charitable
Trust, The *331*
Norman Family Charitable
Trust, The *337*
Oakdale Trust, The *343*
Owen Family Trust, The *348*
PF Charitable Trust *350*
Peppiatt Charitable Trust, The
Brian *359*
Pilkington Charitable Trust,
Cecil *363*
Richard Charitable Trust, The
Cliff *383*
Sainsbury Charitable Fund Ltd,
The *402*
Sargeant's Charitable Trust,
Mrs M E *407*
Schuster Charitable Trust, The
410
Skelton Bounty, The *423*
South Square Trust *430*
Stevens Foundation, The June
437
Summer's and I May's
Charitable Settlement, The
Late Misses (A N) *442*
Sumner's Trust Section 'A', Sir
John *443*
Sussman Charitable Trust,
Adrienne & Leslie *443*
Tisbury Telegraph Trust, The
457
Webber Trust Fund, Ethel *483*
Wyford Charitable Trust, The
507
Wylde Memorial Charity, The
Anthony and Gwendoline
507
Yorkshire Agricultural Society
509

■ **Annual meetings**
  see Community services

■ **Anti-racism**
  see Cultural & religious
  teaching

■ **Archaeology**
  see also Academic subjects,
  sciences & research
  Funding priority
Ball Charitable Trust, The Bruce
  31
British Institute of Archaeology
  at Ankara 62
Kiln Charitable Trust, Robert
  254
Mediterranean Archaeological
  Trust 304

■ **Architecture**
  see also Arts & arts facilities
  Funding priority
David Trust, The Lesley 124
Lyndhurst Settlement 287
Mitchell Trust, Esme 315
Northern Arts 339

  Will consider
Arts Council of Wales, The 23
Astor Foundation, The 26
Barbour Trust, The 33
Bulmer Charitable Trust, Becket
  68
Campbell Charitable
  Foundation, The Ellis 79
Coates Charitable Trust, The
  John 103
Digby Charitable Trust, Simon
  133
Education Services 145
Franklin Trust, Jill 170
Garnett Charitable Trust, The
  178
Granada Foundation, The 190
Greenaway Foundation, The Sir
  Derek 194
Halkes Settlement, John Robert
  204
Holly Hill Charitable Trust 224
Howard Charitable Trust, John
  & Ruth 229
Hudson Benevolent Trust, The
  Thomas 230
Hughes Charitable Trust, The
  Geoffery C 230
Ireland Funds, The 237
Laing Charitable Trust, The
  David 260
Laing Foundation, The
  Christopher 260

Lawson Charitable Trust,
  Raymond and Blanche 267
Leche Trust, The 268
Lee Foundation, The Edgar
  269
Manifold Charitable Trust, The
  295
Music Sales Charitable Trust,
  The 324
New Court Charitable Trust
  332
North West Arts Board 337
Notgrove Trust, The 341
Owen Family Trust, The 348
Rookes Charitable Trust, C A
  390
Royal Commission for the
  Exhibition of 1851 395
St Katharine & Shadwell Trust
  404
Schuster Charitable Trust, The
  410
Somerfield Curtis Will Trust,
  The Dorothy 430
South Square Trust 430
Summerfield Charitable Trust,
  The 442
Taylor Charitable Trust, The B R
  450
Wates Foundation, The 481
Williams Charitable Trust,
  Alfred 493
Worshipful Company of
  Engineers' Charitable Trust
  Fund, The 504

■ **Art galleries &
cultural centres**
  see also Community
  facilities
  Funding priority
Burn Charity Trust, The J H 70
Chase Charity, The 91
Daiwa Anglo-Japanese
  Foundation, The 122
David Trust, The Lesley 124
Grange Farm Centre Trust 191
Gwent County Council Welsh
  Church Fund 200
Horne Foundation, The 228
Ireland Funds, The 237
Morel Charitable Trust, The
  318
Northern Arts 339
Pilkington Trust, The Austin
  and Hope 363
Reekie Trust, R A & V B 381
Southern Arts 432
Spoore, Merry & Rixman
  Foundation, The 434
Wolfson Foundation, The 499

  Will consider
Abbey National Charitable
  Trust 4
Ammco Trust, The 15
Angler's Inn Trust 17
Aquarius Charitable
  Foundation, The 19
Ashley Foundation, The Laura
  24
Astor Foundation, The 26
Astor of Hever Trust, The 26
Avenal 27
Barbour Trust, The 33
Beckwith Charitable
  Settlement, The Heather 39
Beit Trust, The 40
Bowland Charitable Trust, The
  57
Brand Trust, The 59
Brooke Benevolent Fund,
  William 65
Bullough Tompson Settlement,
  The 68
Burton 1960 Charitable
  Settlement, Audrey &
  Stanley 70
Butler's Trust, Lord 71
Cadbury Charitable Trust
  (Incorporated), Edward 75
Campden Charities, The 79
Carnegie Dunfermline Trust 82
Chase Charity, The 91
Chiddick Charitable Trust 92
Clutterbuck Charitable Trust,
  Robert 102
Coates Charitable Trust, The
  John 103
Cobb Charity 103
Colyer-Fergusson Charitable
  Trust, The 107
County Durham Foundation
  115
Dahl Foundation, The Roald
  122
de Freitas Charitable Trust, The
  Helen and Geoffrey 126
Digby Charitable Trust, Simon
  133
Dulverton Trust, The 139
Dumbreck Charity 139
Early's Charitable Settlement,
  Richard 142
Edgar Foundation, The Gilbert
  and Eileen 145
Feeney Charitable Bequest, The
  John 161
Fletcher Charitable Trust, The
  Joyce 164
Fogel Charitable Trust, The
  Gerald 165
Follett Trust, The 166
Forbes Trust, The 166
Four Lanes Trust, The 168
Frognal Trust 174
Gardner Charitable Trust, R & J
  178
Great Britain Sasakawa
  Foundation, The 193

Greenaway Foundation, The Sir
Derek *194*
Grocers' Charity *197*
Halkes Settlement, John Robert
204
Hamlyn Foundation, The Paul
205
Harbinson Charitable Trust,
Roderick *208*
Harford Charitable Trust *209*
Hillards Charitable Trust, Gay &
Peter Hartley's *220*
Hudson Benevolent Trust, The
Thomas *230*
Humanitarian Trust, The *230*
Hunter Charitable Trust, The
Claire *231*
Inverforth Charitable Trust, The
236
Isle of Dogs Community
Foundation *238*
Knott Trust, Sir James *258*
Kroch Foundation, The Heinz &
Anna *259*
Laing Charitable Trust, The
David *260*
Laing Foundation, The
Christopher *260*
Lankelly Foundation, The *264*
Lawson Charitable Trust,
Raymond and Blanche *267*
Leach Fourteenth Trust, The
267
Leche Trust, The *268*
Lee Foundation, The Edgar
269
Littler Foundation, The Emile
277
(Lloyds) TSB Foundation for
England and Wales *279*
Merchants House of Glasgow
307
Needham Cooper Charitable
Trust, The *331*
Norfolk's Family Charitable
Trust, Lavinia *336*
North West Arts Board *337*
Noswad Charity, The *341*
Oakdale Trust, The *343*
Owen Family Trust, The *348*
PF Charitable Trust *350*
Persula Foundation, The *360*
Porter Foundation *366*
Provincial Trust for Kendal, The
370
Rayner Charitable Trust, The
John *380*
Richard Charitable Trust, The
Cliff *383*
Ripley's Charitable Trust, Pat
386
Rookes Charitable Trust, C A
390
Save & Prosper Educational
Trust *408*
Schuster Charitable Trust, The
410

Shepherd Family Charitable
Trust, The Sir Peter *418*
South Square Trust *430*
Spoore, Merry & Rixman
Foundation, The *434*
Strauss Charitable Trust *440*
Summerfield Charitable Trust,
The *442*
Symons Charitable Trust, The
Stella *446*
TSB Foundation for Scotland
447
Tyne & Wear Foundation *466*
Wagstaff Charitable Trust, Bob
475
Wakefield (Tower Hill, Trinity
Square) Trust *476*
Wall Trust, Thomas *478*
Whitaker Charitable Trust *489*
Williams Charitable Trust,
Alfred *493*
Wills 1962 Charitable Trust,
P J H *494*
Wingate Foundation, The
Harold Hyam *496*
Wingfield's Charitable Trust,
Mrs *496*
Wylde Memorial Charity, The
Anthony and Gwendoline
507
Yorkshire Bank Charitable
Trust, The *510*

....

■ Arthritis & rheumatism

Funding priority
Archer Trust, The *20*
Arthritis and Rheumatism
Council for Research in
Great Britain and the
Commonwealth, The *22*
Betard Bequest *46*
Psoriasis Association Research
Fund (1968), The *371*
Sidbury Trust, The Second *421*
Smith Foundation, The Leslie
427
Summer's and I May's
Charitable Settlement, The
Late Misses (A N) *442*

....

■ Arts activities

see also Community arts &
recreation

Funding priority
Calypso Browning Trust *78*
Carnegie United Kingdom
Trust, The *82*
County Durham Foundation
115
Eden Arts Trust *145*
Finzi Charitable Trust, Gerald
162

Fletcher Charitable Trust, The
Joyce *164*
Ireland Funds, The *237*
North West Arts Board *337*
Northern Arts *339*
Northern Ireland Voluntary
Trust *339*
St Katharine & Shadwell Trust
404
South Square Trust *430*
Wylde Memorial Charity, The
Anthony and Gwendoline
507
Yorkshire and Humberside Arts
510

Will consider
Arts Council of England, The
23
Ashden Charitable Trust, The
24
Astor Foundation, The *26*
Barbour Trust, The *33*
Beit Trust, The *40*
Brooke Benevolent Fund,
William *65*
Bulmer Charitable Trust, Becket
68
Cadbury Trust (1928), The
Edward & Dorothy *76*
Carlton Television Trust *81*
Carnegie Dunfermline Trust *82*
David Trust, The Lesley *124*
de Freitas Charitable Trust, The
Helen and Geoffrey *126*
Debtors' Relief Fund Charity
128
Digby Charitable Trust, Simon
133
Edgar Foundation, The Gilbert
and Eileen *145*
Education Services *145*
Fogel Charitable Trust, The
Gerald *165*
Follett Trust, The *166*
Granada Foundation, The *190*
Great Britain Sasakawa
Foundation, The *193*
Grocers' Charity *197*
Gwent County Council Welsh
Church Fund *200*
Halkes Settlement, John Robert
204
Hamlyn Foundation, The Paul
205
Hinrichsen Foundation, The
221
Holly Hill Charitable Trust *224*
Howard Charitable Trust, John
& Ruth *229*
Hudson Benevolent Trust, The
Thomas *230*
Hunter Charitable Trust, The
Claire *231*
Lawley Foundation, The Edgar
E *267*

Lawson Charitable Trust, Raymond and Blanche *267*
Leche Trust, The *268*
Lee Foundation, The Edgar *269*
Linford Charitable Trust, The Fred *276*
Lynn Foundation, The *288*
Mackintosh Foundation, The *292*
Mid Moss Charitable Trust, The *309*
Milton Keynes Community Trust Ltd, The *312*
Mitchell Trust, Esme *315*
Needham Cooper Charitable Trust, The *331*
Noswad Charity, The *341*
Oldham Foundation *345*
Owen Family Trust, The *348*
Persula Foundation, The *360*
Reader's Digest Trust, The *380*
Snipe Charitable Trust *428*
Sobell Welsh People's Charitable Association, Michael *429*
Spoore, Merry & Rixman Foundation, The *434*
Summerfield Charitable Trust, The *442*
Sykes Trust, The Charles *445*
Wates Charitable Trust, John *481*
Wates Foundation, The *481*
Whitaker Charitable Trust *489*
Williams Charitable Trust, Alfred *493*
Woodlands Trust *501*

....

■ Arts & arts facilities

***see also* Residential facilities & services**

Funding priority

AHJ Charitable Trust, The *3*
Astor of Hever Trust, The *26*
Astor's 1969 Charity, The Hon M L *26*
Barnsbury Charitable Trust *35*
Bergqvist Charitable Trust *44*
Brook Charitable Settlement, R E *64*
Cinderford Charitable Trust, The *96*
Clark Charitable Trust, J Anthony *98*
Construction Industry Trust for Youth, The *110*
Crescent Trust, The *117*
Daiwa Anglo-Japanese Foundation, The *122*
De Avenley Foundation, The *126*
Denton Charitable Trust, The *130*
Deutsch Charitable Trust, The Andre *131*

Djanogly Foundation, The *135*
D'Oyly Carte Charitable Trust, The *137*
Drayton Trust, The *138*
East Midlands Arts Board Ltd *143*
Eastern Arts Board *143*
Ecclesiastical Music Trust, The *144*
Elephant Trust, The *146*
Fairbairn Charitable Trust, The Esmee *157*
Feeney Charitable Bequest, The John *161*
Franklin Trust, Jill *170*
Gillett Charitable Trust, J A *183*
Gill's Charitable Trust, Mrs M M *184*
Granada Foundation, The *190*
Hawthorne Charitable Trust, The *212*
Heinz Company Limited Charitable Trust, The H J *215*
Hinrichsen Foundation, The *221*
Hitachi Charitable Trust, The *222*
Hornby Charitable Trust, Miss D *227*
Horne Foundation, The *228*
Hornton Trust, The *228*
Kobler Trust, The *258*
Kreitman Foundation *258*
Liebes Charitable Trust, The Martha Bud *274*
London Arts Board *280*
Lucas Charitable Trust Limited, The Joseph *286*
Lyons Charitable Trust, Sir Jack *288*
MacRobert Trusts, The *294*
Mellows Charitable Settlement, The Anthony and Elizabeth *305*
Millichope Foundation, The *312*
Milton Keynes Community Trust Ltd, The *312*
Moores Foundation, The Peter *318*
Morel Charitable Trust, The *318*
Northern Arts *339*
Oppenheimer Charitable Trust *346*
Owen Trust, Margaret *348*
PDC Trust, The *349*
Pilkington Charitable Trust, Cecil *363*
Pilkington Trust, The Austin and Hope *363*
Pitman Charitable Trust, The John *364*
Powell Foundation, The *367*
Powys Welsh Church Fund *367*
QAS Charitable Trust *373*

Rayne Foundation, The *379*
Reekie Trust, R A & V B *381*
Rodewald's Charitable Settlement, Mr C A *389*
South West Arts *431*
Southern Arts *432*
TSB Foundation for Scotland *447*
Tesco Charity Trust *452*
Wade & Others, The Charity of Thomas *475*
Wates Foundation, The *481*
West Midlands Regional Arts Board *486*
Wohl Charitable Foundation, The Maurice *498*
Wohl Charitable Trust, The Maurice *498*
Wolfson Family Charitable Trust, The *499*
Wolfson Foundation, The *499*

Will consider

Achiezer Association Limited *6*
Airflow Community Ltd, The *9*
Aleh Charitable Foundation, The *10*
Allied Domecq Trust *13*
Alper Charitable Trust, The *15*
Ammco Trust, The *15*
Anderson Trust, Andrew *16*
Angler's Inn Trust *17*
Anglo Hong Kong Trust, The *17*
Appelbe Trust, Ambrose & Ann *19*
Aquarius Charitable Foundation, The *19*
Aquinas Trust *20*
Askew Charitable Trust, The Ian *25*
Assembled Church of Christ Trust, The *25*
Assheton-Smith Charitable Trust *25*
Astor Foundation, The *26*
Astor's Charitable Trust, The Hon M L *26*
Avenal *27*
BBC Children in Need Appeal, The *29*
Balfour Trust, The Nancy *31*
Baring Foundation, The *34*
Barnby's Foundation Appointed Fund, Lord *35*
Barnby's Foundation, Lord *35*
Barton Trust, Eleanor *37*
Bateman Charitable Trust, Lady Margaret *37*
Bealey Foundation, The *38*
Beaverbrook Foundation, The *39*
Beckwith Charitable Trust, The Peter *40*
Beckwith-Smith's Charitable Settlement, Mrs *40*

Behrens Charitable Trust, E M *40*

Beit Trust, The *40*

Benlian Trust, The *44*

Black Foundation, The Bertie *51*

Blagrave Charitable Trust, The Herbert and Peter *52*

Blakenham's Charity Trust, Lady *53*

Blakey Charitable Trust, The Celia and Conrad *53*

Blank Donations Ltd, The David *54*

Boltons Trust, The *55*

Borthwick Memorial Trust, The Oliver *56*

Bottom Charitable Trust, Harry *56*

Bowland Charitable Trust, The *57*

Brand Trust, The *59*

British Sugar Foundation *63*

Brookhouse's Will Trust, Mr John Charles *65*

Brotherton Trust, The Charles *65*

Bullough Tompson Settlement, The *68*

Burn Charity Trust, The J H *70*

Burns Charity, The Dorothy *70*

Burry Charitable Trust, The *70*

Burton Charitable Trust, The Geoffrey *71*

Burton Charitable Trust, R M *71*

Butler's Trust, Lord *71*

Butler's Trust, Lucilla *72*

Buxton Trust, Denis *72*

CHK Charities Limited *74*

Cadbury Schweppes Foundation, The *76*

Cadbury Trust (1928), The Edward & Dorothy *76*

Cardiff & Swansea Methodist District Charitable Trust Fund *80*

Carron Charitable Trust, The *83*

Castang Charitable Trust, H and M *85*

Charity Projects *90*

Chase Charity, The *91*

Chiddick Charitable Trust *92*

Chippindale Foundation, Sam *93*

Closehelm Ltd *101*

Clutterbuck Charitable Trust, Robert *102*

Coates Charitable Settlement, The *102*

Coates Charitable Trust 1969, Lance *103*

Coates Charitable Trust, The John *103*

Cobb Charity *103*

Cohen Charitable Trust, The Vivienne and Samuel *104*

Cohen Charity Trust, Lucy *104*

Cohen Foundation, The John S *104*

Company of Tobacco Pipe Makers and Tobacco Blenders Benevolent Fund *109*

Condon Family Trust *109*

Cope Charitable Trust, Alfred *112*

Curry Charitable Trust, Dennis *119*

Curzon Charitable Trust, The Wallace *120*

Cymerman Trust Limited, Itzchok Meyer *120*

Daily Telegraph Charitable Trust *122*

Dandeen Charitable Trust *123*

Davies Charity, The Gwendoline and Margaret *125*

Davy Foundation, The J *126*

De La Rue Charitable Trust *127*

De Rothschild 1981 Charitable Trust, The Edmund *127*

De Yong Charitable Trust, The Emma *128*

Denby Charitable Foundation, The *130*

Desmond Charitable Trust, The Richard *131*

Deutsch Charitable Trust, The H & M *131*

Dibs Charitable Trust, The *133*

Dicken Charitable Trust, The Albert *133*

Dinam Charity *134*

Doughty Charity Trust, The *136*

Dunn Charitable Trust, The Harry *140*

Earmark Trust, The *142*

Edinburgh Trust, No 2 Account *145*

Egerton of Tatton Will Trust, Lord *146*

Eling Trust *147*

Elmgrant Trust *149*

Elshore Limited *149*

European Cultural Foundation (UK Committee) *154*

Family Trust, The *158*

Famos Foundation Trust *158*

Finzi Charitable Trust, Gerald *162*

Forbes Trust, The *166*

Foreman Foundation, The Carl & Eve *167*

Four Lanes Trust, The *168*

Foyle Trust, Charles Henry *169*

Franklin Bequest, The Rosalind *169*

Franklin Deceased's New Second Charity, Sydney E *170*

Fry Charitable Trust, Maurice *174*

Garnett Charitable Trust, The *178*

Garthgwynion Charities *179*

Gibson's Charity Trust, The Hon Mr & Mrs Clive *182*

Girdlers' Company Charitable Trust, The *184*

Gladstone Charitable Trust, The E W *184*

Gold Hill Church Trust *186*

Goldberg Charitable Trust, The Lewis *186*

Goldsmiths' Company's Charities, The *188*

Goodman Charitable Foundation, The Everard and Mina *188*

Goodman Trust, The *189*

Gradel Foundation, The *189*

Green Foundation, Constance *194*

Greenaway Foundation, The Sir Derek *194*

Grocers' Charity *197*

Gross Charities Limited, M & R *197*

Grosshill Charitable Trust *197*

Grut Charitable Trust, The *198*

Gulbenkian Foundation (Lisbon) United Kingdom Branch, Calouste *199*

HB Charitable Trust *201*

Hacking & Sons Ltd Charitable Trust, C G *201*

Hamilton Educational Trust, Eleanor *205*

Hampstead Wells and Campden Trust *206*

Harbour Foundation Ltd, The *208*

Harford Charitable Trust *209*

Hargreaves Trust, The Kenneth *210*

Harvey Charitable Trust, Gordon *211*

Held Settlement, The Gisela *215*

Hillards Charitable Trust, Gay & Peter Hartley's *220*

Holford Trust Fund *224*

Hoover Foundation, The *226*

Horn Trust, The Cuthbert *227*

IPE Charitable Trust, The *233*

Idlewild Trust, The *234*

Inman Charity, The *235*

Inverforth Charitable Trust, The *236*

Ireland Fund of Great Britain, The *237*

Isle of Dogs Community Foundation *238*

Jacobs Charitable Trust, The J P *240*

James Foundation, The Catherine and Lady Grace *241*

Jarrold Trust Ltd, John *243*
Jones Trust, Cemlyn *248*
KC Charitable Trust, The *250*
Karten Charitable Trust, The
Ian *250*
Keyes Trust, The Ursula *253*
Kingsgrove Charitable Trust,
The *255*
Kinnison Charitable Trust, R O
256
Kleinwort Charitable Trust, The
Ernest *257*
Knott Trust, Sir James *258*
Kulika Charitable Trust, The
259
Kweller Charitable Trust, The
Harry *259*
Laing Charitable Trust, The
David *260*
Laing Foundation, The Kirby
261
Landy Charitable Trust, Harry
and Gertrude *263*
Lankelly Foundation, The *264*
Lanvern Foundation *265*
Laski Memorial Charitable
Trust, Nathan *265*
Laspen Trust *265*
Lauffer Charitable Foundation,
The R & D *266*
Lavender Trust, The *267*
Lawley Foundation, The Edgar
E *267*
Leach Fourteenth Trust, The
267
Lee Foundation, The Edgar
269
Leigh-Bramwell Trust 'E', P *270*
Levy Charitable Foundation,
Joseph *272*
Liffe Benefit *274*
Lingwood Charitable Trust, The
276
Lloyd Charity, The S and D *278*
Localtrust Ltd *279*
Lottery Arts Fund for England,
Scotland, Wales and
Northern Ireland *281*
Low & Bonar Charitable Fund,
The *284*
Lunzer Charitable Trust, The
Ruth & Jack *287*
Lynwood Charitable Trust, The
288
Lyons Charitable Trust, The
288
MDM Memorial Trust *289*
MacAndrew Trust, The E M
289
McKechnie Foundation, A N
292
McKenzie Trust, The Robert
292
McLaren Foundation *292*
McLaren Memorial Trust. The
Martin *293*
Margadale Charitable Trust,
Lord *297*

Marks Charitable Trust,
Michael *298*
Markus Charitable Foundation,
The Erich *298*
Marriage's Charitable Trust,
Miss G M *299*
Marr-Munning Trust *299*
Marshall Charitable Trust, The
Charlotte *300*
Martin Trust, The Sir George
300
Material World Charitable
Foundation Limited, The
301
Mattock Charitable Trust, The
W T *302*
Mayfair Charities Limited *303*
Measures Charity, The James
Frederick and Ethel Anne
303
Medlock Charitable Trust, The
304
Millett Charitable Trust, The
Alan and Janet *312*
Modiano Charitable Trust *315*
Montefiore Trust, The David
316
Moore Charitable Trust, The
Horace *316*
Moore Stephens Charitable
Foundation, The *317*
Morgan Crucible Company plc
Charitable Trust, The *319*
Morris Charitable Trust, The
Willie & Mabel *320*
Moulton Charitable Trust, The
321
Newcastle's 1986 Charitable
Trust, Duke of *333*
Newman Charitable Trust, Mr
and Mrs F E F *334*
Newstead Charity, The *334*
Norfolk's Family Charitable
Trust, Lavinia *336*
Northcott Charity Trust, The
338
Northern Electric Employee
Charity Association *339*
Northern Ireland Voluntary
Trust *339*
Old Possums Practical Trust,
The *344*
Oldham Foundation *345*
PJD Charitable Trust *350*
Palmer Trust, The Gerald *352*
Park Hill Trust, The *353*
Pascoe Charitable Trust, Alan
354
Paul Charitable Trust, The Late
Barbara May *355*
Paul Charitable Trust, Margaret
Jeanne *355*
Paul Charitable Trust, Pamela
Milton *355*
Paul Foundation, The *355*
Paul's Charitable Trust, R J *355*
Payne Charitable Trust, The
355

Pelech Charitable Trust, The
358
Perry Charitable Trust, Miss
Frances Lucille *359*
Pershore Nashdom & Elmore
Trust Ltd, The *360*
Peskin Charitable Trust, The
Hazel and Leslie *360*
Phillips Charitable Foundation,
Reginald M *361*
Pilgrim Trust, The *362*
Pitt Trust, Headley *364*
Prendergast Charitable Trust,
The Simone *368*
Puebla Charitable Trust
Limited, The *371*
Quothquan Charitable Trust,
The Second *373*
RT Trust, The *374*
Rackham Charitable Trust, The
Mr & Mrs Philip *375*
Rae Charity, H J *375*
Rainford Trust, The *376*
Rav Chesed Trust, The *379*
Rayner Charitable Trust, The
John *380*
Reuter Foundation, The *382*
Richard Charitable Trust, The
Cliff *383*
Richards Charity, The Clive *384*
Richmond Parish Lands Charity
384
Rivendell Trust, The *387*
Robbins Trust, The Cheshire
387
Rogers Charitable Settlement,
The Richard *390*
Rolfe Charitable Trust, The *390*
Rosen Foundation, Cecil *392*
S Group Charitable Trust *399*
St Jude's Trust *403*
Salters Charities *405*
Samuel Charitable Trust, M J
406
Save & Prosper Foundation
409
Scarr-Hall Memorial Trust, The
409
Seva Trust, Rampaba Sadhu
415
Sherman Charitable Trust, The
Archie *419*
Shifrin Charitable Trust, The
Maurice and Hilda *419*
Sidbury Trust, The Second *421*
Silvester Charitable Gift Trust
422
Simon's Charity *422*
Skelton Bounty, The *423*
Skinners' Company Lady Neville
Charity *424*
Sobell Welsh People's
Charitable Association,
Michael *429*
Society of Friends of the Torah,
The *429*
Solomons Charitable Trust,
David *430*

South East Arts Board *430*
Stanley Foundation Limited *435*
Stewart Charitable Trust, Mary Stephanie *437*
Sumner's Trust Section 'A', Sir John *443*
Symons Charitable Trust, The Stella *446*
Tait Charity, The Richard *448*
Terry Charitable Trust, Noel Goddard *451*
Tesler Foundation, The *452*
3i Charitable Trust, The *455*
van Geest Foundation, The John and Lucille *470*
Van Norden's Charitable Foundation, Mrs Maud *471*
Vincent Trust Fund, Eric W *473*
Vineyard Christian Fellowship of South West *473*
Vinson Charity Trust, The 1969 *473*
Vogel Charitable Trust, The Nathan *474*
Wakefield (Tower Hill, Trinity Square) Trust *476*
Wakefield Trust, The *476*
Ward Blenkinsop Trust, The *480*
Weinstock Fund, The *484*
Welby Trust, The Barbara *484*
Whetherly's Charitable Trust, The Hon Mrs R G A *489*
Whitehead Charitable Trust, J E *490*
Whittington Charitable Trust, The *491*
Wiggins Charity Trust, Cyril *491*
Wilde Charitable Trust, The Felicity *492*
Wills 1961 Charitable Trust, Major Michael Thomas *494*
Wingate Foundation, The Harold Hyam *496*
Wingfield's Charitable Trust, Mrs *496*
Winstone Foundation, Hyman *497*
Woburn 1986 Charitable Trust *498*
Wolff Charity Trust *498*
Woodhouse Charitable Trust, Edwin *501*
Woods Charitable Foundation, Geoffrey *502*
Worms Charitable Trust, The Freda and Della *504*
Worshipful Company of Needlemakers' Charitable Fund *505*
Wright Deceased Trust, John William *506*
Wychdale Limited *507*

Youell Foundation Ltd, The *510*
Zaiger Trust, The Elizabeth and Prince *512*

....

■ Arts education

see also **Community arts & recreation**

Funding priority

Arts Council of England, The *23*
Ball Charitable Trust, The Bruce *31*
Bugden Charitable Trust, The Rosemary *67*
Calypso Browning Trust *78*
Carlton Television Trust *81*
Carnegie United Kingdom Trust, The *82*
City Parochial Foundation *96*
Clifford Charity Oxford, The *100*
Cobb Charity *103*
County Durham Foundation *115*
Eden Arts Trust *145*
Fletcher Charitable Trust, The Joyce *164*
Garnett Charitable Trust, The *178*
International Arab Women's Council Charities Fund *236*
Ireland Funds, The *237*
Lawley Foundation, The Edgar E *267*
Lewin Charitable Trust, The Robert and Rena *273*
(Lloyds) TSB Foundation for England and Wales *279*
North West Arts Board *337*
Northern Arts *339*
Northern Ireland Voluntary Trust *339*
St Katharine & Shadwell Trust *404*
South Square Trust *430*
Southern Arts *432*
Spoore, Merry & Rixman Foundation, The *434*
Trust Fund for the Training of Handicapped Children in Arts and Crafts *462*
Tutton Charitable Trust, Miss S M *465*
Yorkshire and Humberside Arts *510*

Will consider

Ashden Charitable Trust, The *24*
Ashley Foundation, The Laura *24*
Astor Foundation, The *26*
Barbour Trust, The *33*
Brooke Benevolent Fund, William *65*

Brough Charitable Trust, Joseph *65*
Bulmer Charitable Trust, Becket *68*
Cadbury Trust (1928), The Edward & Dorothy *76*
Campbell Charitable Foundation, The Ellis *79*
David Trust, The Lesley *124*
de Freitas Charitable Trust, The Helen and Geoffrey *126*
Debtors' Relief Fund Charity *128*
Digby Charitable Trust, Simon *133*
Edgar Foundation, The Gilbert and Eileen *145*
Education Services *145*
Finzi Charitable Trust, Gerald *162*
Follett Trust, The *166*
Granada Foundation, The *190*
Great Britain Sasakawa Foundation, The *193*
Grocers' Charity *197*
Gwent County Council Welsh Church Fund *200*
Halkes Settlement, John Robert *204*
Hamlyn Foundation, The Paul *205*
Hinrichsen Foundation, The *221*
Holly Hill Charitable Trust *224*
Howard Charitable Trust, John & Ruth *229*
Hudson Benevolent Trust, The Thomas *230*
Hunter Charitable Trust, The Claire *231*
Lee Foundation, The Edgar *269*
Lewis Foundation, The John Spedan *274*
Linford Charitable Trust, The Fred *276*
Lynn Foundation, The *288*
Mackintosh Foundation, The *292*
Marchday Charitable Fund, The *296*
Mid Moss Charitable Trust, The *309*
Milton Keynes Community Trust Ltd, The *312*
Mitchell Trust, Esme *315*
Needham Cooper Charitable Trust, The *331*
Noswad Charity, The *341*
Oldham Foundation *345*
Owen Family Trust, The *348*
Persula Foundation, The *360*
Reader's Digest Trust, The *380*
Royal Commission for the Exhibition of 1851 *395*
Sheepdrove Trust, The *417*
Snipe Charitable Trust *428*

....

Summerfield Charitable Trust, The *442*

Turner Trust, The Douglas *464*

Wakefield (Tower Hill, Trinity Square) Trust *476*

Wates Charitable Trust, John *481*

Wates Foundation, The *481*

Whitaker Charitable Trust *489*

Williams Charitable Trust, Alfred *493*

■ **Assisted places**
see Costs of study

■ **Asthma**
Funding priority

Asthma Allergy and Inflammation Research Trust *25*

Rackham Charitable Trust, The Mr & Mrs Philip *375*

Smith Foundation, The Leslie *427*

■ **At risk groups**
Funding priority

Alexandra Trust *11*

Ammco Trust, The *15*

Archer Trust, The *20*

Buxton Trust, Denis *72*

Carlton Television Trust *81*

Carnegie United Kingdom Trust, The *82*

Clifford Charity Oxford, The *100*

Cobb Charity *103*

Curriers Company Charitable Fund *119*

Fletcher Trust, Roy *165*

HACT (The Housing Association's Charitable Trust) *201*

Hamlyn Foundation, The Helen *205*

Hampstead Wells and Campden Trust *206*

Hanley Trust (1987), The *207*

Hayward Foundation, The *213*

Hertfordshire Community Trust, The *217*

Hiley Trust, Joseph and Mary *219*

Isle of Dogs Community Foundation *238*

Music for World Development *323*

Noel Buxton Trust, The *335*

Norton Foundation, The *340*

Nunburnholme Trust, The Incorporated Trustees of the *342*

Paristamen Foundation, The *352*

Persula Foundation, The *360*

Reeve's Foundation *382*

Said Foundation, The Karim Rida *401*

Seagram Distillers Charitable Trust *413*

Swale Charity Trust *443*

TSB Foundation for Scotland *447*

Wates Foundation, The *481*

Weavers' Company Benevolent Fund, The *482*

Wiltshire Community Foundation *495*

Will consider

AB Charitable Trust *3*

Adnams Charity, The *7*

Andrew Charitable Trust, The Prince *16*

Askew Trust, The Dorothy *25*

Astor Foundation, The *26*

Ballinger Charitable Trust, The *32*

Barbour Trust, The *33*

Barnabas Charitable Trust *34*

Bartholomew Christian Trust *36*

Beckwith Charitable Settlement, The Heather *39*

Bell Charitable Trust, John *41*

Blake Charitable Trust, The Morgan *53*

Boots Charitable Trust *56*

Bridge Trust, The *60*

Brotherton Trust, The Charles *65*

Burdall Charity, H M *69*

Butlin Charity Trust, Bill *72*

Camelot Foundation, The *78*

Campbell Charitable Foundation, The Ellis *79*

Catto Charitable Settlement, The Thomas Sivewright *86*

Challice Trust, The *87*

Charity Projects *90*

Clark 1965 Charitable Trust, Stephen *98*

Clinton's Charitable Trust, Lord *100*

Cole Charitable Trust, The *105*

Coutts Charitable Trust, The *116*

De Yong Charitable Trust, The Emma *128*

Digbeth Trust Ltd, The *133*

Direct Response *134*

Dorus Trust *136*

Ebb and Flow Charitable Trust *144*

Edgar Foundation, The Gilbert and Eileen *145*

Edgar Trust, The Gilbert *145*

Elkes Charity Fund, The Wilfred & Elsie *147*

Emmaus Christian Foundation *150*

Epigoni Trust *152*

Ericson Trust *152*

Essex Radio Helping Hands Trust, The *154*

Eveson Charitable Trust, The *155*

Ferguson Benevolent Fund Limited *161*

Fletcher Charitable Trust, The Joyce *164*

Four Winds Trust *168*

GNC Trust *175*

Gibson Charitable Trust, The Simon *182*

Gluckstein Charitable Settlement, The Penelope *185*

Goldsmiths' Company's Charities, The *188*

Grant Foundation, The Raymond *191*

Grant-Lawson Charitable Trust, Lady Virginia *192*

Groves Charitable Trust, The *197*

Handicapped Children's Aid Committee *207*

Harbour Foundation Ltd, The *208*

Held Settlement, The Gisela *215*

Hudson Benevolent Trust, The Thomas *230*

Hudson Charitable Trust, The *230*

Iris Trust, The *237*

Irving Charitable Trust, The Charles *237*

JCSCJ Charitable Trust, The *238*

JMK Charitable Trust *239*

Jarrold Trust Ltd, John *243*

Johnson Foundation, The *246*

Johnson Group Cleaners Charity *247*

Keeling Charitable Trust, The Petronella *251*

King Charitable Trust, The Lorna *254*

King's Fund, The *255*

Kyte Charitable Trust, The *259*

Laing Charitable Trust, The David *260*

Laing Foundation, The Christopher *260*

Laing Foundation, The Kirby *261*

Laing Foundation, The Maurice *261*

Laing Trust, Beatrice *261*

Lane Foundation, The Allen *263*

Laspen Trust *265*

Lawson Charitable Trust, Raymond and Blanche *267*

Leach Fourteenth Trust, The *267*

Lloyd Charity, The S and D *278*

Lloyd's Charities Trust *278*

(Lloyds) TSB Foundation for England and Wales *279*

Low & Bonar Charitable Fund, The *284*

Lyons Charitable Trust, The *288*

McCarthy Foundation, The John *290*

Mackintosh Foundation, The *292*

Manning Trust, Leslie & Lilian *296*

Margaret Foundation, The *297*

Marriage's Charitable Trust, Miss G M *299*

Mental Health Foundation, The *305*

Metropolitan Hospital-Sunday Fund, The *308*

Milburn Charitable Trust, Frederick *310*

Milton Keynes Community Trust Ltd, The *312*

Minet Trust, The Peter *313*

Minge's Gift *314*

Moore Foundation, The George A *316*

Moores Foundation, John *318*

Morris Charitable Trust, The Douglas *320*

NR Charitable Trust, The *325*

Nathan Charitable Trust *326*

Natwest Staff Samaritan Fund *330*

Needham Cooper Charitable Trust, The *331*

New Court Charitable Trust *332*

New Durlston Trust, The *332*

Newby Trust Ltd *332*

Oakdale Trust, The *343*

Oldham Foundation *345*

Owen Family Trust, The *348*

Parivar Trust, The *353*

Paterson Charitable Foundation, The Constance *354*

Paterson Charitable Trust, Arthur James *354*

Pratt Charitable Trust, The W L *367*

Pye Christian Trust, The *371*

Pyke Charity Trust *372*

Ravenscroft Foundation, The *379*

Rest-Harrow Trust, The *382*

Robinson Brothers (Ryders Green) Ltd, Charitable Trust *388*

Rope Third Charitable Settlement, The Mrs *391*

Royal's Memorial Fund, Princess *396*

Sainsbury Charitable Fund Ltd, The *402*

St Christopher's Trust, The *402*

Sargeant's Charitable Trust, Mrs M E *407*

Schuster Charitable Trust, The *410*

Scott Bader Commonwealth Ltd, The *411*

Sheldon Trust, The *417*

Smith & Mount Trust, The Mrs *426*

South Square Trust *430*

Sport Aid 88 Trust *434*

Stevens Foundation, The June *437*

Stoate Charitable Trust, The Leonard Laity *438*

Stonehouse Trust Ltd, Eric *438*

Summerfield Charitable Trust, The *442*

Swan Mountain Trust *444*

Swann-Morton Foundation, The *444*

TSB Foundation for Northern Ireland *447*

Tear Fund *450*

Thackray General Charitable Trust, The P & L *452*

Thornton-Smith Trust, The *455*

Thorpe Charity Trust, The *455*

Tisbury Telegraph Trust, The *457*

Trust for the Homeless *462*

Tudor Trust, The *463*

Van Berchem Charitable Trust, The Alec *470*

Van Leer Foundation UK Trust, Bernard *470*

Variety Club Children's Charity Limited, The *471*

Vec Acorn Trust, The *472*

Wagstaff Charitable Trust, Bob *475*

Wakefield (Tower Hill, Trinity Square) Trust *476*

Wakeham Trust, The *476*

Wallace Charity Trust, The A F *478*

Weir Foundation, The James *484*

Wesleyan Charitable Trust, The *485*

Whitecourt Charitable Trust, The *490*

Wills 1961 Charitable Trust, Mr Frederick *493*

Wimpey Charitable Trust, The George *495*

Wix Charitable Trust, Michael and Anna *497*

Woodlands Trust *501*

Woodroffe Benton Foundation, The *502*

Worshipful Company of Glass Sellers' Charity Trust, The *505*

Yapp Welfare Trust, The *508*

■ Autism

Funding priority

Tudor Trust, The *463*

■ Ballet

see Dance & ballet

■ Baptists

Funding priority

Chownes Foundation, The *93*

Fabry Trust, W F *157*

Strict And Particular Baptist Trust Corporation, The *440*

Timson Family Charitable Trust *457*

Webber Trust Fund, Ethel *483*

■ Bird sanctuaries

see also Animal facilities & services

Funding priority

Carron Charitable Trust, The *83*

Cobb Charity *103*

Coote Animal Charity Fund, The Marjorie *111*

GW Trust, The *176*

Sainsbury Animal Welfare Trust, Jean *401*

Will consider

Ammco Trust, The *15*

Animal Defence Trust, The *18*

Astor Foundation, The *26*

BP Conservation Programme *29*

Barnby's Foundation, Lord *35*

Brotherton Trust, The Charles *65*

Bullough Tompson Settlement, The *68*

Butler Charitable Trust, The A S *71*

Buxton Trust, Denis *72*

CLA Charitable Trust *74*

Community Trust for Greater Manchester, The *108*

Corden Trust, Cyril *113*

Digby Charitable Trust, Simon *133*

Dinam Charity *134*

Dumbreck Charity *139*

Elkes Charity Fund, The Wilfred & Elsie *147*

Evetts & Robert Luff Animal Welfare Trust, Beryl *156*

Ford of Britain Trust *166*

Friends of the Animals *173*

Garnett Charitable Trust, The *178*

Great Britain Sasakawa Foundation, The *193*

Green Memorial Fund, The
Barry *194*
Greenaway Foundation, The Sir
Derek *194*
Holly Hill Charitable Trust *224*
Jarrold Trust Ltd, John *243*
Laing Foundation, The Kirby
261
Laing Foundation, The Maurice
261
Lankelly Foundation, The *264*
Leach Fourteenth Trust, The
267
Lee Foundation, The Edgar
269
Lewis Foundation, The John
Spedan *274*
Lloyd Charity, The S and D *278*
Lowe Trust, Mrs D G *285*
MacKintosh Charitable Trust,
Viscount *292*
Marchig Animal Welfare Trust
297
Marriage's Charitable Trust,
Miss G M *299*
Mitchell Trust *315*
Nathan Charitable Trust, Peter
326
Norman Family Charitable
Trust, The *337*
Oakdale Trust, The *343*
Owen Family Trust, The *348*
Peppiatt Charitable Trust, The
Brian *359*
Perry Charitable Trust, Miss
Frances Lucille *359*
Pilkington Charitable Trust,
Cecil *363*
Richard Charitable Trust, The
Cliff *383*
Sargeant's Charitable Trust,
Mrs M E *407*
Sobell Welsh People's
Charitable Association,
Michael *429*
South Square Trust *430*
3i Charitable Trust, The *455*
Tisbury Telegraph Trust, The
457
Vincent Wildlife Trust, The *473*
Walker 597 Trust, The *477*
Wylde Memorial Charity, The
Anthony and Gwendoline
507
Wyre Animal Welfare *507*
Zaiger Trust, The Elizabeth and
Prince *512*

■ **Blindness**
see Sight loss

■ **Blood disorders &
haemophilia**
Funding priority
Dahl Foundation, The Roald
122
Haemophilia Society, The *202*

■ **Books**
see Costs of study

■ **Botany**
see also Environment &
animal sciences
Funding priority
Cobb Charity *103*
Gatsby Charitable Foundation,
The *179*
Pilkington Charitable Trust,
Cecil *363*
Royal Botanical & Horticultural
Society of Manchester and
the Northern Counties, The
395
Smith (UK) Horticultural Trust,
Stanley *428*

Will consider
Allied Domecq Trust *13*
Ashley Foundation, The Laura
24
Astor Foundation, The *26*
Bentall Charity Trust, Rowan
44
Butler Charitable Trust, The A S
71
Carnegie Dunfermline Trust *82*
Chippindale Foundation, Sam
93
Clark 1965 Charitable Trust,
Stephen *98*
Clutterbuck Charitable Trust,
Robert *102*
Coates Charitable Trust 1969,
Lance *103*
Countryside Trust, The *115*
D'Avigdor Goldsmid Charitable
Trust, The Sarah *125*
Digby Charitable Trust, Simon
133
Earwicker Trust *142*
Great Britain Sasakawa
Foundation, The *193*
Greenaway Foundation, The Sir
Derek *194*
Hayward Foundation, The *213*
Horn Trust, The Cuthbert *227*
Isle of Dogs Community
Foundation *238*
MacRobert Trusts, The *294*
Mattock Charitable Trust, The
W T *302*

Measures Charity, The James
Frederick and Ethel Anne
303
Mitchell Trust *315*
Oldacre Foundation, The John
345
Shaw Foundation, The Linley
416
Summerfield Charitable Trust,
The *442*
Yorkshire Agricultural Society
509
Young Explorers' Trust *511*

■ **Broadcasting**
see Film, video, multimedia,
broadcasting

■ **Buddhists & Jainists**
Funding priority
Shah Trust, The Dr N K *416*

■ **Building services**
see also Infrastructure &
technical support
Funding priority
Homeless International *225*
Hood's Charitable Trust, Sir
Harold *226*
Lyndhurst Trust, The *287*

Will consider
County Durham Foundation
115
Daily Telegraph Charitable
Trust *122*
Digby Charitable Trust, Simon
133
Direct Response *134*
IBM United Kingdom Trust
233
Isle of Dogs Community
Foundation *238*
Laing Foundation, The
Christopher *260*
Licensed Trade Charities Trust,
The *274*
Newby Trust Ltd *332*
Northern Arts *339*
Paristamen Foundation, The
352
Whitaker Charitable Trust *489*

■ **Burial grounds**
see Cemeteries & burial
grounds

■ Bursaries & fees

see also Costs of study

Funding priority

Alcohol Education and
Research Council *9*
Carnegie Trust for the
Universities of Scotland *82*
Company of Chartered
Surveyors Charitable Trust
Fund, The *108*
Dove-Bowerman Trust *137*
Groves Charitable Trust, The
197
Hopkinson Educational Trust,
Robert Addy *227*
Howard Charitable Trust, John
& Ruth *229*
Jeffreys Road Fund, Rees *243*
McCallum Bequest Fund *290*
Neave Trust, The Airey *330*
Needham Cooper Charitable
Trust, The *331*
Newitt Fund, Richard *333*
Oldacre Foundation, The John
345
RVW Trust *374*
Richard III and Yorkist History
Trust *384*
Shipwrights' Company
Educational Trust, The *420*
South Square Trust *430*
Thriplow Charitable Trust *456*
Trades Union Congress
Educational Trust *460*
Van Berchem Charitable Trust,
The Alec *470*

Will consider

Abbeydale Trust *5*
Ammco Trust, The *15*
Arts Council of Wales, The *23*
Ashby Charitable Trust, The *23*
Ashley Foundation, The Laura
24
Beit Trust, The *40*
Bulmer Charitable Trust, Becket
68
Burden Trust, The *69*
Campden Charities, The *79*
Carlton Television Trust *81*
Clinton's Charitable Trust, Lord
100
Cooper Charitable Trust *111*
Cripplegate Foundation *118*
Digby Charitable Trust, Simon
133
Dixon Charitable Trust, F E *134*
Earley Charity, The *142*
Education Services *145*
Emanuel Charitable Settlement,
Ralph and Muriel *150*
Firdale Christian Trust, The *162*
GABO Trust for Sculpture
Conservation *175*
Gelston Charitable Trust, The
179

Goldsmiths' Company's
Charities, The *188*
Hertfordshire Community
Trust, The *217*
Hockerill Educational
Foundation *223*
Holly Hill Charitable Trust *224*
Hudson Benevolent Trust, The
Thomas *230*
Humanitarian Trust, The *230*
Hyde Park Place Estate Charity,
The *232*
Ireland Funds, The *237*
James Charitable Trust, John
241
Lee Foundation, The Edgar
269
Licensed Trade Charities Trust,
The *274*
Mackintosh Foundation, The
292
Milward Charity, The Edgar
313
NR Charitable Trust, The *325*
Newby Trust Ltd *332*
Noswad Charity, The *341*
Oldham Foundation *345*
Owen Family Trust, The *348*
Paristamen Foundation, The
352
Pilkington Charitable Trust,
Cecil *363*
Radcliffe's Trust, Dr *375*
Rainbow Charitable Trust *376*
Rayner Charitable Trust, The
John *380*
Rhodes Trust – Public Purposes
Fund, The *383*
Ripley's Charitable Trust, Pat
386
Rothley Trust, The *392*
Royal Botanical & Horticultural
Society of Manchester and
the Northern Counties, The
395
Royal Commission for the
Exhibition of 1851 *395*
Smallpeice Trust, The *425*
Summerfield Charitable Trust,
The *442*
Tisbury Telegraph Trust, The
457
Wall Trust, Thomas *478*
Wates Foundation, The *481*
Woolmen's Company
Charitable Trust, The *503*

■ Business schools

see also Schools & colleges

Funding priority

Clark Charitable Trust, J
Anthony *98*
Dulverton Trust, The *139*
Foundation for Management
Education *168*

Will consider

Arbib Foundation *20*
Boots Charitable Trust *56*
Dibden Allotments Charity *132*
Digby Charitable Trust, Simon
133
Direct Response *134*
Great Britain Sasakawa
Foundation, The *193*
Hillards Charitable Trust, Gay &
Peter Hartley's *220*
Holly Hill Charitable Trust *224*
Hudson Benevolent Trust, The
Thomas *230*
Lewis Foundation, The John
Spedan *274*
Littler Foundation, The Emile
277
Montefiore Trust, The David
316
Newcomen Collett Foundation
333
Oldham Foundation *345*
St Katharine & Shadwell Trust
404
Thriplow Charitable Trust *456*
Whitehead Charitable Trust, J E
490
Worshipful Company of
Engineers' Charitable Trust
Fund, The *504*

■ Campaigning (health)

see also Health education,
Health issues, Health
promotion

Funding priority

Aga Khan Foundation (UK) *7*
Alexander Charitable Trust,
Mrs K L *11*
Aquinas Trust *20*
Astor of Hever Trust, The *26*
Avins Trustees, The John *28*
Bealey Foundation, The *38*
Beauland Ltd *39*
Beckwith-Smith's Charitable
Settlement, Mrs *40*
Birmingham District Nursing
Charitable Trust *49*
Blakey Charitable Trust, The
Celia and Conrad *53*
Boltons Trust, The *55*
British Diabetic Association,
The *61*
British Heart Foundation *62*
British Sugar Foundation *63*
Brook Charitable Settlement,
R E *64*
Burns Charity, The Dorothy *70*
Carron Charitable Trust, The
83
Carter Trust, The Frederick
William *84*
Cinderford Charitable Trust,
The *96*

Clark Charitable Trust, J
Anthony *98*
Cohen Charitable Trust, The
Vivienne and Samuel *104*
Condon Family Trust *109*
Crawford Children's Charity,
Michael *117*
Crescent Trust, The *117*
Delmar Charitable Trust *129*
Djanogly Foundation, The *135*
D'Oyly Carte Charitable Trust,
The *137*
Dunn Charitable Trust, The
Harry *140*
Elvetham Charitable Trust, The
149
Fry Charitable Trust, Maurice
174
Gibson's Charity Trust, The Hon
Mr & Mrs Clive *182*
Girdlers' Company Charitable
Trust, The *184*
Goodman Charitable
Foundation, The Everard
and Mina *188*
Goodman Trust, The *189*
Gradel Foundation, The *189*
Green Foundation, Constance
194
Greenwood Charitable Trust,
The G B *195*
Hitachi Charitable Trust, The
222
IPE Charitable Trust, The *233*
Jones Trust, Cemlyn *248*
Keyes Trust, The Ursula *253*
Kobler Trust, The *258*
Lacy Charity Trust, The Late Sir
Pierce *260*
Landy Charitable Trust, Harry
and Gertrude *263*
Lanvern Foundation *265*
Lauffer Charitable Foundation,
The R & D *266*
Levy Charitable Foundation,
Joseph *272*
Liffe Benefit *274*
Lucas Charitable Trust Limited,
The Joseph *286*
MacAndrew Trust, The E M
289
MacRobert Trusts, The *294*
Medlock Charitable Trust, The
304
Millichope Foundation, The
312
Minet Trust, The Peter *313*
Moore Charitable Trust, The
Horace *316*
Moulton Charitable Trust, The
321
Newstead Charity, The *334*
Northern Dairies Educational
Trust *339*
Northern Electric Employee
Charity Association *339*
Oppenheimer Charitable Trust
346

Palmer Trust, The Gerald *352*
Pascoe Charitable Trust, Alan
354
Paul Foundation, The *355*
Peskin Charitable Trust, The
Hazel and Leslie *360*
Pick Charitable Trust, The
George and Jessie *362*
Pilkington Trust, The Austin
and Hope *363*
QAS Charitable Trust *373*
Reekie Trust, R A & V B *381*
Richards Charity, The Violet M
384
Robbins Trust, The Cheshire
387
Sherman Charitable Trust, The
Archie *419*
Shifrin Charitable Trust, The
Maurice and Hilda *419*
Taylor Charitable Trust, The B R
450
Valentine Charitable Trust, The
470
Wesleyan Charitable Trust, The
485
Westcroft Trust *486*
Whittington Charitable Trust,
The *491*
Wilde Charitable Trust, The
Felicity *492*
Wohl Charitable Foundation,
The Maurice *498*
Wohl Charitable Trust, The
Maurice *498*
Wolfson Family Charitable
Trust, The *499*
Wolfson Foundation, The *499*
Woodcote Trust, The *501*
Woolf Charitable Trust, The
502

Will consider

AHJ Charitable Trust, The *3*
Achiezer Association Limited *6*
Airflow Community Ltd, The *9*
Aleh Charitable Foundation,
The *10*
Alliance Family Foundation
Limited *13*
Allsop Charitable Trust, Pat *14*
Ammco Trust, The *15*
Anderson Trust, Andrew *16*
Angler's Inn Trust *17*
Appelbe Trust, Ambrose & Ann
19
Arthritis and Rheumatism
Council for Research in
Great Britain and the
Commonwealth, The *22*
Askew Charitable Trust, The
Ian *25*
Askew Trust, The Dorothy *25*
Assembled Church of Christ
Trust, The *25*
Assheton-Smith Charitable
Trust *25*

Asthma Allergy and
Inflammation Research Trust
25
Astor Foundation, The *26*
Astor's 1969 Charity, The Hon
M L *26*
BBC Children in Need Appeal,
The *29*
BUPA Foundation, The *29*
Barbour Trust, The *33*
Baring Foundation, The *34*
Barnby's Foundation, Lord *35*
Barnsbury Charitable Trust *35*
Bateman Charitable Trust, Lady
Margaret *37*
Beckwith Charitable Trust, The
Peter *40*
Bergqvist Charitable Trust *44*
Bilton Charity, The Percy *48*
Black Foundation, The Bertie
51
Blagrave Charitable Trust, The
Herbert and Peter *52*
Blake Charitable Trust, The
Hubert *53*
Blakenham's Charity Trust,
Lady *53*
Blank Donations Ltd, The David
54
Borthwick Memorial Trust, The
Oliver *56*
Bottom Charitable Trust, Harry
56
Bowland Charitable Trust, The
57
Brookhouse's Will Trust, Mr
John Charles *65*
Brough Charitable Trust,
Joseph *65*
Burn Charity Trust, The J H *70*
Burry Charitable Trust, The *70*
Burton Charitable Trust, The
Geoffrey *71*
Butler's Trust, Lord *71*
Butler's Trust, Lucilla *72*
Cadbury Schweppes
Foundation, The *76*
Cardiff & Swansea Methodist
District Charitable Trust
Fund *80*
Castang Charitable Trust, H
and M *85*
Charity Projects *90*
Christian Aid *94*
Closehelm Ltd *101*
Clutterbuck Charitable Trust,
Robert *102*
Coates Charitable Settlement,
The *102*
Coates Charitable Trust 1969,
Lance *103*
Cohen Charity Trust, Lucy *104*
Company of Tobacco Pipe
Makers and Tobacco
Blenders Benevolent Fund
109
Cope Charitable Trust, Alfred
112

Cotton Trust, The *114*
Curry Charitable Trust, Dennis *119*
Cymerman Trust Limited, Itzchok Meyer *120*
Daily Telegraph Charitable Trust *122*
Dandeen Charitable Trust *123*
Davy Foundation, The J *126*
De Avenley Foundation, The *126*
De La Rue Charitable Trust *127*
De Rothschild 1981 Charitable Trust, The Edmund *127*
De Yong Charitable Trust, The Emma *128*
Denton Charitable Trust, The *130*
Desmond Charitable Trust, The Richard *131*
Deutsch Charitable Trust, The Andre *131*
Deutsch Charitable Trust, The H & M *131*
Dicken Charitable Trust, The Albert *133*
Dinam Charity *134*
Doughty Charity Trust, The *136*
Drayton Trust, The *138*
Earmark Trust, The *142*
Edinburgh Trust, No 2 Account *145*
Egerton of Tatton Will Trust, Lord *146*
Eling Trust *147*
Elkes Charity Fund, The Wilfred & Elsie *147*
Elshore Limited *149*
Emmandjay Charitable Trust *150*
Esperanza Charitable Trust, The *153*
Family Trust, The *158*
Famos Foundation Trust *158*
Federation of Jewish Relief Organisations *160*
Fishmongers' Company's Charitable Trust *163*
Foyle Trust, Charles Henry *169*
Franklin Bequest, The Rosalind *169*
Franklin Deceased's New Second Charity, Sydney E *170*
Frazer Charities Trust, The *171*
Frome Christian Fellowship *174*
Galinski Charitable Trust *177*
Garthgwynion Charities *179*
Gillett Charitable Trust, J A *183*
Gill's Charitable Trust, Mrs M M *184*
Gold Hill Church Trust *186*
Goldberg Charitable Trust, The Lewis *186*

Greenaway Foundation, The Sir Derek *194*
Gross Charities Limited, M & R *197*
Grosshill Charitable Trust *197*
Grundy Foundation, The Stanley *198*
Grut Charitable Trust, The *198*
HB Charitable Trust *201*
Hacking & Sons Ltd Charitable Trust, C G *201*
Haemophilia Society, The *202*
Haines Charitable Trust, The Alfred *203*
Hamilton Educational Trust, Eleanor *205*
Harbour Foundation Ltd, The *208*
Hargreaves Trust, The Kenneth *210*
Harvey Charitable Trust, Gordon *211*
Hawley Residuary Fund, Harry Fieldsend *212*
Hawthorne Charitable Trust, The *212*
Heinz Company Limited Charitable Trust, The H J *215*
Held Settlement, The Gisela *215*
Hertfordshire Community Trust, The *217*
Higgs Charitable Trust, The *218*
Hillards Charitable Trust, Gay & Peter Hartley's *220*
Hoover Foundation, The *226*
Horn Trust, The Cuthbert *227*
Hornby Charitable Trust, Miss D *227*
Hornton Trust, The *228*
Hudson Benevolent Trust, The Thomas *230*
Hughes Charitable Trust, The Geoffery C *230*
Hyde Park Place Estate Charity, The *232*
Inman Charity, The *235*
Irving Charitable Trust, The Charles *237*
JCSCJ Charitable Trust, The *238*
James Foundation, The Catherine and Lady Grace *241*
Jarrold Trust Ltd, John *243*
Johnson Foundation, The *246*
Jubilee Outreach Yorkshire *248*
KC Charitable Trust, The *250*
Karten Charitable Trust, The Ian *250*
Kingsgrove Charitable Trust, The *255*
Kinnison Charitable Trust, R O *256*

Kleinwort Charitable Trust, The Ernest *257*
Kreitman Foundation *258*
Kulika Charitable Trust, The *259*
Kweller Charitable Trust, The Harry *259*
Laing Foundation, The Christopher *260*
Lambourne Memorial Trust, The Emma *262*
Langley Charitable Trust, The *264*
Lankelly Foundation, The *264*
Laski Memorial Charitable Trust, Nathan *265*
Laspen Trust *265*
Lavender Trust, The *267*
Lawley Foundation, The Edgar E *267*
Leach Fourteenth Trust, The *267*
Leigh-Bramwell Trust 'E', P *270*
Lewis Family Charitable Trust, The *273*
Lingwood Charitable Trust, The *276*
Livesley 1992 Charitable Trust, Mrs C M *277*
Localtrent Ltd *279*
Low & Bonar Charitable Fund, The *284*
Lunzer Charitable Trust, The Ruth & Jack *287*
Lynwood Charitable Trust, The *288*
Lyons Charitable Trust, The *288*
Lyons Charitable Trust, Sir Jack *288*
MDM Memorial Trust *289*
McKechnie Foundation, A N *292*
McKenzie Trust, The Robert *292*
McLaren Foundation *292*
McLaren Memorial Trust, The Martin *293*
Margadale Charitable Trust, Lord *297*
Margaret Foundation, The *297*
Marks Charitable Trust, Michael *298*
Marks Foundation, The Hilda and Samuel *298*
Markus Charitable Foundation, The Erich *298*
Marriage's Charitable Trust, Miss G M *299*
Marr-Munning Trust *299*
Marshall Charitable Trust, The Charlotte *300*
Martin Trust, The Sir George *300*
Matchan Fund Limited, The Leonard *301*

Material World Charitable Foundation Limited, The 301

Mattock Charitable Trust, The W T 302

Mayfair Charities Limited 303

Medical Aid Trust 304

Mellows Charitable Settlement, The Anthony and Elizabeth 305

Millett Charitable Trust, The Alan and Janet 312

Modiano Charitable Trust 315

Montefiore Trust, The David 316

Moore Stephens Charitable Foundation, The 317

Morel Charitable Trust, The 318

Morgan Crucible Company plc Charitable Trust, The 319

Morphy Memorial Fund, Arthur 319

Morris Charitable Trust, The Willie & Mabel 320

Music Sales Charitable Trust, The 324

Muslim Hands 324

National Lottery Charities Board 328

National Power Charitable Trust, The 330

Newcastle's 1986 Charitable Trust, Duke of 333

Newman Charitable Trust, Mr and Mrs F E F 334

North West Arts Board 337

Northcott Charity Trust, The 338

Northern Ireland Voluntary Trust 339

Nuffield Foundation 342

Old Possums Practical Trust, The 344

Owen Trust, Margaret 348

PDC Trust, The 349

PF Charitable Trust 350

PJD Charitable Trust 350

PPP Healthcare Medical Trust Limited 350

Patients' Aid Association Hospital and Medical Charities Trust 354

Paul Charitable Trust, The Late Barbara May 355

Paul Charitable Trust, Margaret Jeanne 355

Paul Charitable Trust, Pamela Milton 355

Paul's Charitable Trust, R J 355

Payne Charitable Trust, The 355

Pelech Charitable Trust, The 358

Perry Charitable Trust, Miss Frances Lucille 359

Pershore Nashdom & Elmore Trust Ltd, The 360

Personal Assurance Charitable Trust 360

Phillips Charitable Foundation, Reginald M 361

Pilkington Charitable Trust, Cecil 363

Pitt Trust, Headley 364

Porter Foundation 366

Powys Welsh Church Fund 367

Puebla Charitable Trust Limited, The 371

Quothquan Charitable Trust, The Second 373

RT Trust, The 374

Rackham Charitable Trust, The Mr & Mrs Philip 375

Radley Charitable Trust 375

Rae Charity, H J 375

Rainford Trust, The 376

Rav Chesed Trust, The 379

Rayne Foundation, The 379

Reuter Foundation, The 382

Richard Charitable Trust, The Cliff 383

Richards Charity, The Clive 384

Rivendell Trust, The 387

Rodewald's Charitable Settlement, Mr C A 389

Rogers Charitable Settlement, The Richard 390

Rokeby Charitable Trust 390

Rolfe Charitable Trust, The 390

Rosen Foundation, Cecil 392

Rozel Trust, The 397

S Group Charitable Trust 399

Said Foundation, The Karim Rida 401

St Jude's Trust 403

Salters Charities 405

Samuel Charitable Trust, M J 406

Save & Prosper Foundation 409

Scarr-Hall Memorial Trust, The 409

Seva Trust, Rampaba Sadhu 415

Sidbury Trust, The Second 421

Silvester Charitable Gift Trust 422

Skinners' Company Lady Neville Charity 424

Salter Trust Ltd 424

Society of Friends of the Torah, The 429

Solomons Charitable Trust, David 430

Somerfield Curtis Will Trust, The Dorothy 430

Stanley Foundation Limited 435

Stewart Charitable Trust, Mary Stephanie 437

Street Charitable Foundation, W O 440

Sumner's Trust Section 'A', Sir John 443

Swann-Morton Foundation, The 444

Symons Charitable Trust, The Stella 446

TSB Foundation for Scotland 447

TSB Foundation for the Channel Islands 447

Terry Charitable Trust, Noel Goddard 451

Tesco Charity Trust 452

Tesler Foundation, The 452

Thompson Charitable Trust, The 453

3i Charitable Trust, The 455

Toler Foundation, The 457

Toyota (GB) Charitable Trust, The 459

Travis Charitable Trust, Constance 460

Tyne & Wear Foundation 466

Upjohn Charitable Trust, The 469

van Geest Foundation, The John and Lucille 470

Van Norden's Charitable Foundation, Mrs Maud 471

Vineyard Christian Fellowship of South West 473

Vinson Charity Trust, The 1969 473

Vogel Charitable Trust, The Nathan 474

Wakefield Trust, The 476

Wander Charitable Fund, The Dr Albert 479

War on Want 479

Ward Blenkinsop Trust, The 480

Weinstock Fund, The 484

Welby Trust, The Barbara 484

Whetherly's Charitable Trust, The Hon Mrs R G A 489

White Rose Children's Aid International Charity 489

Whitehead Charitable Trust, J E 490

Wiggins Charity Trust, Cyril 491

Wills 1961 Charitable Trust, Major Michael Thomas 494

Wiltshire Community Foundation 495

Woburn 1986 Charitable Trust 498

Wolff Charity Trust 498

Woods Charitable Foundation, Geoffrey 502

Worms Charitable Trust, The Freda and Della 504

Worshipful Company of Needlemakers' Charitable Fund 505

Wychdale Limited 507

Youell Foundation Ltd, The 510

Zaiger Trust, The Elizabeth and Prince 512

■ Campaigning (social issues)

see also Community issues, Development proposals, Gay & lesbian rights, International rights of the individual, Penal reform, Racial equality, discrimination, relations, Transport proposals, Unborn children's rights

Funding priority

Allied Dunbar Charitable Trust Limited, The *13*
Anderson Trust, Andrew *16*
Cadbury Trust, The Barrow *76*
Condon Family Trust *109*
Fairbairn Charitable Trust, The Esmee *157*
Franklin Trust, Jill *170*
Green Foundation, Constance *194*
Hacking & Sons Ltd Charitable Trust, C G *201*
Jones Trust, Cemlyn *248*
Lester Trust Fund, The *271*
Melchett Children's Trust, The Violet *305*
Millfield House Foundation *312*
Northern Ireland Voluntary Trust *339*
Paget Trust, The *351*
Pelly Charitable Settlement, The Joanne *358*
Polden-Puckham Charitable Foundation, The *365*
Rodewald's Charitable Settlement, Mr C A *389*
Rowan Charitable Trust, The *393*
Swan Mountain Trust *444*
War on Want *479*
West Midlands Regional Arts Board *486*
Westcroft Trust *486*

Will consider

AB Charitable Trust *3*
AHJ Charitable Trust, The *3*
Achiezer Association Limited *6*
Aga Khan Foundation (UK) *7*
Airflow Community Ltd, The *9*
Ajahma Charitable Trust, The *9*
Aleh Charitable Foundation, The *10*
Angler's Inn Trust *17*
Appelbe Trust, Ambrose & Ann *19*
Aquinas Trust *20*
Askew Charitable Trust, The Ian *25*
Assembled Church of Christ Trust, The *25*
Astor of Hever Trust, The *26*

Astor's 1969 Charity, The Hon M L *26*
Austin of Longbridge Will Trust, The Rt Hon Herbert, Baron *27*
BBC Children in Need Appeal, The *29*
Baring Foundation, The *34*
Barnabas Charitable Trust *34*
Barnby's Foundation, Lord *35*
Barnsbury Charitable Trust *35*
Barton Trust, Eleanor *37*
Bateman Charitable Trust, Lady Margaret *37*
Bealey Foundation, The *38*
Beckwith Charitable Trust, The Peter *40*
Beckwith-Smith's Charitable Settlement, Mrs *40*
Bergqvist Charitable Trust *44*
Bilton Charity, The Percy *48*
Black Foundation, The Bertie *51*
Blagrave Charitable Trust, The Herbert and Peter *52*
Blakenham's Charity Trust, Lady *53*
Blakey Charitable Trust, The Celia and Conrad *53*
Blank Donations Ltd, The David *54*
Boltons Trust, The *55*
Borthwick Memorial Trust, The Oliver *56*
Bottom Charitable Trust, Harry *56*
Bowland Charitable Trust, The *57*
Brand Trust, The *59*
British Sugar Foundation *63*
Brook Charitable Settlement, R E *64*
Brookhouse's Will Trust, Mr John Charles *65*
Burn Charity Trust, The J H *70*
Burns Charity, The Dorothy *70*
Burry Charitable Trust, The *70*
Burton Charitable Trust, The Geoffrey *71*
Butler's Trust, Lord *71*
Butler's Trust, Lucilla *72*
Buxton Trust, Denis *72*
Cadbury Schweppes Foundation, The *76*
Cardiff & Swansea Methodist District Charitable Trust Fund *80*
Carron Charitable Trust, The *83*
Castang Charitable Trust, H and M *85*
Charity Projects *90*
Chippindale Foundation, Sam *93*
Christian Aid *94*
Church Urban Fund *95*
Cinderford Charitable Trust, The *96*

Clark Charitable Trust, J Anthony *98*
Closehelm Ltd *101*
Clutterbuck Charitable Trust, Robert *102*
Coates Charitable Settlement, The *102*
Coates Charitable Trust 1969, Lance *103*
Cohen Charitable Trust, The Vivienne and Samuel *104*
Cohen Charity Trust, Lucy *104*
Company of Tobacco Pipe Makers and Tobacco Blenders Benevolent Fund *109*
Cope Charitable Trust, Alfred *112*
Cotton Trust, The *114*
Crescent Trust, The *117*
Curry Charitable Trust, Dennis *119*
Cymerman Trust Limited, Itzchok Meyer *120*
Daily Telegraph Charitable Trust *122*
Dandeen Charitable Trust *123*
David Trust, The Lesley *124*
Davy Foundation, The J *126*
De Avenley Foundation, The *126*
De La Rue Charitable Trust *127*
De Rothschild 1981 Charitable Trust, The Edmund *127*
De Yong Charitable Trust, The Emma *128*
Denby Charitable Foundation, The *130*
Denton Charitable Trust, The *130*
Desmond Charitable Trust, The Richard *131*
Deutsch Charitable Trust, The Andre *131*
Deutsch Charitable Trust, The H & M *131*
Dicken Charitable Trust, The Albert *133*
Dinam Charity *134*
Djanogly Foundation, The *135*
Doughty Charity Trust, The *136*
D'Oyly Carte Charitable Trust, The *137*
Drayton Trust, The *138*
Dulverton Trust, The *139*
Dunn Charitable Trust, The Harry *140*
Earmark Trust, The *142*
Edinburgh Trust, No 2 Account *145*
Eling Trust *147*
Elshore Limited *149*
Elvetham Charitable Trust, The *149*
Family Trust, The *158*
Famos Foundation Trust *158*

Federation of Jewish Relief
Organisations *160*
Foreman Foundation, The Carl
& Eve *167*
Foyle Trust, Charles Henry *169*
Franklin Bequest, The Rosalind
169
Franklin Deceased's New
Second Charity, Sydney E
170
Friarsgate Trust *172*
Frome Christian Fellowship
174
Fry Charitable Trust, Maurice
174
Galinski Charitable Trust *177*
Gibson's Charity Trust, The Hon
Mr & Mrs Clive *182*
Gillett Charitable Trust, J A
183
Gill's Charitable Trust, Mrs M M
184
Girdlers' Company Charitable
Trust, The *184*
Glynde Place Charitable Trust
(1974), The *186*
Gold Hill Church Trust *186*
Goldberg Charitable Trust, The
Lewis *186*
Goodman Charitable
Foundation, The Everard
and Mina *188*
Goodman Trust, The *189*
Goodman Trust, The S & F *189*
Gradel Foundation, The *189*
Gross Charities Limited, M & R
197
Grut Charitable Trust, The *198*
Gulbenkian Foundation
(Lisbon) United Kingdom
Branch, Calouste *199*
Gwent County Council Welsh
Church Fund *200*
HB Charitable Trust *201*
Hamilton Educational Trust,
Eleanor *205*
Harbour Foundation Ltd, The
208
Harvey Charitable Trust,
Gordon *211*
Hawthorne Charitable Trust,
The *212*
Heinz Company Limited
Charitable Trust, The H J
215
Held Settlement, The Gisela
215
Hillards Charitable Trust, Gay &
Peter Hartley's *220*
Hitachi Charitable Trust, The
222
Holford Trust Fund *224*
Hoover Foundation, The *226*
Horn Trust, The Cuthbert *227*
Hornby Charitable Trust, Miss
D *227*
Hornton Trust, The *228*

Hospital of God at Greatham ,
The *229*
Hughes Charitable Trust, The
Geoffery C *230*
IPE Charitable Trust, The *233*
Inman Charity, The *235*
Isle of Dogs Community
Foundation *238*
James Foundation, The
Catherine and Lady Grace
241
KC Charitable Trust, The *250*
Karten Charitable Trust, The
Ian *250*
Keyes Trust, The Ursula *253*
Kingsgrove Charitable Trust,
The *255*
Kinnison Charitable Trust, R O
256
Kleinwort Charitable Trust, The
Ernest *257*
Kobler Trust, The *258*
Kreitman Foundation *258*
Kulika Charitable Trust, The
259
Kweller Charitable Trust, The
Harry *259*
Landy Charitable Trust, Harry
and Gertrude *263*
Langley Charitable Trust, The
264
Lanvern Foundation *265*
Laski Memorial Charitable
Trust, Nathan *265*
Lauffer Charitable Foundation,
The R & D *266*
Lavender Trust, The *267*
Lawley Foundation, The Edgar
E *267*
Leigh-Bramwell Trust 'E', P *270*
Levy Charitable Foundation,
Joseph *272*
Lewis Family Charitable Trust,
The *273*
Liffe Benefit *274*
Lingwood Charitable Trust, The
276
Localtrent Ltd *279*
Lucas Charitable Trust Limited,
The Joseph *286*
Lunzer Charitable Trust, The
Ruth & Jack *287*
Lynwood Charitable Trust, The
288
Lyons Charitable Trust, The
288
Lyons Charitable Trust, Sir Jack
288
MDM Memorial Trust *289*
MacAndrew Trust, The E M
289
Maccabi Foundation, The *290*
McKechnie Foundation, A N
292
McKenzie Trust, The Robert
292
McLaren Foundation *292*

McLaren Memorial Trust, The
Martin *293*
MacRobert Trusts, The *294*
Margadale Charitable Trust,
Lord *297*
Marks Charitable Trust,
Michael *298*
Markus Charitable Foundation,
The Erich *298*
Marr-Munning Trust *299*
Marshall Charitable Trust, The
Charlotte *300*
Martin Trust, The Sir George
300
Matchan Fund Limited, The
Leonard *301*
Material World Charitable
Foundation Limited, The
301
Mattock Charitable Trust, The
W T *302*
Mayfair Charities Limited *303*
Medlock Charitable Trust, The
304
Mellows Charitable Settlement,
The Anthony and Elizabeth
305
Mid Moss Charitable Trust, The
309
Millett Charitable Trust, The
Alan and Janet *312*
Millichope Foundation, The
312
Modiano Charitable Trust *315*
Montefiore Trust, The David
316
Moore Charitable Trust, The
Horace *316*
Morgan Crucible Company plc
Charitable Trust, The *319*
Morris Charitable Trust, The
Willie & Mabel *320*
Moulton Charitable Trust, The
321
Music Sales Charitable Trust,
The *324*
National Lottery Charities
Board *328*
Newcastle Children's Mission &
Institute *333*
Newcastle's 1986 Charitable
Trust, Duke of *333*
Newman Charitable Trust, Mr
and Mrs F E F *334*
Newstead Charity, The *334*
Norman Trust, The *337*
Northcott Charity Trust, The
338
Northern Arts *339*
Northern Dairies Educational
Trust *339*
Northern Electric Employee
Charity Association *339*
Old Possums Practical Trust,
The *344*
Oldham Foundation *345*
Oppenheimer Charitable Trust
346

Owen Trust, Margaret *348*
PDC Trust, The *349*
PJD Charitable Trust *350*
Palmer Trust, The Gerald *352*
Paristamen Foundation, The *352*
Pascoe Charitable Trust, Alan *354*
Paul Charitable Trust, The Late Barbara May *355*
Paul Charitable Trust, Margaret Jeanne *355*
Paul Charitable Trust, Pamela Milton *355*
Paul Foundation, The *355*
Paul's Charitable Trust, R J *355*
Payne Charitable Trust, The *355*
Pelech Charitable Trust, The *358*
Perry Charitable Trust, Miss Frances Lucille *359*
Pershore Nashdom & Elmore Trust Ltd, The *360*
Peskin Charitable Trust, The Hazel and Leslie *360*
Phillips Charitable Foundation, Reginald M *361*
Pilkington Charitable Trust, Cecil *363*
Pitt Trust, Headley *364*
Powys Welsh Church Fund *367*
QAS Charitable Trust *373*
Quothquan Charitable Trust, The Second *373*
RT Trust, The *374*
Rackham Charitable Trust, The Mr & Mrs Philip *375*
Radley Charitable Trust *375*
Rae Charity, H J *375*
Rav Chesed Trust, The *379*
Reekie Trust, R A & V B *381*
Rest-Harrow Trust, The *382*
Reuter Foundation, The *382*
Richards Charity, The Clive *384*
Richmond Parish Lands Charity *384*
Riley-Smith Charitable Trust, The F A *386*
Rivendell Trust, The *387*
Robbins Trust, The Cheshire *387*
Rogers Charitable Settlement, The Richard *390*
Rolfe Charitable Trust, The *390*
Rope Third Charitable Settlement, The Mrs *391*
Rosen Foundation, Cecil *392*
S Group Charitable Trust *399*
St Jude's Trust *403*
Samuel Charitable Trust, M J *406*
Save & Prosper Foundation *409*
Scarr-Hall Memorial Trust, The *409*
Scott Charitable Trust, The Francis C *412*

Seva Trust, Rampaba Sadhu *415*
Shepherd Family Charitable Trust, The Sir Peter *418*
Sherman Charitable Trust, The Archie *419*
Shifrin Charitable Trust, The Maurice and Hilda *419*
Shine No 2 Charitable Trust, The Barnett and Sylvia *420*
Shuttlewood Clarke Foundation, The *421*
Sidbury Trust, The Second *421*
Silvester Charitable Gift Trust *422*
Singer Foundation *423*
Salter Trust Ltd *424*
Society of Friends of the Torah, The *429*
Solomons Charitable Trust, David *430*
Somerfield Curtis Will Trust, The Dorothy *430*
Stanley Foundation Limited *435*
Stewart Charitable Trust, Mary Stephanie *437*
Street Charitable Foundation, W O *440*
TSB Foundation for the Channel Islands *447*
Taylor Charitable Trust, The B R *450*
Terry Charitable Trust, Noel Goddard *451*
Tesco Charity Trust *452*
Tesler Foundation, The *452*
Unitek Foundation *469*
van Geest Foundation, The John and Lucille *470*
Van Norden's Charitable Foundation, Mrs Maud *471*
Vineyard Christian Fellowship of South West *473*
Vinson Charity Trust, The 1969 *473*
Vogel Charitable Trust, The Nathan *474*
Wakefield Trust, The *476*
Ward Blenkinsop Trust, The *480*
Weinstock Fund, The *484*
Whetherly's Charitable Trust, The Hon Mrs R G A *489*
Whitehead Charitable Trust, J E *490*
Whittington Charitable Trust, The *491*
Wiggins Charity Trust, Cyril *491*
Wilde Charitable Trust, The Felicity *492*
Wiltshire Community Foundation *495*
Woburn 1986 Charitable Trust *498*
Wohl Charitable Foundation, The Maurice *498*

Wohl Charitable Trust, The Maurice *498*
Wolff Charity Trust *498*
Wolfson Family Charitable Trust, The *499*
Woods Charitable Foundation, Geoffrey *502*
Worms Charitable Trust, The Freda and Della *504*
Worshipful Company of Needlemakers' Charitable Fund *505*
Wychdale Limited *507*
Youell Foundation Ltd, The *510*
Zaiger Trust, The Elizabeth and Prince *512*

....
■ Cancer research

see also **Medical studies & research**

Funding priority
Ammco Trust, The *15*
Ashby Charitable Trust, The *23*
Assheton-Smith Charitable Trust *25*
Beckwith Charitable Settlement, The Heather *39*
Breast Cancer Research Trust, The *59*
Cancer Research Campaign *80*
Denton Charitable Trust, The *130*
Dimbleby Cancer Fund, The Richard *134*
Earmark Trust, The *142*
Edgar Trust, The Gilbert *145*
Emmandjay Charitable Trust *150*
Fane Research Trust, The Edmund *159*
Firdale Christian Trust, The *162*
Flanagan Leukaemia Fund, Bud *164*
Fogel Charitable Trust, The Gerald *165*
Garnett's 1973 Charitable Trust, Mrs A M *178*
Garthgwynion Charities *179*
Gilley Charitable Trust, The L & R *183*
HB Charitable Trust *201*
Hawthorne Charitable Trust, The *212*
Heath Charitable Trust *214*
Hill Memorial Trust, L E *219*
Hodge Charitable Trust, The Sir Julian *223*
Hodge Foundation, The Jane *223*
Hornby Charitable Trust, Miss D *227*
Humphreys Charitable Settlement, J A M *231*
Hutchinson Charitable Trust, E B *232*

Kroch Foundation, The Heinz & Anna 259
Lawson Charitable Trust, Raymond and Blanche 267
Lewis Family Charitable Trust 273
Lowenthal Charitable Trust, The L and C 285
Lynall Foundation, The D G 287
Man of the People Fund 295
Melville Trust for Care and Cure of Cancer 305
North West Cancer Research Fund 338
Noswad Charity, The 341
Owen Trust, Margaret 348
Pratt Charitable Trust, The W L 367
Prophit, Charity of James Maxwell Grant 370
Pryor Charitable Trust, The John 370
Roberts Charitable Trust, F G 388
Sargeant's Charitable Trust, Mrs M E 407
Silvester Charitable Gift Trust 422
Sportsman's Aid Charity Ltd, The 434
Summer's and I May's Charitable Settlement, The Late Misses (A N) 442
Tenovus – The Cancer Charity 451
Tyneside Leukaemia Research Association, The 466
Webber Trust Fund, Ethel 483
Whetherly's Charitable Trust, The Hon Mrs R G A 489

Will consider
Anstey Charitable Settlement, J C W 18
Arbib Foundation 20
Archer Trust, The 20
Astor Foundation, The 26
Avenal 27
Avon Trust, The 28
Aylesfield Foundation, The 28
Balney Charitable Trust, The 32
Bancroft Trust, The 33
Barbour Trust, The 33
Barratt Charitable Trust, The Elaine 36
Bourne-May Charitable Trust, The 57
Broadley Charitable Trust, The 64
Buckinghamshire Masonic Centenary Fund 67
Cadbury Trust (1928), The Edward & Dorothy 76
Cancer Relief Macmillan Fund 79

Chownes Foundation, The 93
Clarke Charitable Settlement, The 99
Clinton's Charitable Trust, Lord 100
Coates Charitable Trust, The John 103
Cottingham Charitable Trust, Mrs Diana Mary 114
Coutts Charitable Trust, The 116
Denne Charitable Trust 130
Digby Charitable Trust, Simon 133
Direct Response 134
Dorus Trust 136
Early's Charitable Settlement, Richard 142
Edgar Foundation, The Gilbert and Eileen 145
Elkes Charity Fund, The Wilfred & Elsie 147
Emmaus Christian Foundation 150
Epigoni Trust 152
Eventhall Family Charitable Trust, The 155
Fleming Charitable Trust, The Ian 164
Gluckstein Charitable Settlement, The Penelope 185
Glynde Place Charitable Trust (1974), The 186
Graham Charitable Trust, Reginald 190
Grant Foundation, The Raymond 191
Gray Charitable Trust, R B 192
Great Britain Sasakawa Foundation, The 193
Greenaway Foundation, The Alan 194
Greenaway Foundation, The Sir Derek 194
Hannay Charitable Trust, Lennox 208
Harford Charitable Trust 209
Haywood Charitable Trust 214
Henderson's Settlement, J R 216
Hunter Charitable Trust, The Claire 231
Jarman Charitable Trust, The 243
Kiln Charitable Trust, Robert 254
Kyte Charitable Trust, The 259
Laing Charitable Trust, The David 260
Lee Foundation, The Edgar 269
Leech Charity, The William 269
Linmardon Trust 276
London Law Trust 280
Lowe Trust, Mrs D G 285
MacKintosh Charitable Trust, Viscount 292

Mackintosh Foundation, The 292
Manning Trust, Leslie & Lilian 296
Milburn Charitable Trust, Frederick 310
Needham Cooper Charitable Trust, The 331
New Court Charitable Trust 332
Newby Trust Ltd 332
Norman Family Charitable Trust, The 337
Oakdale Trust, The 343
Owen Family Trust, The 348
Peppiatt Charitable Trust, The Brian 359
Persula Foundation, The 360
Ravenscroft Foundation, The 379
Rest-Harrow Trust, The 382
St Christopher's Trust, The 402
Schuster Charitable Trust, The 410
Shepherd Charitable Trust, The Sylvia and Colin 418
South Square Trust 430
Sussman Charitable Trust, Adrienne & Leslie 443
Sykes Trust, The Charles 445
Tisbury Telegraph Trust, The 457
Toy Trust, The 459
Travis Charitable Trust, Constance 460
Will Charitable Trust, The 492
Wingfield's Charitable Trust, Mrs 496
Wolfe Family's Charitable Trust, The 498
Woolmen's Company Charitable Trust, The 503
Woolton Charitable Trust, The 503
Worshipful Company of Engineers' Charitable Trust Fund, The 504

■ **Cancers**
Funding priority
Archer Trust, The 20
Ballinger Charitable Trust, The 32
Balney Charitable Trust, The 32
Breast Cancer Research Trust, The 59
Cancer Relief Macmillan Fund 79
Cancer Research Campaign 80
Chownes Foundation, The 93
Denton Charitable Trust, The 130
Dimbleby Cancer Fund, The Richard 134
Earmark Trust, The 142

Flanagan Leukaemia Fund, Bud *164*

Fleming Charitable Trust, The Ian *164*

Franklin Trust, Jill *170*

Garnett's 1973 Charitable Trust, Mrs A M *178*

HB Charitable Trust *201*

Harbinson Charitable Trust, Roderick *208*

Hornby Charitable Trust, Miss D *227*

Hutchinson Charitable Trust, E B *232*

Kendall Leukaemia Fund, Kay *252*

Lowenthal Charitable Trust, The L and C *285*

Mackintosh Foundation, The *292*

Melville Trust for Care and Cure of Cancer *305*

North West Cancer Research Fund *338*

Prophit, Charity of James Maxwell Grant *370*

RT Trust, The *374*

Rest-Harrow Trust, The *382*

St Christopher's Trust, The *402*

Summer's and I May's Charitable Settlement, The Late Misses (A N) *442*

Tyneside Leukaemia Research Association, The *466*

■ Care for carers

see **Respite care, care for carers**

■ Care in the community

see also **Community services**

Funding priority

AB Charitable Trust *3*

Alexandra Trust *11*

Army Benevolent Fund, The *22*

Avon Trust, The *28*

Beit Trust, The *40*

Berkshire Community Trust *45*

Chrimes Family Charitable Trust, The *93*

Cloudesley's Charity/School Parents & Friends Association, Richard *102*

Community Trust for Greater Manchester, The *108*

County Durham Foundation *115*

Coutts Charitable Trust, The *116*

Curriers Company Charitable Fund *119*

Dahl Foundation, The Roald *122*

David Trust, The Lesley *124*

Derbyshire Trust, J N *130*

Eaton Fund for Artists, Nurses and Gentlewomen *144*

Eventhall Family Charitable Trust, The *155*

Fletcher Trust, Roy *165*

Gatsby Charitable Foundation, The *179*

Grant Foundation, The Raymond *191*

HACT (The Housing Association's Charitable Trust) *201*

Harford Charitable Trust *209*

Hartley Memorial Trust, The N & P *211*

Hayward Foundation, The *213*

Home Housing Trust *225*

Hudson Benevolent Trust, The Thomas *230*

Humphreys Charitable Settlement, J A M *231*

Hyde Charitable Trust *232*

Johnson Group Cleaners Charity *247*

King Charitable Trust, The Lorna *254*

Kroch Foundation, The Heinz & Anna *259*

Lloyd's Charities Trust *278*

Margaret Foundation, The *297*

Mental Health Foundation, The *305*

Merchant Taylors' Consolidated Charities for the Infirm *306*

National Power Charitable Trust, The *330*

Nunburnholme Trust, The Incorporated Trustees of the *342*

Oldham Foundation *345*

Paterson Charitable Foundation, The Constance *354*

Paterson Charitable Trust, Arthur James *354*

Robinson Brothers (Ryders Green) Ltd, Charitable Trust *388*

Rocket Club Benevolent Fund, The *389*

Royal Theatrical Fund, The *396*

SMB Trust, The *400*

Skerritt Trust *423*

Swan Mountain Trust *444*

TSB Foundation for Scotland *447*

Wakeham Trust, The *476*

Wates Foundation, The *481*

Whitaker Charitable Trust *489*

Wiltshire Community Foundation *495*

Will consider

Abbey National Charitable Trust *4*

Abel Charitable Trust *5*

Alexis Trust, The *11*

Ammco Trust, The *15*

Anstey Charitable Settlement, J C W *18*

Aquarius Charitable Foundation, The *19*

Archer Trust, The *20*

Ashley Foundation, The Laura *24*

Askew Trust, The Dorothy *25*

Astor Foundation, The *26*

Aylesfield Foundation, The *28*

Bancroft Trust, The *33*

Barbour Trust, The *33*

Barratt Charitable Trust, The Elaine *36*

Barrie Charitable Trust, The Misses *36*

Berris Charitable Trust *45*

Betard Bequest *46*

Blackburn Trust, The *51*

Blakenham's Charity Trust, Lady *53*

Boots Charitable Trust *56*

Bowland Charitable Trust, The *57*

Bridge Trust, The *60*

Brighton & Hove Charitable Youth Trust *60*

Brooke Benevolent Fund, William *65*

Brough Charitable Trust, Joseph *65*

Buckinghamshire Masonic Centenary Fund *67*

Burdall Charity, H M *69*

Burton 1960 Charitable Settlement, Audrey & Stanley *70*

Butlin Charity Trust, Bill *72*

CLA Charitable Trust *74*

Cadbury Charitable Trust (Incorporated), Edward *75*

Camelot Foundation, The *78*

Campden Charities, The *79*

Cathedral Nursing Society Charitable Trust *85*

Catto Charitable Settlement, The Thomas Sivewright *86*

Challice Trust, The *87*

Clark 1965 Charitable Trust, Stephen *98*

Cleopatra Trust *99*

Clifford Charity Oxford, The *100*

Clinton's Charitable Trust, Lord *100*

Curzon Charitable Trust, The Wallace *120*

Debtors' Relief Fund Charity *128*

Denne Charitable Trust *130*

Digby Charitable Trust, Simon *133*

Direct Response *134*
Dorus Trust *136*
Dumbreck Charity *139*
Early's Charitable Settlement, Richard *142*
Earwicker Trust *142*
Edgar Foundation, The Gilbert and Eileen *145*
Edgar Trust, The Gilbert *145*
Education Services *145*
Egerton of Tatton Will Trust, Lord *146*
Elkes Charity Fund, The Wilfred & Elsie *147*
Emanuel Charitable Settlement, Ralph and Muriel *150*
Emmandjay Charitable Trust *150*
Emmaus Christian Foundation *150*
Epigoni Trust *152*
Ferguson Benevolent Fund Limited *161*
Fishmongers' Company's Charitable Trust *163*
Fogel Charitable Trust, The Gerald *165*
Follett Trust, The *166*
Four Winds Trust *168*
Franklin Trust, Jill *170*
Gardner Charitable Trust, R & J *178*
Garnett Charitable Trust, The *178*
Gelston Charitable Trust, The *179*
Gibbins Trust, The *181*
Great Britain Sasakawa Foundation, The *193*
Greenaway Foundation, The Sir Derek *194*
Griffiths Trust, The E E and D M *196*
Grocers' Charity *197*
Grosshill Charitable Trust *197*
Halkes Settlement, John Robert *204*
Harding's Charity, William *209*
Heath Charitable Trust *214*
Henderson's Settlement, J R *216*
Hertfordshire Community Trust, The *217*
Homfray Trust, The *226*
Ibbett Trust, The *233*
Ingles Charitable Trust, The *234*
Iris Trust, The *237*
Isle of Dogs Community Foundation *238*
JDM Charitable Trust *239*
Jarrold Trust Ltd, John *243*
Johnson Foundation, The *246*
King Charitable Settlement, Philip *254*
Knott Trust, Sir James *258*
Kyte Charitable Trust, The *259*

Laing Foundation, The Christopher *260*
Laing Trust, Beatrice *261*
Lancaster's Trust, Bryan *263*
Lane Foundation, The Allen *263*
Lankelly Foundation, The *264*
Lawson Charitable Trust, Raymond and Blanche *267*
Leach Fourteenth Trust, The *267*
League of the Helping Hand, The *268*
Leech Charity, The William *269*
Lewis Partnership, John *274*
Licensed Trade Charities Trust, The *274*
Linmardon Trust *276*
(Lloyds) TSB Foundation for England and Wales *279*
Lowe Trust, Mrs D G *285*
Luke Trust, The *286*
Lynall Foundation, The D G *287*
Lyndhurst Settlement *287*
MacKintosh Charitable Trust, Viscount *292*
Mackintosh Foundation, The *292*
Manning Trust, Leslie & Lilian *296*
Marchday Charitable Fund, The *296*
Measures Charity, The James Frederick and Ethel Anne *303*
Metropolitan Hospital-Sunday Fund, The *308*
Milburn Charitable Trust, Frederick *310*
Multithon Trust, The *323*
Music for World Development *323*
NR Charitable Trust, The *325*
Natwest Staff Samaritan Fund *330*
Needham Cooper Charitable Trust, The *331*
New Court Charitable Trust *332*
Newby Trust Ltd *332*
Noah Trust, The *335*
Norfolk's Family Charitable Trust, Lavinia *336*
Norman Family Charitable Trust, The *337*
North British Hotel Trust *337*
Northcott Devon Foundation *338*
Norton Foundation, The *340*
Oakdale Trust, The *343*
Owen Family Trust, The *348*
PF Charitable Trust *350*
Paget Trust, The *351*
Parivar Trust, The *353*
Patients' Aid Association Hospital and Medical Charities Trust *354*

Payne Trust, The Harry *356*
Persula Foundation, The *360*
Pilkington Trust, The Austin and Hope *363*
Powell Foundation, The *367*
Pratt Charitable Trust, The W L *367*
Pye Christian Trust, The *371*
Pyke Charity Trust *372*
Rayner Charitable Trust, The John *380*
Rest-Harrow Trust, The *382*
Richard Charitable Trust, The Cliff *383*
Rope Third Charitable Settlement, The Mrs *391*
Rowbotham Charitable Trust, The Christopher *393*
Rowntree Foundation, Joseph *394*
St Christopher's Trust, The *402*
Saint Edmund King and Martyr Trust *402*
Saint Sarkis Charity Trust *404*
Sheepdrove Trust, The *417*
Sheldon Trust, The *417*
Shelroy Charitable Trust, The *417*
Shepherd Charitable Trust, The Sylvia and Colin *418*
Shepherd Family Charitable Trust, The Sir Peter *418*
Skelton Bounty, The *423*
Slater Foundation Ltd, The *424*
Smith & Mount Trust, The Mrs *426*
South Square Trust *430*
Sparkhill Trust, The *433*
Stoate Charitable Trust, The Leonard Laity *438*
Stonehouse Trust Ltd, Eric *438*
Summerfield Charitable Trust, The *442*
Summer's and I May's Charitable Settlement, The Late Misses (A N) *442*
Sussman Charitable Trust, Adrienne & Leslie *443*
TSB Foundation for Northern Ireland *447*
Thackray General Charitable Trust, The P & L *452*
Thomson Foundation, The Sue *454*
Torquay Charities, The *458*
Towler Charity Trust, The Fred *459*
Travis Charitable Trust, Constance *460*
Tudor Trust, The *463*
Tyne & Wear Foundation *466*
Upjohn Charitable Trust, The *469*
Van Berchem Charitable Trust, The Alec *470*
Victoria & Johnson Memorial Trust, Queen *472*

Wakefield (Tower Hill, Trinity Square) Trust *476*
Wall Trust, Thomas *478*
Wander Charitable Fund, The Dr Albert *479*
Webber Trust Fund, Ethel *483*
Wesleyan Charitable Trust, The *485*
Westcroft Trust *486*
Whitecourt Charitable Trust, The *490*
Wills 1961 Charitable Trust, Mr Frederick *493*
Wingate Foundation, The Harold Hyam *496*
Wolfe Family's Charitable Trust, The *498*
Women Caring Trust, The *500*
Woodlands Trust *501*
Worshipful Company of Glass Sellers' Charity Trust, The *505*
Yorkshire Bank Charitable Trust, The *510*

■ Care services
see Community services

■ Carers

Funding priority
Ammco Trust, The *15*
Archer Trust, The *20*
Cobb Charity *103*
Essex Radio Helping Hands Trust, The *154*
Franklin Trust, Jill *170*
GW Trust, The *176*
Hampstead Wells and Campden Trust *206*
Hertfordshire Community Trust, The *217*
Hiley Trust, Joseph and Mary *219*
Johnson Group Cleaners Charity *247*
League of the Helping Hand, The *268*
(Lloyds) TSB Foundation for England and Wales *279*
Meridian Broadcasting Charitable Trust *307*
Moores Foundation, John *318*
Paget Trust, The *351*
Sainsbury Charitable Fund Ltd, The *402*
Swale Charity Trust *443*
TSB Foundation for Scotland *447*
Van Berchem Charitable Trust, The Alec *470*
Wakeham Trust, The *476*
Wiltshire Community Foundation *495*

Will consider
Abbey National Charitable Trust *4*
Adnams Charity, The *7*
Andrew Charitable Trust, The Prince *16*
Ashley Foundation, The Laura *24*
Astor Foundation, The *26*
Ballinger Charitable Trust, The *32*
Bancroft Trust, The *33*
Barbour Trust, The *33*
Barratt Charitable Trust, The Elaine *36*
Barrie Charitable Trust, The Misses *36*
Beckwith Charitable Settlement, The Heather *39*
Bell Charitable Trust, John *41*
Bentall Charity Trust, Rowan *44*
Berris Charitable Trust *45*
Bewley Charitable Trust, The *46*
Birtwistle Memorial Trust, The G E *50*
Blake Charitable Trust, The Morgan *53*
Boots Charitable Trust *56*
Bowring (Charities Fund) Ltd, C T *57*
Brotherton Trust, The Charles *65*
Buckinghamshire Masonic Centenary Fund *67*
Burdall Charity, H M *69*
Butlin Charity Trust, Bill *72*
Buxton Trust, Denis *72*
Camelot Foundation, The *78*
Campbell Charitable Foundation, The Ellis *79*
Carlton Television Trust *81*
Catto Charitable Settlement, The Thomas Sivewright *86*
Challice Trust, The *87*
Charity Projects *90*
Cole Charitable Trust, The *105*
Collier Charitable Trust, The *105*
Cottingham Charitable Trust, Mrs Diana Mary *114*
Coutts Charitable Trust, The *116*
Curriers Company Charitable Fund *119*
David Trust, The Lesley *124*
De Yong Charitable Trust, The Emma *128*
Digbeth Trust Ltd, The *133*
Direct Response *134*
Dorus Trust *136*
Dumbreck Charity *139*
Earley Charity, The *142*
Early's Charitable Settlement, Richard *142*
Ebb and Flow Charitable Trust *144*

Edgar Foundation, The Gilbert and Eileen *145*
Edgar Trust, The Gilbert *145*
Elkes Charity Fund, The Wilfred & Elsie *147*
Emmaus Christian Foundation *150*
Epigoni Trust *152*
Ericson Trust *152*
Fane Research Trust, The Edmund *159*
Ferguson Benevolent Fund Limited *161*
Fishmongers' Company's Charitable Trust *163*
Fletcher Charitable Trust, The Joyce *164*
Fletcher Trust, Roy *165*
Fortune Trust, The *167*
Four Winds Trust *168*
GNC Trust *175*
Gibson Charitable Trust, The Simon *182*
Goldsmiths' Company's Charities, The *188*
Good Neighbours Trust, The *188*
Grant-Lawson Charitable Trust, Lady Virginia *192*
Groves Charitable Trust, The *197*
Hanley Trust (1987), The *207*
Harbour Foundation Ltd, The *208*
Held Settlement, The Gisela *215*
Hudson Benevolent Trust, The Thomas *230*
Hudson Charitable Trust, The *230*
Inverforth Charitable Trust, The *236*
Irving Charitable Trust, The Charles *237*
Isle of Dogs Community Foundation *238*
JCSCJ Charitable Trust, The *238*
Jarrold Trust Ltd, John *243*
Johnson Foundation, The *246*
Johnson Foundation, The Beth *247*
Keeling Charitable Trust, The Petronella *251*
King Charitable Trust, The Lorna *254*
King's Fund, The *255*
Kyte Charitable Trust, The *259*
Laing Charitable Trust, The David *260*
Laing Foundation, The Christopher *260*
Laing Foundation, The Kirby *261*
Laing Foundation, The Maurice *261*
Laing Trust, Beatrice *261*

Lane Foundation, The Allen 263

Laspen Trust 265

Lawson Charitable Trust, Raymond and Blanche 267

Leach Fourteenth Trust, The 267

Linford Charitable Trust, The Fred 276

Lloyd Charity, The S and D 278

Lloyd's Charities Trust 278

Low & Bonar Charitable Fund, The 284

Lynall Foundation, The D G 287

Lyndhurst Settlement 287

Lyons Charitable Trust, The 288

McCarthy Foundation, The John 290

Manning Trust, Leslie & Lilian 296

Margaret Foundation, The 297

Marriage's Charitable Trust, Miss G M 299

Matthews Wrightson Charity Trust 301

Mental Health Foundation, The 305

Metropolitan Hospital-Sunday Fund, The 308

Milburn Charitable Trust, Frederick 310

Milton Keynes Community Trust Ltd, The 312

Minet Trust, The Peter 313

Minge's Gift 314

Moore Foundation, The George A 316

Morris Charitable Trust, The Douglas 320

Multithon Trust, The 323

Music for World Development 323

NR Charitable Trust, The 325

Nathan Charitable Trust 326

Needham Cooper Charitable Trust, The 331

New Court Charitable Trust 332

New Durlston Trust, The 332

Newby Trust Ltd 332

Oakdale Trust, The 343

Oldham Foundation 345

Owen Family Trust, The 348

Paristamen Foundation, The 352

Parivar Trust, The 353

Paterson Charitable Foundation, The Constance 354

Paterson Charitable Trust, Arthur James 354

Payne Trust, The Harry 356

Persula Foundation, The 360

Pye Christian Trust, The 371

Pyke Charity Trust 372

Ravenscroft Foundation, The 379

Reeve's Foundation 382

Rest-Harrow Trust, The 382

Robinson Brothers (Ryders Green) Ltd, Charitable Trust 388

Robinson Trust 4, The J C 388

Rope Third Charitable Settlement, The Mrs 391

Rowbotham Charitable Trust, The Christopher 393

Rowntree Foundation, Joseph 394

St Christopher's Trust, The 402

Sargeant's Charitable Trust, Mrs M E 407

Schuster Charitable Trust, The 410

Seagram Distillers Charitable Trust 413

Sheldon Trust, The 417

Shelroy Charitable Trust, The 417

Shepherd Charitable Trust, The Sylvia and Colin 418

Smith & Mount Trust, The Mrs 426

South Square Trust 430

Stevens Foundation, The June 437

Stoate Charitable Trust, The Leonard Laity 438

Stonehouse Trust Ltd, Eric 438

Summerfield Charitable Trust, The 442

Swan Mountain Trust 444

Swann-Morton Foundation, The 444

TSB Foundation for Northern Ireland 447

Thackray General Charitable Trust, The P & L 452

Thomson Foundation, The Sue 454

Thornton-Smith Trust, The 455

Tisbury Telegraph Trust, The 457

Tudor Trust, The 463

Van Leer Foundation UK Trust, Bernard 470

Variety Club Children's Charity Limited, The 471

Wagstaff Charitable Trust, Bob 475

Wakefield (Tower Hill, Trinity Square) Trust 476

Wates Foundation, The 481

Weir Foundation, The James 484

Wesleyan Charitable Trust, The 485

Whitecourt Charitable Trust, The 490

Wix Charitable Trust, Michael and Anna 497

Wolfe Family's Charitable Trust, The 498

Woodlands Trust 501

Woodroffe Benton Foundation, The 502

Woolton Charitable Trust, The 503

■ Catholic bodies

see also **Religious umbrella bodies**

Funding priority

Aid to the Church in Need (United Kingdom) 8

Catholic Charitable Trust 86

Catholic Foreign Missions 86

Lacy Charity Trust, The Late Sir Pierce 260

Lloyd Foundation, The Charles 278

Marshall Charitable Trust, The Charlotte 300

National Catholic Fund 327

Sylvanus Charitable Trust, The 446

Will consider

Avenal 27

Brampton Trust, The 58

Chownes Foundation, The 93

Digby Charitable Trust, Simon 133

Fattorini Charitable Trust, James J 160

Hudson Benevolent Trust, The Thomas 230

Jerusalem Trust 244

Norfolk's Family Charitable Trust, Lavinia 336

Rope Third Charitable Settlement, The Mrs 391

Shepherd Charitable Trust, The Sylvia and Colin 418

Stanley Residuary Trust, Bishop 435

Summerfield Charitable Trust, The 442

Thorpe Charity Trust, The 455

Welby Trust, The Barbara 484

■ Catholics

see **Roman Catholics**

■ Cats – catteries & other facilities for cats

see also **Animal facilities & services**

Funding priority

Heath Charitable Trust 214

Marchig Animal Welfare Trust 297

Sainsbury Animal Welfare Trust, Jean *401*

Zaiger Trust, The Elizabeth and Prince *512*

Will consider

Animal Defence Trust, The *18*

Astor Foundation, The *26*

Barnby's Foundation, Lord *35*

Body Charitable Trust, Bernard Richard *55*

Carron Charitable Trust, The *83*

Community Trust for Greater Manchester, The *108*

Coote Animal Charity Fund, The Marjorie *111*

Corden Trust, Cyril *113*

Digby Charitable Trust, Simon *133*

Dinam Charity *134*

Dumbreck Charity *139*

Elkes Charity Fund, The Wilfred & Elsie *147*

Evetts & Robert Luff Animal Welfare Trust, Beryl *156*

Ford of Britain Trust *166*

Friends of the Animals *173*

Green Memorial Fund, The Barry *194*

Greenaway Foundation, The Sir Derek *194*

Lee Foundation, The Edgar *269*

Lowe Trust, Mrs D G *285*

MacKintosh Charitable Trust, Viscount *292*

Marriage's Charitable Trust, Miss G M *299*

Nathan Charitable Trust, Peter *326*

Needham Cooper Charitable Trust, The *331*

Norman Family Charitable Trust, The *337*

Perry Charitable Trust, Miss Frances Lucille *359*

Vincent Wildlife Trust, The *473*

Walker 597 Trust, The *477*

Wylde Memorial Charity, The Anthony and Gwendoline *507*

Wyre Animal Welfare *507*

■ Catteries

see Cats – catteries & other facilities for cats

■ Cemeteries & burial grounds

see also Religious buildings

Funding priority

Cohen and William Leech Foundation, Sebag *103*

Gwent County Council Welsh Church Fund *200*

Will consider

Beckwith-Smith's Charitable Settlement, Mrs *40*

Chesters Settlement for Methodist Church Purposes, Mr H G *91*

David Trust, The Lesley *124*

Digby Charitable Trust, Simon *133*

Greenaway Foundation, The Sir Derek *194*

Haddon Charitable Trust, William *202*

Hillards Charitable Trust, Gay & Peter Hartley's *220*

Laspen Trust *265*

Lloyd Charity, The S and D *278*

Marriage's Charitable Trust, Miss G M *299*

Moore Charitable Trust, The Horace *316*

Norfolk's Family Charitable Trust, Lavinia *336*

Peppiatt Charitable Trust, The Brian *359*

Saunderson Foundation, The *408*

Wills 1961 Charitable Trust, Mr Frederick *493*

■ Cerebral palsy

Funding priority

SCOPE *410*

■ Charity or voluntary umbrella bodies

see also Council for Voluntary Service (CVS), Rural Community Council (RCC), Volunteer bureaux

Funding priority

Aga Khan Foundation (UK) *7*

Baring Foundation, The *34*

Community Trust for Greater Manchester, The *108*

International Bar Association Educational Trust *236*

(Lloyds) TSB Foundation for England and Wales *279*

Millfield House Foundation *312*

Wakeham Trust, The *476*

Westminster Amalgamated Charity *487*

Will consider

AHJ Charitable Trust, The *3*

Achiezer Association Limited *6*

Airflow Community Ltd, The *9*

Ajahma Charitable Trust, The *9*

Aleh Charitable Foundation, The *10*

Allachy Trust, The *12*

Anderson Trust, Andrew *16*

Andrew Charitable Trust, The Prince *16*

Angler's Inn Trust *17*

Appelbe Trust, Ambrose & Ann *19*

Aquarius Charitable Foundation, The *19*

Aquinas Trust *20*

Askew Charitable Trust, The Ian *25*

Assembled Church of Christ Trust, The *25*

Assheton-Smith Charitable Trust *25*

Astor Foundation, The *26*

Astor of Hever Trust, The *26*

Astor's 1969 Charity, The Hon M L *26*

Barbour Trust, The *33*

Barnby's Foundation, Lord *35*

Barnsbury Charitable Trust *35*

Barton Trust, Eleanor *37*

Bateman Charitable Trust, Lady Margaret *37*

Bealey Foundation, The *38*

Beattie Charitable Trust, The James *39*

Beckwith Charitable Trust, The Peter *40*

Beckwith-Smith's Charitable Settlement, Mrs *40*

Bergqvist Charitable Trust *44*

Black Foundation, The Bertie *51*

Blagrave Charitable Trust, The Herbert and Peter *52*

Blakenham's Charity Trust, Lady *53*

Blakey Charitable Trust, The Celia and Conrad *53*

Blank Donations Ltd, The David *54*

Boltons Trust, The *55*

Borthwick Memorial Trust, The Oliver *56*

Bottom Charitable Trust, Harry *56*

Bowland Charitable Trust, The *57*

British Sugar Foundation *63*

Brook Charitable Settlement, R E *64*

Brookhouse's Will Trust, Mr John Charles 65

Brough Charitable Trust, Joseph 65

Burn Charity Trust, The J H 70

Burns Charity, The Dorothy 70

Burry Charitable Trust, The 70

Butler's Trust, Lord 71

Butler's Trust, Lucilla 72

Buxton Trust, Denis 72

Cadbury Schweppes Foundation, The 76

Campden Charities, The 79

Cardiff & Swansea Methodist District Charitable Trust Fund 80

Carnegie United Kingdom Trust, The 82

Carron Charitable Trust, The 83

Castang Charitable Trust, H and M 85

Catto Charitable Settlement, The Thomas Sivewright 86

Challice Trust, The 87

Charity Projects 90

Chase Charity, The 91

Chrimes Family Charitable Trust, The 93

Christian Aid 94

Cinderford Charitable Trust, The 96

Clark Charitable Trust, J Anthony 98

Closehelm Ltd 101

Clutterbuck Charitable Trust, Robert 102

Coates Charitable Settlement, The 102

Coates Charitable Trust 1969, Lance 103

Cohen Charitable Trust, The Vivienne and Samuel 104

Cohen Charity Trust, Lucy 104

Collier Charitable Trust, The 105

Company of Tobacco Pipe Makers and Tobacco Blenders Benevolent Fund 109

Condon Family Trust 109

Cope Charitable Trust, Alfred 112

Crescent Trust, The 117

Cripplegate Foundation 118

Curry Charitable Trust, Dennis 119

Cymerman Trust Limited, Itzchok Meyer 120

Daily Telegraph Charitable Trust 122

Dandeen Charitable Trust 123

Davy Foundation, The J 126

De Avenley Foundation, The 126

de Freitas Charitable Trust, The Helen and Geoffrey 126

De La Rue Charitable Trust 127

De Rothschild 1981 Charitable Trust, The Edmund 127

De Yong Charitable Trust, The Emma 128

Delmar Charitable Trust 129

Denton Charitable Trust, The 130

Desmond Charitable Trust, The Richard 131

Deutsch Charitable Trust, The Andre 131

Deutsch Charitable Trust, The H & M 131

Dicken Charitable Trust, The Albert 133

Dinam Charity 134

Djanogly Foundation, The 135

Doughty Charity Trust, The 136

D'Oyly Carte Charitable Trust, The 137

Drayton Trust, The 138

Dulverton Trust, The 139

Dunn Charitable Trust, The Harry 140

Earmark Trust, The 142

Edinburgh Trust, No 2 Account 145

Egerton of Tatton Will Trust, Lord 146

Eling Trust 147

Ellis 1985 Charitable Trust, Edith M 148

Elshore Limited 149

Family Trust, The 158

Famos Foundation Trust 158

Fletcher Trust, Roy 165

Foreman Foundation, The Carl & Eve 167

Foyle Trust, Charles Henry 169

Franklin Bequest, The Rosalind 169

Franklin Deceased's New Second Charity, Sydney E 170

Franklin Trust, Jill 170

Fry Charitable Trust, Maurice 174

Gardner Charitable Trust, R & J 178

Garthgwynion Charities 179

Gibson's Charity Trust, The Hon Mr & Mrs Clive 182

Gillett Charitable Trust, J A 183

Gill's Charitable Trust, Mrs M M 184

Girdlers' Company Charitable Trust, The 184

Gold Hill Church Trust 186

Goldberg Charitable Trust, The Lewis 186

Goldsmiths' Company's Charities, The 188

Goodman Charitable Foundation, The Everard and Mina 188

Goodman Trust, The 189

Gradel Foundation, The 189

Graves Charitable Trust, J G 192

Green Foundation, Constance 194

Gross Charities Limited, M & R 197

Grosshill Charitable Trust 197

Grut Charitable Trust, The 198

HB Charitable Trust 201

Hacking & Sons Ltd Charitable Trust, C G 201

Hamilton Educational Trust, Eleanor 205

Harbour Foundation Ltd, The 208

Harvey Charitable Trust, Gordon 211

Hawthorne Charitable Trust, The 212

Heinz Company Limited Charitable Trust, The H J 215

Held Settlement, The Gisela 215

Hertfordshire Community Trust, The 217

Hillards Charitable Trust, Gay & Peter Hartley's 220

Hobbs Trust Limited, The Betty 222

Holford Trust Fund 224

Hoover Foundation, The 226

Horn Trust, The Cuthbert 227

Hornby Charitable Trust, Miss D 227

Hornton Trust, The 228

Hughes Charitable Trust, The Geoffery C 230

Hyde Park Place Estate Charity, The 232

IBM United Kingdom Trust 233

IPE Charitable Trust, The 233

Inman Charity, The 235

Ireland Funds, The 237

James Foundation, The Catherine and Lady Grace 241

Jones Trust, Cemlyn 248

Jubilee Outreach Yorkshire 248

KC Charitable Trust, The 250

Karten Charitable Trust, The Ian 250

Keyes Trust, The Ursula 253

Kingsgrove Charitable Trust, The 255

Kinnison Charitable Trust, R O 256

Kleinwort Charitable Trust, The Ernest 257

Kobler Trust, The 258

Kreitman Foundation 258

Kulika Charitable Trust, The 259
Kweller Charitable Trust, The Harry 259
Lacy Charity Trust, The Late Sir Pierce 260
Laing Charitable Trust, The David 260
Laing Foundation, The Christopher 260
Landy Charitable Trust, Harry and Gertrude 263
Lane Foundation, The Allen 263
Lankelly Foundation, The 264
Lanvern Foundation 265
Laski Memorial Charitable Trust, Nathan 265
Laspen Trust 265
Lauffer Charitable Foundation, The R & D 266
Lavender Trust, The 267
Lawley Foundation, The Edgar E 267
Lawson Charitable Trust, Raymond and Blanche 267
Leigh-Bramwell Trust 'E', P 270
Levy Charitable Foundation, Joseph 272
Liffe Benefit 274
Lingwood Charitable Trust, The 276
Lloyd's Charities Trust 278
Localtrent Ltd 279
London Law Trust 280
Low & Bonar Charitable Fund, The 284
Lucas Charitable Trust Limited, The Joseph 286
Lunzer Charitable Trust, The Ruth & Jack 287
Lynwood Charitable Trust, The 288
Lyons Charitable Trust, The 288
MacAndrew Trust, The E M 289
McKechnie Foundation, A N 292
McKenzie Trust, The Robert 292
McLaren Foundation 292
McLaren Memorial Trust, The Martin 293
MacRobert Trusts, The 294
Margadale Charitable Trust, Lord 297
Marks Charitable Trust, Michael 298
Markus Charitable Foundation, The Erich 298
Marr-Munning Trust 299
Marshall Charitable Trust, The Charlotte 300
Martin Trust, The Sir George 300

Material World Charitable Foundation Limited, The 301
Mattock Charitable Trust, The W T 302
Mayfair Charities Limited 303
Medlock Charitable Trust, The 304
Mellows Charitable Settlement, The Anthony and Elizabeth 305
Millett Charitable Trust, The Alan and Janet 312
Millichope Foundation, The 312
Modiano Charitable Trust 315
Montefiore Trust, The David 316
Moore Charitable Trust, The Horace 316
Moores Foundation, John 318
Morel Charitable Trust, The 318
Morgan Crucible Company plc Charitable Trust, The 319
Morris Charitable Trust, The Willie & Mabel 320
Moulton Charitable Trust, The 321
Music for World Development 323
Music Sales Charitable Trust, The 324
National Lottery Charities Board 328
National Power Charitable Trust, The 330
Newcastle's 1986 Charitable Trust, Duke of 333
Newman Charitable Trust, Mr and Mrs F E F 334
Newstead Charity, The 334
Noel Buxton Trust, The 335
Norfolk's Family Charitable Trust, Lavinia 336
Northcott Charity Trust, The 338
Northern Electric Employee Charity Association 339
Northern Ireland Voluntary Trust 339
Noswad Charity, The 341
Old Possums Practical Trust, The 344
Oppenheimer Charitable Trust 346
Owen Trust, Margaret 348
PDC Trust, The 349
PJD Charitable Trust 350
Palmer Trust, The Gerald 352
Paristamen Foundation, The 352
Pascoe Charitable Trust, Alan 354
Paul Charitable Trust, The Late Barbara May 355
Paul Charitable Trust, Margaret Jeanne 355

Paul Charitable Trust, Pamela Milton 355
Paul Foundation, The 355
Paul's Charitable Trust, R J 355
Payne Charitable Trust, The 355
Pelech Charitable Trust, The 358
Perry Charitable Trust, Miss Frances Lucille 359
Pershore Nashdom & Elmore Trust Ltd, The 360
Persula Foundation, The 360
Peskin Charitable Trust, The Hazel and Leslie 360
Phillips Charitable Foundation, Reginald M 361
Pitt Trust, Headley 364
Powys Welsh Church Fund 367
Puebla Charitable Trust Limited, The 371
QAS Charitable Trust 373
Quothquan Charitable Trust, The Second 373
RT Trust, The 374
Rackham Charitable Trust, The Mr & Mrs Philip 375
Radley Charitable Trust 375
Rae Charity, H J 375
Rav Chesed Trust, The 379
Reekie Trust, R A & V B 381
Richard Charitable Trust, The Cliff 383
Richards Charity, The Clive 384
Richmond Parish Lands Charity 384
Riley-Smith Charitable Trust, The F A 386
Ripley's Charitable Trust, Pat 386
Rivendell Trust, The 387
Robbins Trust, The Cheshire 387
Rodewald's Charitable Settlement, Mr C A 389
Rogers Charitable Settlement, The Richard 390
Rolfe Charitable Trust, The 390
Rosen Foundation, Cecil 392
Rothley Trust, The 392
Rowan Charitable Trust, The 393
S Group Charitable Trust 399
St Jude's Trust 403
Samuel Charitable Trust, M J 406
Save & Prosper Foundation 409
Scarr-Hall Memorial Trust, The 409
Scott Bader Commonwealth Ltd, The 411
Seva Trust, Rampaba Sadhu 415
Sherman Charitable Trust, The Archie 419
Shifrin Charitable Trust, The Maurice and Hilda 419

Chemists

Sidbury Trust, The Second *421*
Silvester Charitable Gift Trust *422*
Skelton Bounty, The *423*
Society of Friends of the Torah, The *429*
Solomons Charitable Trust, David *430*
Somerfield Curtis Will Trust, The Dorothy *430*
Stanley Foundation Limited *435*
Stewart Charitable Trust, Mary Stephanie *437*
Symons Charitable Trust, The Stella *446*
TSB Foundation for Northern Ireland *447*
TSB Foundation for Scotland *447*
Taylor Charitable Trust, The B R *450*
Terry Charitable Trust, Noel Goddard *451*
Tesco Charity Trust *452*
Tesler Foundation, The *452*
Tyne & Wear Foundation *466*
Van Norden's Charitable Foundation, Mrs Maud *471*
Victoria & Johnson Memorial Trust, Queen *472*
Vineyard Christian Fellowship of South West *473*
Vinson Charity Trust, The 1969 *473*
Vogel Charitable Trust, The Nathan *474*
Wakefield Trust, The *476*
War on Want *479*
Ward Blenkinsop Trust, The *480*
Weinstock Fund, The *484*
Weir Foundation, The James *484*
Wetherly's Charitable Trust, The Hon Mrs R G A *489*
Whitehead Charitable Trust, J E *490*
Whittington Charitable Trust, The *491*
Wiggins Charity Trust, Cyril *491*
Wilde Charitable Trust, The Felicity *492*
Wiltshire Community Foundation *495*
Woburn 1986 Charitable Trust *498*
Wohl Charitable Trust, The Maurice *498*
Wolff Charity Trust *498*
Woodhouse Charitable Trust, Edwin *501*
Woods Charitable Foundation, Geoffrey *502*
Worms Charitable Trust, The Freda and Della *504*

Worshipful Company of Needlemakers' Charitable Fund *505*
Wychdale Limited *507*
Youell Foundation Ltd, The *510*
Zaiger Trust, The Elizabeth and Prince *512*

....

■ Chemists
Funding priority
Asthma Allergy and Inflammation Research Trust *25*
Leverhulme Trade Charities Trust, The *272*

....

■ Children
see also Parents & children
Funding priority
AHJ Charitable Trust, The *3*
Abrahams 2nd Charitable Foundation, The Henry and Grete *5*
Access 4 Trust *6*
Ainsworth and Family Benevolent Fund, Green and Lilian F M *8*
Alexandra Rose Day *11*
Ammco Trust, The *15*
Angler's Inn Trust *17*
Aquinas Trust *20*
Arnopa Trust, The *22*
Arts Council of Wales, The *23*
Astor of Hever Trust, The *26*
Austin of Longbridge Will Trust, The Rt Hon Herbert, Baron *27*
Aylesfield Foundation, The *28*
BBC Children in Need Appeal, The *29*
Bachad Fellowship – Friends of Bnei Akiva *30*
Baker Charitable Trust, The *30*
Balint Charitable Trust, Paul *31*
Ballard Charitable Trust, The Stanton *32*
Ballinger Charitable Trust, The *32*
Baronets Trust, The *35*
Barratt Charitable Trust, The Elaine *36*
Bergqvist Charitable Trust *44*
Betteshanger Charitable Trust *46*
Betton's Charity (Educational), Mr Thomas *46*
Bilton Charity, The Percy *48*
Black Charitable Trust, The Cyril W *51*
Black Charitable Trust, Edna *51*
Black Charitable Trust, Sydney *51*

Blackburn Trust, The *51*
Blagrave Charitable Trust, The Herbert and Peter *52*
Blakey Charitable Trust, The Celia and Conrad *53*
Bowland Charitable Trust, The *57*
Bramall Charitable Trust, The Tony *58*
Bridge Trust, The *60*
Brighton & Hove Charitable Youth Trust *60*
British Friends of Chinuch Atzmai Trust, The *62*
Brook Charitable Trust *64*
Burn Charity Trust, The J H *70*
Burton Charitable Trust, The Harriet *71*
Butler's Trust, Lord *71*
Butler's Trust, Lucilla *72*
Butlin Charity Trust, Bill *72*
Cadbury Charitable Trust, Richard *75*
Campbell Charitable Foundation, The Ellis *79*
Carlton Television Trust *81*
Cass's Foundation, Sir John *85*
Catholic Education Service for England and Wales *86*
Challice Trust, The *87*
Charity Projects *90*
Child Growth Foundation *92*
Children's Research Fund, The *92*
Chownes Foundation, The *93*
Christmas Cracker Trust *95*
Chronicle Cinderella Home Fund No 1, The *95*
Clarke Trust, The Thomas Edward *99*
Clifford Charity Oxford, The *100*
Clipsham Charitable Settlement, R E *101*
Clover Trust *102*
Cobb Charity *103*
Cohen and William Leech Foundation, Sebag *103*
Collinson Charitable Trust, The Norman *106*
Condon Family Trust *109*
Construction Industry Trust for Youth, The *110*
Corbett's Charity, Thomas *112*
Coxen Trust Fund, Sir William *116*
Crawford Children's Charity, Michael *117*
Curtis Charitable Trust, The Thomas *120*
Curzon Charitable Trust, The Wallace *120*
Dahl Foundation, The Roald *122*
Davenport's Charity Trust, Baron *124*
Dawson Educational Foundation, Thomas *126*

De Yong Charitable Trust, The
Emma *128*
De Yong's Charitable Trust
1984, Nicholas *128*
Delmar Charitable Trust *129*
Denton Charitable Trust, The
130
Derbyshire Trust, J N *130*
Desmond Charitable Trust, The
Richard *131*
Diamond Industry Educational
Charity, The *132*
Dibden Allotments Charity *132*
Dinam Charity *134*
Djanogly Foundation, The *135*
Dulverton Trust, The *139*
Dumbreck Charity *139*
Duveen Trust, The *141*
Earmark Trust, The *142*
Edgar Trust, The Gilbert *145*
Egerton of Tatton Will Trust,
Lord *146*
Ellbridge Trust, The *148*
Emerton-Christie Charity *150*
Eveson Charitable Trust, The
155
Feeney Charitable Bequest, The
John *161*
Foreman 1980 Charitable Trust,
The Russell and Mary *167*
Fortune Trust, The *167*
Franklin Deceased's New
Second Charity, Sydney E
170
French Charitable Trust,
Charles S *171*
Friarsgate Trust *172*
Gallagher Memorial Fund,
Angela *177*
Gannochy Trust, The *177*
Garnett Charitable Trust, The
178
Gatsby Charitable Foundation,
The *179*
Gibson's Charity Trust, The Hon
Mr & Mrs Clive *182*
Gill's Charitable Trust, Mrs M M
184
Glebe Charitable Trust *185*
Gluckstein Charitable
Settlement, The Penelope
185
Golders Green Foundation *187*
Goodman Charitable
Foundation, The Everard
and Mina *188*
Gough Charitable Trust, The
189
Grange Farm Centre Trust *191*
Grant Charitable Trust, The
191
Grant-Lawson Charitable Trust,
Lady Virginia *192*
Green Foundation, The *193*
Grocers' Charity *197*
Gunnell Charitable Trust, The
199
HB Charitable Trust *201*

Hale Trust, The *203*
Hall Charitable Trust, E F &
M G *204*
Harding's Charity, William *209*
Harford Charitable Trust *209*
Harris Charity, The *211*
Hartley Memorial Trust, The N
& P *211*
Hattori Foundation, The *212*
Hawley Residuary Fund, Harry
Fieldsend *212*
Hawthorne Charitable Trust,
The *212*
Hertfordshire Community
Trust, The *217*
Historic Churches Preservation
Trust, The *221*
Hopkins, The Charity of Joseph
227
Hornby Charitable Trust, Miss
D *227*
Horne Foundation, The *228*
Hudson Charitable Trust, The
230
Humphreys Charitable
Settlement, J A M *231*
Hussey Trust, The *232*
Ibbett Trust, The *233*
Ingles Charitable Trust, The
234
Isle of Dogs Community
Foundation *238*
JJ Charitable Trust, The *239*
Jacobson Charitable Trust, The
Yvette and Hermione *241*
Jewish Childs' Day *245*
Keller Charitable Trust, Samuel
251
Knightly Charitable Trust, The
David *257*
Laing Charitable Trust, The
David *260*
Lalonde Trust *262*
Lambourne Memorial Trust,
The Emma *262*
Langdale Trust *264*
Levy Charitable Foundation,
Joseph *272*
Lewis Foundation, The John
Spedan *274*
Lewis Partnership, John *274*
Lister Charitable Trust, The
277
Liverpool Child Welfare
Association Incorporated
277
Living and Waking Naturally
278
London Law Trust *280*
Lord's Taverners, The *281*
Lowndes Charitable Trust, The
Vanessa *285*
Lyons Charitable Trust, The
288
Lyon's Charity, John *288*
MacAndrew Trust, The E M
289
Maccabi Foundation, The *290*

Mackintosh Foundation, The
292
Man of the People Fund *295*
Marmor Charitable Trust, The
Julie *299*
Material World Charitable
Foundation Limited, The
301
Melchett Children's Trust, The
Violet *305*
Mellows Charitable Settlement,
The Anthony and Elizabeth
305
Mental Health Foundation, The
305
Merchants House of Glasgow
307
Mijoda Charitable Trust, The
310
Milton Mount Foundation *313*
Minet Trust, The Peter *313*
Moore Charitable Trust, The
Horace *316*
Moores Family Charity
Foundation, The *317*
Morgan Crucible Company plc
Charitable Trust, The *319*
Murphy-Neumann Charity
Company Limited *323*
Music Sales Charitable Trust,
The *324*
Muslim Hands *324*
New Chasers Charitable Trust,
The *332*
Newcastle Children's Mission &
Institute *333*
Newcastle's 1986 Charitable
Trust, Duke of *333*
Newcomen Collett Foundation
333
Noel Buxton Trust, The *335*
Norman Trust, The *337*
Norton Foundation, The *340*
Noswad Charity, The *341*
Ogilvie Charities (Deed No 2)
344
Older's School Charity, William
345
Oppenheimer Charitable Trust
346
Ormsby Charitable Trust, The
347
Ouseley Trust, The *347*
PDC Trust, The *349*
Paddington Charitable Estates
Educational Fund *351*
Paget Trust, The *351*
Parivar Trust, The *353*
Pascoe Charitable Trust, Alan
354
Paul's Charitable Trust, R J *355*
Pearson Foundation, The Frank
357
Peirce Memorial Trust, The Joe
358
Pickford Charitable
Foundation, The David *362*

Priestman Trust, S H and E C
368
Proctor Charitable Trust, The
Albert Edward 370
REMEDI (Rehabilitation and
Medical Research Trust) 374
Rangoonwala Foundation,
ZVM 376
Rank Xerox Trust, The 378
Rayne Foundation, The 379
Rayner Charitable Trust, The
John 380
Roberts Charitable Trust, F G
388
Robyn Charitable Trust 389
Rocket Club Benevolent Fund,
The 389
Roedean School Mission Fund
390
Rolfe Charitable Trust, The 390
Rosca Trust 391
Royal Gardeners' Orphan Fund,
The 395
Royle Memorial Trust, Kirstin
397
Said Foundation, The Karim
Rida 401
St Francis Leprosy Guild 402
St Hilda's Trust 403
Sarum St Michael Educational
Charity, The 408
Save & Prosper Educational
Trust 408
Save & Prosper Foundation
409
Scopus Jewish Educational
Trust 411
Scott Charitable Trust, The
Francis C 412
Seagram Distillers Charitable
Trust 413
Sedbury Trust, The 414
Sharon Trust, The 416
Sheldon Trust; The 417
Shuttleworth Memorial Trust,
Barbara A 421
Silvester Charitable Gift Trust
422
Singer Foundation 423
Slater Foundation Ltd, The 424
Salter Trust Ltd 424
Smith Foundation, The Leslie
427
Southover Manor General
Education Trust Ltd 433
Sparkes Charitable Trust, The
Eric F 433
Spoore, Merry & Rixman
Foundation, The 434
Sport Aid 88 Trust 434
Stevens Foundation, The June
437
Swindon Charitable Trust, The
Walter 445
Sykes Trust, The Charles 445
Thompson Charitable Trust,
The 453

Thompson Memorial Fund, The
Edwin John 453
Toy Trust, The 459
Trust Fund for the Training of
Handicapped Children in
Arts and Crafts 462
Turner Charitable Settlement,
The Sir Mark and Lady 464
29th May 1961 Charity, The
465
United Kingdom Friends for
Further Education in Israel
468
van Geest Foundation, The
John and Lucille 470
Variety Club Children's Charity
Limited, The 471
Vodafone Group Charitable
Trust, The 474
Wates Foundation, The 481
Watson Foundation, The Bertie
482
Watson's Trust, John 482
Wedge, The 483
Weinberg Foundation, The
483
Westcroft Trust 486
White Rose Children's Aid
International Charity 489
Wohl Charitable Foundation,
The Maurice 498
Wohl Charitable Trust, The
Maurice 498
Woodhouse Charitable Trust,
Edwin 501
Woodroffe Benton Foundation,
The 502
Woolf Charitable Trust, The
502
Worms Charitable Trust, The
Freda and Della 504
Worshipful Company of Glass
Sellers' Charity Trust, The
505
Yorkshire Field Studies Trust
510
Youth Appeal for Eastern
Europe 511

Will consider

Adnams Charity, The 7
Alexis Trust, The 11
Ambika Paul Foundation 15
Anstey Charitable Settlement,
J C W 18
Assembled Church of Christ
Trust, The 25
Assheton-Smith Charitable
Trust 25
Astor Foundation, The 26
Avenal 27
Barnabas Charitable Trust 34
Bateman Charitable Trust, Lady
Margaret 37
Beckwith Charitable
Settlement, The Heather 39

Behrens Charitable Trust, E M
40
Benlian Trust, The 44
Bentall Charity Trust, Rowan
44
Birtwistle Memorial Trust, The
G E 50
Blakenham's Charity Trust,
Lady 53
Blott Charitable Settlement,
Robert Orpwood 55
Bonhomie United Charity
Society 56
Borthwick Memorial Trust, The
Oliver 56
Bottom Charitable Trust, Harry
56
Brotherton Trust, The Charles
65
Buccleuch Place Trust 67
Buckingham Trust 67
Buckinghamshire Masonic
Centenary Fund 67
Bulmer Charitable Trust, Becket
68
Chandris Foundation, The 88
Chase Charity, The 91
Christian Renewal Trust, The
94
Clinton's Charitable Trust, Lord
100
Commonweal Fund of the
Trades House of Glasgow,
The 108
Cope Charitable Trust, Alfred
112
Dacorum Community Trust 121
David Trust, The Lesley 124
Dean Refugee Trust Fund, The
Miriam 128
Denne Charitable Trust 130
Digby Charitable Trust, Simon
133
Direct Response 134
Doughty Charity Trust, The
136
Dunhill Medical Trust, The 140
Earley Charity, The 142
Early's Charitable Settlement,
Richard 142
Education Services 145
Englass Charitable Trust, The
151
Family Trust, The 158
Fletcher Charitable Trust, The
Joyce 164
Fogel Charitable Trust, The
Gerald 165
GW Trust, The 176
Gale Charitable Trust, A W 176
Garbacz Charitable Trust, The
Bernard & Vera 178
Gardner Memorial Trust, The
Samuel 178
Gold Hill Church Trust 186
Grand Metropolitan Charitable
Trust, The 191
Gray Trust, The 192

CA - CATHOLIC
A - ANGLICAN
M - Methodist   E = EVANGELICAL.
G = General.

Greater Bristol Foundation 193

Handicapped Children's Aid Committee 207

Hanley Trust (1987), The 207

Harding Trust, The 209

Hobbs Trust Limited, The Betty 222

Homfray Trust, The 226

Horn Trust, The Cuthbert 227

Hornsey Parochial Charities (Educational and Vocational Foundation), The 228

Hurst Will Trust, Arthur 231

Hutchinson Charitable Trust, E B 232

Inman Charity, The 235

Iris Trust, The 237

Jackson Trust for Charity, The Isaac and Harriet 240

Jacobsen Foundation Limited 240

James Charitable Trust, John 241

Joseph Charitable Trust, J E 248

Kleinwort Charitable Trust, The Ernest 257

Lane Foundation, The Allen 263

Lankelly Foundation, The 264

Lawley Foundation, The Edgar E 267

Leadbeater Trust, The Alfred 268

Lee Foundation, The Edgar 269

Licensed Trade Charities Trust, The 274

Littler Foundation, The Emile 277

(Lloyds) TSB Foundation for England and Wales 279

London Taxi Drivers' Fund for Underprivileged Children, The 280

Lowenthal Charitable Trust, The L and C 285

Lunn-Rockliffe Charitable Trust, Paul 286

Lynn Foundation, The 288

Margadale Charitable Trust, Lord 297

Milward Charity, The Edgar 313

Minge's Gift 314

Montefiore Trust, The David 316

Needham Cooper Charitable Trust, The 331

New Durlston Trust, The 332

Newby Trust Ltd 332

Nidditch Foundation, The Laurie 335

Norman, The Educational Foundation of Alderman John 337

Norman Family Charitable Trust, The 337

Northcott Devon Foundation 338

Oakdale Trust, The 343

PJD Charitable Trust 350

Paragon Concert Society 352

Paul Charitable Trust, The Late Barbara May 355

Paul Charitable Trust, Margaret Jeanne 355

Paul Charitable Trust, Pamela Milton 355

Peppiatt Charitable Trust, The Brian 359

Persula Foundation, The 360

Pettit Charitable Trust 360

Pitt Trust, Headley 364

Radcliffe's Trust, Dr 375

Rae Charity, H J 375

Rest-Harrow Trust, The 382

Richards Charity, The Violet M 384

Rothley Trust, The 392

Rothschild Group Charitable Trust, The J 393

Rowntree Foundation, Joseph 394

Shepherd Charitable Trust, The Sylvia and Colin 418

Shepherd Family Charitable Trust, The Sir Peter 418

Slaughter Charitable Trust, The Ernest William 425

Smith (Estates Charities), Henry 426

Smith Trust, The Sydney 428

Southdown Trust 432

Stewards' Charitable Trust, The 437

Street Charitable Foundation, W O 440

Sugden-Wilson's Charitable Trust, Mrs Gabrielle Mary 441

Summerfield Charitable Trust, The 442

Timson Family Charitable Trust 457

Travis Charitable Trust, Constance 460

Turkish Women's Philanthropic Association of England 463

Van Leer Foundation UK Trust, Bernard 470

Van Neste Foundation, The 471

Van Norden's Charitable Foundation, Mrs Maud 471

Vincent Trust Fund, Eric W 473

Wakeham Trust, The 476

Waley-Cohen Charitable Trust, Robert & Felicity 477

Walker Trust, The 477

Weinstock Fund, The 484

Whitehall Charitable Foundation Limited 490

Whitehead's Charitable Trust, Sydney Dean 490

Whitley Trust, Sheila 491

Wills 1961 Charitable Trust, Frederick 493

Wimpey Charitable Trust, The George 495

Wix Charitable Trust, Michael and Anna 497

Woburn 1986 Charitable Trust 498

Women Caring Trust, The 500

Woodhead Charitable Trust, Michael 501

Wylde Memorial Charity, The Anthony and Gwendoline 507

Yapp Welfare Trust, The 508

Yorkshire Agricultural Society 509

....

■ Children's illnesses

see **Paediatric diseases**

....

■ Christian outreach

see also **Advancement of religion**

Funding priority

CA Aid to the Church in Need (United Kingdom) 8

? Almond Trust, The 14

?. Assembled Church of Christ Trust, The 25

M /Avon Trust, The 28

? Barleycorn Trust, The 34

C Bartholomew Christian Trust 36

? Billingsgate Christian Mission Charitable Trust 48

G Black Charitable Trust, The Cyril W 51

G Black Charitable Trust, Edna 51

? Britland Charitable Trust, The 63

? Candap Trust, The 80

G Childs Charitable Trust, The 92

? Christian Renewal Trust, The 94

? Christian Vision 94

? Church Urban Fund 95

? Collier Charitable Trust, The 105

E Dicken Charitable Trust, The Albert 133

E Drummond Trust, The 138

G Earmark Trust, The 142

? Emmaus Christian Foundation 150

? Family Trust, The 158

CA Fattorini Charitable Trust, James J 160

? Firtree Trust, The 163

? Frome Christian Fellowship 174

? Gelston Charitable Trust, The 179

G THE CAMILLA Trust

....

Gold Hill Church Trust *186*
Griffiths Trust, The E E and D M *196*
Groves Charitable Trust, The *197*
Growth Building Trust, The *198*
Hobbs Trust Limited, The Betty *222*
James Charitable Trust, John *241*
James Trust, The *242*
Jarman Charitable Trust, The *243*
Jerusalem Trust *244*
Laing Foundation, The Maurice *261*
Laing Trust, Beatrice *261*
Langley Charitable Trust, The *264*
Latham Trust, The *266*
Lingwood Charitable Trust, The *276*
Lunn-Rockliffe Charitable Trust, Paul *286*
Milward Charity, The Edgar *313*
Moores Foundation, The Peter *318*
NR Charitable Trust, The *325*
Ogle Trust, The *344*
Owen Family Trust, The *348*
Paristamen Foundation, The *352*
Pershore Nashdom & Elmore Trust Ltd, The *360*
Proctor Charitable Trust, The Albert Edward *370*
Pye Christian Trust, The *371*
Quothquan Charitable Trust, The Second *373*
Richard Charitable Trust, The Cliff *383*
Riley-Smith Charitable Trust, The F A *386*
River Trust, The *387*
Robbins Trust, The Cheshire *387*
Rozel Trust, The *397*
Rudabede *397*
SMB Trust, The *400*
St George's Trust, The *403*
Saunderson Foundation, The *408*
Seedfield Trust, The *414*
Skinner Charitable Trust, Edward *424*
Stathern Chapel Close Trust, The *436*
Stewart Trust, Sir Halley *437*
Stow Allen Trust, The *439*
Swansea and Brecon Diocesan Board of Finance Ltd *444*
Taylor Charitable Trust, The *449*
Teman Trust, The *450*
Tisbury Telegraph Trust, The *457*

Tunstall Charitable Trust *463*
Tyndale Trust *466*
United Society for the Propagation of the Gospel *468*
Vineyard Christian Fellowship of South West *473*
Whitecourt Charitable Trust, The *490*
Whiteley Trust, Norman *490*
Wiggins Charity Trust, Cyril *491*

Will consider
Abel Charitable Trust *5*
Appleton Trust, The *19*
Archer Trust, The *20*
Aston Charities Trust Ltd *25*
Astor Foundation, The *26*
Barnabas Charitable Trust *34*
Blackman Foundation, Isabel *52*
Brooke Benevolent Fund, William *65*
Burden Trust, The *69*
Cadbury Charitable Trust (Incorporated), Edward *75*
Chickadee Trust, The *91*
Clarke Charitable Settlement, The *99*
Debtors' Relief Fund Charity *128*
Digby Charitable Trust, Simon *133*
Ebenezer Family Trust *144*
Feed the Minds *160*
Fulham Cross Christian Mission *175*
Gardner Charitable Trust, R & J *178*
Greenaway Foundation, The Sir Derek *194*
Haines Charitable Trust, The Alfred *203*
Halkes Settlement, John Robert *204*
Hannay Memorial Charity, Kathleen *208*
Hudson Benevolent Trust, The Thomas *230*
Hussey for Africans, Charity of Rebecca *231*
Laing Charitable Trust, The David *260*
Laing Foundation, The Kirby *261*
Laspen Trust *265*
Leech Charity, The William *269*
Littler Foundation, The Emile *277*
Lloyd Charity, The S and D *278*
New Durlston Trust, The *332*
Nightingale Trust, The *335*
Peppiatt Charitable Trust, The Brian *359*
Pettit Charitable Trust *360*
Rainbow Charitable Trust *376*

Rainford Trust, The *376*
St Christopher's Trust, The *402*
Saint Edmund King and Martyr Trust *402*
Sharon Trust, The *416*
Shelroy Charitable Trust, The *417*
Shone Memorial Trust, J A *420*
Sparkhill Trust, The *433*
Stonehouse Trust Ltd, Eric *438*
Summerfield Charitable Trust, The *442*
Tear Fund *450*
Thorpe Charity Trust, The *455*
Tindall's Charitable Trust, Mrs R P *457*
Trust for the Homeless *462*
United Society for Christian Literature *468*
Waghorn Charitable Trust, The Albert *475*
Wagstaff Charitable Trust, Bob *475*
Wallington Missionary Mart & Auctions *478*
Warren Foundation, The John *480*
Wates Charitable Trust, John *481*
Welfare Charity Establishment *485*
Williams Trust, James *493*
Wills 1961 Charitable Trust, Mr Frederick *493*
Wills 1962 Charitable Trust, P J H *494*

■ Christians
Funding priority
Almond Trust, The *14*
Aston Charities Trust Ltd *25*
Barleycorn Trust, The *34*
Bartholomew Christian Trust *36*
Beacon Trust *38*
BibleLands *47*
Brand Charitable Trust *58*
Britland Charitable Trust, The *63*
Campbell Charitable Foundation, The Ellis *79*
Candap Trust, The *80*
Chickadee Trust, The *91*
Childs Charitable Trust, The *92*
Christendom Trust, The *94*
Church Urban Fund *95*
Cohen Charity Trust, Lucy *104*
Collier Charitable Trust, The *105*
Dashe Trust, The *124*
Dibdin Foundation, Thomas Peter *132*
Dicken Charitable Trust, The Albert *133*
Ebenezer Trust *144*
Elijah Trust *147*

Eling Trust *147*
Englefield Charitable Trust, The *151*
Feed the Minds *160*
Firtree Trust, The *163*
Frome Christian Fellowship *174*
Fulham Cross Christian Mission *175*
Gelston Charitable Trust, The *179*
Gregson Trust, The John *195*
Griffiths Trust, The E E and D M *196*
Groves Charitable Trust, The *197*
Growth Building Trust, The *198*
Haines Charitable Trust, The Alfred *203*
Hiley Trust, Joseph and Mary *219*
Hockerill Educational Foundation *223*
Hurst Will Trust, Arthur *231*
Inlight *235*
James Foundation, John & Rhys Thomas *242*
James Trust, The *242*
Jerusalem Trust *244*
Jesus Lane Trust, The *245*
Jubilee Outreach Yorkshire *248*
Laspen Trust *265*
Lingwood Charitable Trust, The *276*
Listeners, The *276*
Lyndhurst Trust, The *287*
Marriage's Charitable Trust, Miss G M *299*
NR Charitable Trust, The *325*
Naaman Trust, The *325*
National Committee of The Women's World Day of Prayer for England, Wales and Northern Ireland, The *327*
New Durlston Trust, The *332*
Owen Family Trust, The *348*
Palmer Trust, The Gerald *352*
Paristamen Foundation, The *352*
Pedmore Trust *357*
Pickford Charitable Foundation, The David *362*
Poulden Charitable Trust, The Frank and Dorothy *366*
Quothquan Charitable Trust, The Second *373*
Rae Charity, H J *375*
Rainbow Charitable Trust *376*
Riggs Charity, The *386*
Rope Third Charitable Settlement, The Mrs *391*
Rozel Trust, The *397*
Rudabede *397*
Rutland Historic Churches Preservation Trust *399*

Saunderson Foundation, The *408*
Seedfield Trust, The *414*
Sheepdrove Trust, The *417*
Skinner Charitable Trust, Edward *424*
Swansea and Brecon Diocesan Board of Finance Ltd *444*
Thorpe Charity Trust, The *455*
Tisbury Telegraph Trust, The *457*
Torchbearer Trust *458*
Tunstall Charitable Trust *463*
United Society for Christian Literature *468*
Wallington Missionary Mart & Auctions *478*
Welfare Charity Establishment *485*
Westcroft Trust *486*
Wright Deceased Trust, John William *506*

....

■ Church buildings

see also Conservation

Funding priority

Alec-Smith Charitable Trust, R A *10*
Barnby's Foundation, Lord *35*
Bellahouston Bequest Fund *42*
Brook Charitable Settlement, R E *64*
Buckinghamshire Historic Churches Trust *67*
Cadbury Charitable Trust, J & L A *75*
Chase Charity, The *91*
Colyer-Fergusson Charitable Trust, The *107*
Cripps Foundation *118*
David Trust, The Lesley *124*
Franklin Trust, Jill *170*
Friends of Essex Churches, The *172*
Friends of Friendless Churches, The *173*
Friends of Kent Churches *173*
Greenaway Foundation, The Sir Derek *194*
Gregson Trust, The John *195*
Grimthorpe's Charity Fund, The First Lord *196*
Gwent County Council Welsh Church Fund *200*
Haddon Charitable Trust, William *202*
Historic Churches Preservation Trust, The *221*
Humphreys Charitable Settlement, J A M *231*
Incorporated Church Building Society, The *234*
Jarman Charitable Trust, The *243*
Leech Charity, The William *269*

Lower Hall Charitable Trust *285*
Luke Trust, The *286*
MacKintosh Charitable Trust, Viscount *292*
Mellows Charitable Settlement, The Anthony and Elizabeth *305*
Mitchell Trust, Esme *315*
Norfolk Churches Trust Ltd *336*
Peppiatt Charitable Trust, The Brian *359*
Powys Welsh Church Fund *367*
Swale Charity Trust *443*
Wakefield Trust, The *476*
Whitley Animal Protection Trust *491*

Will consider

Ammco Trust, The *15*
Amory Charitable Trust, Viscount *16*
Askew Charitable Trust, The Ian *25*
Astor Foundation, The *26*
Balney Charitable Trust, The *32*
Barbour Trust, The *33*
Barrie Charitable Trust, The Misses *36*
Body Charitable Trust, Bernard Richard *55*
Bourne-May Charitable Trust, The *57*
Bridge Trust, The *60*
Broadley Charitable Trust, The *64*
Brough Charitable Trust, Joseph *65*
Butlin Charity Trust, Bill *72*
Cadbury Trust (1928), The Edward & Dorothy *76*
Community Trust for Greater Manchester, The *108*
Cripplegate Foundation *118*
D'Avigdor Goldsmid Charitable Trust, The Sarah *125*
de Freitas Charitable Trust, The Helen and Geoffrey *126*
Digby Charitable Trust, Simon *133*
Direct Response *134*
Early's Charitable Settlement, Richard *142*
Edgar Foundation, The Gilbert and Eileen *145*
Fishmongers' Company's Charitable Trust *163*
Fletcher Trust, Roy *165*
Garnett Charitable Trust, The *178*
Getty Jr General Charitable Trust, J Paul *181*
Gladstone Charitable Trust, The E W *184*

Glynde Place Charitable Trust (1974), The *186*
Goldsmiths' Company's Charities, The *188*
Hannay Memorial Charity, Kathleen *208*
Hawthorne Charitable Trust, The *212*
Idlewild Trust, The *234*
Inverforth Charitable Trust, The *236*
Isle of Dogs Community Foundation *238*
Jarrold Trust Ltd, John *243*
King Charitable Trust, The Lorna *254*
Lacy Charity Trust, The Late Sir Pierce *260*
Lankelly Foundation, The *264*
Leach Fourteenth Trust, The *267*
Lee Foundation, The Edgar *269*
Lloyd's Charities Trust *278*
Lyndhurst Settlement *287*
Mitchell Trust *315*
NR Charitable Trust, The *325*
Needham Cooper Charitable Trust, The *331*
Newby Trust Ltd *332*
Owen Family Trust, The *348*
Persula Foundation, The *360*
Pilgrim Trust, The *362*
Prince's Trust - BRO, The *369*
Provincial Trust for Kendal, The *370*
Pye Christian Trust, The *371*
Pyke Charity Trust *372*
Robinson Brothers (Ryders Green) Ltd, Charitable Trust *388*
Rookes Charitable Trust, C A *390*
Rowbotham Charitable Trust, The Christopher *393*
Sargeant's Charitable Trust, Mrs M E *407*
Seagram Distillers Charitable Trust *413*
Sharon Trust, The *416*
Shepherd Charitable Trust, The Sylvia and Colin *418*
South Square Trust *430*
Stevens Foundation, The June *437*
Strauss Charitable Trust *440*
Sykes Trust, The Charles *445*
Terry Charitable Trust, Noel Goddard *451*
Tisbury Telegraph Trust, The *457*
Vincent Trust Fund, Eric W *473*
Webber Trust Fund, Ethel *483*
Wingfield's Charitable Trust, Mrs *496*
Woodlands Trust *501*
Woodroffe Benton Foundation, The *502*

Worshipful Company of Engineers' Charitable Trust Fund, The *504*
Wylde Memorial Charity, The Anthony and Gwendoline *507*

■ Church of England
Funding priority
Anglo-Catholic Ordination Candidates Fund, The *18*
Appleton Trust, The *19*
Betton's Charity (Educational), Mr Thomas *46*
Cloudesley's Charity/School Parents & Friends Association, Richard *102*
David Trust, The Lesley *124*
Gough Charitable Trust, The *189*
Grimthorpe's Charity Fund, The First Lord *196*
Hockerill Educational Foundation *223*
Kingston Religious Trust Fund, The *256*
Marshall's Charity *300*
Paddington Charitable Estates Educational Fund *351*
Poulden Charitable Trust, The Frank and Dorothy *366*
Saint Edmund King and Martyr Trust *402*
St Hilda's Trust *403*
Sarum St Michael Educational Charity, The *408*
United Society for the Propagation of the Gospel *468*

■ Church schools
***see also* Schools & colleges**
Funding priority
Bayne Benefaction *38*

■ Churches
***see also* Religious buildings**
Funding priority
Aid to the Church in Need (United Kingdom) *8*
Avon Trust, The *28*
Barleycorn Trust, The *34*
Beckwith-Smith's Charitable Settlement, Mrs *40*
Bellahouston Bequest Fund *42*
Buckinghamshire Historic Churches Trust *67*
Cadbury Charitable Trust, J & L A *75*
Candap Trust, The *80*
Carmichael-Montgomery Charitable Trust, The *81*

Catholic Charitable Trust *86*
Chesters Settlement for Methodist Church Purposes, Mr H G *91*
Childs Charitable Trust, The *92*
Church Urban Fund *95*
Clarke Charitable Settlement, The *99*
Cloudesley's Charity/School Parents & Friends Association, Richard *102*
David Trust, The Lesley *124*
Fencewood Trust, The *161*
Friends of Friendless Churches, The *173*
Friends of Kent Churches *173*
Greenaway Foundation, The Sir Derek *194*
Gregson Trust, The John *195*
Grimthorpe's Charity Fund, The First Lord *196*
Haddon Charitable Trust, William *202*
Hillards Charitable Trust, Gay & Peter Hartley's *220*
Historic Churches Preservation Trust, The *221*
Hudson Benevolent Trust, The Thomas *230*
Humphreys Charitable Settlement, J A M *231*
Incorporated Church Building Society, The *234*
Jarman Charitable Trust, The *243*
Kingston Religious Trust Fund, The *256*
Laing Trust, Beatrice *261*
Lingwood Charitable Trust, The *276*
Lloyd Foundation, The Charles *278*
Lower Hall Charitable Trust *285*
Luke Trust, The *286*
Marshall Charitable Trust, The Charlotte *300*
Marshall's Charity *300*
Moore Charitable Trust, The Horace *316*
Moores Foundation, The Peter *318*
Norfolk Churches Trust Ltd *336*
Norwood Settlement *340*
Peppiatt Charitable Trust, The Brian *359*
Powys Welsh Church Fund *367*
St George's Trust, The *403*
Saunderson Foundation, The *408*
Swansea and Brecon Diocesan Board of Finance Ltd *444*
Tisbury Telegraph Trust, The *457*
Tyndale Memorial Trust Ltd *465*
Tyndale Trust *466*

United Society for the Propagation of the Gospel 468

Vineyard Christian Fellowship of South West 473

Wakefield Trust, The 476

Warren Foundation, The John 480

Will consider

Almond Trust, The 14

Assembled Church of Christ Trust, The 25

Astor Foundation, The 26

Bentall Charity Trust, Rowan 44

Black Charitable Trust, Edna 51

Brampton Trust, The 58

Britland Charitable Trust, The 63

Brough Charitable Trust, Joseph 65

Bullough Tompson Settlement, The 68

Cadbury Charitable Trust (Incorporated), Edward 75

Cardiff & Swansea Methodist District Charitable Trust Fund 80

Catholic Foreign Missions 86

Catto Charitable Settlement, The Thomas Sivewright 86

Christian Renewal Trust, The 94

Cottingham Charitable Trust, Mrs Diana Mary 114

Davies Charity, The Gwendoline and Margaret 125

Dibdin Foundation, Thomas Peter 132

Digby Charitable Trust, Simon 133

Early's Charitable Settlement, Richard 142

Eling Trust 147

Emmaus Christian Foundation 150

Fattorini Charitable Trust, James J 160

Fulham Cross Christian Mission 175

Gladstone Charitable Trust, The E W 184

Glynde Place Charitable Trust (1974), The 186

Goldsmiths' Company's Charities, The 188

Grant-Lawson Charitable Trust, Lady Virginia 192

Halkes Settlement, John Robert 204

Hannay Charitable Trust, The Lennox 208

Hussey for Africans, Charity of Rebecca 231

JCSCJ Charitable Trust, The 238

James Trust, The 242

Jarrold Trust Ltd, John 243

Jerusalem Trust 244

Laing Foundation, The Christopher 260

Laing Foundation, The Kirby 261

Laing Foundation, The Maurice 261

Laspen Trust 265

Leach Fourteenth Trust, The 267

Leech Charity, The William 269

Lloyd Charity, The S and D 278

Lloyd's Charities Trust 278

MacRobert Trusts, The 294

Marriage's Charitable Trust, Miss G M 299

Milward Charity, The Edgar 313

NR Charitable Trust, The 325

Needham Cooper Charitable Trust, The 331

Norfolk's Family Charitable Trust, Lavinia 336

Ormonde Foundation 347

Owen Family Trust, The 348

PF Charitable Trust 350

Paristamen Foundation, The 352

Payne Trust, The Harry 356

Pitt Trust, Headley 364

Proctor Charitable Trust, The Albert Edward 370

Pye Christian Trust, The 371

Rainbow Charitable Trust 376

Rainford Trust, The 376

River Trust, The 387

Robbins Trust, The Cheshire 387

Robinson Brothers (Ryders Green) Ltd, Charitable Trust 388

Rozel Trust, The 397

Rudabede 397

SMB Trust, The 400

Shelroy Charitable Trust, The 417

Shepherd Charitable Trust, The Sylvia and Colin 418

Skinner Charitable Trust, Edward 424

South Square Trust 430

Southall Charitable Trust, Kenneth & Phyllis 431

Sparkhill Trust, The 433

Stathern Chapel Close Trust, The 436

Stewardship Trust Ripon, The 437

Stonehouse Trust Ltd, Eric 438

Summer's and I May's Charitable Settlement, The Late Misses (A N) 442

Templeton Goodwill Trust 451

Tindall's Charitable Trust, Mrs R P 457

Wagstaff Charitable Trust, Bob 475

Webber Trust Fund, Ethel 483

Whitecourt Charitable Trust, The 490

Wills 1961 Charitable Trust, Mr Frederick 493

Woodroffe Benton Foundation, The 502

Wright Deceased Trust, John William 506

Wylde Memorial Charity, The Anthony and Gwendoline 507

....

■ **Clergy**

Funding priority

Anglo-Catholic Ordination Candidates Fund, The 18

Ballinger Charitable Trust, The 32

Bayne Benefaction 38

Brand Charitable Trust 58

Britland Charitable Trust, The 63

Burden Trust, The 69

Corbett's Charity, Thomas 112

Hurst Will Trust, Arthur 231

Marshall's Charity 300

Milton Mount Foundation 313

Milward Charity, The Edgar 313

Summer's and I May's Charitable Settlement, The Late Misses (A N) 442

Swansea and Brecon Diocesan Board of Finance Ltd 444

Thornton Fund, The 455

....

■ **Clubs**

see also Community services

Funding priority

AB Charitable Trust 3

Aldwyns Trust, The 10

Aston Charities Trust Ltd 25

Bowland Charitable Trust, The 57

Brotherton Trust, The Charles 65

Clarke Trust, The Thomas Edward 99

Clipsham Charitable Settlement, R E 101

Curriers Company Charitable Fund 119

Dahl Foundation, The Roald 122

Fairway Trust, The 158

Garnett Charitable Trust, The 178

Grange Farm Centre Trust 191

Grant-Lawson Charitable Trust, Lady Virginia *192*
Haslemere Estates Charitable Trust *212*
Isle of Dogs Community Foundation *238*
Johnson Group Cleaners Charity *247*
Paul's Charitable Trust, R J *355*
Sell Charitable Trust, Leslie *415*
Singer Foundation *423*
Sulgrave Charitable Trust *442*
TSB Foundation for Scotland *447*
Wates Foundation, The *481*

Will consider

Alexandra Trust *11*
Amory Charitable Trust, Viscount *16*
Anstey Charitable Settlement, J C W *18*
Aquarius Charitable Foundation, The *19*
Askew Trust, The Dorothy *25*
Barbour Trust, The *33*
Berkshire Community Trust *45*
Bewley Charitable Trust, The *46*
BibleLands *47*
Birtwistle Memorial Trust, The G E *50*
Bisgood Trust, The *50*
Bisgood's Charitable Trust, Miss Jeanne *50*
Blakenham's Charity Trust, Lady *53*
Blanchminster Trust, The *54*
Boots Charitable Trust *56*
Bridge Trust, The *60*
Brighton & Hove Charitable Youth Trust *60*
Brough Charitable Trust, Joseph *65*
Butlin Charity Trust, Bill *72*
Cadbury Charitable Trust (Incorporated), Edward *75*
Camelot Foundation, The *78*
Campden Charities, The *79*
Carnegie Dunfermline Trust *82*
Challice Trust, The *87*
Chapman Foundation *88*
Chrimes Family Charitable Trust, The *93*
Community Trust for Greater Manchester, The *108*
County Durham Foundation *115*
Coutts Charitable Trust, The *116*
Curzon Charitable Trust, The Wallace *120*
Derbyshire Trust, J N *130*
Digby Charitable Trust, Simon *133*
Dixon Charitable Trust, F E *134*
Dumbreck Charity *139*

Edgar Foundation, The Gilbert and Eileen *145*
Edgar Trust, The Gilbert *145*
Egerton of Tatton Will Trust, Lord *146*
Elkes Charity Fund, The Wilfred & Elsie *147*
Emmandjay Charitable Trust *150*
Ferguson Benevolent Fund Limited *161*
Fletcher Charitable Trust, The Joyce *164*
Fletcher Trust, Roy *165*
Follett Trust, The *166*
Four Lanes Trust, The *168*
Four Winds Trust *168*
Gardner Charitable Trust, R & J *178*
Gibbins Trust, The *181*
Grant Foundation, The Raymond *191*
Great Britain Sasakawa Foundation, The *193*
Greenaway Foundation, The Sir Derek *194*
Grocers' Charity *197*
Grosshill Charitable Trust *197*
Grundy Foundation, The Stanley *198*
Hamlyn Foundation, The Paul *205*
Harding's Charity, William *209*
Harford Charitable Trust *209*
Henderson's Settlement, J R *216*
Hertfordshire Community Trust, The *217*
Hudson Benevolent Trust, The Thomas *230*
Ingles Charitable Trust, The *234*
Ireland Funds, The *237*
Iris Trust, The *237*
JDM Charitable Trust *239*
Jarrold Trust Ltd, John *243*
Johnson Foundation, The *246*
King Charitable Settlement, Philip *254*
King Charitable Trust, The Lorna *254*
Knott Trust, Sir James *258*
Laing Foundation, The Christopher *260*
Lancaster's Trust, Bryan *263*
Lane Foundation, The Allen *263*
Lawson Charitable Trust, Raymond and Blanche *267*
Leech Charity, The William *269*
Lewis Partnership, John *274*
Lloyd's Charities Trust *278*
(Lloyds) TSB Foundation for England and Wales *279*
London Taxi Drivers' Fund for Underprivileged Children, The *280*
Lord's Taverners, The *281*

Lunn-Rockliffe Charitable Trust, Paul *286*
MacKintosh Charitable Trust, Viscount *292*
Measures Charity, The James Frederick and Ethel Anne *303*
Milburn Charitable Trust, Frederick *310*
Minet Trust, The Peter *313*
Moore Foundation, The George A *316*
National Power Charitable Trust, The *330*
Needham Cooper Charitable Trust, The *331*
New Chasers Charitable Trust, The *332*
New Court Charitable Trust *332*
Newby Trust Ltd *332*
Norman Family Charitable Trust, The *337*
Northcott Devon Foundation *338*
Norton Foundation, The *340*
Oakdale Trust, The *343*
Oldham Foundation *345*
Owen Family Trust, The *348*
PF Charitable Trust *350*
Payne Trust, The Harry *356*
Persula Foundation, The *360*
Porter Foundation *366*
Powell Foundation, The *367*
Pratt Charitable Trust, The W L *367*
Provincial Trust for Kendal, The *370*
Pyke Charity Trust *372*
Ravenscroft Foundation, The *379*
Rayner Charitable Trust, The John *380*
Rest-Harrow Trust, The *382*
Ripley's Charitable Trust, Pat *386*
Robinson Brothers (Ryders Green) Ltd, Charitable Trust *388*
Rope Third Charitable Settlement, The Mrs *391*
Rowbotham Charitable Trust, The Christopher *393*
Sainsbury Charitable Fund Ltd, The *402*
Saint Edmund King and Martyr Trust *402*
St Katharine & Shadwell Trust *404*
Schuster Charitable Trust, The *410*
Seagram Distillers Charitable Trust *413*
Sheldon Trust, The *417*
Shelroy Charitable Trust, The *417*
Shepherd Family Charitable Trust, The Sir Peter *418*

Skelton Bounty, The *423*

South Square Trust *430*

Sparkhill Trust, The *433*

Spooner Charitable Trust, W W *434*

Stoate Charitable Trust, The Leonard Laity *438*

Stonehouse Trust Ltd, Eric *438*

Summerfield Charitable Trust, The *442*

Sussman Charitable Trust, Adrienne & Leslie *443*

Swan Mountain Trust *444*

Sykes Trust, The Charles *445*

TSB Foundation for Northern Ireland *447*

Tear Fund *450*

Thomson Foundation, The Sue *454*

Tisbury Telegraph Trust, The *457*

Torquay Charities, The *458*

Towler Charity Trust, The Fred *459*

Travis Charitable Trust, Constance *460*

Truemark Trust, The *461*

Tudor Trust, The *463*

Tyne & Wear Foundation *466*

Upjohn Charitable Trust, The *469*

Wade & Others, The Charity of Thomas *475*

Wakefield (Tower Hill, Trinity Square) Trust *476*

Wakeham Trust, The *476*

Wall Trust, Thomas *478*

Wander Charitable Fund, The Dr Albert *479*

Watson Foundation, The Bertie *482*

Wesleyan Charitable Trust, The *485*

Westcroft Trust *486*

Whitaker Charitable Trust *489*

Whitecourt Charitable Trust, The *490*

Wills 1961 Charitable Trust, Mr Frederick *493*

Wingate Foundation, The Harold Hyam *496*

Woodlands Trust *501*

Wylde Memorial Charity, The Anthony and Gwendoline *507*

Yorkshire Bank Charitable Trust, The *510*

■ Colleges

see **Schools & colleges**

■ Combined arts

see also **Arts & arts facilities**

Funding priority

North West Arts Board *337*

■ Community arts & recreation

see also **Arts activities, Arts education, Dance groups, Opera companies, opera groups, Orchestras, Theatrical companies, theatre groups**

Funding priority

AHJ Charitable Trust, The *3*

Arts Council of Wales, The *23*

Astor of Hever Trust, The *26*

Astor's 1969 Charity, The Hon M L *26*

Baring Foundation, The *34*

Barnsbury Charitable Trust *35*

Barton Trust, Eleanor *37*

Bergqvist Charitable Trust *44*

Brook Charitable Settlement, R E *64*

Burrough Charitable Trust, The Alan & Rosemary *70*

Chase Charity, The *91*

Cinderford Charitable Trust, The *96*

Clark Charitable Trust, J Anthony *98*

Crescent Trust, The *117*

Daiwa Anglo-Japanese Foundation, The *122*

De Avenley Foundation, The *126*

Denton Charitable Trust, The *130*

Deutsch Charitable Trust, The Andre *131*

Djanogly Foundation, The *135*

D'Oyly Carte Charitable Trust, The *137*

Drayton Trust, The *138*

East Midlands Arts Board Ltd *143*

Eastern Arts Board *143*

Elephant Trust, The *146*

Elmgrant Trust *149*

Fairbairn Charitable Trust, The Esmee *157*

Franklin Trust, Jill *170*

Garthgwynion Charities *179*

Gillett Charitable Trust, J A *183*

Gill's Charitable Trust, Mrs M M *184*

Harewood's Charitable Settlement, Lord *209*

Hargreaves Trust, The Kenneth *210*

Hawthorne Charitable Trust, The *212*

Heinz Company Limited Charitable Trust, The H J *215*

Hitachi Charitable Trust, The *222*

Hornby Charitable Trust, Miss D *227*

Horne Foundation, The *228*

Hornton Trust, The *228*

Kobler Trust, The *258*

Kreitman Foundation *258*

Liebes Charitable Trust, The Martha Bud *274*

London Arts Board *280*

Lucas Charitable Trust Limited, The Joseph *286*

Ludgate Trust, The *286*

Lyons Charitable Trust, Sir Jack *288*

MacKintosh Charitable Trust, Viscount *292*

MacRobert Trusts, The *294*

Marchday Charitable Fund, The *296*

Mellows Charitable Settlement, The Anthony and Elizabeth *305*

Millichope Foundation, The *312*

Moores Foundation, The Peter *318*

Morel Charitable Trust, The *318*

Northern Arts *339*

Oppenheimer Charitable Trust *346*

Owen Trust, Margaret *348*

PDC Trust, The *349*

Pilkington Charitable Trust, Cecil *363*

Pilkington Trust, The Austin and Hope *363*

Pitman Charitable Trust, The John *364*

Powell Foundation, The *367*

Powys Welsh Church Fund *367*

QAS Charitable Trust *373*

Rayne Foundation, The *379*

Reekie Trust, R A & V B *381*

Rodewald's Charitable Settlement, Mr C A *389*

Sheldon Trust, The *417*

Smith (UK) Horticultural Trust, Stanley *428*

South West Arts *431*

Southern Arts *432*

Stewards' Charitable Trust, The *437*

Tesco Charity Trust *452*

Truemark Trust, The *461*

Wade & Others, The Charity of Thomas *475*

Wates Foundation, The *481*

West Midlands Regional Arts Board *486*

Westminster Amalgamated Charity *487*

Wohl Charitable Foundation, The Maurice 498
Wohl Charitable Trust, The Maurice 498
Wolfson Family Charitable Trust, The 499
Wolfson Foundation, The 499

Will consider
Achiezer Association Limited 6
Airflow Community Ltd, The 9
Aleh Charitable Foundation, The 10
Allied Domecq Trust 13
Alper Charitable Trust, The 15
Ammco Trust, The 15
Anderson Trust, Andrew 16
Angler's Inn Trust 17
Anglo Hong Kong Trust, The 17
Appelbe Trust, Ambrose & Ann 19
Aquarius Charitable Foundation, The 19
Aquinas Trust 20
Askew Charitable Trust, The Ian 25
Assembled Church of Christ Trust, The 25
Assheton-Smith Charitable Trust 25
Astor Foundation, The 26
Astor's Charitable Trust, The Hon M L 26
BBC Children in Need Appeal, The 29
Barnby's Foundation, Lord 35
Bateman Charitable Trust, Lady Margaret 37
Bealey Foundation, The 38
Beckwith Charitable Trust, The Peter 40
Beckwith-Smith's Charitable Settlement, Mrs 40
Behrens Charitable Trust, E M 40
Beit Trust, The 40
Benlian Trust, The 44
Black Foundation, The Bertie 51
Blagrave Charitable Trust, The Herbert and Peter 52
Blakenham's Charity Trust, Lady 53
Blakey Charitable Trust, The Celia and Conrad 53
Blank Donations Ltd, The David 54
Boltons Trust, The 55
Borthwick Memorial Trust, The Oliver 56
Bottom Charitable Trust, Harry 56
Bowland Charitable Trust, The 57
British Sugar Foundation 63

Brookhouse's Will Trust, Mr John Charles 65
Brotherton Trust, The Charles 65
Bullough Tompson Settlement, The 68
Burn Charity Trust, The J H 70
Burns Charity, The Dorothy 70
Burry Charitable Trust, The 70
Burton Charitable Trust, The Geoffrey 71
Butler's Trust, Lord 71
Butler's Trust, Lucilla 72
Buxton Trust, Denis 72
CHK Charities Limited 74
Cadbury Schweppes Foundation, The 76
Cadbury Trust (1928), The Edward & Dorothy 76
Campden Charities, The 79
Cardiff & Swansea Methodist District Charitable Trust Fund 80
Carron Charitable Trust, The 83
Castang Charitable Trust, H and M 85
Chapman Foundation 88
Charity Projects 90
Chiddick Charitable Trust 92
Chippindale Foundation, Sam 93
Closehelm Ltd 101
Clutterbuck Charitable Trust, Robert 102
Coates Charitable Settlement, The 102
Coates Charitable Trust 1969, Lance 103
Coates Charitable Trust, The John 103
Cohen Charitable Trust, The Vivienne and Samuel 104
Cohen Charity Trust, Lucy 104
Cohen Foundation, The John S 104
Cole Charitable Trust, The 105
Community Trust for Greater Manchester, The 108
Company of Tobacco Pipe Makers and Tobacco Blenders Benevolent Fund 109
Condon Family Trust 109
Cope Charitable Trust, Alfred 112
Cripplegate Foundation 118
Curry Charitable Trust, Dennis 119
Cymerman Trust Limited, Itzchok Meyer 120
Daily Telegraph Charitable Trust 122
Dandeen Charitable Trust 123
Davies Charity, The Gwendoline and Margaret 125
Davy Foundation, The J 126

De La Rue Charitable Trust 127
De Rothschild 1981 Charitable Trust, The Edmund 127
De Yong Charitable Trust, The Emma 128
Denby Charitable Foundation, The 130
Desmond Charitable Trust, The Richard 131
Deutsch Charitable Trust, The H & M 131
Dibden Allotments Charity 132
Dibs Charitable Trust, The 133
Dicken Charitable Trust, The Albert 133
Dinam Charity 134
Doughty Charity Trust, The 136
Dunn Charitable Trust, The Harry 140
Earmark Trust, The 142
Edinburgh Trust, No 2 Account 145
Egerton of Tatton Will Trust, Lord 146
Eling Trust 147
Elshore Limited 149
European Cultural Foundation (UK Committee) 154
Family Trust, The 158
Famos Foundation Trust 158
Finzi Charitable Trust, Gerald 162
Foreman Foundation, The Carl & Eve 167
Four Lanes Trust, The 168
Foyle Trust, Charles Henry 169
Franklin Bequest, The Rosalind 169
Franklin Deceased's New Second Charity, Sydney E 170
Fry Charitable Trust, Maurice 174
Gannochy Trust, The 177
Gibson's Charity Trust, The Hon Mr & Mrs Clive 182
Girdlers' Company Charitable Trust, The 184
Gold Hill Church Trust 186
Goldberg Charitable Trust, The Lewis 186
Goldsmiths' Company's Charities, The 188
Goodman Charitable Foundation, The Everard and Mina 188
Goodman Trust, The 189
Gradel Foundation, The 189
Green Foundation, Constance 194
Greenaway Foundation, The Sir Derek 194
Gross Charities Limited, M & R 197
Grosshill Charitable Trust 197

Grundy Foundation, The
Stanley 198

Grut Charitable Trust, The 198

Gulbenkian Foundation
(Lisbon) United Kingdom
Branch, Calouste 199

HB Charitable Trust 201

Hacking & Sons Ltd Charitable
Trust, C G 201

Halkes Settlement, John Robert
204

Hamilton Educational Trust,
Eleanor 205

Hampstead Wells and
Campden Trust 206

Harbour Foundation Ltd, The
208

Harford Charitable Trust 209

Harvey Charitable Trust,
Gordon 211

Held Settlement, The Gisela
215

Hillards Charitable Trust, Gay &
Peter Hartley's 220

Holford Trust Fund 224

Hoover Foundation, The 226

Horn Trust, The Cuthbert 227

Hughes Charitable Trust, The
Geoffery C 230

IPE Charitable Trust, The 233

Inman Charity, The 235

Ireland Fund of Great Britain,
The 237

Isle of Dogs Community
Foundation 238

James Foundation, The
Catherine and Lady Grace
241

Jarrold Trust Ltd, John 243

Jones Trust, Cemlyn 248

Joseph Charitable Trust, J E
248

KC Charitable Trust, The 250

Karten Charitable Trust, The
Ian 250

Keyes Trust, The Ursula 253

Kingsgrove Charitable Trust,
The 255

Kinnison Charitable Trust, R O
256

Kleinwort Charitable Trust, The
Ernest 257

Knott Trust, Sir James 258

Kulika Charitable Trust, The
259

Kweller Charitable Trust, The
Harry 259

Laing Charitable Trust, The
David 260

Laing Foundation, The
Christopher 260

Landy Charitable Trust, Harry
and Gertrude 263

Lankelly Foundation, The 264

Lanvern Foundation 265

Laski Memorial Charitable
Trust, Nathan 265

Laspen Trust 265

Lauffer Charitable Foundation,
The R & D 266

Lavender Trust, The 267

Leach Fourteenth Trust, The
267

Leigh-Bramwell Trust 'E', P 270

Levy Charitable Foundation,
Joseph 272

Liffe Benefit 274

Lingwood Charitable Trust, The
276

Lloyd Charity, The S and D 278

Localtrent Ltd 279

Lottery Arts Fund for England,
Scotland, Wales and
Northern Ireland 281

Low & Bonar Charitable Fund,
The 284

Lunzer Charitable Trust, The
Ruth & Jack 287

Lynwood Charitable Trust, The
288

Lyons Charitable Trust, The
288

MDM Memorial Trust 289

MacAndrew Trust, The E M
289

McKechnie Foundation, A N
292

McKenzie Trust, The Robert
292

McLaren Foundation 292

McLaren Memorial Trust, The
Martin 293

Margadale Charitable Trust,
Lord 297

Marks Charitable Trust,
Michael 298

Markus Charitable Foundation,
The Erich 298

Marriage's Charitable Trust,
Miss G M 299

Marr-Munning Trust 299

Marshall Charitable Trust, The
Charlotte 300

Martin Trust, The Sir George
300

Material World Charitable
Foundation Limited, The
301

Mattock Charitable Trust, The
W T 302

Mayfair Charities Limited 303

Measures Charity, The James
Frederick and Ethel Anne
303

Medlock Charitable Trust, The
304

Merchants House of Glasgow
307

Millett Charitable Trust, The
Alan and Janet 312

Minet Trust, The Peter 313

Modiano Charitable Trust 315

Montefiore Trust, The David
316

Moore Charitable Trust, The
Horace 316

Moore Stephens Charitable
Foundation, The 317

Morgan Crucible Company plc
Charitable Trust, The 319

Morris Charitable Trust, The
Willie & Mabel 320

Moulton Charitable Trust, The
321

Music Sales Charitable Trust,
The 324

Newcastle's 1986 Charitable
Trust, Duke of 333

Newman Charitable Trust, Mr
and Mrs F E F 334

Newstead Charity, The 334

Norfolk's Family Charitable
Trust, Lavinia 336

North West Arts Board 337

Northcott Charity Trust, The
338

Northern Electric Employee
Charity Association 339

Old Possums Practical Trust,
The 344

Oldham Foundation 345

Owen Family Trust, The 348

PJD Charitable Trust 350

Palmer Trust, The Gerald 352

Park Hill Trust, The 353

Pascoe Charitable Trust, Alan
354

Paul Charitable Trust, The Late
Barbara May 355

Paul Charitable Trust, Margaret
Jeanne 355

Paul Charitable Trust, Pamela
Milton 355

Paul Foundation, The 355

Paul's Charitable Trust, R J 355

Payne Charitable Trust, The
355

Pelech Charitable Trust, The
358

Perry Charitable Trust, Miss
Frances Lucille 359

Pershore Nashdom & Elmore
Trust Ltd, The 360

Persula Foundation, The 360

Peskin Charitable Trust, The
Hazel and Leslie 360

Phillips Charitable Foundation,
Reginald M 361

Pitt Trust, Headley 364

Porter Foundation 366

Provincial Trust for Kendal, The
370

Puebla Charitable Trust
Limited, The 371

Quothquan Charitable Trust,
The Second 373

RT Trust, The 374

Rackham Charitable Trust, The
Mr & Mrs Philip 375

Rae Charity, H J 375

Rainford Trust, The 376

Rav Chesed Trust, The 379

Rayner Charitable Trust, The
John 380

Reuter Foundation, The *382*
Richards Charity, The Clive *384*
Richmond Parish Lands Charity *384*
Rivendell Trust, The *387*
Robbins Trust, The Cheshire *387*
Rogers Charitable Settlement, The Richard *390*
Rolfe Charitable Trust, The *390*
Rosen Foundation, Cecil *392*
S Group Charitable Trust *399*
St Jude's Trust *403*
Salters Charities *405*
Samuel Charitable Trust, M J *406*
Save & Prosper Educational Trust *408*
Save & Prosper Foundation *409*
Scarr-Hall Memorial Trust, The *409*
Seva Trust, Rampaba Sadhu *415*
Sherman Charitable Trust, The Archie *419*
Shifrin Charitable Trust, The Maurice and Hilda *419*
Sidbury Trust, The Second *421*
Silvester Charitable Gift Trust *422*
Simon's Charity *422*
Skelton Bounty, The *423*
Skinners' Company Lady Neville Charity *424*
Sobell Welsh People's Charitable Association, Michael *429*
Society of Friends of the Torah, The *429*
Solomons Charitable Trust, David *430*
Somerfield Curtis Will Trust, The Dorothy *430*
South East Arts Board *430*
Stanley Foundation Limited *435*
Stewart Charitable Trust, Mary Stephanie *437*
Strauss Charitable Trust *440*
Sumner's Trust Section 'A', Sir John *443*
Symons Charitable Trust, The Stella *446*
TSB Foundation for Scotland *447*
Tait Charity, The Richard *448*
Taylor Charitable Trust, The B R *450*
Terry Charitable Trust, Noel Goddard *451*
Tesler Foundation, The *452*
Thomson Foundation, The Sue *454*
Tyne & Wear Foundation *466*
van Geest Foundation, The John and Lucille *470*

Van Norden's Charitable Foundation, Mrs Maud *471*
Vincent Trust Fund, Eric W *473*
Vineyard Christian Fellowship of South West *473*
Vinson Charity Trust, The 1969 *473*
Vogel Charitable Trust, The Nathan *474*
Wakefield Trust, The *476*
Wakeham Trust, The *476*
Walker Trust, The *477*
Wall Trust, Thomas *478*
Ward Blenkinsop Trust, The *480*
Weinstock Fund, The *484*
Welby Trust, The Barbara *484*
Whetherly's Charitable Trust, The Hon Mrs R G A *489*
Whitehead Charitable Trust, J E *490*
Whittington Charitable Trust, The *491*
Wiggins Charity Trust, Cyril *491*
Wilde Charitable Trust, The Felicity *492*
Wills 1961 Charitable Trust, Major Michael Thomas *494*
Wingate Foundation, The Harold Hyam *496*
Wingfield's Charitable Trust, Mrs *496*
Winstone Foundation, Hyman *497*
Woburn 1986 Charitable Trust *498*
Wolff Charity Trust *498*
Woodhouse Charitable Trust, Edwin *501*
Woods Charitable Foundation, Geoffrey *502*
Worms Charitable Trust, The Freda and Della *504*
Worshipful Company of Needlemakers' Charitable Fund *505*
Wright Deceased Trust, John William *506*
Wychdale Limited *507*
Youell Foundation Ltd, The *510*
Zaiger Trust, The Elizabeth and Prince *512*

....

■ Community businesses

see also Infrastructure development

Funding priority
Baring Foundation, The *34*
Ferguson Benevolent Fund Limited *161*
Homeless International *225*
St Katharine & Shadwell Trust *404*

Will consider
Ashby Charitable Trust, The *23*
Aston Charities Trust Ltd *25*
Berkshire Community Trust *45*
Body Shop Foundation, The *55*
British Sugar Foundation *63*
Collier Charitable Trust, The *105*
County Durham Foundation *115*
Coutts Charitable Trust, The *116*
de Freitas Charitable Trust, The Helen and Geoffrey *126*
Digby Charitable Trust, Simon *133*
Direct Response *134*
Ford of Britain Trust *166*
Four Lanes Trust, The *168*
Goldsmiths' Company's Charities, The *188*
Graves Charitable Trust, J G *192*
Greenaway Foundation, The Sir Derek *194*
Humanitarian Trust, The *230*
Hussey for Africans, Charity of Rebecca *231*
Ireland Funds, The *237*
Isle of Dogs Community Foundation *238*
Knott Trust, Sir James *258*
Lane Foundation, The Allen *263*
Leech Charity, The William *269*
Lewis Foundation, The John Spedan *274*
London Law Trust *280*
Marr-Munning Trust *299*
National Power Charitable Trust, The *330*
Noah Trust, The *335*
Puebla Charitable Trust Limited, The *371*
Rope Third Charitable Settlement, The Mrs *391*
Sainsbury Charitable Fund Ltd, The *402*
Summerfield Charitable Trust, The *442*
Tear Fund *450*
Tyne & Wear Foundation *466*
Wall Trust, Thomas *478*

....

■ Community centres & village halls

see also Community facilities

Funding priority
Aston Charities Trust Ltd *25*
Carnegie United Kingdom Trust, The *82*
Chapman Foundation *88*
Community Trust for Greater Manchester, The *108*

County Durham Foundation
115
Dixon Charitable Trust, F E *134*
Ford of Britain Trust *166*
Grange Farm Centre Trust *191*
Hillards Charitable Trust, Gay &
Peter Hartley's *220*
Isle of Dogs Community
Foundation *238*
King Charitable Trust, The
Lorna *254*
Lancaster's Trust, Bryan *263*
Moore Foundation, The
George A *316*
Rothley Trust, The *392*
Skerritt Trust *423*
TSB Foundation for Scotland
447
Wates Foundation, The *481*

Will consider
Ammco Trust, The *15*
Amory Charitable Trust,
Viscount *16*
Andrew Charitable Trust, The
Prince *16*
Angler's Inn Trust *17*
Aquarius Charitable
Foundation, The *19*
Ashley Foundation, The Laura
24
Astor of Hever Trust, The *26*
Barbour Trust, The *33*
Barratt Charitable Trust, The
Elaine *36*
Barrie Charitable Trust, The
Misses *36*
Beit Trust, The *40*
Berkshire Community Trust *45*
Blanchminster Trust, The *54*
Boots Charitable Trust *56*
Bowland Charitable Trust, The
57
Brand Trust, The *59*
Bridge Trust, The *60*
Brough Charitable Trust,
Joseph *65*
Buckinghamshire Masonic
Centenary Fund *67*
Bullough Tompson Settlement,
The *68*
Burdall Charity, H M *69*
Butler's Trust, Lord *71*
Butlin Charity Trust, Bill *72*
Cadbury Charitable Trust
(Incorporated), Edward *75*
Camelot Foundation, The *78*
Campden Charities, The *79*
Carnegie Dunfermline Trust *82*
Challice Trust, The *87*
Chase Charity, The *91*
Chrimes Family Charitable
Trust, The *93*
Clark 1965 Charitable Trust,
Stephen *98*
Clifford Charity Oxford, The
100

Clinton's Charitable Trust, Lord
100
Cloudesley's Charity/School
Parents & Friends
Association, Richard *102*
Clutterbuck Charitable Trust,
Robert *102*
Construction Industry Trust for
Youth, The *110*
Coutts Charitable Trust, The
116
Dahl Foundation, The Roald
122
de Freitas Charitable Trust, The
Helen and Geoffrey *126*
Dean Refugee Trust Fund, The
Miriam *128*
Derbyshire Trust, J N *130*
Dibden Allotments Charity *132*
Dibs Charitable Trust, The *133*
Digby Charitable Trust, Simon
133
Direct Response *134*
Dulverton Trust, The *139*
Dumbreck Charity *139*
Early's Charitable Settlement,
Richard *142*
Edgar Foundation, The Gilbert
and Eileen *145*
Education Services *145*
Elkes Charity Fund, The Wilfred
& Elsie *147*
Emmandjay Charitable Trust
150
Fletcher Charitable Trust, The
Joyce *164*
Fletcher Trust, Roy *165*
Follett Trust, The *166*
Four Lanes Trust, The *168*
Frognal Trust *174*
Grant-Lawson Charitable Trust,
Lady Virginia *192*
Great Britain Sasakawa
Foundation, The *193*
Greenaway Foundation, The Sir
Derek *194*
Gwent County Council Welsh
Church Fund *200*
Halkes Settlement, John Robert
204
Hamlyn Foundation, The Paul
205
Harford Charitable Trust *209*
Hartley Memorial Trust, The N
& P *211*
Henderson's Settlement, J R
216
Hudson Benevolent Trust, The
Thomas *230*
Hussey for Africans, Charity of
Rebecca *231*
Ingles Charitable Trust, The
234
Ireland Funds, The *237*
JCSCJ Charitable Trust, The
238
JDM Charitable Trust *239*
Johnson Foundation, The *246*

Johnson Group Cleaners
Charity *247*
Knott Trust, Sir James *258*
Laing Charitable Trust, The
David *260*
Laing Foundation, The
Christopher *260*
Lane Foundation, The Allen
263
Lankelly Foundation, The *264*
Lawson Charitable Trust,
Raymond and Blanche *267*
Leach Fourteenth Trust, The
267
Lee Foundation, The Edgar
269
Leech Charity, The William *269*
Littler Foundation, The Emile
277
Living and Waking Naturally
278
(Lloyds) TSB Foundation for
England and Wales *279*
Lyndhurst Settlement *287*
MacKintosh Charitable Trust,
Viscount *292*
Marriage's Charitable Trust,
Miss G M *299*
Middlesex County Rugby
Football Union Memorial
Fund *309*
Milburn Charitable Trust,
Frederick *310*
Moores Foundation, John *318*
Morel Charitable Trust, The
318
National Power Charitable
Trust, The *330*
Needham Cooper Charitable
Trust, The *331*
Newby Trust Ltd *332*
Norfolk's Family Charitable
Trust, Lavinia *336*
Norman Family Charitable
Trust, The *337*
North British Hotel Trust *337*
North West Arts Board *337*
Northcott Devon Foundation
338
Norton Foundation, The *340*
Oakdale Trust, The *343*
Owen Family Trust, The *348*
Paristamen Foundation, The
352
Patients' Aid Association
Hospital and Medical
Charities Trust *354*
Payne Trust, The Harry *356*
Persula Foundation, The *360*
Porter Foundation *366*
Provincial Trust for Kendal, The
370
Pye Christian Trust, The *371*
Pyke Charity Trust *372*
Rayner Charitable Trust, The
John *380*
Reekie Trust, R A & V B *381*

Ripley's Charitable Trust, Pat 386

Rookes Charitable Trust, C A 390

SMB Trust, The 400

Saint Sarkis Charity Trust 404

Scott Charitable Trust, The Francis C 412

Seagram Distillers Charitable Trust 413

Sheepdrove Trust, The 417

Shelroy Charitable Trust, The 417

Shepherd Family Charitable Trust, The Sir Peter 418

Skelton Bounty, The 423

Smith & Mount Trust, The Mrs 426

Sobell Welsh People's Charitable Association, Michael 429

Southern Arts 432

Spoore, Merry & Rixman Foundation, The 434

Stevens Foundation, The June 437

Stoate Charitable Trust, The Leonard Laity 438

Summerfield Charitable Trust, The 442

Sussman Charitable Trust, Adrienne & Leslie 443

Swan Mountain Trust 444

Sykes Trust, The Charles 445

Symons Charitable Trust, The Stella 446

TSB Foundation for Northern Ireland 447

Torquay Charities, The 458

Towler Charity Trust, The Fred 459

Travis Charitable Trust, Constance 460

Truemark Trust, The 461

Tudor Trust, The 463

Tyne & Wear Foundation 466

Upjohn Charitable Trust, The 469

Victoria & Johnson Memorial Trust, Queen 472

Wagstaff Charitable Trust, Bob 475

Wakefield (Tower Hill, Trinity Square) Trust 476

Wall Trust, Thomas 478

Wander Charitable Fund, The Dr Albert 479

Wesleyan Charitable Trust, The 485

Whitaker Charitable Trust 489

Williams Charitable Trust, Alfred 493

Wills 1961 Charitable Trust, Mr Frederick 493

Wills 1962 Charitable Trust, P J H 494

Wingfield's Charitable Trust, Mrs 496

Wolfe Family's Charitable Trust, The 498

Women Caring Trust, The 500

Wylde Memorial Charity, The Anthony and Gwendoline 507

Yorkshire Bank Charitable Trust, The 510

....

■ Community development

see also Infrastructure development, Training for community development

Funding priority

Aston Charities Trust Ltd 25

Baring Foundation, The 34

County Durham Foundation 115

De La Rue Charitable Trust 127

Ferguson Benevolent Fund Limited 161

HACT (The Housing Association's Charitable Trust) 201

Hertfordshire Community Trust, The 217

Homeless International 225

Hood's Charitable Trust, Sir Harold 226

Marr-Munning Trust 299

Moores Foundation, John 318

National Power Charitable Trust, The 330

Northern Ireland Voluntary Trust 339

Puebla Charitable Trust Limited, The 371

St Katharine & Shadwell Trust 404

Wiltshire Community Foundation 495

Will consider

Abel Charitable Trust 5

Barbour Trust, The 33

Berkshire Community Trust 45

BibleLands 47

Blake Charitable Trust, The Hubert 53

Body Shop Foundation, The 55

British Sugar Foundation 63

Brotherton Trust, The Charles 65

Brough Charitable Trust, Joseph 65

Camelot Foundation, The 78

Campden Charities, The 79

Cleopatra Trust 99

Collier Charitable Trust, The 105

Community Trust for Greater Manchester, The 108

Coutts Charitable Trust, The 116

Cripplegate Foundation 118

de Freitas Charitable Trust, The Helen and Geoffrey 126

Derbyshire Trust, J N 130

Digby Charitable Trust, Simon 133

Direct Response 134

Ford of Britain Trust 166

Four Lanes Trust, The 168

Four Winds Trust 168

Goldsmiths' Company's Charities, The 188

Great Britain Sasakawa Foundation, The 193

Greenaway Foundation, The Sir Derek 194

Growth Building Trust, The 198

Humanitarian Trust, The 230

Hussey for Africans, Charity of Rebecca 231

Hyde Park Place Estate Charity, The 232

IBM United Kingdom Trust 233

Ireland Funds, The 237

Isle of Dogs Community Foundation 238

Johnson Foundation, The 246

Knott Trust, Sir James 258

Lane Foundation, The Allen 263

Leech Charity, The William 269

Lloyd's Charities Trust 278

London Law Trust 280

Low & Bonar Charitable Fund, The 284

Manning Trust, Leslie & Lilian 296

Milton Keynes Community Trust Ltd, The 312

Minet Trust, The Peter 313

New Chasers Charitable Trust, The 332

Newby Trust Ltd 332

Noah Trust, The 335

Norwich Church of England Young Men's Society 340

Owen Family Trust, The 348

Paristamen Foundation, The 352

Parivar Trust, The 353

Powell Foundation, The 367

Prince's Trust (now includes King George's Jubilee Trust (1935) and the Queen's Silver Jubilee Trust (1977)), The 369

Richmond Parish Lands Charity 384

Rope Third Charitable Settlement, The Mrs 391

Rowntree Foundation, Joseph 394

Sainsbury Charitable Fund Ltd, The 402

Scott Bader Commonwealth Ltd, The *411*
Sheldon Trust, The *417*
Singer Foundation *423*
Skelton Bounty, The *423*
Smith & Mount Trust, The Mrs *426*
South Yorkshire Community Foundation *431*
Summerfield Charitable Trust, The *442*
TSB Foundation for Northern Ireland *447*
Tear Fund *450*
Thomson Foundation, The Sue *454*
Tudor Trust, The *463*
Tyne & Wear Foundation *466*
Van Leer Foundation UK Trust, Bernard *470*
Wade & Others, The Charity of Thomas *475*
Wakefield (Tower Hill, Trinity Square) Trust *476*
Wall Trust, Thomas *478*
War on Want *479*
Whesby Ltd *488*
Whitaker Charitable Trust *489*
Woodlands Trust *501*
Woolton Charitable Trust, The *503*

....

■ Community facilities

see also **Art galleries & cultural centres, Community centres & village halls, Libraries & museums, Parks, Playgrounds, Recreation grounds, Sports centres, Theatres & opera houses**

Funding priority
Aga Khan Foundation (UK) *7*
Allachy Trust, The *12*
Anderson Trust, Andrew *16*
Angler's Inn Trust *17*
Army Benevolent Fund, The *22*
Barnby's Foundation, Lord *35*
Barnes Workhouse Fund *35*
Barnsbury Charitable Trust *35*
Bilton Charity, The Percy *48*
Brook Charitable Settlement, R E *64*
Brough Charitable Trust, Joseph *65*
Burton Charitable Trust, The Geoffrey *71*
Chippindale Foundation, Sam *93*
Clarke Trust, The Thomas Edward *99*
Condon Family Trust *109*
Corbett's Charity, Thomas *112*
De La Rue Charitable Trust *127*
Djanogly Foundation, The *135*

Elvetham Charitable Trust, The *149*
Fairbairn Charitable Trust, The Esmee *157*
Friarsgate Trust *172*
Garthgwynion Charities *179*
George's Fund for Sailors, King *180*
Good Neighbours Trust, The *188*
Green Foundation, Constance *194*
HB Charitable Trust *201*
Hacking & Sons Ltd Charitable Trust, C G *201*
Hampton Fuel Allotment Charity *207*
Hawthorne Charitable Trust, The *212*
Ireland Fund of Great Britain, The *237*
Irving Charitable Trust, The Charles *237*
Jerusalem Trust *244*
Jones Trust, Cemlyn *248*
KC Charitable Trust, The *250*
Lester Trust Fund, The *271*
Lister Charitable Trust, The *277*
Living and Waking Naturally *278*
Lord's Taverners, The *281*
Lyons Charitable Trust, Sir Jack *288*
MacRobert Trusts, The *294*
Martin Trust, The Sir George *300*
Millfield House Foundation *312*
Millichope Foundation, The *312*
Moores Foundation, The Peter *318*
Morgan Crucible Company plc Charitable Trust, The *319*
Munro Charitable Trust, The *323*
Owen Family Trust, The *348*
Owen Trust, Margaret *348*
Pitman Charitable Trust, The John *364*
Powys Welsh Church Fund *367*
Robyn Charitable Trust *389*
Rodewald's Charitable Settlement, Mr C A *389*
Shuttlewood Clarke Foundation, The *421*
Southall Charitable Trust, Kenneth & Phyllis *431*
Street Charitable Foundation, W O *440*
TSB Foundation for the Channel Islands *447*
Tesco Charity Trust *452*
Watson's Trust, John *482*
Wohl Charitable Foundation, The Maurice *498*

Wohl Charitable Trust, The Maurice *498*
Yapp Welfare Trust, The *508*

Will consider
AB Charitable Trust, The *3*
AHJ Charitable Trust, The *3*
Achiezer Association Limited *6*
Airflow Community Ltd, The *9*
Ajahma Charitable Trust, The *9*
Aleh Charitable Foundation, The *10*
Alexandra Trust *11*
Appelbe Trust, Ambrose & Ann *19*
Aquarian Healing Trust *19*
Aquarius Charitable Foundation, The *19*
Aquinas Trust *20*
Arnopa Trust, The *22*
Ashley Foundation, The Laura *24*
Askew Charitable Trust, The Ian *25*
Assembled Church of Christ Trust, The *25*
Assheton-Smith Charitable Trust *25*
Astor Foundation, The *26*
Astor's 1969 Charity, The Hon M L *26*
Austin of Longbridge Will Trust, The Rt Hon Herbert, Baron *27*
Baker Charitable Trust, The *30*
Baring Foundation, The *34*
Barnabas Charitable Trust *34*
Barratt Charitable Trust, The Elaine *36*
Barton Trust, Eleanor *37*
Bateman Charitable Trust, Lady Margaret *37*
Bealey Foundation, The *38*
Bear Mordechai Ltd *39*
Beattie Charitable Trust, The James *39*
Beckwith Charitable Trust, The Peter *40*
Beckwith-Smith's Charitable Settlement, Mrs *40*
Bergqvist Charitable Trust *44*
Black Charitable Trust, Edna *51*
Black Charitable Trust, Sydney *51*
Black Foundation, The Bertie *51*
Blagrave Charitable Trust, The Herbert and Peter *52*
Blakenham's Charity Trust, Lady *53*
Blakey Charitable Trust, The Celia and Conrad *53*
Blank Donations Ltd, The David *54*

Bloom Foundation, Abraham Algy *54*
Boltons Trust, The *55*
Borthwick Memorial Trust, The Oliver *56*
Bottom Charitable Trust, Harry *56*
Brand Trust, The *59*
British Sugar Foundation *63*
Brookhouse's Will Trust, Mr John Charles *65*
Brotherton Trust, The Charles *65*
Burn Charity Trust, The J H *70*
Burns Charity, The Dorothy *70*
Burry Charitable Trust, The *70*
Butler's Trust, Lucilla *72*
Buxton Trust, Denis *72*
Cadbury Charitable Trust (Incorporated), Edward *75*
Cadbury Schweppes Foundation, The *76*
Cadbury Trust (1928), The Edward & Dorothy *76*
Cardiff & Swansea Methodist District Charitable Trust Fund *80*
Carron Charitable Trust, The *83*
Castang Charitable Trust, H and M *85*
Chapman Foundation *88*
Charity for Change *89*
Charity Projects *90*
Chrimes Family Charitable Trust, The *93*
Christian Aid *94*
Church Urban Fund *95*
Cinderford Charitable Trust, The *96*
City and Metropolitan Welfare Charity, The *96*
Clark Charitable Trust *98*
Clark Charitable Trust, J Anthony *98*
Closehelm Ltd *101*
Coates Charitable Settlement, The *102*
Coates Charitable Trust 1969, Lance *103*
Cohen Charitable Trust, The Vivienne and Samuel *104*
Cohen Charity Trust, Lucy *104*
Cohen Foundation, The John S *104*
Cole Charitable Trust, The *105*
Company of Tobacco Pipe Makers and Tobacco Blenders Benevolent Fund *109*
Cope Charitable Trust, Alfred *112*
Cotton Trust, The *114*
Crescent Trust, The *117*
Cripplegate Foundation *118*
Curry Charitable Trust, Dennis *119*

Cymerman Trust Limited, Itzchok Meyer *120*
Daily Telegraph Charitable Trust *122*
Dandeen Charitable Trust *123*
Davies Charity, The Gwendoline and Margaret *125*
Davy Foundation, The J *126*
De Avenley Foundation, The *126*
De Rothschild 1981 Charitable Trust, The Edmund *127*
De Yong Charitable Trust, The Emma *128*
Denton Charitable Trust, The *130*
Desmond Charitable Trust, The Richard *131*
Deutsch Charitable Trust, The Andre *131*
Deutsch Charitable Trust, The H & M *131*
Dicken Charitable Trust, The Albert *133*
Dinam Charity *134*
Doughty Charity Trust, The *136*
D'Oyly Carte Charitable Trust, The *137*
Drapers' Charitable Fund *137*
Drayton Trust, The *138*
Dunn Charitable Trust, The Harry *140*
Edinburgh Trust, No 2 Account *145*
Eling Trust *147*
Ellis 1985 Charitable Trust, Edith M *148*
Elshore Limited *149*
Emanuel Charitable Settlement, Ralph and Muriel *150*
Family Trust, The *158*
Famos Foundation Trust *158*
Federation of Jewish Relief Organisations *160*
Foreman Foundation, The Carl & Eve *167*
Foyle Trust, Charles Henry *169*
Franklin Bequest, The Rosalind *169*
Franklin Deceased's New Second Charity, Sydney E *170*
Frome Christian Fellowship *174*
Fry Charitable Trust, Maurice *174*
Galinski Charitable Trust *177*
Gibbs Charitable Trusts, The *181*
Gibson's Charity Trust, The Hon Mr & Mrs Clive *182*
Gillett Charitable Trust, J A *183*
Gill's Charitable Trust, Mrs M M *184*

Girdlers' Company Charitable Trust, The *184*
Gladstone Charitable Trust, The E W *184*
Glynde Place Charitable Trust (1974), The *186*
Gold Hill Church Trust *186*
Goldberg Charitable Trust, The Lewis *186*
Golders Green Foundation *187*
Goldsmiths' Company's Charities, The *188*
Goodman Charitable Foundation, The Everard and Mina *188*
Goodman Trust, The *189*
Goodman Trust, The S & F *189*
Gradel Foundation, The *189*
Graves Charitable Trust, J G *192*
Greenaway Foundation, The Sir Derek *194*
Gross Charities Limited, M & R *197*
Grosshill Charitable Trust *197*
Grut Charitable Trust, The *198*
Gulbenkian Foundation (Lisbon) United Kingdom Branch, Calouste *199*
Halkes Settlement, John Robert *204*
Hamilton Educational Trust, Eleanor *205*
Hampstead Wells and Campden Trust *206*
Harbour Foundation Ltd, The *208*
Hargreaves Trust, The Kenneth *210*
Harvey Charitable Trust, Gordon *211*
Heinz Company Limited Charitable Trust, The H J *215*
Held Settlement, The Gisela *215*
Hitachi Charitable Trust, The *222*
Holford Trust Fund *224*
Hoover Foundation, The *226*
Horn Trust, The Cuthbert *227*
Hornby Charitable Trust, Miss D *227*
Hornton Trust, The *228*
Hughes Charitable Trust, The Geoffery C *230*
Hyde Park Place Estate Charity, The *232*
IPE Charitable Trust, The *233*
Inman Charity, The *235*
Isle of Dogs Community Foundation *238*
JCA Charitable Foundation *238*
Jacobs Charitable Trust, The J P *240*
James Foundation, The Catherine and Lady Grace *241*

Jubilee Outreach Yorkshire *248*

Karten Charitable Trust, The Ian *250*

Keyes Trust, The Ursula *253*

Kingsgrove Charitable Trust, The *255*

Kinnison Charitable Trust, R O *256*

Kleinwort Charitable Trust, The Ernest *257*

Kobler Trust, The *258*

Kreitman Foundation *258*

Kulika Charitable Trust, The *259*

Kweller Charitable Trust, The Harry *259*

Laing Charitable Trust, The David *260*

Laing's Charitable Trust *262*

Landy Charitable Trust, Harry and Gertrude *263*

Langley Charitable Trust, The *264*

Lanvern Foundation *265*

Laski Memorial Charitable Trust, Nathan *265*

Laspen Trust *265*

Lauffer Charitable Foundation, The R & D *266*

Lavender Trust, The *267*

Lawley Foundation, The Edgar E *267*

Leach Fourteenth Trust, The *267*

Lee Foundation, The Edgar *269*

Leigh-Bramwell Trust 'E', P *270*

Levy Charitable Foundation, Joseph *272*

Lewis Family Charitable Trust, The *273*

Liffe Benefit *274*

Lingwood Charitable Trust, The *276*

Littler Foundation, The Emile *277*

Localtrent Ltd *279*

Lottery Sports Funds for England, Northern Ireland, Scotland and Wales *283*

Lucas Charitable Trust Limited, The Joseph *286*

Lunzer Charitable Trust, The Ruth & Jack *287*

Lynn Foundation, The *288*

Lynwood Charitable Trust, The *288*

Lyons Charitable Trust, The *288*

Lyon's Charity, John *288*

MDM Memorial Trust *289*

MacAndrew Trust, The E M *289*

Maccabi Foundation, The *290*

McKechnie Foundation, A N *292*

McKenzie Trust, The Robert *292*

McLaren Foundation *292*

McLaren Memorial Trust, The Martin *293*

Margadale Charitable Trust, Lord *297*

Marks Charitable Trust, Michael *298*

Marks Foundation, The Hilda and Samuel *298*

Markus Charitable Foundation, The Erich *298*

Marr-Munning Trust *299*

Marshall Charitable Trust, The Charlotte *300*

Matchan Fund Limited, The Leonard *301*

Material World Charitable Foundation Limited, The *301*

Mattock Charitable Trust, The W T *302*

Mayfair Charities Limited *303*

Measures Charity, The James Frederick and Ethel Anne *303*

Medlock Charitable Trust, The *304*

Mellows Charitable Settlement, The Anthony and Elizabeth *305*

Mid Moss Charitable Trust, The *309*

Milburn Charitable Trust, Frederick *310*

Millett Charitable Trust, The Alan and Janet *312*

Minet Trust, The Peter *313*

Modiano Charitable Trust *315*

Montefiore Trust, The David *316*

Moore Charitable Trust, The Horace *316*

Morris Charitable Trust, The Willie & Mabel *320*

Moulton Charitable Trust, The *321*

Music Sales Charitable Trust, The *324*

National Lottery Charities Board *328*

Newcastle Children's Mission & Institute *333*

Newcastle's 1986 Charitable Trust, Duke of *333*

Newman Charitable Trust, Mr and Mrs F E F *334*

Newstead Charity, The *334*

Norfolk's Family Charitable Trust, Lavinia *336*

Northcott Charity Trust, The *338*

Northern Dairies Educational Trust *339*

Northern Electric Employee Charity Association *339*

Northern Ireland Voluntary Trust *339*

Old Possums Practical Trust, The *344*

Oppenheimer Charitable Trust *346*

PDC Trust, The *349*

PJD Charitable Trust *350*

Palmer Trust, The Gerald *352*

Park Hill Trust, The *353*

Pascoe Charitable Trust, Alan *354*

Paul Charitable Trust, The Late Barbara May *355*

Paul Charitable Trust, Margaret Jeanne *355*

Paul Charitable Trust, Pamela Milton *355*

Paul Foundation, The *355*

Paul's Charitable Trust, R J *355*

Payne Charitable Trust, The *355*

Pelech Charitable Trust, The *358*

Peppiatt Charitable Trust, The Brian *359*

Perry Charitable Trust, Miss Frances Lucille *359*

Pershore Nashdom & Elmore Trust Ltd, The *360*

Personal Assurance Charitable Trust *360*

Peskin Charitable Trust, The Hazel and Leslie *360*

Phillips Charitable Foundation, Reginald M *361*

Pilkington Charitable Trust, Cecil *363*

Pitt Trust, Headley *364*

Powell Foundation, The *367*

Puebla Charitable Trust Limited, The *371*

QAS Charitable Trust *373*

Quothquan Charitable Trust, The Second *373*

RT Trust, The *374*

Rackham Charitable Trust, The Mr & Mrs Philip *375*

Radley Charitable Trust *375*

Rae Charity, H J *375*

Rainford Trust, The *376*

Rav Chesed Trust, The *379*

Rayne Foundation, The *379*

Reader's Digest Trust, The *380*

Reuter Foundation, The *382*

Richards Charity, The Clive *384*

Richmond Parish Lands Charity *384*

Riley-Smith Charitable Trust, The F A *386*

Rivendell Trust, The *387*

Robbins Trust, The Cheshire *387*

Rogers Charitable Settlement, The Richard *390*

Rokeby Charitable Trust *390*

Rolfe Charitable Trust, The *390*

Rosen Foundation, Cecil *392*

Community issues (campaigning)

Trusts by field of interest and type of beneficiary

Rozel Trust, The *397*
S Group Charitable Trust *399*
St Jude's Trust *403*
St Katharine & Shadwell Trust *404*
Salters Charities *405*
Samuel Charitable Trust, M J *406*
Sassoon Charitable Trust, The Late Aaron D *408*
Save & Prosper Foundation *409*
Scarr-Hall Memorial Trust, The *409*
Seva Trust, Rampaba Sadhu *415*
Sherman Charitable Trust, The Archie *419*
Shifrin Charitable Trust, The Maurice and Hilda *419*
Shine No 2 Charitable Trust, The Barnett and Sylvia *420*
Sidbury Trust, The Second *421*
Silvester Charitable Gift Trust *422*
Simon's Charity *422*
Singer Foundation *423*
Skinners' Company Lady Neville Charity *424*
Slater Foundation Ltd, The *424*
Salter Trust Ltd *424*
Society of Friends of the Torah, The *429*
Solomons Charitable Trust, David *430*
Somerfield Curtis Will Trust, The Dorothy *430*
Southall Trust, W F *432*
Stanley Foundation Limited *435*
Stewart Charitable Trust, Mary Stephanie *437*
Sumner's Trust Section 'A', Sir John *443*
Symons Charitable Trust, The Stella *446*
Taylor Charitable Trust, The B R *450*
Terry Charitable Trust, Noel Goddard *451*
Tesler Foundation, The *452*
3i Charitable Trust, The *455*
Turner Charitable Settlement, The Sir Mark and Lady *464*
Turner Trust, The Douglas *464*
Unitek Foundation *469*
van Geest Foundation, The John and Lucille *470*
Van Norden's Charitable Foundation, Mrs Maud *471*
Vincent Trust Fund, Eric W *473*
Vineyard Christian Fellowship of South West *473*
Vinson Charity Trust, The 1969 *473*
Vogel Charitable Trust, The Nathan *474*
Wakefield Trust, The *476*

Ward Blenkinsop Trust, The *480*
Weinstock Fund, The *484*
Welby Trust, The Barbara *484*
Westminster Amalgamated Charity *487*
Whetherly's Charitable Trust, The Hon Mrs R G A *489*
Whitehead Charitable Trust, J E *490*
Whittington Charitable Trust, The *491*
Wiggins Charity Trust, Cyril *491*
Wilde Charitable Trust, The Felicity *492*
Wills 1961 Charitable Trust, Major Michael Thomas *494*
Winstone Foundation, Hyman *497*
Woburn 1986 Charitable Trust *498*
Wolff Charity Trust *498*
Wolfson Family Charitable Trust, The *499*
Wolfson Foundation, The *499*
Wolverhampton Rotary Club Charitable Trust *500*
Woodhouse Charitable Trust, Edwin *501*
Woods Charitable Foundation, Geoffrey *502*
Worms Charitable Trust, The Freda and Della *504*
Worshipful Company of Needlemakers' Charitable Fund *505*
Wright Deceased Trust, John William *506*
Wychdale Limited *507*
Wylde Memorial Charity, The Anthony and Gwendoline *507*
Youell Foundation Ltd, The *510*
Zaiger Trust, The Elizabeth and Prince *512*

see also **Campaigning (social issues)**

■ Community issues (campaigning)
Funding priority
Allachy Trust, The *12*
Aston Charities Trust Ltd *25*
Cadbury Trust, The Barrow *76*
City Parochial Foundation *96*
Garthgwynion Charities *179*
Heinz Company Limited Charitable Trust, The H J *215*
Ireland Fund of Great Britain, The *237*
National Power Charitable Trust, The *330*

Northern Ireland Voluntary Trust *339*
Puebla Charitable Trust Limited, The *371*
Wiltshire Community Foundation *495*

Will consider
Abel Charitable Trust *5*
Astor Foundation, The *26*
Avenal *27*
Barrie Charitable Trust, The Misses *36*
Body Shop Foundation, The *55*
Chrimes Family Charitable Trust, The *93*
Coutts Charitable Trust, The *116*
Curriers Company Charitable Fund *119*
David Trust, The Lesley *124*
Dibs Charitable Trust, The *133*
Digby Charitable Trust, Simon *133*
Dorus Trust *136*
Dumbreck Charity *139*
Epigoni Trust *152*
Fletcher Trust, Roy *165*
Four Winds Trust *168*
Gardner Charitable Trust, R & J *178*
Great Britain Sasakawa Foundation, The *193*
Hamlyn Foundation, The Paul *205*
Harford Charitable Trust *209*
Hyde Charitable Trust *232*
Ireland Funds, The *237*
Iris Trust, The *237*
Irving Charitable Trust, The Charles *237*
Isle of Dogs Community Foundation *238*
JCSCJ Charitable Trust, The *238*
Knott Trust, Sir James *258*
Laing Foundation, The Christopher *260*
Lane Foundation, The Allen *263*
Leech Charity, The William *269*
Lyndhurst Settlement *287*
Minet Trust, The Peter *313*
Morel Charitable Trust, The *318*
Needham Cooper Charitable Trust, The *331*
New Court Charitable Trust *332*
Noah Trust, The *335*
North West Arts Board *337*
Oldham Foundation *345*
Owen Family Trust, The *348*
Patients' Aid Association Hospital and Medical Charities Trust *354*

128

Page references refer to Volume Two

Shelroy Charitable Trust, The
417
Shepherd Family Charitable
Trust, The Sir Peter 418
Skelton Bounty, The 423
Summerfield Charitable Trust,
The 442
Symons Charitable Trust, The
Stella 446
TSB Foundation for Northern
Ireland 447
Tear Fund 450
Tisbury Telegraph Trust, The
457
Tyne & Wear Foundation 466
Wakefield (Tower Hill, Trinity
Square) Trust 476
Wingfield's Charitable Trust,
Mrs 496
Woodhouse Charitable Trust,
Edwin 501

■ Community services

see also **Adoption & fostering services, Care in the community, Clubs, Community transport, Counselling (social issues), Crime prevention schemes, Day centres, Emergency care, refugees, famine, Holidays & outings, Income support & maintenance, Meals provision, Playschemes**

Funding priority

AHJ Charitable Trust, The 3
Access 4 Trust 6
Achiezer Association Limited 6
Aga Khan Foundation (UK) 7
Airflow Community Ltd, The 9
Ajahma Charitable Trust, The
9
Aldwyns Trust, The 10
Allachy Trust, The 12
Allied Dunbar Charitable Trust
Limited, The 13
Allied Dunbar Staff Charity
Fund 13
Allsop Charitable Trust, Pat 14
Anderson Trust, Andrew 16
Angler's Inn Trust 17
Aquinas Trust 20
Arnopa Trust, The 22
Assembled Church of Christ
Trust, The 25
Astor of Hever Trust, The 26
Austin of Longbridge Will
Trust, The Rt Hon Herbert,
Baron 27
Baker Charitable Trust, The 30
Balint Charitable Trust, Paul 31
Ball Charitable Trust, The Bruce
31

Ballinger Charitable Trust, The
32
Barnby's Foundation
Appointed Fund, Lord 35
Barnes Workhouse Fund 35
Barnsbury Charitable Trust 35
Bateman Charitable Trust, Lady
Margaret 37
Bear Mordechai Ltd 39
Beckwith Charitable Trust, The
Peter 40
Betteshanger Charitable Trust
46
Bilton Charity, The Percy 48
Bisgood Trust, The 50
Bisgood's Charitable Trust, Miss
Jeanne 50
Black Charitable Trust, The
Cyril W 51
Black Charitable Trust, Edna
51
Black Charitable Trust, Sydney
51
Black Foundation, The Bertie
51
Blagrave Charitable Trust, The
Herbert and Peter 52
Blakey Charitable Trust, The
Celia and Conrad 53
Brand Charitable Trust 58
Brand Trust, The 59
Brook Charitable Settlement,
R E 64
Brough Charitable Trust,
Joseph 65
Burn Charity Trust, The J H 70
Burrough Charitable Trust, The
Alan & Rosemary 70
Burton Charitable Trust, The
Geoffrey 71
Butler's Trust, Lord 71
Butler's Trust, Lucilla 72
CLA Charitable Trust 74
Cadbury Schweppes
Foundation, The 76
Carlton Television Trust 81
Carter Trust, The Frederick
William 84
Charity Projects 90
Chase Charity, The 91
City and Metropolitan Welfare
Charity, The 96
Clarke Trust, The Thomas
Edward 99
Coates Charitable Settlement,
The 102
Cohen Charitable Trust, The
Vivienne and Samuel 104
Condon Family Trust 109
Construction Industry Trust for
Youth, The 110
Corbett's Charity, Thomas 112
Cotton Trust, The 114
Curtis Charitable Trust, The
Thomas 120
Davenport's Charity Trust,
Baron 124

De La Rue Charitable Trust
127
De Yong Charitable Trust, The
Emma 128
Debtors' Relief Fund Charity
128
Denby Charitable Foundation,
The 130
Denton Charitable Trust, The
130
Devon Association for the
Blind 131
Dibs Charitable Trust, The 133
Dinam Charity 134
Djanogly Foundation, The 135
Doughty Charity Trust, The
136
D'Oyly Carte Charitable Trust,
The 137
Dulverton Trust, The 139
Dunn Charitable Trust, The
Harry 140
Duveen Trust, The 141
Earmark Trust, The 142
Elvetham Charitable Trust, The
149
Fairbairn Charitable Trust, The
Esmee 157
Federation of Jewish Relief
Organisations 160
Fishmongers' Company's
Charitable Trust 163
Fleurus Trust, The 165
Foreman 1980 Charitable Trust,
The Russell and Mary 167
Franklin Deceased's New
Second Charity, Sydney E
170
Franklin Trust, Jill 170
Friarsgate Trust 172
Frome Christian Fellowship
174
Fry Charitable Trust, Maurice
174
Gannochy Trust, The 177
Gardner's Trust for the Blind
178
Garthgwynion Charities 179
Gatsby Charitable Foundation,
The 179
Gibson's Charity Trust, The Hon
Mr & Mrs Clive 182
Glebe Charitable Trust 185
Gold Hill Church Trust 186
Goldberg Charitable Trust, The
Lewis 186
Golders Green Foundation 187
Good Neighbours Trust, The
188
Gough Charitable Trust, The
189
Green Foundation, Constance
194
Grimley Charity, The 196
Gwent County Council Welsh
Church Fund 200
HB Charitable Trust 201

Haberdashers' Eleemosynary Charity 201
Hacking & Sons Ltd Charitable Trust, C G 201
Hale Trust, The 203
Hamlyn Foundation, The Helen 205
Hampton Fuel Allotment Charity 207
Hawthorne Charitable Trust, The 212
Heinz Company Limited Charitable Trust, The H J 215
Held Settlement, The Gisela 215
Hillards Charitable Trust, Gay & Peter Hartley's 220
Hitachi Charitable Trust, The 222
Hobbs Trust Limited, The Betty 222
Hoover Foundation, The 226
Horne Foundation, The 228
IPE Charitable Trust, The 233
Inman Charity, The 235
International Arab Women's Council Charities Fund 236
Ireland Fund of Great Britain, The 237
Irving Charitable Trust, The Charles 237
JCSCJ Charitable Trust, The 238
JL Charity Trust, The 239
Jewish Philanthropic Association for Israel and the Middle East, The 245
Jones Trust, Cemlyn 248
KC Charitable Trust, The 250
Keyes Trust, The Ursula 253
Kinnison Charitable Trust, R O 256
Kleinwort Charitable Trust, The Ernest 257
Lacy Charity Trust, The Late Sir Pierce 260
Langley Charitable Trust, The 264
Layton Charity Trust, The Julian 267
Lester Trust Fund, The 271
Levy Charitable Foundation, Joseph 272
Liebes Charitable Trust, The Martha Bud 274
Lord's Taverners, The 281
Lucas Charitable Trust Limited, The Joseph 286
Lynn Foundation, The 288
Lyons Charitable Trust, The 288
Lyons Charitable Trust, Sir Jack 288
Lyon's Charity, John 288
MacAndrew Trust, The E M 289

McCarthy Foundation, The John 290
McKechnie Foundation, A N 292
McLaren Foundation 292
MacRobert Trusts, The 294
Man of the People Fund 295
Marchday Charitable Fund, The 296
Margadale Charitable Trust, Lord 297
Marks Foundation, The Hilda and Samuel 298
Markus Charitable Foundation, The Erich 298
Marmor Charitable Trust, The Julie 299
Martin Trust, The Sir George 300
Mattock Charitable Trust, The W T 302
Measures Charity, The James Frederick and Ethel Anne 303
Medlock Charitable Trust, The 304
Merchants House of Glasgow 307
Millfield House Foundation 312
Millichope Foundation, The 312
Moore Charitable Trust, The Horace 316
Moores Family Charity Foundation, The 317
Morel Charitable Trust, The 318
Morgan Crucible Company plc Charitable Trust, The 319
Natwest Staff Samaritan Fund 330
Newcastle Children's Mission & Institute 333
Newcastle's 1986 Charitable Trust, Duke of 333
Newman Charitable Trust, Mr and Mrs F E F 334
Newstead Charity, The 334
Northcott Charity Trust, The 338
Northcott Devon Foundation 338
Northern Dairies Educational Trust 339
Northern Electric Employee Charity Association 339
Northern Ireland Voluntary Trust 339
Noswad Charity, The 341
Oliver Trust, Kate Wilson 345
Oppenheimer Charitable Trust 346
Owen Trust, Margaret 348
PDC Trust, The 349
PJD Charitable Trust 350
Paristamen Foundation, The 352

Paul Charitable Trust, Margaret Jeanne 355
Paul's Charitable Trust, R J 355
Pershore Nashdom & Elmore Trust Ltd, The 360
Pick Charitable Trust, The George and Jessie 362
Pickford Charitable Foundation, The David 362
Pitman Charitable Trust, The John 364
Podde Trust 365
Powys Welsh Church Fund 367
Proctor Charitable Trust, The Albert Edward 370
Puebla Charitable Trust Limited, The 371
Rae Charity, H J 375
Rank Xerox Trust, The 378
Ravenscroft Foundation, The 379
Rayne Foundation, The 379
Reekie Trust, R A & V B 381
Richards Charity, The Clive 384
Richards Charity, The Violet M 384
Riley-Smith Charitable Trust, The F A 386
Rivendell Trust, The 387
Robyn Charitable Trust 389
Rodewald's Charitable Settlement, Mr C A 389
Rope Third Charitable Settlement, The Mrs 391
Rosen Foundation, Cecil 392
Rowan Charitable Trust, The 393
Rozel Trust, The 397
Saint Sarkis Charity Trust 404
Sassoon Charitable Trust, The Late Aaron D 408
Scott Charitable Trust, The Francis C 412
Sell Charitable Trust, Leslie 415
Shifrin Charitable Trust, The Maurice and Hilda 419
Shine No 2 Charitable Trust, The Barnett and Sylvia 420
Shuttlewood Clarke Foundation, The 421
Salter Trust Ltd 424
Smith Foundation, The Leslie 427
Southall Charitable Trust, Kenneth & Phyllis 431
Southall Trust, W F 432
Sparkes Charitable Trust, The Eric F 433
Spurgin Charitable Trust, The 434
Street Charitable Foundation, W O 440
TSB Foundation for the Channel Islands 447
Talteg Ltd 448
Tesco Charity Trust 452
Thornton-Smith Trust, The 455

Timson Family Charitable Trust 457

Turkish Women's Philanthropic Association of England 463

Turner Charitable Settlement, The Sir Mark and Lady 464

van Geest Foundation, The John and Lucille 470

Van Norden's Charitable Foundation, Mrs Maud 471

Vision Charity 474

Wander Charitable Fund, The Dr Albert 479

War on Want 479

Weavers' Company Benevolent Fund, The 482

Wedge, The 483

Weinstock Fund, The 484

Welfare Charity Establishment 485

West & Others, Charity of John 486

Westcroft Trust 486

Westminster Amalgamated Charity 487

Whitley Trust, Sheila 491

Whittington Charitable Trust, The 491

Wohl Charitable Foundation, The Maurice 498

Wohl Charitable Trust, The Maurice 498

Wolverhampton Rotary Club Charitable Trust 500

Worshipful Company of Shipwrights Charitable Fund, The 506

Yapp Welfare Trust, The 508

Will consider

AB Charitable Trust 3

AB Charitable Trust, The 3

Aleh Charitable Foundation, The 10

Ancaster Trust, The 16

Andrew Charitable Trust, The Prince 16

Appelbe Trust, Ambrose & Ann 19

Aquarian Healing Trust 19

Aquarius Charitable Foundation, The 19

Askew Charitable Trust, The Ian 25

Assheton-Smith Charitable Trust 25

Astor Foundation, The 26

Astor's 1969 Charity, The Hon M L 26

BBC Children in Need Appeal, The 29

Baring Foundation, The 34

Barnabas Charitable Trust 34

Barnby's Foundation, Lord 35

Barratt Charitable Trust, The Elaine 36

Barton Trust, Eleanor 37

Bealey Foundation, The 38

Beattie Charitable Trust, The James 39

Beckwith-Smith's Charitable Settlement, Mrs 40

Bellahouston Bequest Fund 42

Belljoe Tzedoko Ltd 42

Belmont Trust, The 42

Bergqvist Charitable Trust 44

Blackman Foundation, Isabel 52

Blank Donations Ltd, The David 54

Boltons Trust, The 55

Borthwick Memorial Trust, The Oliver 56

Bottom Charitable Trust, Harry 56

British Sugar Foundation 63

Brookhouse's Will Trust, Mr John Charles 65

Brushmill Ltd 66

Buckingham Trust 67

Burgess Trust, The Michael 69

Burns Charity, The Dorothy 70

Burry Charitable Trust, The 70

Buxton Trust, Denis 72

Cadbury Trust (1928), The Edward & Dorothy 76

Cardiff & Swansea Methodist District Charitable Trust Fund 80

Carron Charitable Trust, The 83

Castang Charitable Trust, H and M 85

Childtime Trust, The 92

Chippindale Foundation, Sam 93

Christian Aid 94

Christian Renewal Trust, The 94

Church Urban Fund 95

Cinderford Charitable Trust, The 96

Clark Charitable Trust 98

Clark Charitable Trust, J Anthony 98

Closehelm Ltd 101

Clutterbuck Charitable Trust, Robert 102

Coates Charitable Trust 1969, Lance 103

Cohen Charity Trust, Lucy 104

Cohen Foundation, The John S 104

Cole Charitable Trust, The 105

Collier Charitable Trust, The 105

Collinson Charitable Trust, The Norman 106

Company of Tobacco Pipe Makers and Tobacco Blenders Benevolent Fund 109

Cope Charitable Trust, Alfred 112

Crawford Children's Charity, Michael 117

Crescent Trust, The 117

Cripplegate Foundation 118

Curry Charitable Trust, Dennis 119

Cymerman Trust Limited, Itzchok Meyer 120

Daily Telegraph Charitable Trust 122

Dandeen Charitable Trust 123

Davy Foundation, The J 126

De Avenley Foundation, The 126

De Rothschild 1981 Charitable Trust, The Edmund 127

Delmar Charitable Trust 129

Desmond Charitable Trust, The Richard 131

Deutsch Charitable Trust, The Andre 131

Deutsch Charitable Trust, The H & M 131

Dibden Allotments Charity 132

Dicken Charitable Trust, The Albert 133

Drapers' Charitable Fund 137

Drayton Trust, The 138

Edinburgh Trust, No 2 Account 145

Eling Trust 147

Elkes Charity Fund, The Wilfred & Elsie 147

Ellis 1985 Charitable Trust, Edith M 148

Elshore Limited 149

Eventhall Family Charitable Trust, The 155

Family Trust, The 158

Famos Foundation Trust 158

Ford of Britain Trust 166

Foreman Foundation, The Carl & Eve 167

Foyle Trust, Charles Henry 169

Franklin Bequest, The Rosalind 169

Galinski Charitable Trust 177

Gibbs Charitable Trusts, The 181

Gillett Charitable Trust, J A 183

Gill's Charitable Trust, Mrs M M 184

Girdlers' Company Charitable Trust, The 184

Glynde Place Charitable Trust (1974), The 186

Goldsmiths' Company's Charities, The 188

Goodman Charitable Foundation, The Everard and Mina 188

Goodman Trust, The 189

Goodman Trust, The S & F 189

Gradel Foundation, The 189

Grahame Charitable Foundation, The 190

Graves Charitable Trust, J G 192

Greenaway Foundation, The Alan 194

Greenaway Foundation, The Sir Derek 194

Gross Charities Limited, M & R 197

Grundy Foundation, The Stanley 198

Grut Charitable Trust, The 198

Gulbenkian Foundation (Lisbon) United Kingdom Branch, Calouste 199

Haines Charitable Trust, The Alfred 203

Hamilton Educational Trust, Eleanor 205

Hampstead Wells and Campden Trust 206

Harbour Foundation Ltd, The 208

Hargreaves Trust, The Kenneth 210

Harvey Charitable Trust, Gordon 211

Holford Trust Fund 224

Hopkins, The Charity of Joseph 227

Horn Trust, The Cuthbert 227

Hornby Charitable Trust, Miss D 227

Hornton Trust, The 228

Hospital of God at Greatham , The 229

Hughes Charitable Trust, The Geoffery C 230

Hyde Park Place Estate Charity, The 232

Isle of Dogs Community Foundation 238

JCA Charitable Foundation 238

Jacobs Charitable Trust, The J P 240

James Foundation, The Catherine and Lady Grace 241

Jewish Childs' Day 245

Johnson Foundation, The Beth 247

Jubilee Outreach Yorkshire 248

Karten Charitable Trust, The Ian 250

Kingsgrove Charitable Trust, The 255

Kobler Trust, The 258

Kreitman Foundation 258

Kulika Charitable Trust, The 259

Kweller Charitable Trust, The Harry 259

Landy Charitable Trust, Harry and Gertrude 263

Lankelly Foundation, The 264

Lanvern Foundation 265

Laski Memorial Charitable Trust, Nathan 265

Laspen Trust 265

Lauffer Charitable Foundation, The R & D 266

Lavender Trust, The 267

Lawley Foundation, The Edgar E 267

Leach Fourteenth Trust, The 267

Lee Foundation, The Edgar 269

Leigh-Bramwell Trust 'E', P 270

Lewis Family Charitable Trust, The 273

Liffe Benefit 274

Lingwood Charitable Trust, The 276

Localtrent Ltd 279

Low & Bonar Charitable Fund, The 284

Lunzer Charitable Trust, The Ruth & Jack 287

Lynwood Charitable Trust, The 288

MDM Memorial Trust 289

Maccabi Foundation, The 290

McKenzie Trust, The Robert 292

McLaren Memorial Trust, The Martin 293

Manchester and Salford Medical Charities Fund 295

Margaret Foundation, The 297

Marks Charitable Trust, Michael 298

Marriage's Charitable Trust, Miss G M 299

Marr-Munning Trust 299

Marshall Charitable Trust, The Charlotte 300

Matchan Fund Limited, The Leonard 301

Material World Charitable Foundation Limited, The 301

Mayfair Charities Limited 303

Melchett Children's Trust, The Violet 305

Mellows Charitable Settlement, The Anthony and Elizabeth 305

Mid Moss Charitable Trust, The 309

Milburn Charitable Trust, Frederick 310

Millett Charitable Trust, The Alan and Janet 312

Modiano Charitable Trust 315

Montefiore Trust, The David 316

Morgan Foundation, The Mr & Mrs J T 319

Morris Charitable Trust, The Willie & Mabel 320

Morrison Bequest Fund, Thomas Wharrie 320

Moulton Charitable Trust, The 321

Munro Charitable Trust, The 323

Music Sales Charitable Trust, The 324

Muslim Hands 324

National Lottery Charities Board 328

Northern Arts 339

Nuffield Foundation 342

Old Possums Practical Trust, The 344

Palmer Trust, The Gerald 352

Park Hill Trust, The 353

Pascoe Charitable Trust, Alan 354

Paterson Charitable Foundation, The Constance 354

Paterson Charitable Trust, Arthur James 354

Paul Charitable Trust, The Late Barbara May 355

Paul Charitable Trust, Pamela Milton 355

Paul Foundation, The 355

Payne Charitable Trust, The 355

Pelech Charitable Trust, The 358

Perry Charitable Trust, Miss Frances Lucille 359

Personal Assurance Charitable Trust 360

Peskin Charitable Trust, The Hazel and Leslie 360

Phillips Charitable Foundation, Reginald M 361

Pilgrim Trust, The 362

Pilkington Charitable Trust, Cecil 363

Pitt Trust, Headley 364

QAS Charitable Trust 373

Quothquan Charitable Trust, The Second 373

RT Trust, The 374

Rackham Charitable Trust, The Mr & Mrs Philip 375

Radley Charitable Trust 375

Rainford Trust, The 376

Rav Chesed Trust, The 379

Rest-Harrow Trust, The 382

Reuter Foundation, The 382

Richmond Parish Lands Charity 384

Robbins Trust, The Cheshire 387

Rogers Charitable Settlement, The Richard 390

Rokeby Charitable Trust 390

Rolfe Charitable Trust, The 390

S Group Charitable Trust 399

St Jude's Trust 403

St Katharine & Shadwell Trust 404

Salters Charities 405

Samuel Charitable Trust, M J 406

Sargeant's Charitable Trust, Mrs M E *407*

Save & Prosper Foundation *409*

Scarr-Hall Memorial Trust, The *409*

Seedfield Trust, The *414*

Seva Trust, Rampaba Sadhu *415*

Shepherd Family Charitable Trust, The Sir Peter *418*

Sherman Charitable Trust, The Archie *419*

Sidbury Trust, The Second *421*

Silvester Charitable Gift Trust *422*

Simon's Charity *422*

Singer Foundation *423*

Skinners' Company Lady Neville Charity *424*

Slater Foundation Ltd, The *424*

Smith (Estates Charities), Henry *426*

Smith Trust, Metcalfe *427*

Society of Friends of the Torah, The *429*

Solomons Charitable Trust, David *430*

Somerfield Curtis Will Trust, The Dorothy *430*

Stanley Foundation Limited *435*

Stewart Charitable Trust, Mary Stephanie *437*

Sumner's Trust Section 'A', Sir John *443*

Symons Charitable Trust, The Stella *446*

Taylor Charitable Trust, The B R *450*

Templeton Goodwill Trust *451*

Terry Charitable Trust, Noel Goddard *451*

Tesler Foundation, The *452*

3i Charitable Trust, The *455*

Turner Trust, The Douglas *464*

Tyndale Trust *466*

Unitek Foundation *469*

Veronique Charitable Trust *472*

Vincent Trust Fund, Eric W *473*

Vineyard Christian Fellowship of South West *473*

Vinson Charity Trust, The 1969 *473*

Vogel Charitable Trust, The Nathan *474*

Wagstaff Charitable Trust, Bob *475*

Wakefield Trust, The *476*

Ward Blenkinsop Trust, The *480*

Welby Trust, The Barbara *484*

Whesby Ltd *488*

Whetherly's Charitable Trust, The Hon Mrs R G A *489*

Whitehead Charitable Trust, J E *490*

Wiggins Charity Trust, Cyril *491*

Wilde Charitable Trust, The Felicity *492*

Wills 1961 Charitable Trust, Major Michael Thomas *494*

Wiltshire Community Foundation *495*

Winstone Foundation, Hyman *497*

Wix Charitable Trust, Michael and Anna *497*

Woburn 1986 Charitable Trust *498*

Wolff Charity Trust *498*

Wolfson Family Charitable Trust, The *499*

Woodhouse Charitable Trust, Edwin *501*

Woods Charitable Foundation, Geoffrey *502*

Worms Charitable Trust, The Freda and Della *504*

Worshipful Company of Founders Charities, The *505*

Worshipful Company of Needlemakers' Charitable Fund *505*

Wychdale Limited *507*

Wylde Memorial Charity, The Anthony and Gwendoline *507*

Youell Foundation Ltd, The *510*

Zaiger Trust, The Elizabeth and Prince *512*

....

■ **Community transport**

see also **Community services**

Funding priority

AB Charitable Trust *3*

Army Benevolent Fund, The *22*

Christmas Cracker Trust *95*

Curriers Company Charitable Fund *119*

Hertfordshire Community Trust, The *217*

Hudson Benevolent Trust, The Thomas *230*

Isle of Dogs Community Foundation *238*

Johnson Group Cleaners Charity *247*

Merchant Taylors' Consolidated Charities for the Infirm *306*

SMB Trust, The *400*

St Katharine & Shadwell Trust *404*

Skerritt Trust *423*

TSB Foundation for Scotland *447*

Wates Foundation, The *481*

Wiltshire Community Foundation *495*

Will consider

Abbey National Charitable Trust *4*

Alexis Trust, The *11*

Amory Charitable Trust, Viscount *16*

Aquarius Charitable Foundation, The *19*

Askew Trust, The Dorothy *25*

Avon Trust, The *28*

Bancroft Trust, The *33*

Barbour Trust, The *33*

Berkshire Community Trust *45*

Bisgood Trust, The *50*

Bisgood's Charitable Trust, Miss Jeanne *50*

Blakenham's Charity Trust, Lady *53*

Boots Charitable Trust *56*

Bowland Charitable Trust, The *57*

Bridge Trust, The *60*

Brotherton Trust, The Charles *65*

Brough Charitable Trust, Joseph *65*

Burdall Charity, H M *69*

Butlin Charity Trust, Bill *72*

CLA Charitable Trust *74*

Cadbury Charitable Trust (Incorporated), Edward *75*

Camelot Foundation, The *78*

Campden Charities, The *79*

Challice Trust, The *87*

Chrimes Family Charitable Trust, The *93*

Clark 1965 Charitable Trust, Stephen *98*

Cloudesley's Charity/School Parents & Friends Association, Richard *102*

Community Trust for Greater Manchester, The *108*

County Durham Foundation *115*

Coutts Charitable Trust, The *116*

Davies Charity, The Gwendoline and Margaret *125*

Derbyshire Trust, J N *130*

Digby Charitable Trust, Simon *133*

Direct Response *134*

Dumbreck Charity *139*

Early's Charitable Settlement, Richard *142*

Ebb and Flow Charitable Trust *144*

Edgar Foundation, The Gilbert and Eileen *145*

Egerton of Tatton Will Trust, Lord *146*

Elkes Charity Fund, The Wilfred & Elsie *147*

Emmandjay Charitable Trust *150*

Fletcher Charitable Trust, The
Joyce *164*
Fletcher Trust, Roy *165*
Gibbins Trust, The *181*
Grant Foundation, The
Raymond *191*
Grant-Lawson Charitable Trust,
Lady Virginia *192*
Great Britain Sasakawa
Foundation, The *193*
Greenaway Foundation, The Sir
Derek *194*
Grocers' Charity *197*
Grosshill Charitable Trust *197*
Harding's Charity, William *209*
Harford Charitable Trust *209*
Hartley Memorial Trust, The N
& P *211*
Henderson's Settlement, J R
216
Homfray Trust, The *226*
Humanitarian Trust, The *230*
Ingles Charitable Trust, The
234
JDM Charitable Trust *239*
Jarman Charitable Trust, The
243
Jarrold Trust Ltd, John *243*
Johnson Foundation, The *246*
King Charitable Trust, The
Lorna *254*
Knott Trust, Sir James *258*
Kroch Foundation, The Heinz &
Anna *259*
Laing Charitable Trust, The
David *260*
Laing Foundation, The
Christopher *260*
Lancaster's Trust, Bryan *263*
Lane Foundation, The Allen
263
Lankelly Foundation, The *264*
Lawson Charitable Trust,
Raymond and Blanche *267*
Leach Fourteenth Trust, The
267
Leech Charity, The William *269*
Lewis Partnership, John *274*
Lloyd's Charities Trust *278*
(Lloyds) TSB Foundation for
England and Wales *279*
Lowe Trust, Mrs D G *285*
Lyndhurst Settlement *287*
MacKintosh Charitable Trust,
Viscount *292*
Marchday Charitable Fund, The
296
Measures Charity, The James
Frederick and Ethel Anne
303
Mental Health Foundation, The
305
Metropolitan Hospital-Sunday
Fund, The *308*
Minet Trust, The Peter *313*
Moore Foundation, The
George A *316*
NR Charitable Trust, The *325*

National Power Charitable
Trust, The *330*
Needham Cooper Charitable
Trust, The *331*
New Chasers Charitable Trust,
The *332*
New Court Charitable Trust
332
Newby Trust Ltd *332*
Noah Trust, The *335*
Norman Family Charitable
Trust, The *337*
Northcott Devon Foundation
338
Norton Foundation, The *340*
Notgrove Trust, The *341*
Oakdale Trust, The *343*
Oldham Foundation *345*
Owen Family Trust, The *348*
Patients' Aid Association
Hospital and Medical
Charities Trust *354*
Persula Foundation, The *360*
Powell Foundation, The *367*
Pratt Charitable Trust, The W L
367
Pyke Charity Trust *372*
Ravenscroft Foundation, The
379
Rayner Charitable Trust, The
John *380*
Richard Charitable Trust, The
Cliff *383*
Ripley's Charitable Trust, Pat
386
Rope Third Charitable
Settlement, The Mrs *391*
Rothley Trust, The *392*
Rowbotham Charitable Trust,
The Christopher *393*
Sainsbury Charitable Fund Ltd,
The *402*
Saint Sarkis Charity Trust *404*
Seagram Distillers Charitable
Trust *413*
Sheldon Trust, The *417*
Shelroy Charitable Trust, The
417
Shepherd Family Charitable
Trust, The Sir Peter *418*
Skelton Bounty, The *423*
Sobell Welsh People's
Charitable Association,
Michael *429*
South Square Trust *430*
Sparkhill Trust, The *433*
Stoate Charitable Trust, The
Leonard Laity *438*
Summerfield Charitable Trust,
The *442*
Summer's and I May's
Charitable Settlement, The
Late Misses (A N) *442*
Sussman Charitable Trust,
Adrienne & Leslie *443*
Swan Mountain Trust *444*
Sykes Trust, The Charles *445*

TSB Foundation for Northern
Ireland *447*
Thackray General Charitable
Trust, The P & L *452*
Thomson Foundation, The Sue
454
Tisbury Telegraph Trust, The
457
Torquay Charities, The *458*
Towler Charity Trust, The Fred
459
Travis Charitable Trust,
Constance *460*
Truemark Trust, The *461*
Tyne & Wear Foundation *466*
Victoria & Johnson Memorial
Trust, Queen *472*
Wakefield (Tower Hill, Trinity
Square) Trust *476*
Wall Trust, Thomas *478*
Wander Charitable Fund, The
Dr Albert *479*
Webber Trust Fund, Ethel *483*
Wedge, The *483*
Wesleyan Charitable Trust, The
485
Westcroft Trust *486*
Whitaker Charitable Trust *489*
Whitecourt Charitable Trust,
The *490*
Wills 1961 Charitable Trust, Mr
Frederick *493*
Wills 1962 Charitable Trust,
P J H *494*
Wingate Foundation, The
Harold Hyam *496*
Wolfe Family's Charitable
Trust, The *498*
Women Caring Trust, The *500*
Woodlands Trust *501*
Wylde Memorial Charity, The
Anthony and Gwendoline
507
Yorkshire Bank Charitable
Trust, The *510*

....

■ **Computers**

see **Information technology
& computers**

....

■ **Conflict resolution**

see **Academic subjects,
sciences & research**

■ Conservation

see also **Church buildings, Fauna, Flora, Historic buildings, Lakes, Landscapes, Memorials & monuments, Nature reserves, Waterways**

Funding priority

Alexander Charitable Trust, Mrs K L *11*
Allachy Trust, The *12*
Astor of Hever Trust, The *26*
Astor's 1969 Charity, The Hon M L *26*
BP Conservation Programme *29*
Ball Charitable Trust, The Bruce *31*
Barnsbury Charitable Trust *35*
Bateman Charitable Trust, Lady Margaret *37*
Bell Trust and Additional Fund, The Barron *41*
Bergqvist Charitable Trust *44*
Bonham-Carter Charitable Trust, The Charlotte *55*
British Sugar Foundation *63*
Brotherton Trust, The Charles *65*
Brough Charitable Trust, Joseph *65*
Burton Charitable Trust, The Geoffrey *71*
Cadbury Schweppes Foundation, The *76*
Campbell Charitable Foundation, The Ellis *79*
Chippindale Foundation, Sam *93*
Cobb Charity *103*
Conservation Foundation, The *110*
Daiwa Anglo-Japanese Foundation, The *122*
De Rothschild 1981 Charitable Trust, The Edmund *127*
Dinam Charity *134*
D'Oyly Carte Charitable Trust, The *137*
Dunn Charitable Trust, The Harry *140*
Egerton of Tatton Will Trust, Lord *146*
Elvetham Charitable Trust, The *149*
Essex Heritage Trust *153*
Evans Memorial Trust, The Alan *155*
Fairbairn Charitable Trust, The Esmee *157*
Frognal Trust *174*
Fry Charitable Trust, Maurice *174*
Goodman Trust, The *189*
Greenaway Foundation, The Sir Derek *194*
Hamamelis Trust, The *204*

Hargreaves Trust, The Kenneth *210*
Heinz Company Limited Charitable Trust, The H J *215*
Hitachi Charitable Trust, The *222*
Horn Trust, The Cuthbert *227*
Hudson Benevolent Trust, The Thomas *230*
Hughes Charitable Trust, The Geoffery C *230*
IBM United Kingdom Trust *233*
IPE Charitable Trust, The *233*
Jeffreys Road Fund, Rees *243*
Jones Trust, Cemlyn *248*
Kilverstone Wildlife Charitable Trust, The *254*
Kinnison Charitable Trust, R O *256*
Kleinwort Charitable Trust, The Ernest *257*
Kulika Charitable Trust, The *259*
Living and Waking Naturally *278*
Lucas Charitable Trust Limited, The Joseph *286*
McLaren Foundation *292*
Marks Charitable Trust, Michael *298*
Material World Charitable Foundation Limited, The *301*
Millichope Foundation, The *312*
Nickerson Charitable Foundation, The Joseph *335*
Pilkington Charitable Trust, Cecil *363*
Pitman Charitable Trust, The John *364*
Plaisterers' Company Charitable Trust, The *364*
Reekie Trust, R A & V B *381*
Riley-Smith Charitable Trust, The F A *386*
Sainsbury Charitable Fund Ltd, The *402*
Samuel Charitable Trust, M J *406*
Scarfe Charitable Trust, The *409*
Southall Charitable Trust, Kenneth & Phyllis *431*
Sykes Trust, The Charles *445*
Valentine Charitable Trust, The *470*
Van Norden's Charitable Foundation, Mrs Maud *471*
Williams Charitable Trust, Alfred *493*
Yorkshire Field Studies Trust *510*

Will consider

AHJ Charitable Trust, The *3*
Achiezer Association Limited *6*
Airflow Community Ltd, The *9*
Aleh Charitable Foundation, The *10*
Allied Domecq Trust *13*
Ammco Trust, The *15*
Ancaster Trust, The *16*
Anderson Trust, Andrew *16*
Angler's Inn Trust *17*
Appelbe Trust, Ambrose & Ann *19*
Aquarius Charitable Foundation, The *19*
Aquinas Trust *20*
Arbib Foundation *20*
Assembled Church of Christ Trust, The *25*
Astor Foundation, The *26*
Astor's Charitable Trust, The Hon M L *26*
Barton Trust, Eleanor *37*
Bealey Foundation, The *38*
Beattie Charitable Trust, The James *39*
Beckwith Charitable Trust, The Peter *40*
Beckwith-Smith's Charitable Settlement, Mrs *40*
Behrens Charitable Trust, E M *40*
Black Foundation, The Bertie *51*
Blagrave Charitable Trust, The Herbert and Peter *52*
Blakenham's Charity Trust, Lady *53*
Blakey Charitable Trust, The Celia and Conrad *53*
Blank Donations Ltd, The David *54*
Boltons Trust, The *55*
Borthwick Memorial Trust, The Oliver *56*
Bottom Charitable Trust, Harry *56*
Bowland Charitable Trust, The *57*
Brand Trust, The *59*
Brookhouse's Will Trust, Mr John Charles *65*
Bullough Tompson Settlement, The *68*
Bulmer Charitable Trust, Becket *68*
Burn Charity Trust, The J H *70*
Burns Charity, The Dorothy *70*
Burry Charitable Trust, The *70*
Butler's Trust, Lord *71*
Butler's Trust, Lucilla *72*
Buxton Trust, Denis *72*
CHK Charities Limited *74*
Cadbury Trust (1928), The Edward & Dorothy *76*
Cardiff & Swansea Methodist District Charitable Trust Fund *80*

Carron Charitable Trust, The 83

Carter Charitable Trust, The Leslie Mary 83

Castang Charitable Trust, H and M 85

Catto Charitable Settlement, The Thomas Sivewright 86

Charity for Change 89

Charity Projects 90

Childtime Trust, The 92

Christian Aid 94

Cinderford Charitable Trust, The 96

Closehelm Ltd 101

Clutterbuck Charitable Trust, Robert 102

Coates Charitable Settlement, The 102

Coates Charitable Trust 1969, Lance 103

Cohen Charitable Trust, The Vivienne and Samuel 104

Cohen Charity Trust, Lucy 104

Cohen Foundation, The John S 104

Company of Tobacco Pipe Makers and Tobacco Blenders Benevolent Fund 109

Condon Family Trust 109

Cook Trust, The Ernest 110

Cope Charitable Trust, Alfred 112

Crescent Trust, The 117

Curry Charitable Trust, Dennis 119

Cymerman Trust Limited, Itzchok Meyer 120

Daily Telegraph Charitable Trust 122

Dandeen Charitable Trust 123

Davy Foundation, The J 126

De Avenley Foundation, The 126

De La Rue Charitable Trust 127

De Yong Charitable Trust, The Emma 128

Denby Charitable Foundation, The 130

Denton Charitable Trust, The 130

Desmond Charitable Trust, The Richard 131

Deutsch Charitable Trust, The Andre 131

Deutsch Charitable Trust, The H & M 131

Dicken Charitable Trust, The Albert 133

Djanogly Foundation, The 135

Doughty Charity Trust, The 136

Drayton Trust, The 138

Earmark Trust, The 142

Edinburgh Trust, No 2 Account 145

Eling Trust 147

Elshore Limited 149

Family Trust, The 158

Famos Foundation Trust 158

Ford of Britain Trust 166

Foreman Foundation, The Carl & Eve 167

Foyle Trust, Charles Henry 169

Franklin Bequest, The Rosalind 169

Franklin Deceased's New Second Charity, Sydney E 170

Frazer Charities Trust, The 171

Garthgwynion Charities 179

Gibson's Charity Trust, The Hon Mr & Mrs Clive 182

Gillett Charitable Trust, J A 183

Gill's Charitable Trust, Mrs M M 184

Girdlers' Company Charitable Trust, The 184

Gladstone Charitable Trust, The E W 184

Gold Hill Church Trust 186

Goldberg Charitable Trust, The Lewis 186

Goodman Charitable Foundation, The Everard and Mina 188

Gough Charitable Trust, The 189

Gradel Foundation, The 189

Graves Charitable Trust, J G 192

Greater Bristol Foundation 193

Green Foundation, Constance 194

Gross Charities Limited, M & R 197

Grosshill Charitable Trust 197

Grut Charitable Trust, The 198

HB Charitable Trust 201

Hacking & Sons Ltd Charitable Trust, C G 201

Halkes Settlement, John Robert 204

Hamilton Educational Trust, Eleanor 205

Harbour Foundation Ltd, The 208

Harford Charitable Trust 209

Harvey Charitable Trust, Gordon 211

Held Settlement, The Gisela 215

Henhurst Charitable Trust, The 216

Heritage Lottery Fund 216

Hillards Charitable Trust, Gay & Peter Hartley's 220

Holford Trust Fund 224

Hoover Foundation, The 226

Hornby Charitable Trust, Miss D 227

Hornton Trust, The 228

Hyde Park Place Estate Charity, The 232

Inman Charity, The 235

JCSCJ Charitable Trust, The 238

James Foundation, The Catherine and Lady Grace 241

KC Charitable Trust, The 250

Karten Charitable Trust, The Ian 250

Keyes Trust, The Ursula 253

Kingsgrove Charitable Trust, The 255

Knott Trust, Sir James 258

Kobler Trust, The 258

Kreitman Foundation 258

Kweller Charitable Trust, The Harry 259

Laing Charitable Trust, The David 260

Laing Foundation, The Christopher 260

Laing's Charitable Trust 262

Lalonde Trust 262

Landy Charitable Trust, Harry and Gertrude 263

Lanvern Foundation 265

Laski Memorial Charitable Trust, Nathan 265

Laspen Trust 265

Lauffer Charitable Foundation, The R & D 266

Lavender Trust, The 267

Lawley Foundation, The Edgar E 267

Leach Fourteenth Trust, The 267

Lee Foundation, The Edgar 269

Leigh-Bramwell Trust 'E', P 270

Levy Charitable Foundation, Joseph 272

Lingwood Charitable Trust, The 276

Lloyd Charity, The S and D 278

Localtrent Ltd 279

Lunzer Charitable Trust, The Ruth & Jack 287

Lynwood Charitable Trust, The 288

Lyons Charitable Trust, The 288

MDM Memorial Trust 289

MacAndrew Trust, The E M 289

McKechnie Foundation, A N 292

McKenzie Trust, The Robert 292

McLaren Memorial Trust, The Martin 293

MacRobert Trusts, The 294

Manifold Charitable Trust, The 295

Margadale Charitable Trust, Lord 297

Markus Charitable Foundation, The Erich *298*

Marriage's Charitable Trust, Miss G M *299*

Marr-Munning Trust *299*

Marshall Charitable Trust, The Charlotte *300*

Martin Trust, The Sir George *300*

Mattock Charitable Trust, The W T *302*

Mayfair Charities Limited *303*

Measures Charity, The James Frederick and Ethel Anne *303*

Medlock Charitable Trust, The *304*

Millett Charitable Trust, The Alan and Janet *312*

Modiano Charitable Trust *315*

Montefiore Trust, The David *316*

Moore Charitable Trust, The Horace *316*

Moore Stephens Charitable Foundation, The *317*

Morel Charitable Trust, The *318*

Morphy Memorial Fund, Arthur *319*

Morris Charitable Trust, The Willie & Mabel *320*

Moulton Charitable Trust, The *321*

Music Sales Charitable Trust, The *324*

Newcastle's 1986 Charitable Trust, Duke of *333*

Newman Charitable Trust, Mr and Mrs F E F *334*

Newstead Charity, The *334*

Norfolk's Family Charitable Trust, Lavinia *336*

Northcott Charity Trust, The *338*

Northern Arts *339*

Northern Dairies Educational Trust *339*

Northern Electric Employee Charity Association *339*

Northern Ireland Voluntary Trust *339*

Notgrove Trust, The *341*

Old Possums Practical Trust, The *344*

Oppenheimer Charitable Trust *346*

Owen Trust, Margaret *348*

PDC Trust, The *349*

PF Charitable Trust *350*

PJD Charitable Trust *350*

Palmer Trust, The Gerald *352*

Park Hill Trust, The *353*

Pascoe Charitable Trust, Alan *354*

Paul Charitable Trust, The Late Barbara May *355*

Paul Charitable Trust, Margaret Jeanne *355*

Paul Charitable Trust, Pamela Milton *355*

Paul Foundation, The *355*

Paul's Charitable Trust, R J *355*

Payne Charitable Trust, The *355*

Pelech Charitable Trust, The *358*

Perry Charitable Trust, Miss Frances Lucille *359*

Pershore Nashdom & Elmore Trust Ltd, The *360*

Peskin Charitable Trust, The Hazel and Leslie *360*

Phillips Charitable Foundation, Reginald M *361*

Pike Woodlands Trust, Claude & Margaret *362*

Pitt Trust, Headley *364*

Porter Foundation *366*

Prendergast Charitable Trust, The Simone *368*

Puebla Charitable Trust Limited, The *371*

QAS Charitable Trust *373*

Quothquan Charitable Trust, The Second *373*

RT Trust, The *374*

Rackham Charitable Trust, The Mr & Mrs Philip *375*

Radley Charitable Trust *375*

Rae Charity, H J *375*

Rainford Trust, The *376*

Rav Chesed Trust, The *379*

Rayner Charitable Trust, The John *380*

Reuter Foundation, The *382*

Richards Charity, The Clive *384*

Richmond Parish Lands Charity *384*

Ripley's Charitable Trust, Pat *386*

Rivendell Trust, The *387*

Robbins Trust, The Cheshire *387*

Rodewald's Charitable Settlement, Mr C A *389*

Rogers Charitable Settlement, The Richard *390*

Rolfe Charitable Trust, The *390*

Rosen Foundation, Cecil *392*

Rowan Charitable Trust, The *393*

S Group Charitable Trust *399*

St Jude's Trust *403*

Salters Charities *405*

Save & Prosper Foundation *409*

Scarr-Hall Memorial Trust, The *409*

Seva Trust, Rampaba Sadhu *415*

Shaw Foundation, The Linley *416*

Sheepdrove Trust, The *417*

Shepherd Conservation Foundation, The David *418*

Sherman Charitable Trust, The Archie *419*

Shifrin Charitable Trust, The Maurice and Hilda *419*

Sidbury Trust, The Second *421*

Silvester Charitable Gift Trust *422*

Skinners' Company Lady Neville Charity *424*

Society of Friends of the Torah, The *429*

Solomons Charitable Trust, David *430*

Somerfield Curtis Will Trust, The Dorothy *430*

Stanley Foundation Limited *435*

Stevens Foundation, The June *437*

Stewart Charitable Trust, Mary Stephanie *437*

Stoate Charitable Trust, The Leonard Laity *438*

Sumner's Trust Section 'A', Sir John *443*

Swann-Morton Foundation, The *444*

Tait Charity, The Richard *448*

Taylor Charitable Trust, The B R *450*

Tesco Charity Trust *452*

Tesler Foundation, The *452*

3i Charitable Trust, The *455*

Turner Trust, The Douglas *464*

van Geest Foundation, The John and Lucille *470*

Vineyard Christian Fellowship of South West *473*

Vinson Charity Trust, The 1969 *473*

Vogel Charitable Trust, The Nathan *474*

Wagstaff Charitable Trust, Bob *475*

Wakefield Trust, The *476*

Ward Blenkinsop Trust, The *480*

Weinstock Fund, The *484*

Welby Trust, The Barbara *484*

Whetherly's Charitable Trust, The Hon Mrs R G A *489*

Whitehead Charitable Trust, J E *490*

Whitley Animal Protection Trust *491*

Whittington Charitable Trust, The *491*

Wiggins Charity Trust, Cyril *491*

Wilde Charitable Trust, The Felicity *492*

Will Charitable Trust, The *492*

Wills 1961 Charitable Trust, Major Michael Thomas *494*

Winstone Foundation, Hyman *497*

Woburn 1986 Charitable Trust
 498
Wohl Charitable Foundation,
 The Maurice *498*
Wohl Charitable Trust, The
 Maurice *498*
Wolff Charity Trust *498*
Wolfson Family Charitable
 Trust, The *499*
Woodhouse Charitable Trust,
 Edwin *501*
Woods Charitable Foundation,
 Geoffrey *502*
Worms Charitable Trust, The
 Freda and Della *504*
Worshipful Company of
 Founders Charities, The *505*
Worshipful Company of
 Needlemakers' Charitable
 Fund *505*
Wright Deceased Trust, John
 William *506*
Wychdale Limited *507*
Wylde Memorial Charity, The
 Anthony and Gwendoline
 507
Youell Foundation Ltd, The
 510
Zaiger Trust, The Elizabeth and
 Prince *512*

....

■ **Conservation &
 campaigning**
 see also **Endangered
 species, Environmental
 issues, Heritage, Nuclear
 energy, nuclear power,
 Renewable energy,
 renewable power,
 Transport & alternative
 transport**

Funding priority
Alexander Charitable Trust,
 Mrs K L *11*
Allachy Trust, The *12*
Ashden Charitable Trust, The
 24
Astor of Hever Trust, The *26*
Astor's 1969 Charity, The Hon
 M L *26*
Barnsbury Charitable Trust *35*
Bateman Charitable Trust, Lady
 Margaret *37*
Bergqvist Charitable Trust *44*
Bonham-Carter Charitable
 Trust, The Charlotte *55*
British Sugar Foundation *63*
Burton Charitable Trust, The
 Geoffrey *71*
Cadbury Schweppes
 Foundation, The *76*
Clark Charitable Trust, J
 Anthony *98*
Conservation Foundation, The
 110

Daiwa Anglo-Japanese
 Foundation, The *122*
David Trust, The Lesley *124*
De Rothschild 1981 Charitable
 Trust, The Edmund *127*
Dinam Charity *134*
D'Oyly Carte Charitable Trust,
 The *137*
Dulverton Trust, The *139*
Dunn Charitable Trust, The
 Harry *140*
Elvetham Charitable Trust, The
 149
Evans Memorial Trust, The
 Alan *155*
Fairbairn Charitable Trust, The
 Esmee *157*
Fry Charitable Trust, Maurice
 174
Goodman Trust, The *189*
Hamamelis Trust, The *204*
Hargreaves Trust, The Kenneth
 210
Heinz Company Limited
 Charitable Trust, The H J
 215
Hitachi Charitable Trust, The
 222
Horn Trust, The Cuthbert *227*
Hughes Charitable Trust, The
 Geoffery C *230*
IBM United Kingdom Trust
 233
IPE Charitable Trust, The *233*
JJ Charitable Trust, The *239*
Jones Trust, Cemlyn *248*
Kinnison Charitable Trust, R O
 256
Kleinwort Charitable Trust, The
 Ernest *257*
Lucas Charitable Trust Limited,
 The Joseph *286*
Marks Charitable Trust,
 Michael *298*
Material World Charitable
 Foundation Limited, The
 301
Millichope Foundation, The
 312
Northern Dairies Educational
 Trust *339*
Paget Trust, The *351*
Panton Trust, The *352*
Persula Foundation, The *360*
Riley-Smith Charitable Trust,
 The F A *386*
Samuel Charitable Trust, M J
 406
Scarfe Charitable Trust, The
 409
Southall Charitable Trust,
 Kenneth & Phyllis *431*
Valentine Charitable Trust, The
 470
Van Norden's Charitable
 Foundation, Mrs Maud *471*

Will consider
AHJ Charitable Trust, The *3*
Achiezer Association Limited *6*
Airflow Community Ltd, The *9*
Aleh Charitable Foundation,
 The *10*
Ancaster Trust, The *16*
Anderson Trust, Andrew *16*
Angler's Inn Trust *17*
Appelbe Trust, Ambrose & Ann
 19
Aquinas Trust *20*
Askew Charitable Trust, The
 Ian *25*
Assembled Church of Christ
 Trust, The *25*
Astor Foundation, The *26*
Astor's Charitable Trust, The
 Hon M L *26*
Barton Trust, Eleanor *37*
Bealey Foundation, The *38*
Beattie Charitable Trust, The
 James *39*
Beckwith Charitable Trust, The
 Peter *40*
Benham Charitable Trust,
 Hervey *43*
Black Foundation, The Bertie
 51
Blagrave Charitable Trust, The
 Herbert and Peter *52*
Blakenham's Charity Trust,
 Lady *53*
Blakey Charitable Trust, The
 Celia and Conrad *53*
Blank Donations Ltd, The David
 54
Boltons Trust, The *55*
Borthwick Memorial Trust, The
 Oliver *56*
Bottom Charitable Trust, Harry
 56
Bowland Charitable Trust, The
 57
Brook Charitable Settlement,
 R E *64*
Brookhouse's Will Trust, Mr
 John Charles *65*
Brotherton Trust, The Charles
 65
Burn Charity Trust, The J H *70*
Burns Charity, The Dorothy *70*
Burry Charitable Trust, The *70*
Butler's Trust, Lord *71*
Butler's Trust, Lucilla *72*
Cardiff & Swansea Methodist
 District Charitable Trust
 Fund *80*
Carter Charitable Trust, The
 Leslie Mary *83*
Castang Charitable Trust, H
 and M *85*
Charity Projects *90*
Childtime Trust, The *92*
Chippindale Foundation, Sam
 93
Christian Aid *94*

Cinderford Charitable Trust, The *96*

Clark 1965 Charitable Trust, Stephen *98*

Closehelm Ltd *101*

Clutterbuck Charitable Trust, Robert *102*

Coates Charitable Settlement, The *102*

Cohen Charitable Trust, The Vivienne and Samuel *104*

Cohen Charity Trust, Lucy *104*

Cohen Foundation, The John S *104*

Cole Charitable Trust, The *105*

Company of Tobacco Pipe Makers and Tobacco Blenders Benevolent Fund *109*

Condon Family Trust *109*

Cook Trust, The Ernest *110*

Cope Charitable Trust, Alfred *112*

Crescent Trust, The *117*

Curry Charitable Trust, Dennis *119*

Cymerman Trust Limited, Itzchok Meyer *120*

Daily Telegraph Charitable Trust *122*

Dandeen Charitable Trust *123*

Davy Foundation, The J *126*

De Avenley Foundation, The *126*

De La Rue Charitable Trust *127*

De Yong Charitable Trust, The Emma *128*

Denton Charitable Trust, The *130*

Desmond Charitable Trust, The Richard *131*

Deutsch Charitable Trust, The Andre *131*

Deutsch Charitable Trust, The H & M *131*

Dicken Charitable Trust, The Albert *133*

Digby Charitable Trust, Simon *133*

Djanogly Foundation, The *135*

Doughty Charity Trust, The *136*

Drayton Trust, The *138*

Earmark Trust, The *142*

Edinburgh Trust, No 2 Account *145*

Eling Trust *147*

Elshore Limited *149*

Family Trust, The *158*

Famos Foundation Trust *158*

Foreman Foundation, The Carl & Eve *167*

Foyle Trust, Charles Henry *169*

Franklin Bequest, The Rosalind *169*

Franklin Deceased's New Second Charity, Sydney E *170*

GW Trust, The *176*

Garnett Charitable Trust, The *178*

Garthgwynion Charities *179*

Gibson's Charity Trust, The Hon Mr & Mrs Clive *182*

Gillett Charitable Trust, J A *183*

Gill's Charitable Trust, Mrs M M *184*

Girdlers' Company Charitable Trust, The *184*

Gold Hill Church Trust *186*

Goldberg Charitable Trust, The Lewis *186*

Goodman Charitable Foundation, The Everard and Mina *188*

Gradel Foundation, The *189*

Green Foundation, Constance *194*

Greenaway Foundation, The Sir Derek *194*

Gross Charities Limited, M & R *197*

Grosshill Charitable Trust *197*

Grut Charitable Trust, The *198*

HB Charitable Trust *201*

Hacking & Sons Ltd Charitable Trust, C G *201*

Halkes Settlement, John Robert *204*

Hamilton Educational Trust, Eleanor *205*

Harbour Foundation Ltd, The *208*

Harford Charitable Trust *209*

Harvey Charitable Trust, Gordon *211*

Hawthorne Charitable Trust, The *212*

Held Settlement, The Gisela *215*

Henhurst Charitable Trust, The *216*

Hillards Charitable Trust, Gay & Peter Hartley's *220*

Holford Trust Fund *224*

Hoover Foundation, The *226*

Hornby Charitable Trust, Miss D *227*

Hornton Trust, The *228*

Hudson Benevolent Trust, The Thomas *230*

Inman Charity, The *235*

JCSCJ Charitable Trust, The *238*

James Foundation, The Catherine and Lady Grace *241*

KC Charitable Trust, The *250*

Karten Charitable Trust, The Ian *250*

Keyes Trust, The Ursula *253*

Kingsgrove Charitable Trust, The *255*

Kobler Trust, The *258*

Kreitman Foundation *258*

Kulika Charitable Trust, The *259*

Kweller Charitable Trust, The Harry *259*

Laing Charitable Trust, The David *260*

Lalonde Trust *262*

Landy Charitable Trust, Harry and Gertrude *263*

Lanvern Foundation *265*

Laski Memorial Charitable Trust, Nathan *265*

Laspen Trust *265*

Lauffer Charitable Foundation, The R & D *266*

Lavender Trust, The *267*

Lawley Foundation, The Edgar E *267*

Leigh-Bramwell Trust 'E', P *270*

Levy Charitable Foundation, Joseph *272*

Lingwood Charitable Trust, The *276*

Localtrent Ltd *279*

Lunzer Charitable Trust, The Ruth & Jack *287*

Lynwood Charitable Trust, The *288*

Lyons Charitable Trust, The *288*

MDM Memorial Trust *289*

MacAndrew Trust, The E M *289*

McKechnie Foundation, A N *292*

McKenzie Trust, The Robert *292*

McLaren Foundation *292*

McLaren Memorial Trust, The Martin *293*

MacRobert Trusts, The *294*

Marchig Animal Welfare Trust *297*

Margadale Charitable Trust, Lord *297*

Markus Charitable Foundation, The Erich *298*

Marriage's Charitable Trust, Miss G M *299*

Marr-Munning Trust *299*

Marshall Charitable Trust, The Charlotte *300*

Martin Trust, The Sir George *300*

Mattock Charitable Trust, The W T *302*

Mayfair Charities Limited *303*

Medlock Charitable Trust, The *304*

Millett Charitable Trust, The Alan and Janet *312*

Modiano Charitable Trust *315*

Montefiore Trust, The David *316*

Moore Charitable Trust, The Horace 316

Morel Charitable Trust, The 318

Morphy Memorial Fund, Arthur 319

Morris Charitable Trust, The Willie & Mabel 320

Moulton Charitable Trust, The 321

Music Sales Charitable Trust, The 324

National Lottery Charities Board 328

Newcastle's 1986 Charitable Trust, Duke of 333

Newman Charitable Trust, Mr and Mrs F E F 334

Newstead Charity, The 334

Nickerson Charitable Foundation, The Joseph 335

Norman Trust, The 337

Northcott Charity Trust, The 338

Northern Electric Employee Charity Association 339

Northern Ireland Voluntary Trust 339

Old Possums Practical Trust, The 344

Oldham Foundation 345

Oppenheimer Charitable Trust 346

Owen Family Trust, The 348

Owen Trust, Margaret 348

PDC Trust, The 349

PJD Charitable Trust 350

Palmer Trust, The Gerald 352

Pascoe Charitable Trust, Alan 354

Paul Charitable Trust, The Late Barbara May 355

Paul Charitable Trust, Margaret Jeanne 355

Paul Charitable Trust, Pamela Milton 355

Paul Foundation, The 355

Paul's Charitable Trust, R J 355

Payne Charitable Trust, The 355

Pelech Charitable Trust, The 358

Perry Charitable Trust, Miss Frances Lucille 359

Pershore Nashdom & Elmore Trust Ltd, The 360

Peskin Charitable Trust, The Hazel and Leslie 360

Phillips Charitable Foundation, Reginald M 361

Pitt Trust, Headley 364

Porter Foundation 366

Powys Welsh Church Fund 367

Prince's Trust - BRO, The 369

Puebla Charitable Trust Limited, The 371

Pyke Charity Trust 372

QAS Charitable Trust 373

Quothquan Charitable Trust, The Second 373

RT Trust, The 374

Rackham Charitable Trust, The Mr & Mrs Philip 375

Radley Charitable Trust 375

Rae Charity, H J 375

Rainford Trust, The 376

Rav Chesed Trust, The 379

Reekie Trust, R A & V B 381

Reuter Foundation, The 382

Richard Charitable Trust, The Cliff 383

Richards Charity, The Clive 384

Rivendell Trust, The 387

Robbins Trust, The Cheshire 387

Rodewald's Charitable Settlement, Mr C A 389

Rogers Charitable Settlement, The Richard 390

Rolfe Charitable Trust, The 390

Rosen Foundation, Cecil 392

Rowan Charitable Trust, The 393

St Jude's Trust 403

Salters Charities 405

Sargeant's Charitable Trust, Mrs M E 407

Save & Prosper Foundation 409

Scarr-Hall Memorial Trust, The 409

Seva Trust, Rampaba Sadhu 415

Shaw Foundation, The Linley 416

Sheepdrove Trust, The 417

Sherman Charitable Trust, The Archie 419

Shifrin Charitable Trust, The Maurice and Hilda 419

Sidbury Trust, The Second 421

Silvester Charitable Gift Trust 422

Skinners' Company Lady Neville Charity 424

Society of Friends of the Torah, The 429

Solomons Charitable Trust, David 430

Somerfield Curtis Will Trust, The Dorothy 430

Stanley Foundation Limited 435

Stewart Charitable Trust, Mary Stephanie 437

Swann-Morton Foundation, The 444

Symons Charitable Trust, The Stella 446

Taylor Charitable Trust, The B R 450

Terry Charitable Trust, Noel Goddard 451

Tesco Charity Trust 452

Tesler Foundation, The 452

van Geest Foundation, The John and Lucille 470

Vineyard Christian Fellowship of South West 473

Vinson Charity Trust, The 1969 473

Vogel Charitable Trust, The Nathan 474

Wakefield Trust, The 476

Ward Blenkinsop Trust, The 480

Weinstock Fund, The 484

Welby Trust, The Barbara 484

Whetherly's Charitable Trust, The Hon Mrs R G A 489

Whitehead Charitable Trust, J E 490

Whittington Charitable Trust, The 491

Wiggins Charity Trust, Cyril 491

Wilde Charitable Trust, The Felicity 492

Wills 1961 Charitable Trust, Major Michael Thomas 494

Winstone Foundation, Hyman 497

Woburn 1986 Charitable Trust 498

Wohl Charitable Foundation, The Maurice 498

Wohl Charitable Trust, The Maurice 498

Wolff Charity Trust 498

Wolfson Family Charitable Trust, The 499

Woods Charitable Foundation, Geoffrey 502

Worms Charitable Trust, The Freda and Della 504

Worshipful Company of Needlemakers' Charitable Fund 505

Wright Deceased Trust, John William 506

Wychdale Limited 507

Youell Foundation Ltd, The 510

Zaiger Trust, The Elizabeth and Prince 512

···················

■ Conservation education & training

see Education & training

···················

■ Convalescent homes

see also Health facilities & buildings

Funding priority

Andrew Convalescent Trust, The Frederick 17

Cohen Charity Trust, Lucy 104

Holinsworth Fund of Help, The
C B and A B *224*

Merton and George Woofindin
Convalescent Trust, The
Zachary *307*

Royal Theatrical Fund, The *396*

Sassoon Charitable Trust, The
Late Aaron D *408*

....

■ Costs of study

see also **Bursaries & fees,
Fellowships, Scholarships**

Funding priority

AB Charitable Trust, The *3*

Achiezer Association Limited *6*

Aga Khan Foundation (UK) *7*

Airflow Community Ltd, The *9*

Aleh Charitable Foundation,
The *10*

Alexander Charitable Trust,
The *10*

Alexander Charitable Trust,
Mrs K L *11*

Alliance Family Foundation
Limited *13*

Allsop Charitable Trust, Pat *14*

Anglo-Catholic Ordination
Candidates Fund, The *18*

Appelbe Trust, Ambrose & Ann
19

Arts Council of Wales, The *23*

Ashton Foundation, The
Norman C *24*

Astor of Hever Trust, The *26*

Baker Trust, The C Alma *31*

Bear Mordechai Ltd *39*

Beit Trust, The *40*

Bestway Foundation, The *46*

Black Foundation, The Bertie
51

Blank Donations Ltd, The David
54

Bottom Charitable Trust, Harry
56

Brand Charitable Trust *58*

Bridgeman TRA Foundation,
The Dick *60*

British Schools and Universities
Foundation (Inc) *62*

Burden Trust, The *69*

Cadbury Schweppes
Foundation, The *76*

Campden Charities, The *79*

Carnegie Trust for the
Universities of Scotland *82*

Carron Charitable Trust, The
83

Carter Trust, The Frederick
William *84*

Cassel Educational Trust
(Overseas Research Grants),
Sir Ernest *84*

Cen Foundation, The Hyman
87

Chippindale Foundation, Sam
93

Ciba Fellowship Trust, The *95*

Clark Charitable Trust *98*

Clark Charitable Trust, J
Anthony *98*

Coates Charitable Settlement,
The *102*

Cohen Charitable Trust, The
Vivienne and Samuel *104*

Company of Chartered
Surveyors Charitable Trust
Fund, The *108*

Company of Tobacco Pipe
Makers and Tobacco
Blenders Benevolent Fund
109

Crescent Trust, The *117*

Curry Charitable Trust, Dennis
119

Daily Telegraph Charitable
Trust *122*

Daiwa Anglo-Japanese
Foundation, The *122*

Dandeen Charitable Trust *123*

Davy Foundation, The J *126*

De La Rue Charitable Trust
127

Deutsch Charitable Trust, The
Andre *131*

Deutsch Charitable Trust, The
H & M *131*

Diamond Industry Educational
Charity, The *132*

Djanogly Foundation, The *135*

Dove-Bowerman Trust *137*

Dulverton Trust, The *139*

Edgar Foundation, The Gilbert
and Eileen *145*

Edinburgh Trust, No 2 Account
145

Elephant Jobs Charity *146*

Ellis 1985 Charitable Trust,
Edith M *148*

Fairbairn Charitable Trust, The
Esmee *157*

Fairway Trust, The *158*

Famos Foundation Trust *158*

Farmers' Company Charitable
Fund, The *159*

Follett Trust, The *166*

Franklin Bequest, The Rosalind
169

Franklin Deceased's New
Second Charity, Sydney E
170

Franklin Trust, Jill *170*

Garnett Charitable Trust, The
178

Gatsby Charitable Foundation,
The *179*

Gibbs Charitable Trusts, The
181

Gilchrist Educational Trust *183*

Girdlers' Company Charitable
Trust, The *184*

Goodman Charitable
Foundation, The Everard
and Mina *188*

Goodman Trust, The *189*

Grahame Charitable
Foundation, The *190*

Greenwood Charitable Trust,
The G B *195*

Griffiths Trust, The E E and
D M *196*

Gross Charities Limited, M & R
197

Grosshill Charitable Trust *197*

Gwent County Council Welsh
Church Fund *200*

Hamilton Educational Trust,
Eleanor *205*

Hamlyn Foundation, The Paul
205

Harbour Foundation Ltd, The
208

Harding's Charity, William *209*

Hargreaves Trust, The Kenneth
210

Heinz Company Limited
Charitable Trust, The H J
215

Held Settlement, The Gisela
215

Highcroft Charitable Trust *218*

Hitachi Charitable Trust, The
222

Hopkinson Educational Trust,
Robert Addy *227*

Horne Foundation, The *228*

Hornsey Parochial Charities
(Educational and Vocational
Foundation), The *228*

Hyde Park Place Estate Charity,
The *232*

IBM United Kingdom Trust
233

IPE Charitable Trust, The *233*

Ireland Funds, The *237*

JCA Charitable Foundation *238*

James Foundation, The
Catherine and Lady Grace
241

Jeffreys Road Fund, Rees *243*

Jewish Philanthropic
Association for Israel and
the Middle East, The *245*

Jones Trust, Cemlyn *248*

Kahn Charitable Trust, Bernard
250

Karten Charitable Trust, The
Ian *250*

Kings Medical Research Trust,
The *255*

Kobler Trust, The *258*

Kreitman Foundation *258*

Kulika Charitable Trust, The
259

Kweller Charitable Trust, The
Harry *259*

Landy Charitable Trust, Harry
and Gertrude *263*

Lanvern Foundation *265*

Laski Memorial Charitable
Trust, Nathan *265*

Lauffer Charitable Foundation,
The R & D *266*

Leche Trust, The *268*
Leigh-Bramwell Trust 'E', P *270*
Lester Trust Fund, The *271*
Lucas Charitable Trust Limited,
The Joseph *286*
Lunzer Charitable Trust, The
Ruth & Jack *287*
Lyons Charitable Trust, Sir Jack
288
Maccabi Foundation, The *290*
McKenzie Trust, The Robert
292
MacRobert Trusts, The *294*
Marks Foundation, The Hilda
and Samuel *298*
Marmor Charitable Trust, The
Julie *299*
Marshall Charitable Trust, The
Charlotte *300*
Martin Trust, The Sir George
300
Mayfair Charities Limited *303*
Medlock Charitable Trust, The
304
Mellows Charitable Settlement,
The Anthony and Elizabeth
305
Mercers' Company Educational
Trust Fund, The *306*
Millett Charitable Trust, The
Alan and Janet *312*
Modiano Charitable Trust *315*
Montefiore Trust, The David
316
Moore Charitable Trust, The
Horace *316*
Moores Foundation, The Peter
318
Morgan Foundation, The Mr &
Mrs J T *319*
Muslim Hands *324*
Needham Cooper Charitable
Trust, The *331*
Newitt Fund, Richard *333*
Newman Charitable Trust, Mr
and Mrs F E F *334*
Noah Trust, The *335*
Northern Dairies Educational
Trust *339*
Old Possums Practical Trust,
The *344*
Oldacre Foundation, The John
345
Ouseley Trust, The *347*
Oxford Trust, The *349*
Peacock Charitable Foundation,
The Michael *356*
Pelech Charitable Trust, The
358
QAS Charitable Trust *373*
RVW Trust *374*
Rayne Foundation, The *379*
Rhodes Trust – Public Purposes
Fund, The *383*
Richard III and Yorkist History
Trust *384*
Robbins Trust, The Cheshire
387

Rosen Foundation, Cecil *392*
Royal Commission for the
Exhibition of 1851 *395*
Rozel Trust, The *397*
Said Foundation, The Karim
Rida *401*
St Jude's Trust *403*
Save & Prosper Foundation
409
Scarr-Hall Memorial Trust, The
409
Seva Trust, Rampaba Sadhu
415
Shah Trust, The Dr N K *416*
Sherman Charitable Trust, The
Archie *419*
Shine No 2 Charitable Trust,
The Barnett and Sylvia *420*
Shipwrights' Company
Educational Trust, The *420*
Sidbury Trust, The Second *421*
Simon Population Trust, The
422
Salter Trust Ltd *424*
Society of Friends of the Torah,
The *429*
South Square Trust *430*
Southall Charitable Trust,
Kenneth & Phyllis *431*
Southall Trust, W F *432*
Spoore, Merry & Rixman
Foundation, The *434*
Stanley Foundation Limited
435
Stathern Chapel Close Trust,
The *436*
Stewart Charitable Trust, Mary
Stephanie *437*
Street Charitable Foundation,
W O *440*
TSB Foundation for the
Channel Islands *447*
Tesco Charity Trust *452*
Tesler Foundation, The *452*
Thompson Memorial Fund, The
Edwin John *453*
Thriplow Charitable Trust *456*
Timson Family Charitable Trust
457
Tyndale Trust *466*
United Kingdom Friends for
Further Education in Israel
468
Watson's Trust, John *482*
Weinstock Fund, The *484*
White Rose Children's Aid
International Charity *489*
Wingate Foundation, The
Harold Hyam *496*
Wolff Charity Trust *498*
Wolfson Family Charitable
Trust, The *499*
Wolfson (Scotland) Trust, The
Edith & Isaac *500*
Wolverhampton Rotary Club
Charitable Trust *500*
Woods Charitable Foundation,
Geoffrey *502*

Worms Charitable Trust, The
Freda and Della *504*
Worshipful Company of
Engineers' Charitable Trust
Fund, The *504*
Worshipful Company of
Needlemakers' Charitable
Fund *505*
Zaiger Trust, The Elizabeth and
Prince *512*

Will consider

AHJ Charitable Trust, The *3*
Abbeydale Trust *5*
Acacia Charitable Trust *6*
All Saints Educational Trust *12*
Allnatt Charitable Foundation,
Angus *14*
Ambika Paul Foundation *15*
Amory Charitable Trust,
Viscount *16*
Angler's Inn Trust *17*
Anglo Hong Kong Trust, The
17
Anglo-German Foundation for
the Study of Industrial
Society *18*
Aquarian Healing Trust *19*
Aquinas Trust *20*
Arkleton Trust, The *21*
Armourers' & Brasiers' Gauntlet
Trust, The *21*
Army Benevolent Fund, The *22*
Ashley Foundation, The Laura
24
Askew Charitable Trust, The
Ian *25*
Assembled Church of Christ
Trust, The *25*
Asthma Allergy and
Inflammation Research Trust
25
Astor's 1969 Charity, The Hon
M L *26*
BUPA Foundation, The *29*
Bachad Fellowship – Friends of
Bnei Akiva *30*
Barnby's Foundation, Lord *35*
Barnes Workhouse Fund *35*
Barnsbury Charitable Trust *35*
Barton Trust, Eleanor *37*
Bateman Charitable Trust, Lady
Margaret *37*
Bealey Foundation, The *38*
Beckwith Charitable Trust, The
Peter *40*
Beckwith-Smith's Charitable
Settlement, Mrs *40*
Behrens Charitable Trust, E M
40
Bergqvist Charitable Trust *44*
Biological Trust, The *49*
Blagrave Charitable Trust, The
Herbert and Peter *52*
Blakey Charitable Trust, The
Celia and Conrad *53*
Blanchminster Trust, The *54*

Boltons Trust, The 55

Borthwick Memorial Trust, The Oliver 56

Bowland Charitable Trust, The 57

Brighton & Hove Charitable Youth Trust 60

British Friends of Chinuch Atzmai Trust, The 62

Brook Charitable Settlement, R E 64

Brookhouse's Will Trust, Mr John Charles 65

Bugden Charitable Trust, The Rosemary 67

Bullough Tompson Settlement, The 68

Bulmer Charitable Trust, Becket 68

Burn Charity Trust, The J H 70

Burns Charity, The Dorothy 70

Burry Charitable Trust, The 70

Burton Charitable Trust, The Geoffrey 71

Butler's Trust, Lord 71

Butler's Trust, Lucilla 72

Campden Charities, The 79

Canine Supporters Charity, The 80

Cardiff & Swansea Methodist District Charitable Trust Fund 80

Carlton Television Trust 81

Cass's Foundation, Sir John 85

Castang Charitable Trust, H and M 85

Charity Projects 90

Chartered Institute of Management Accountants' General Charitable Trust, The 90

Christian Aid 94

Cinderford Charitable Trust, The 96

Closehelm Ltd 101

Clutterbuck Charitable Trust, Robert 102

Coates Charitable Trust 1969, Lance 103

Coates Charitable Trust, The John 103

Cohen Charity Trust, Lucy 104

Cohen Foundation, The John S 104

Condon Family Trust 109

Cooper Charitable Trust 111

Cope Charitable Trust, Alfred 112

Curriers Company Charitable Fund 119

Curzon Charitable Trust, The Wallace 120

Cymerman Trust Limited, Itzchok Meyer 120

De Avenley Foundation, The 126

De Rothschild 1981 Charitable Trust, The Edmund 127

De Yong Charitable Trust, The Emma 128

Denton Charitable Trust, The 130

Desmond Charitable Trust, The Richard 131

Dicken Charitable Trust, The Albert 133

Digby Charitable Trust, Simon 133

Dinam Charity 134

Dixon Charitable Trust, F E 134

Doughty Charity Trust, The 136

D'Oyly Carte Charitable Trust, The 137

Drapers' Charitable Fund 137

Drayton Trust, The 138

Dunn Charitable Trust, The Harry 140

Earley Charity, The 142

Earmark Trust, The 142

Ebb and Flow Charitable Trust 144

Education Services 145

Eling Trust 147

Ellinson Foundation Limited 148

Elmchurch Trust, The 148

Elshore Limited 149

Emanuel Charitable Settlement, Ralph and Muriel 150

Family Trust, The 158

Federation of Jewish Relief Organisations 160

Fletcher Trust, Roy 165

Follett Trust, The 166

Foreman Foundation, The Carl & Eve 167

Foyle Trust, Charles Henry 169

Fry Charitable Trust, Maurice 174

Gardner Memorial Trust, The Samuel 178

Garthgwynion Charities 179

Gibson's Charity Trust, The Hon Mr & Mrs Clive 182

Gillett Charitable Trust, J A 183

Gill's Charitable Trust, Mrs M M 184

Glebe Charitable Trust 185

Glynde Place Charitable Trust (1974), The 186

Gold Hill Church Trust 186

Goldberg Charitable Trust, The Lewis 186

Goldsmiths' Company's Charities, The 188

Goodman Trust, The S & F 189

Gradel Foundation, The 189

Green Foundation, Constance 194

Greenaway Foundation, The Sir Derek 194

Groves Charitable Trust, The 197

Grut Charitable Trust, The 198

Gulbenkian Foundation (Lisbon) United Kingdom Branch, Calouste 199

HB Charitable Trust 201

Hacking & Sons Ltd Charitable Trust, C G 201

Hale Trust, The 203

Hamlyn Foundation, The Paul 205

Hampton Fuel Allotment Charity 207

Harvey Charitable Trust, Gordon 211

Hawthorne Charitable Trust, The 212

Hertfordshire Community Trust, The 217

Hewett/Driver Education Trust, The 217

Hillards Charitable Trust, Gay & Peter Hartley's 220

Hodge Foundation, The Jane 223

Holford Trust Fund 224

Holly Hill Charitable Trust 224

Hoover Foundation, The 226

Hopkins Charitable Foundation, The Sir Anthony 226

Horn Trust, The Cuthbert 227

Hornby Charitable Trust, Miss D 227

Hornton Trust, The 228

Howard Charitable Trust, John & Ruth 229

Hudson Benevolent Trust, The Thomas 230

Hughes Charitable Trust, The Geoffery C 230

Humanitarian Trust, The 230

Idlewild Trust, The 234

Inman Charity, The 235

KC Charitable Trust, The 250

Kalms Foundation, The Stanley 250

Keyes Trust, The Ursula 253

Kingsgrove Charitable Trust, The 255

Kinnison Charitable Trust, R O 256

Kleinwort Charitable Trust, The Ernest 257

Lavender Trust, The 267

Lawley Foundation, The Edgar E 267

Levy Charitable Foundation, Joseph 272

Lewis Foundation, The John Spedan 274

Licensed Trade Charities Trust, The 274

Liffe Benefit 274

Linford Charitable Trust, The Fred 276

Lingwood Charitable Trust, The 276

Littler Foundation, The Emile 277

Lloyd's Charities Trust 278

Localtrent Ltd *279*
Lunn-Rockliffe Charitable Trust, Paul *286*
Lynwood Charitable Trust, The *288*
Lyons Charitable Trust, The *288*
Lyon's Charity, John *288*
MDM Memorial Trust *289*
MacAndrew Trust, The E M *289*
McKechnie Foundation, A N *292*
Mackintosh Foundation, The *292*
McLaren Foundation *292*
McLaren Memorial Trust, The Martin *293*
Margadale Charitable Trust, Lord *297*
Marks Charitable Trust, Michael *298*
Markus Charitable Foundation, The Erich *298*
Marriage's Charitable Trust, Miss G M *299*
Marr-Munning Trust *299*
Matchan Fund Limited, The Leonard *301*
Material World Charitable Foundation Limited, The *301*
Mattock Charitable Trust, The W T *302*
Measures Charity, The James Frederick and Ethel Anne *303*
Mediterranean Archaeological Trust *304*
Melville Trust for Care and Cure of Cancer *305*
Millichope Foundation, The *312*
Morel Charitable Trust, The *318*
Morgan Crucible Company plc Charitable Trust, The *319*
Morris Charitable Trust, The Willie & Mabel *320*
Moulton Charitable Trust, The *321*
Music Sales Charitable Trust, The *324*
NR Charitable Trust, The *325*
Naaman Trust, The *325*
National Lottery Charities Board *328*
Newcastle's 1986 Charitable Trust, Duke of *333*
Newcomen Collett Foundation *333*
Newstead Charity, The *334*
Nidditch Foundation, The Laurie *335*
Norfolk's Family Charitable Trust, Lavinia *336*
North West Arts Board *337*

Northcott Charity Trust, The *338*
Northern Electric Employee Charity Association *339*
Norton Foundation, The *340*
Nuffield Foundation *342*
Oldham Foundation *345*
Owen Family Trust, The *348*
Owen Trust, Margaret *348*
PDC Trust, The *349*
PJD Charitable Trust *350*
Palmer Trust, The Gerald *352*
Pascoe Charitable Trust, Alan *354*
Patients' Aid Association Hospital and Medical Charities Trust *354*
Paul Charitable Trust, The Late Barbara May *355*
Paul Charitable Trust, Margaret Jeanne *355*
Paul Charitable Trust, Pamela Milton *355*
Paul Foundation, The *355*
Paul's Charitable Trust, R J *355*
Payne Charitable Trust, The *355*
Payne Trust, The Harry *356*
Peel Medical Research Trust, The *358*
Perry Charitable Trust, Miss Frances Lucille *359*
Pershore Nashdom & Elmore Trust Ltd, The *360*
Peskin Charitable Trust, The Hazel and Leslie *360*
Phillips Charitable Foundation, Reginald M *361*
Pilkington Charitable Trust, Cecil *363*
Pitt Trust, Headley *364*
Porcupine Trust, The *366*
Powys Welsh Church Fund *367*
Puebla Charitable Trust Limited, The *371*
Queen Anne Street Educational Trust Limited *373*
RT Trust, The *374*
Rackham Charitable Trust, The Mr & Mrs Philip *375*
Radcliffe's Trust, Dr *375*
Radley Charitable Trust *375*
Rae Charity, H J *375*
Rainford Trust, The *376*
Rav Chesed Trust, The *379*
Rayner Charitable Trust, The John *380*
Reekie Trust, R A & V B *381*
Reuter Foundation, The *382*
Rhodes Trust – Public Purposes Fund, The *383*
Richards Charity, The Clive *384*
Richards Charity, The Violet M *384*
Richmond Parish Lands Charity *384*
Rivendell Trust, The *387*
Robyn Charitable Trust *389*

Rodewald's Charitable Settlement, Mr C A *389*
Rogers Charitable Settlement, The Richard *390*
Rolfe Charitable Trust, The *390*
Rothley Trust, The *392*
S Group Charitable Trust *399*
Salamander Charitable Trust, The *405*
Salters Charities *405*
Samuel Charitable Trust, M J *406*
Sarum St Michael Educational Charity, The *408*
Save & Prosper Educational Trust *408*
Scopus Jewish Educational Trust *411*
Sheepdrove Trust, The *417*
Shifrin Charitable Trust, The Maurice and Hilda *419*
Silvester Charitable Gift Trust *422*
Simon's Charity *422*
Skinners' Company Lady Neville Charity *424*
Solomons Charitable Trust, David *430*
Somerfield Curtis Will Trust, The Dorothy *430*
Summerfield Charitable Trust, The *442*
Sumner's Trust Section 'A', Sir John *443*
Swann-Morton Foundation, The *444*
Taylor Charitable Trust, The B R *450*
Tear Fund *450*
Terry Charitable Trust, Noel Goddard *451*
Thompson Charitable Trust, The *453*
Thomson Charitable Trust, The Arthur *453*
Thomson Foundation, The Sue *454*
Thorpe Charity Trust, The *455*
van Geest Foundation, The John and Lucille *470*
Van Norden's Charitable Foundation, Mrs Maud *471*
Vincent Trust Fund, Eric W *473*
Vineyard Christian Fellowship of South West *473*
Vinson Charity Trust, The 1969 *473*
Vogel Charitable Trust, The Nathan *474*
Wakefield Trust, The *476*
Walker Trust, The *477*
Ward Blenkinsop Trust, The *480*
Wates Charitable Trust, John *481*
Wates Foundation, The *481*
Wellcome Trust, The *485*

Westminster Amalgamated Charity *487*
Whetherly's Charitable Trust, The Hon Mrs R G A *489*
Whitehead Charitable Trust, J E *490*
Whitehead's Charitable Trust, Sydney Dean *490*
Whittington Charitable Trust, The *491*
Wiggins Charity Trust, Cyril *491*
Wilde Charitable Trust, The Felicity *492*
Wills 1961 Charitable Trust, Major Michael Thomas *494*
Wingate Foundation, The Harold Hyam *496*
Wingfield's Charitable Trust, Mrs *496*
Winstone Foundation, Hyman *497*
Wiseman Memorial Fund Limited, The Max *497*
Woburn 1986 Charitable Trust *498*
Woodhouse Charitable Trust, Edwin *501*
Woodroffe Benton Foundation, The *502*
Woolmen's Company Charitable Trust, The *503*
Worshipful Company of Founders Charities, The *505*
Worshipful Company of Weavers Textile Education Fund, The *506*
Wychdale Limited *507*
Yapp Education and Research Trust, The *508*
Yorkshire Agricultural Society *509*
Youell Foundation Ltd, The *510*

....

■ Council for Voluntary Service (CVS)

see also **Charity or voluntary umbrella bodies**

Funding priority
Berkshire Community Trust *45*
City Parochial Foundation *96*
Community Trust for Greater Manchester, The *108*
County Durham Foundation *115*

Will consider
Amory Charitable Trust, Viscount *16*
Barbour Trust, The *33*
Boots Charitable Trust *56*
Brotherton Trust, The Charles *65*

Camelot Foundation, The *78*
Campden Charities, The *79*
Carnegie United Kingdom Trust, The *82*
Coutts Charitable Trust, The *116*
Debtors' Relief Fund Charity *128*
Digby Charitable Trust, Simon *133*
Edgar Foundation, The Gilbert and Eileen *145*
Ford of Britain Trust *166*
Grant-Lawson Charitable Trust, Lady Virginia *192*
Great Britain Sasakawa Foundation, The *193*
Hampstead Wells and Campden Trust *206*
Harford Charitable Trust *209*
Isle of Dogs Community Foundation *238*
Leech Charity, The William *269*
Milton Keynes Community Trust Ltd, The *312*
Minet Trust, The Peter *313*
Newby Trust Ltd *332*
Norman Family Charitable Trust, The *337*
Persula Foundation, The *360*
Pilkington Charitable Trust, Cecil *363*
Pratt Charitable Trust, The W L *367*
Richmond Parish Lands Charity *384*
Rope Third Charitable Settlement, The Mrs *391*
Rowntree Foundation, Joseph *394*
Sainsbury Charitable Fund Ltd, The *402*
Scott Bader Commonwealth Ltd, The *411*
Sheldon Trust, The *417*
Shepherd Charitable Trust, The Sylvia and Colin *418*
Summerfield Charitable Trust, The *442*
Wiltshire Community Foundation *495*
Woodlands Trust *501*
Woolton Charitable Trust, The *503*

....

■ Counselling (health)

see also **Health care**

Funding priority
Allied Dunbar Charitable Trust Limited, The *13*
Artemis Charitable Trust, The *22*
Berkshire Community Trust *45*
Borthwick Memorial Trust, The Oliver *56*

Community Trust for Greater Manchester, The *108*
Kroch Foundation, The Heinz & Anna *259*
Lloyd's Charities Trust *278*
Mental Health Foundation, The *305*
Mercury Phoenix Trust *307*
SMB Trust, The *400*
Van Berchem Charitable Trust, The Alec *470*
Wiltshire Community Foundation *495*

Will consider
Abbey National Charitable Trust *4*
Alcohol Education and Research Council *9*
Allen Trust, Mrs M H *13*
Ammco Trust, The *15*
Andrew Charitable Trust, The Prince *16*
Archer Trust, The *20*
Army Benevolent Fund, The *22*
Astor Foundation, The *26*
Barbour Trust, The *33*
Beit Trust, The *40*
Berris Charitable Trust *45*
BibleLands *47*
Bottom Charitable Trust, Harry *56*
British Dietetic Association General and Education Trust Fund, The *61*
Britton Charitable Trust, The J & M *63*
Burdall Charity, H M *69*
Camelot Foundation, The *78*
Cleopatra Trust *99*
Clinton's Charitable Trust, Lord *100*
Cole Charitable Trust, The *105*
Collier Charitable Trust, The *105*
County Durham Foundation *115*
Cripplegate Foundation *118*
Curzon Charitable Trust, The Wallace *120*
Debtors' Relief Fund Charity *128*
Dibden Allotments Charity *132*
Digby Charitable Trust, Simon *133*
Dorus Trust *136*
Dumbreck Charity *139*
Edgar Foundation, The Gilbert and Eileen *145*
Edgar Trust, The Gilbert *145*
Elkes Charity Fund, The Wilfred & Elsie *147*
Emmandjay Charitable Trust *150*
Epigoni Trust *152*
Fishmongers' Company's Charitable Trust *163*

Foreman Foundation, The Carl
& Eve *167*
GW Trust, The *176*
Gardner Charitable Trust, R & J
178
Gibbins Trust, The *181*
Goldsmiths' Company's
Charities, The *188*
Great Britain Sasakawa
Foundation, The *193*
Greenaway Foundation, The Sir
Derek *194*
Grocers' Charity *197*
Haines Charitable Trust, The
Alfred *203*
Hardy Trust, The Patsy *209*
Hawley Residuary Fund, Harry
Fieldsend *212*
Heritage of London Trust, The
216
Hertfordshire Community
Trust, The *217*
Isle of Dogs Community
Foundation *238*
Lankelly Foundation, The *264*
Lawson Charitable Trust,
Raymond and Blanche *267*
Leadbeater Trust, The Alfred
268
Lee Foundation, The Edgar
269
Leech Charity, The William *269*
(Lloyds) TSB Foundation for
England and Wales *279*
London Law Trust *280*
MacKintosh Charitable Trust,
Viscount *292*
Mackintosh Foundation, The
292
Manning Trust, Leslie & Lilian
296
Marchday Charitable Fund, The
296
Metropolitan Hospital-Sunday
Fund, The *308*
Milton Keynes Community
Trust Ltd, The *312*
Milward Charity, The Edgar
313
Minet Trust, The Peter *313*
Moores Foundation, John *318*
Needham Cooper Charitable
Trust, The *331*
New Court Charitable Trust
332
Noah Trust, The *335*
North British Hotel Trust *337*
Oakdale Trust, The *343*
Payne Trust, The Harry *356*
Persula Foundation, The *360*
Rest-Harrow Trust, The *382*
Rothley Trust, The *392*
Rowbotham Charitable Trust,
The Christopher *393*
Schuster Charitable Trust, The
410
Seagram Distillers Charitable
Trust *413*

Skelton Bounty, The *423*
South Square Trust *430*
Summerfield Charitable Trust,
The *442*
Sussman Charitable Trust,
Adrienne & Leslie *443*
TSB Foundation for Northern
Ireland *447*
Tear Fund *450*
Thackray General Charitable
Trust, The P & L *452*
Thompson Charitable Trust,
The *453*
Torquay Charities, The *458*
Truemark Trust, The *461*
Tudor Trust, The *463*
Tyne & Wear Foundation *466*
Van Leer Foundation UK Trust,
Bernard *470*
Victoria & Johnson Memorial
Trust, Queen *472*
Wakefield (Tower Hill, Trinity
Square) Trust *476*
Weir Foundation, The James
484
Westcroft Trust *486*
Whitaker Charitable Trust *489*
Woodlands Trust *501*
Worshipful Company of
Engineers' Charitable Trust
Fund, The *504*
Wylde Memorial Charity, The
Anthony and Gwendoline
507

....

Counselling (social issues)

see also Community
services

Funding priority

Alexandra Trust *11*
Army Benevolent Fund, The *22*
Aston Charities Trust Ltd *25*
Berkshire Community Trust *45*
Christmas Cracker Trust *95*
Community Trust for Greater
Manchester, The *108*
Egerton of Tatton Will Trust,
Lord *146*
Fletcher Trust, Roy *165*
Isle of Dogs Community
Foundation *238*
Kroch Foundation, The Heinz &
Anna *259*
Lancaster's Trust, Bryan *263*
Lloyd's Charities Trust *278*
Milton Keynes Community
Trust Ltd, The *312*
Moores Family Charity
Foundation, The *317*
National Power Charitable
Trust, The *330*
SMB Trust, The *400*
Smith Foundation, The Leslie
427

TSB Foundation for Scotland
447
Van Berchem Charitable Trust,
The Alec *470*
Wates Foundation, The *481*

Will consider

Abbey National Charitable
Trust *4*
Abel Charitable Trust *5*
Allen Trust, Mrs M H *13*
Aquarius Charitable
Foundation, The *19*
Archer Trust, The *20*
Askew Trust, The Dorothy *25*
Astor Foundation, The *26*
Barbour Trust, The *33*
Beit Trust, The *40*
BibleLands *47*
Blackburn Trust, The *51*
Blakenham's Charity Trust,
Lady *53*
Blanchminster Trust, The *54*
Boots Charitable Trust *56*
Bowland Charitable Trust, The
57
Bridge Trust, The *60*
Brighton & Hove Charitable
Youth Trust *60*
Brough Charitable Trust,
Joseph *65*
Burdall Charity, H M *69*
CLA Charitable Trust *74*
Cadbury Charitable Trust
(Incorporated), Edward *75*
Camelot Foundation, The *78*
Campden Charities, The *79*
Chrimes Family Charitable
Trust, The *93*
Cleopatra Trust *99*
Clifford Charity Oxford, The
100
Clinton's Charitable Trust, Lord
100
Cloudesley's Charity/School
Parents & Friends
Association, Richard *102*
County Durham Foundation
115
Coutts Charitable Trust, The
116
Curriers Company Charitable
Fund *119*
Curzon Charitable Trust, The
Wallace *120*
Debtors' Relief Fund Charity
128
Derbyshire Trust, J N *130*
Digby Charitable Trust, Simon
133
Dorus Trust *136*
Dumbreck Charity *139*
Ebb and Flow Charitable Trust
144
Edgar Foundation, The Gilbert
and Eileen *145*
Edgar Trust, The Gilbert *145*

Education Services *145*
Elkes Charity Fund, The Wilfred & Elsie *147*
Emmandjay Charitable Trust *150*
Epigoni Trust *152*
Fishmongers' Company's Charitable Trust *163*
Fletcher Charitable Trust, The Joyce *164*
Franklin Trust, Jill *170*
GW Trust, The *176*
Gardner Charitable Trust, R & J *178*
Gelston Charitable Trust, The *179*
Gibbins Trust, The *181*
Great Britain Sasakawa Foundation, The *193*
Greenaway Foundation, The Sir Derek *194*
Griffiths Trust, The E E and D M *196*
Grocers' Charity *197*
Grosshill Charitable Trust *197*
Harford Charitable Trust *209*
Hartley Memorial Trust, The N & P *211*
Hertfordshire Community Trust, The *217*
Ibbett Trust, The *233*
Ingles Charitable Trust, The *234*
Inverforth Charitable Trust, The *236*
Ireland Funds, The *237*
Iris Trust, The *237*
Jarman Charitable Trust, The *243*
Jarrold Trust Ltd, John *243*
Johnson Foundation, The *246*
King Charitable Trust, The Lorna *254*
Knott Trust, Sir James *258*
Kyte Charitable Trust, The *259*
Laing Foundation, The Christopher *260*
Lane Foundation, The Allen *263*
Lankelly Foundation, The *264*
Lawson Charitable Trust, Raymond and Blanche *267*
Leech Charity, The William *269*
Lewis Partnership, John *274*
(Lloyds) TSB Foundation for England and Wales *279*
Lunn-Rockliffe Charitable Trust, Paul *286*
Lyndhurst Settlement *287*
MacKintosh Charitable Trust, Viscount *292*
Mackintosh Foundation, The *292*
Manning Trust, Leslie & Lilian *296*
Marchday Charitable Fund, The *296*

Mental Health Foundation, The *305*
Mercury Phoenix Trust *307*
Metropolitan Hospital-Sunday Fund, The *308*
Milburn Charitable Trust, Frederick *310*
Minet Trust, The Peter *313*
Moores Foundation, John *318*
Multithon Trust, The *323*
NR Charitable Trust, The *325*
Needham Cooper Charitable Trust, The *331*
New Court Charitable Trust *332*
Noah Trust, The *335*
Norman Family Charitable Trust, The *337*
North British Hotel Trust *337*
Northcott Devon Foundation *338*
Norton Foundation, The *340*
Oakdale Trust, The *343*
Owen Family Trust, The *348*
PF Charitable Trust *350*
Parivar Trust, The *353*
Payne Trust, The Harry *356*
Persula Foundation, The *360*
Pilkington Trust, The Austin and Hope *363*
Porter Foundation *366*
Powell Foundation, The *367*
Pratt Charitable Trust, The W L *367*
Provincial Trust for Kendal, The *370*
Pye Christian Trust, The *371*
Rest-Harrow Trust, The *382*
Robinson Brothers (Ryders Green) Ltd, Charitable Trust *388*
Rothley Trust, The *392*
Rowbotham Charitable Trust, The Christopher *393*
Saint Edmund King and Martyr Trust *402*
Saint Sarkis Charity Trust *404*
Schuster Charitable Trust, The *410*
Seagram Distillers Charitable Trust *413*
Sheepdrove Trust, The *417*
Sheldon Trust, The *417*
Shepherd Charitable Trust, The Sylvia and Colin *418*
Shepherd Family Charitable Trust, The Sir Peter *418*
Skelton Bounty, The *423*
Smith & Mount Trust, The Mrs *426*
South Square Trust *430*
Sparkhill Trust, The *433*
Staples Trust *435*
Summerfield Charitable Trust, The *442*
Sussman Charitable Trust, Adrienne & Leslie *443*
Swan Mountain Trust *444*

Sykes Trust, The Charles *445*
TSB Foundation for Northern Ireland *447*
Tear Fund *450*
Thackray General Charitable Trust, The P & L *452*
Tindall's Charitable Trust, Mrs R P *457*
Tisbury Telegraph Trust, The *457*
Toler Foundation, The *457*
Torquay Charities, The *458*
Truemark Trust, The *461*
Tudor Trust, The *463*
Tyne & Wear Foundation *466*
Upjohn Charitable Trust, The *469*
Van Leer Foundation UK Trust, Bernard *470*
Victoria & Johnson Memorial Trust, Queen *472*
Wakefield (Tower Hill, Trinity Square) Trust *476*
Wakeham Trust, The *476*
Walker Trust, The *477*
Wall Trust, Thomas *478*
Wander Charitable Fund, The Dr Albert *479*
Weir Foundation, The James *484*
Wesleyan Charitable Trust, The *485*
Westcroft Trust *486*
Whitaker Charitable Trust *489*
Whitecourt Charitable Trust, The *490*
Williams Charitable Trust, Alfred *493*
Wills 1961 Charitable Trust, Mr Frederick *493*
Wiltshire Community Foundation *495*
Wingate Foundation, The Harold Hyam *496*
Woodlands Trust *501*
Worshipful Company of Glass Sellers' Charity Trust, The *505*
Wylde Memorial Charity, The Anthony and Gwendoline *507*
Yorkshire Bank Charitable Trust, The *510*

■ **Crafts**
see also **Arts & arts facilities**
Funding priority
Atwell's Charity (Skinner's Company), Lawrence *27*
North West Arts Board *337*
Radcliffe's Trust, Dr *375*
Southern Arts *432*
Williams Charitable Trust, Alfred *493*

■ Crime

see Victims of crime

■ Crime prevention schemes

see also Community services

Funding priority

Berkshire Community Trust 45
City Parochial Foundation 96
Community Trust for Greater Manchester, The 108
County Durham Foundation 115
Coutts Charitable Trust, The 116
David Trust, The Lesley 124
Isle of Dogs Community Foundation 238
Lloyd's Charities Trust 278
(Lloyds) TSB Foundation for England and Wales 279
Moore Foundation, The George A 316
Noel Buxton Trust, The 335
TSB Foundation for Scotland 447
Wates Foundation, The 481

Will consider

Alexandra Trust 11
Anstey Charitable Settlement, J C W 18
Astor Foundation, The 26
Barbour Trust, The 33
Bewley Charitable Trust, The 46
Blakenham's Charity Trust, Lady 53
Boots Charitable Trust 56
Bowland Charitable Trust, The 57
Bridge Trust, The 60
Brough Charitable Trust, Joseph 65
Buckinghamshire Masonic Centenary Fund 67
CHK Charities Limited 74
CLA Charitable Trust 74
Cadbury Charitable Trust (Incorporated), Edward 75
Camelot Foundation, The 78
Campden Charities, The 79
Carnegie Dunfermline Trust 82
Chrimes Family Charitable Trust, The 93
Clinton's Charitable Trust, Lord 100
Davies Charity, The Gwendoline and Margaret 125
Debtors' Relief Fund Charity 128
Derbyshire Trust, J N 130

Digby Charitable Trust, Simon 133
Dorus Trust 136
Dumbreck Charity 139
Edgar Foundation, The Gilbert and Eileen 145
Edgar Trust, The Gilbert 145
Egerton of Tatton Will Trust, Lord 146
Elkes Charity Fund, The Wilfred & Elsie 147
Emmandjay Charitable Trust 150
Epigoni Trust 152
Fletcher Trust, Roy 165
Grocers' Charity 197
Grosshill Charitable Trust 197
Harford Charitable Trust 209
Hertfordshire Community Trust, The 217
Inverforth Charitable Trust, The 236
Iris Trust, The 237
Jarman Charitable Trust, The 243
Jarrold Trust Ltd, John 243
Johnson Foundation, The 246
Knott Trust, Sir James 258
Kroch Foundation, The Heinz & Anna 259
Laing Charitable Trust, The David 260
Laing Foundation, The Christopher 260
Laing's Charitable Trust 262
Lane Foundation, The Allen 263
Lankelly Foundation, The 264
Lawson Charitable Trust, Raymond and Blanche 267
Leach Fourteenth Trust, The 267
Leech Charity, The William 269
Lewis Partnership, John 274
MacKintosh Charitable Trust, Viscount 292
Manning Trust, Leslie & Lilian 296
Marchday Charitable Fund, The 296
Milburn Charitable Trust, Frederick 310
Minet Trust, The Peter 313
NR Charitable Trust, The 325
National Power Charitable Trust, The 330
New Court Charitable Trust 332
Norfolk's Family Charitable Trust, Lavinia 336
Norman Family Charitable Trust, The 337
Norton Foundation, The 340
Notgrove Trust, The 341
Oldham Foundation 345
Patients' Aid Association Hospital and Medical Charities Trust 354

Payne Trust, The Harry 356
Persula Foundation, The 360
Pratt Charitable Trust, The W L 367
Provincial Trust for Kendal, The 370
Pyke Charity Trust 372
Ravenscroft Foundation, The 379
Rope Third Charitable Settlement, The Mrs 391
Rothley Trust, The 392
Rowbotham Charitable Trust, The Christopher 393
Sainsbury Charitable Fund Ltd, The 402
Schuster Charitable Trust, The 410
Shepherd Charitable Trust, The Sylvia and Colin 418
Shepherd Family Charitable Trust, The Sir Peter 418
Skelton Bounty, The 423
South Square Trust 430
Sykes Trust, The Charles 445
TSB Foundation for Northern Ireland 447
Torquay Charities, The 458
Travis Charitable Trust, Constance 460
Tyne & Wear Foundation 466
Wall Trust, Thomas 478
Wesleyan Charitable Trust, The 485
Whitaker Charitable Trust 489
Wills 1962 Charitable Trust, P J H 494
Wiltshire Community Foundation 495
Wingate Foundation, The Harold Hyam 496
Yorkshire Bank Charitable Trust, The 510

■ Crohn's disease

Funding priority

Stewart Trust, Sir Halley 437

■ Cultural activity

see also Cultural heritage (of national & historical importance)

Funding priority

Cobb Charity 103
David Trust, The Lesley 124
Hudson Benevolent Trust, The Thomas 230
Northern Arts 339
St Katharine & Shadwell Trust 404
Ultach Trust 467

Will consider

Astor Foundation, The *26*
Barbour Trust, The *33*
Beckwith Charitable
  Settlement, The Heather *39*
Beit Trust, The *40*
Broadley Charitable Trust, The
  64
Brooke Benevolent Fund,
  William *65*
Bulmer Charitable Trust, Becket
  68
Cadbury Trust (1928), The
  Edward & Dorothy *76*
County Durham Foundation
  115
Cripplegate Foundation *118*
de Freitas Charitable Trust, The
  Helen and Geoffrey *126*
Digby Charitable Trust, Simon
  133
Fogel Charitable Trust, The
  Gerald *165*
Follett Trust, The *166*
Four Lanes Trust, The *168*
Garnett Charitable Trust, The
  178
Granada Foundation, The *190*
Great Britain Sasakawa
  Foundation, The *193*
Greenaway Foundation, The Sir
  Derek *194*
Harding Trust, The *209*
Harford Charitable Trust *209*
Howard Charitable Trust, John
  & Ruth *229*
Inverforth Charitable Trust, The
  236
Ireland Funds, The *237*
Laspen Trust *265*
Lee Foundation, The Edgar
  269
Mitchell Trust, Esme *315*
Needham Cooper Charitable
  Trust, The *331*
New Court Charitable Trust
  332
North West Arts Board *337*
Oldham Foundation *345*
Owen Family Trust, The *348*
Reader's Digest Trust, The *380*
Rookes Charitable Trust, C A
  390
Royal Commission for the
  Exhibition of 1851 *395*
South Square Trust *430*
Summerfield Charitable Trust,
  The *442*
Tyne & Wear Foundation *466*
Wakefield (Tower Hill, Trinity
  Square) Trust *476*
Whitaker Charitable Trust *489*

■ Cultural & religious teaching

see also **Education & training**

Funding priority

Alexis Trust, The *11*
Anglo-Catholic Ordination
  Candidates Fund, The *18*
Bachad Fellowship – Friends of
  Bnei Akiva *30*
Beacon Trust *38*
Burden Trust, The *69*
Christmas Cracker Trust *95*
Deutsch Charitable Trust, The
  H & M *131*
Doughty Charity Trust, The
  136
Firdale Christian Trust, The *162*
Gelston Charitable Trust, The
  179
Grove Charitable Trust, The
  197
Hockerill Educational
  Foundation *223*
Kalms Foundation, The Stanley
  250
Luke Trust, The *286*
Nemoral Ltd *331*
Nidditch Foundation, The
  Laurie *335*
SMB Trust, The *400*
St Luke's College Foundation
  404
Tisbury Telegraph Trust, The
  457
Ultach Trust *467*
Vogel Charitable Trust, The
  Nathan *474*

Will consider

Barnabas Charitable Trust *34*
BibleLands *47*
Bilton Charity, The Percy *48*
Brand Charitable Trust *58*
Cadbury Trust (1928), The
  Edward & Dorothy *76*
Carlton Television Trust *81*
Cobb Charity *103*
Collier Charitable Trust, The
  105
Dibden Allotments Charity *132*
Digby Charitable Trust, Simon
  133
Emanuel Charitable Settlement,
  Ralph and Muriel *150*
Emmaus Christian Foundation
  150
European Cultural Foundation
  (UK Committee) *154*
Glynde Place Charitable Trust
  (1974), The *186*
Goldsmiths' Company's
  Charities, The *188*
Great Britain Sasakawa
  Foundation, The *193*
Groves Charitable Trust, The
  197

Hamlyn Foundation, The Paul
  205
Holly Hill Charitable Trust *224*
Hudson Benevolent Trust, The
  Thomas *230*
Hussey for Africans, Charity of
  Rebecca *231*
Ireland Funds, The *237*
James Charitable Trust, John
  241
KC Charitable Trust, The *250*
King Charitable Settlement,
  Philip *254*
Leech Charity, The William *269*
Linford Charitable Trust, The
  Fred *276*
Littler Foundation, The Emile
  277
Lloyd Charity, The S and D *278*
Locker Foundation, The *280*
London Law Trust *280*
MacKintosh Charitable Trust,
  Viscount *292*
Milward Charity, The Edgar
  313
NR Charitable Trust, The *325*
Norwood Settlement *340*
Owen Family Trust, The *348*
Paristamen Foundation, The
  352
Pye Christian Trust, The *371*
Rainbow Charitable Trust *376*
Said Foundation, The Karim
  Rida *401*
St Katharine & Shadwell Trust
  404
Sheepdrove Trust, The *417*
Shelroy Charitable Trust, The
  417
Summerfield Charitable Trust,
  The *442*
Tear Fund *450*
Thorpe Charity Trust, The *455*
Vincent Trust Fund, Eric W *473*
Wander Charitable Fund, The
  Dr Albert *479*
Westcroft Trust *486*
Wills 1961 Charitable Trust, Mr
  Frederick *493*
Wingate Foundation, The
  Harold Hyam *496*

■ Cultural centres

see **Art galleries & cultural centres**

■ Cultural heritage (of national & historical importance)

see also Cultural activity, English literature

Funding priority

AHJ Charitable Trust, The *3*
Arts Council of Wales, The *23*
Astor of Hever Trust, The *26*
Astor's 1969 Charity, The Hon M L *26*
Barnsbury Charitable Trust *35*
Bergqvist Charitable Trust *44*
Brook Charitable Settlement, R E *64*
Chase Charity, The *91*
Cinderford Charitable Trust, The *96*
Clark Charitable Trust, J Anthony *98*
Cobb Charity *103*
Crescent Trust, The *117*
Daiwa Anglo-Japanese Foundation, The *122*
David Trust, The Lesley *124*
De Avenley Foundation, The *126*
Denton Charitable Trust, The *130*
Deutsch Charitable Trust, The Andre *131*
Djanogly Foundation, The *135*
D'Oyly Carte Charitable Trust, The *137*
Drayton Trust, The *138*
East Midlands Arts Board Ltd *143*
Elephant Trust, The *146*
Fairbairn Charitable Trust, The Esmee *157*
Garthgwynion Charities *179*
Gillett Charitable Trust, J A *183*
Gill's Charitable Trust, Mrs M M *184*
Golden Charitable Trust *187*
Hawthorne Charitable Trust, The *212*
Heinz Company Limited Charitable Trust, The H J *215*
Hitachi Charitable Trust, The *222*
Hornby Charitable Trust, Miss D *227*
Horne Foundation, The *228*
Hornton Trust, The *228*
Kobler Trust, The *258*
Kreitman Foundation *258*
London Arts Board *280*
Lucas Charitable Trust Limited, The Joseph *286*
Lyons Charitable Trust, Sir Jack *288*
MacRobert Trusts, The *294*

Maritime Trust, The *297*
Mellows Charitable Settlement, The Anthony and Elizabeth *305*
Millichope Foundation, The *312*
Moores Foundation, The Peter *318*
Oppenheimer Charitable Trust *346*
Owen Trust, Margaret *348*
Pilkington Charitable Trust, Cecil *363*
Pitman Charitable Trust, The John *364*
Powys Welsh Church Fund *367*
QAS Charitable Trust *373*
Rayne Foundation, The *379*
Reekie Trust, R A & V B *381*
Rodewald's Charitable Settlement, Mr C A *389*
South West Arts *431*
Southern Arts *432*
Tesco Charity Trust *452*
Wade & Others, The Charity of Thomas *475*
West Midlands Regional Arts Board *486*
Westminster Amalgamated Charity *487*
Wohl Charitable Foundation, The Maurice *498*
Wohl Charitable Trust, The Maurice *498*
Wolfson Family Charitable Trust, The *499*
Wolfson Foundation, The *499*

Will consider

Achiezer Association Limited *6*
Airflow Community Ltd, The *9*
Aleh Charitable Foundation, The *10*
Allied Domecq Trust *13*
Alper Charitable Trust, The *15*
Anderson Trust, Andrew *16*
Angler's Inn Trust *17*
Anglo Hong Kong Trust, The *17*
Appelbe Trust, Ambrose & Ann *19*
Aquarius Charitable Foundation, The *19*
Aquinas Trust *20*
Askew Charitable Trust, The Ian *25*
Assembled Church of Christ Trust, The *25*
Assheton-Smith Charitable Trust *25*
Astor Foundation, The *26*
Astor's Charitable Trust, The Hon M L *26*
BBC Children in Need Appeal, The *29*
Baring Foundation, The *34*
Barnby's Foundation, Lord *35*

Barton Trust, Eleanor *37*
Bateman Charitable Trust, Lady Margaret *37*
Bealey Foundation, The *38*
Beckwith Charitable Trust, The Peter *40*
Beckwith-Smith's Charitable Settlement, Mrs *40*
Beit Trust, The *40*
Benlian Trust, The *44*
Black Foundation, The Bertie *51*
Blagrave Charitable Trust, The Herbert and Peter *52*
Blakenham's Charity Trust, Lady *53*
Blakey Charitable Trust, The Celia and Conrad *53*
Blank Donations Ltd, The David *54*
Boltons Trust, The *55*
Borthwick Memorial Trust, The Oliver *56*
Bottom Charitable Trust, Harry *56*
Bowland Charitable Trust, The *57*
British Sugar Foundation *63*
Brookhouse's Will Trust, Mr John Charles *65*
Bullough Tompson Settlement, The *68*
Burn Charity Trust, The J H *70*
Burns Charity, The Dorothy *70*
Burry Charitable Trust, The *70*
Burton Charitable Trust, The Geoffrey *71*
Butler's Trust, Lord *71*
Butler's Trust, Lucilla *72*
Buxton Trust, Denis *72*
Cadbury Schweppes Foundation, The *76*
Cadbury Trust (1928), The Edward & Dorothy *76*
Cardiff & Swansea Methodist District Charitable Trust Fund *80*
Carnegie Dunfermline Trust *82*
Carnegie United Kingdom Trust, The *82*
Carron Charitable Trust, The *83*
Castang Charitable Trust, H and M *85*
Catto Charitable Settlement, The Thomas Sivewright *86*
Charity Projects *90*
Chiddick Charitable Trust *92*
Chippindale Foundation, Sam *93*
Closehelm Ltd *101*
Clutterbuck Charitable Trust, Robert *102*
Coates Charitable Settlement, The *102*
Coates Charitable Trust 1969, Lance *103*

Coates Charitable Trust, The John *103*

Cohen Charitable Trust, The Vivienne and Samuel *104*

Cohen Charity Trust, Lucy *104*

Cohen Foundation, The John S *104*

Community Trust for Greater Manchester, The *108*

Company of Tobacco Pipe Makers and Tobacco Blenders Benevolent Fund *109*

Condon Family Trust *109*

Cope Charitable Trust, Alfred *112*

Curry Charitable Trust, Dennis *119*

Cymerman Trust Limited, Itzchok Meyer *120*

Daily Telegraph Charitable Trust *122*

Dandeen Charitable Trust *123*

Davies Charity, The Gwendoline and Margaret *125*

Davy Foundation, The J *126*

De La Rue Charitable Trust *127*

De Rothschild 1981 Charitable Trust, The Edmund *127*

De Yong Charitable Trust, The Emma *128*

Desmond Charitable Trust, The Richard *131*

Deutsch Charitable Trust, The H & M *131*

Dibs Charitable Trust, The *133*

Dicken Charitable Trust, The Albert *133*

Dinam Charity *134*

Doughty Charity Trust, The *136*

Dunn Charitable Trust, The Harry *140*

Earmark Trust, The *142*

Eastern Arts Board *143*

Edinburgh Trust, No 2 Account *145*

Egerton of Tatton Will Trust, Lord *146*

Eling Trust *147*

Elshore Limited *149*

Family Trust, The *158*

Famos Foundation Trust *158*

Foreman Foundation, The Carl & Eve *167*

Foyle Trust, Charles Henry *169*

Franklin Bequest, The Rosalind *169*

Franklin Deceased's New Second Charity, Sydney E *170*

Fry Charitable Trust, Maurice *174*

Gibson's Charity Trust, The Hon Mr & Mrs Clive *182*

Girdlers' Company Charitable Trust, The *184*

Gladstone Charitable Trust, The E W *184*

Gold Hill Church Trust *186*

Goldberg Charitable Trust, The Lewis *186*

Goldsmiths' Company's Charities, The *188*

Goodman Charitable Foundation, The Everard and Mina *188*

Goodman Trust, The *189*

Gradel Foundation, The *189*

Green Foundation, Constance *194*

Greenaway Foundation, The Sir Derek *194*

Grocers' Charity *197*

Gross Charities Limited, M & R *197*

Grosshill Charitable Trust *197*

Grut Charitable Trust, The *198*

Gulbenkian Foundation (Lisbon) United Kingdom Branch, Calouste *199*

HB Charitable Trust *201*

Hacking & Sons Ltd Charitable Trust, C G *201*

Halkes Settlement, John Robert *204*

Hamilton Educational Trust, Eleanor *205*

Hampstead Wells and Campden Trust *206*

Harbour Foundation Ltd, The *208*

Hargreaves Trust, The Kenneth *210*

Harvey Charitable Trust, Gordon *211*

Held Settlement, The Gisela *215*

Hillards Charitable Trust, Gay & Peter Hartley's *220*

Holford Trust Fund *224*

Hoover Foundation, The *226*

Horn Trust, The Cuthbert *227*

Hughes Charitable Trust, The Geoffery C *230*

IPE Charitable Trust, The *233*

Idlewild Trust, The *234*

Inman Charity, The *235*

Ireland Fund of Great Britain, The *237*

Isle of Dogs Community Foundation *238*

James Foundation, The Catherine and Lady Grace *241*

Jones Trust, Cemlyn *248*

KC Charitable Trust, The *250*

Karten Charitable Trust, The Ian *250*

Keyes Trust, The Ursula *253*

Kingsgrove Charitable Trust, The *255*

Kinnison Charitable Trust, R O *256*

Kleinwort Charitable Trust, The Ernest *257*

Knott Trust, Sir James *258*

Kulika Charitable Trust, The *259*

Kweller Charitable Trust, The Harry *259*

Laing Charitable Trust, The David *260*

Laing Foundation, The Christopher *260*

Landy Charitable Trust, Harry and Gertrude *263*

Lanvern Foundation *265*

Laski Memorial Charitable Trust, Nathan *265*

Laspen Trust *265*

Lauffer Charitable Foundation, The R & D *266*

Lavender Trust, The *267*

Lawley Foundation, The Edgar E *267*

Leigh-Bramwell Trust 'E', P *270*

Levy Charitable Foundation, Joseph *272*

Liffe Benefit *274*

Lingwood Charitable Trust, The *276*

Lloyd Charity, The S and D *278*

Localtrent Ltd *279*

Lunzer Charitable Trust, The Ruth & Jack *287*

Lynwood Charitable Trust, The *288*

Lyons Charitable Trust, The *288*

MDM Memorial Trust *289*

MacAndrew Trust, The E M *289*

McKechnie Foundation, A N *292*

McKenzie Trust, The Robert *292*

McLaren Foundation *292*

McLaren Memorial Trust, The Martin *293*

Manifold Charitable Trust, The *295*

Margadale Charitable Trust, Lord *297*

Marks Charitable Trust, Michael *298*

Markus Charitable Foundation, The Erich *298*

Marriage's Charitable Trust, Miss G M *299*

Marr-Munning Trust *299*

Marshall Charitable Trust, The Charlotte *300*

Martin Trust, The Sir George *300*

Material World Charitable Foundation Limited, The *301*

Mattock Charitable Trust, The W T *302*

Mayfair Charities Limited *303*
Measures Charity, The James Frederick and Ethel Anne *303*
Medlock Charitable Trust, The *304*
Millett Charitable Trust, The Alan and Janet *312*
Modiano Charitable Trust *315*
Montefiore Trust, The David *316*
Moore Charitable Trust, The Horace *316*
Moore Stephens Charitable Foundation, The *317*
Morel Charitable Trust, The *318*
Morgan Crucible Company plc Charitable Trust, The *319*
Morris Charitable Trust, The Willie & Mabel *320*
Moulton Charitable Trust, The *321*
Music Sales Charitable Trust, The *324*
Nakou Foundation, The Eleni *326*
Newcastle's 1986 Charitable Trust, Duke of *333*
Newman Charitable Trust, Mr and Mrs F E F *334*
Newstead Charity, The *334*
Norfolk's Family Charitable Trust, Lavinia *336*
Northcott Charity Trust, The *338*
Northern Arts *339*
Northern Electric Employee Charity Association *339*
Northern Ireland Voluntary Trust *339*
Old Possums Practical Trust, The *344*
Oldham Foundation *345*
Owen Family Trust, The *348*
PDC Trust, The *349*
PJD Charitable Trust *350*
Palmer Trust, The Gerald *352*
Park Hill Trust, The *353*
Pascoe Charitable Trust, Alan *354*
Paul Charitable Trust, The Late Barbara May *355*
Paul Charitable Trust, Margaret Jeanne *355*
Paul Charitable Trust, Pamela Milton *355*
Paul Foundation, The *355*
Paul's Charitable Trust, R J *355*
Payne Charitable Trust, The *355*
Pelech Charitable Trust, The *358*
Perry Charitable Trust, Miss Frances Lucille *359*
Pershore Nashdom & Elmore Trust Ltd, The *360*

Peskin Charitable Trust, The Hazel and Leslie *360*
Phillips Charitable Foundation, Reginald M *361*
Pitt Trust, Headley *364*
Porter Foundation *366*
Puebla Charitable Trust Limited, The *371*
Quothquan Charitable Trust, The Second *373*
RT Trust, The *374*
Rackham Charitable Trust, The Mr & Mrs Philip *375*
Rae Charity, H J *375*
Rainford Trust, The *376*
Rav Chesed Trust, The *379*
Rayner Charitable Trust, The John *380*
Reuter Foundation, The *382*
Richards Charity, The Clive *384*
Richmond Parish Lands Charity *384*
Ripley's Charitable Trust, Pat *386*
Rivendell Trust, The *387*
Robbins Trust, The Cheshire *387*
Rogers Charitable Settlement, The Richard *390*
Rolfe Charitable Trust, The *390*
Rosen Foundation, Cecil *392*
S Group Charitable Trust *399*
St Jude's Trust *403*
Salters Charities *405*
Samuel Charitable Trust, M J *406*
Save & Prosper Foundation *409*
Scarr-Hall Memorial Trust, The *409*
Seva Trust, Rampaba Sadhu *415*
Sherman Charitable Trust, The Archie *419*
Shifrin Charitable Trust, The Maurice and Hilda *419*
Sidbury Trust, The Second *421*
Silvester Charitable Gift Trust *422*
Simon's Charity *422*
Skinners' Company Lady Neville Charity *424*
Society of Friends of the Torah, The *429*
Solomons Charitable Trust, David *430*
Somerfield Curtis Will Trust, The Dorothy *430*
South East Arts Board *430*
Stanley Foundation Limited *435*
Stewart Charitable Trust, Mary Stephanie *437*
Strauss Charitable Trust *440*
Sumner's Trust Section 'A', Sir John *443*
Symons Charitable Trust, The Stella *446*

TSB Foundation for Scotland *447*
Taylor Charitable Trust, The B R *450*
Terry Charitable Trust, Noel Goddard *451*
Tesler Foundation, The *452*
Turner Trust, The Douglas *464*
van Geest Foundation, The John and Lucille *470*
Van Norden's Charitable Foundation, Mrs Maud *471*
Vincent Trust Fund, Eric W *473*
Vineyard Christian Fellowship of South West *473*
Vinson Charity Trust, The 1969 *473*
Vogel Charitable Trust, The Nathan *474*
Wakefield Trust, The *476*
Ward Blenkinsop Trust, The *480*
Weinstock Fund, The *484*
Welby Trust, The Barbara *484*
Whetherly's Charitable Trust, The Hon Mrs R G A *489*
Whitehead Charitable Trust, J E *490*
Whittington Charitable Trust, The *491*
Wiggins Charity Trust, Cyril *491*
Wilde Charitable Trust, The Felicity *492*
Williams Charitable Trust, Alfred *493*
Wills 1961 Charitable Trust, Major Michael Thomas *494*
Wingate Foundation, The Harold Hyam *496*
Wingfield's Charitable Trust, Mrs *496*
Winstone Foundation, Hyman *497*
Woburn 1986 Charitable Trust *498*
Wolff Charity Trust *498*
Woodhouse Charitable Trust, Edwin *501*
Woods Charitable Foundation, Geoffrey *502*
Worms Charitable Trust, The Freda and Della *504*
Worshipful Company of Engineers' Charitable Trust Fund, The *504*
Worshipful Company of Needlemakers' Charitable Fund *505*
Wright Deceased Trust, John William *506*
Wychdale Limited *507*
Youell Foundation Ltd, The *510*
Zaiger Trust, The Elizabeth and Prince *512*

■ Culture
see Ethnic minority groups

■ Cystic fibrosis
Funding priority
Cystic Fibrosis Trust *121*
Lambourne Memorial Trust,
The Emma *262*
Woodroffe Benton Foundation,
The *502*

■ Dance & ballet
see also Arts & arts facilities
Funding priority
Arts Council of England, The
23
Arts Council of Wales, The *23*
Beckwith Charitable
Settlement, The Heather *39*
Hughes Charitable Trust, The
Geoffery C *230*
North West Arts Board *337*
Northern Arts *339*
Yorkshire and Humberside Arts
510

Will consider
Arbib Foundation *20*
Ashley Foundation, The Laura
24
Astor Foundation, The *26*
Broadley Charitable Trust, The
64
Brooke Benevolent Fund,
William *65*
Bulmer Charitable Trust, Becket
68
Cadbury Trust (1928), The
Edward & Dorothy *76*
Campden Charities, The *79*
Carnegie Dunfermline Trust *82*
Carnegie United Kingdom
Trust, The *82*
Coates Charitable Trust, The
John *103*
Cripplegate Foundation *118*
Debtors' Relief Fund Charity
128
Digby Charitable Trust, Simon
133
Early's Charitable Settlement,
Richard *142*
Edgar Foundation, The Gilbert
and Eileen *145*
Education Services *145*
Finzi Charitable Trust, Gerald
162
Fletcher Charitable Trust, The
Joyce *164*
Follett Trust, The *166*
Granada Foundation, The *190*
Great Britain Sasakawa
Foundation, The *193*

Halkes Settlement, John Robert
204
Hamlyn Foundation, The Paul
205
Harbinson Charitable Trust,
Roderick *208*
Harding Trust, The *209*
Hinrichsen Foundation, The
221
Holly Hill Charitable Trust *224*
Hudson Benevolent Trust, The
Thomas *230*
Inverforth Charitable Trust, The
236
Ireland Funds, The *237*
Laing Charitable Trust, The
David *260*
Laing Foundation, The
Christopher *260*
Leche Trust, The *268*
Lee Foundation, The Edgar
269
Linford Charitable Trust, The
Fred *276*
Littler Foundation, The Emile
277
Lower Hall Charitable Trust
285
Mackintosh Foundation, The
292
Milton Keynes Community
Trust Ltd, The *312*
Music Sales Charitable Trust,
The *324*
Needham Cooper Charitable
Trust, The *331*
Notgrove Trust, The *341*
Oldham Foundation *345*
Owen Family Trust, The *348*
Paragon Concert Society *352*
Provincial Trust for Kendal, The
370
Radcliffe's Trust, Dr *375*
Royal Commission for the
Exhibition of 1851 *395*
St Katharine & Shadwell Trust
404
Snipe Charitable Trust *428*
Somerfield Curtis Will Trust,
The Dorothy *430*
South Square Trust *430*
Strauss Charitable Trust *440*
Summerfield Charitable Trust,
The *442*
Taylor Charitable Trust, The B R
450
Thomson Foundation, The Sue
454
Walker Trust, The *477*
Wates Foundation, The *481*
Williams Charitable Trust,
Alfred *493*

■ Dance groups
see also Community arts &
recreation
Funding priority
Carnegie United Kingdom
Trust, The *82*
County Durham Foundation
115
North West Arts Board *337*
Northern Arts *339*
Yorkshire and Humberside Arts
510

Will consider
Arts Council of England, The
23
Brooke Benevolent Fund,
William *65*
Bulmer Charitable Trust, Becket
68
Cadbury Trust (1928), The
Edward & Dorothy *76*
Calypso Browning Trust *78*
Carlton Television Trust *81*
Carnegie Dunfermline Trust *82*
Clifford Charity Oxford, The
100
Debtors' Relief Fund Charity
128
Digby Charitable Trust, Simon
133
Edgar Foundation, The Gilbert
and Eileen *145*
Finzi Charitable Trust, Gerald
162
Follett Trust, The *166*
Granada Foundation, The *190*
Great Britain Sasakawa
Foundation, The *193*
Grocers' Charity *197*
Hamlyn Foundation, The Paul
205
Harbinson Charitable Trust,
Roderick *208*
Hinrichsen Foundation, The
221
Hudson Benevolent Trust, The
Thomas *230*
Ireland Funds, The *237*
Lawley Foundation, The Edgar
E *267*
Leche Trust, The *268*
Mackintosh Foundation, The
292
Milton Keynes Community
Trust Ltd, The *312*
Needham Cooper Charitable
Trust, The *331*
Northern Ireland Voluntary
Trust *339*
Oldham Foundation *345*
Owen Family Trust, The *348*
Persula Foundation, The *360*
St Katharine & Shadwell Trust
404
South Square Trust *430*

Summerfield Charitable Trust,
The *442*
Wakefield (Tower Hill, Trinity
Square) Trust *476*
Wates Foundation, The *481*
Williams Charitable Trust,
Alfred *493*

■ Day centres

see also Community
services

Funding priority
AB Charitable Trust *3*
Army Benevolent Fund, The *22*
Berkshire Community Trust *45*
Challice Trust, The *87*
Christmas Cracker Trust *95*
Clipsham Charitable
Settlement, R E *101*
Community Trust for Greater
Manchester, The *108*
County Durham Foundation
115
Curriers Company Charitable
Fund *119*
Dahl Foundation, The Roald
122
Egerton of Tatton Will Trust,
Lord *146*
Hertfordshire Community
Trust, The *217*
Isle of Dogs Community
Foundation *238*
Meath, Charity of Mary Jane,
Countess of *304*
Merchant Taylors' Consolidated
Charities for the Infirm *306*
National Power Charitable
Trust, The *330*
Nunburnholme Trust, The
Incorporated Trustees of the
342
Rae Charity, H J *375*
SMB Trust, The *400*
Skerritt Trust *423*
Swan Mountain Trust *444*
TSB Foundation for Scotland
447
Toy Trust, The *459*
Wakeham Trust, The *476*
Wates Foundation, The *481*
Whitaker Charitable Trust *489*

Will consider
Abel Charitable Trust *5*
Alexandra Trust *11*
Alexis Trust, The *11*
Amory Charitable Trust,
Viscount *16*
Anstey Charitable Settlement,
J C W *18*
Aquarius Charitable
Foundation, The *19*
Archer Trust, The *20*
Askew Trust, The Dorothy *25*
Avon Trust, The *28*

Barbour Trust, The *33*
Barratt Charitable Trust, The
Elaine *36*
Beit Trust, The *40*
Betard Bequest *46*
Bisgood Trust, The *50*
Bisgood's Charitable Trust, Miss
Jeanne *50*
Blackburn Trust, The *51*
Blakenham's Charity Trust,
Lady *53*
Blanchminster Trust, The *54*
Boots Charitable Trust *56*
Bowland Charitable Trust, The
57
Bridge Trust, The *60*
Brotherton Trust, The Charles
65
Brough Charitable Trust,
Joseph *65*
Buckinghamshire Masonic
Centenary Fund *67*
Burdall Charity, H M *69*
Burton 1960 Charitable
Settlement, Audrey &
Stanley *70*
CLA Charitable Trust *74*
Cadbury Charitable Trust
(Incorporated), Edward *75*
Camelot Foundation, The *78*
Campden Charities, The *79*
Carnegie Dunfermline Trust *82*
Chrimes Family Charitable
Trust, The *93*
Cleopatra Trust *99*
Clinton's Charitable Trust, Lord
100
Cloudesley's Charity/School
Parents & Friends
Association, Richard *102*
Coutts Charitable Trust, The
116
Curzon Charitable Trust, The
Wallace *120*
de Freitas Charitable Trust, The
Helen and Geoffrey *126*
Debtors' Relief Fund Charity
128
Denne Charitable Trust *130*
Derbyshire Trust, J N *130*
Digby Charitable Trust, Simon
133
Dixon Charitable Trust, F E *134*
Dorus Trust *136*
Dumbreck Charity *139*
Early's Charitable Settlement,
Richard *142*
Ebb and Flow Charitable Trust
144
Edgar Foundation, The Gilbert
and Eileen *145*
Elkes Charity Fund, The Wilfred
& Elsie *147*
Emmandjay Charitable Trust
150
Epigoni Trust *152*
Ferguson Benevolent Fund
Limited *161*

Fishmongers' Company's
Charitable Trust *163*
Fletcher Charitable Trust, The
Joyce *164*
Fletcher Trust, Roy *165*
Follett Trust, The *166*
Four Lanes Trust, The *168*
Four Winds Trust *168*
Gardner Charitable Trust, R & J
178
Gibbins Trust, The *181*
Gluckstein Charitable
Settlement, The Penelope
185
Grange Farm Centre Trust *191*
Grant Foundation, The
Raymond *191*
Greenaway Foundation, The Sir
Derek *194*
Grocers' Charity *197*
Grosshill Charitable Trust *197*
HACT (The Housing
Association's Charitable
Trust) *201*
Hamlyn Foundation, The Paul
205
Harding's Charity, William *209*
Harford Charitable Trust *209*
Hartley Memorial Trust, The N
& P *211*
Henderson's Settlement, J R
216
Hudson Benevolent Trust, The
Thomas *230*
Ingles Charitable Trust, The
234
Ireland Funds, The *237*
Iris Trust, The *237*
JDM Charitable Trust *239*
Jarrold Trust Ltd, John *243*
Johnson Foundation, The *246*
Johnson Group Cleaners
Charity *247*
Keeling Charitable Trust, The
Petronella *251*
King Charitable Trust, The
Lorna *254*
Knott Trust, Sir James *258*
Kyte Charitable Trust, The *259*
Laing Charitable Trust, The
David *260*
Laing Foundation, The
Christopher *260*
Laing Trust, Beatrice *261*
Laing's Charitable Trust *262*
Lancaster's Trust, Bryan *263*
Lane Foundation, The Allen
263
Lankelly Foundation, The *264*
Lawson Charitable Trust,
Raymond and Blanche *267*
Leech Charity, The William *269*
Lewis Partnership, John *274*
Lloyd's Charities Trust *278*
(Lloyds) TSB Foundation for
England and Wales *279*
Lunn-Rockliffe Charitable Trust,
Paul *286*

Lynall Foundation, The D G
287

Marchday Charitable Fund, The
296

Margaret Foundation, The 297

Measures Charity, The James
Frederick and Ethel Anne
303

Mental Health Foundation, The
305

Metropolitan Hospital-Sunday
Fund, The 308

Milton Keynes Community
Trust Ltd, The 312

Minet Trust, The Peter 313

Moore Foundation, The
George A 316

NR Charitable Trust, The 325

Natwest Staff Samaritan Fund
330

Needham Cooper Charitable
Trust, The 331

New Court Charitable Trust
332

Newby Trust Ltd 332

Norfolk's Family Charitable
Trust, Lavinia 336

Norman Family Charitable
Trust, The 337

North British Hotel Trust 337

North West Arts Board 337

Northcott Devon Foundation
338

Norton Foundation, The 340

Oakdale Trust, The 343

Oldham Foundation 345

Owen Family Trust, The 348

PF Charitable Trust 350

Paget Trust, The 351

Parivar Trust, The 353

Paterson Charitable
Foundation, The Constance
354

Paterson Charitable Trust,
Arthur James 354

Patients' Aid Association
Hospital and Medical
Charities Trust 354

Payne Trust, The Harry 356

Persula Foundation, The 360

Porter Foundation 366

Powell Foundation, The 367

Pratt Charitable Trust, The W L
367

Provincial Trust for Kendal, The
370

Pyke Charity Trust 372

Ravenscroft Foundation, The
379

Rayner Charitable Trust, The
John 380

Reader's Digest Trust, The 380

Rest-Harrow Trust, The 382

Richard Charitable Trust, The
Cliff 383

Robinson Brothers (Ryders
Green) Ltd, Charitable Trust
388

Rookes Charitable Trust, C A
390

Rope Third Charitable
Settlement, The Mrs 391

Rothley Trust, The 392

Rowbotham Charitable Trust,
The Christopher 393

Royal's Memorial Fund,
Princess 396

Sainsbury Charitable Fund Ltd,
The 402

Saint Edmund King and Martyr
Trust 402

Seagram Distillers Charitable
Trust 413

Sheepdrove Trust, The 417

Sheldon Trust, The 417

Shelroy Charitable Trust, The
417

Shepherd Family Charitable
Trust, The Sir Peter 418

Skelton Bounty, The 423

Smith & Mount Trust, The Mrs
426

Sparkhill Trust, The 433

Stoate Charitable Trust, The
Leonard Laity 438

Stonehouse Trust Ltd, Eric 438

Summerfield Charitable Trust,
The 442

Sussman Charitable Trust,
Adrienne & Leslie 443

Sykes Trust, The Charles 445

TSB Foundation for Northern
Ireland 447

Tear Fund 450

Thackray General Charitable
Trust, The P & L 452

Thomson Foundation, The Sue
454

Towler Charity Trust, The Fred
459

Truemark Trust, The 461

Trust for the Homeless 462

Tudor Trust, The 463

Tyne & Wear Foundation 466

Van Berchem Charitable Trust,
The Alec 470

Van Leer Foundation UK Trust,
Bernard 470

Victoria & Johnson Memorial
Trust, Queen 472

Wade & Others, The Charity of
Thomas 475

Wakefield (Tower Hill, Trinity
Square) Trust 476

Walker Trust, The 477

Wall Trust, Thomas 478

Wesleyan Charitable Trust, The
485

Westcroft Trust 486

Whitecourt Charitable Trust,
The 490

Wiltshire Community
Foundation 495

Wolfe Family's Charitable
Trust, The 498

Women Caring Trust, The 500

Woodlands Trust 501

Wylde Memorial Charity, The
Anthony and Gwendoline
507

Yorkshire Bank Charitable
Trust, The 510

....

■ Day nurseries
see **Playschemes**

....

■ Deafness
see **Hearing loss**

....

■ Dentistry
see also **Health care**

Funding priority

Heritage of London Trust, The
216

Thomson Charitable Trust, The
Arthur 453

Will consider

Army Benevolent Fund, The 22

Astor Foundation, The 26

Bottom Charitable Trust, Harry
56

Curzon Charitable Trust, The
Wallace 120

Digby Charitable Trust, Simon
133

Edgar Foundation, The Gilbert
and Eileen 145

Foreman Foundation, The Carl
& Eve 167

Hawley Residuary Fund, Harry
Fieldsend 212

Innes Memorial Fund 235

London Law Trust 280

Tear Fund 450

Thompson Charitable Trust,
The 453

....

■ Development activities
see **Infrastructure
development**

see also **Campaigning
(social issues)**

....

■ Development proposals (campaigning)

Funding priority

Aston Charities Trust Ltd 25

City Parochial Foundation 96

Tisbury Telegraph Trust, The
457

Wiltshire Community
Foundation 495

Will consider

Allachy Trust, The 12
Avenal 27
Barrie Charitable Trust, The
 Misses 36
Body Shop Foundation, The 55
Campden Charities, The 79
Chiddick Charitable Trust 92
Chrimes Family Charitable
 Trust, The 93
Coutts Charitable Trust, The
 116
David Trust, The Lesley 124
Dibs Charitable Trust, The 133
Digby Charitable Trust, Simon
 133
Dorus Trust 136
Early's Charitable Settlement,
 Richard 142
Epigoni Trust 152
Four Winds Trust 168
Garthgwynion Charities 179
Great Britain Sasakawa
 Foundation, The 193
Hamlyn Foundation, The Paul
 205
Hyde Charitable Trust 232
Iris Trust, The 237
Isle of Dogs Community
 Foundation 238
JCSCJ Charitable Trust, The
 238
Knott Trust, Sir James 258
Lane Foundation, The Allen
 263
Leech Charity, The William 269
Morel Charitable Trust, The
 318
Music for World Development
 323
National Power Charitable
 Trust, The 330
New Court Charitable Trust
 332
Noah Trust, The 335
North West Arts Board 337
Northern Ireland Voluntary
 Trust 339
Owen Family Trust, The 348
Patients' Aid Association
 Hospital and Medical
 Charities Trust 354
Puebla Charitable Trust
 Limited, The 371
Skelton Bounty, The 423
Summerfield Charitable Trust,
 The 442
Symons Charitable Trust, The
 Stella 446
Tyne & Wear Foundation 466
Williams Charitable Trust,
 Alfred 493
Woodhouse Charitable Trust,
 Edwin 501

■ Diabetes

Funding priority

British Diabetic Association,
 The 61
Ferguson Benevolent Fund
 Limited 161
Grant Foundation, The
 Raymond 191
Lloyd Charity, The S and D 278
Rosen Foundation, Cecil 392

■ Dietary – special dietary needs

Funding priority

Corden Trust, Cyril 113

■ Diocesan boards

see also Religious umbrella
bodies

Funding priority

Bayne Benefaction 38
Marshall's Charity 300
Tisbury Telegraph Trust, The
 457

Will consider

Abel Charitable Trust 5
Avenal 27
Brough Charitable Trust,
 Joseph 65
Burden Trust, The 69
Digby Charitable Trust, Simon
 133
Hockerill Educational
 Foundation 223
Hudson Benevolent Trust, The
 Thomas 230
James Trust, The 242
Jarrold Trust Ltd, John 243
Jerusalem Trust 244
Marriage's Charitable Trust,
 Miss G M 299
Milward Charity, The Edgar
 313
Norfolk's Family Charitable
 Trust, Lavinia 336
Norwich Church of England
 Young Men's Society 340
Peppiatt Charitable Trust, The
 Brian 359
Rope Third Charitable
 Settlement, The Mrs 391
Shepherd Charitable Trust, The
 Sylvia and Colin 418
Summerfield Charitable Trust,
 The 442
United Society for the
 Propagation of the Gospel
 468
Welby Trust, The Barbara 484
Wills 1961 Charitable Trust, Mr
 Frederick 493

■ Disabilities

see Disabled people
(physical, sensory, learning
impairments)

■ Disability rights

see Disabled people
(physical, sensory, learning
impairments) & see
Campaigning (social issues)

■ Disabled people (physical, sensory, learning impairments)

Funding priority

Abrahams 2nd Charitable
 Foundation, The Henry and
 Grete 5
Airflow Community Ltd, The 9
Ammco Trust, The 15
Army Benevolent Fund, The 22
Aylesfield Foundation, The 28
Baker Charitable Trust, The 30
Balint Charitable Trust, Paul 31
Bisgood's Charitable Trust, Miss
 Jeanne 50
Black Charitable Trust, Edna
 51
Black Charitable Trust, Sydney
 51
Blagrave Charitable Trust, The
 Herbert and Peter 52
Blakenham's Charity Trust,
 Lady 53
Blott Charitable Settlement,
 Robert Orpwood 55
Borthwick Memorial Trust, The
 Oliver 56
Bridge Trust, The 60
Brough Charitable Trust,
 Joseph 65
Burrough Charitable Trust, The
 Alan & Rosemary 70
Butler's Trust, Lord 71
Butlin Charity Trust, Bill 72
CLA Charitable Trust 74
Cadbury Charitable Trust,
 Richard 75
Carlton Television Trust 81
Cassel Educational Trust
 (Mountbatten Memorial
 Grants to Commonwealth
 Students), The Sir Ernest 84
Castang Charitable Trust, H
 and M 85
Cathedral Nursing Society
 Charitable Trust 85
Chownes Foundation, The 93
Christian Renewal Trust, The
 94
Chronicle Cinderella Home
 Fund No 1, The 95
City Parochial Foundation 96

Clifford Charity Oxford, The 100

Cloudesley's Charity/School Parents & Friends Association, Richard 102

Cole Charitable Trust, The 105

Cottingham Charitable Trust, Mrs Diana Mary 114

Cotton Trust, The 114

Curtis Charitable Trust, The Thomas 120

D'Avigdor Goldsmid Charitable Trust, The Sarah 125

Doughty Charity Trust, The 136

Dunn Charitable Trust, The Harry 140

Earmark Trust, The 142

Ebb and Flow Charitable Trust 144

Emily Appeal Fund, The 150

Fattorini Charitable Trust, James J 160

Ferguson Benevolent Fund Limited 161

Fishmongers' Company's Charitable Trust 163

Fleurus Trust, The 165

Franklin Trust, Jill 170

Glebe Charitable Trust 185

Good Neighbours Trust, The 188

Goodman Trust, The S & F 189

Grand Charity (of Freemasons under the United Grand Lodge of England), The 190

Grant-Lawson Charitable Trust, Lady Virginia 192

Gray Trust, The 192

Griffiths Trust, The E E and D M 196

Grimley Charity, The 196

Gunnell Charitable Trust, The 199

HACT (The Housing Association's Charitable Trust) 201

HB Charitable Trust 201

Hale Trust, The 203

Hall Charitable Trust, E F & M G 204

Hanley Trust (1987), The 207

Hertfordshire Community Trust, The 217

Hobbs Trust Limited, The Betty 222

Jacobson Charitable Trust, The Yvette and Hermione 241

Kleinwort Charitable Trust, The Ernest 257

Lane Foundation, The Allen 263

League of the Helping Hand, The 268

Lewis Partnership, John 274

Liebes Charitable Trust, The Martha Bud 274

Linford Charitable Trust, The Fred 276

Lloyd Charity, The S and D 278

(Lloyds) TSB Foundation for England and Wales 279

Lord's Taverners, The 281

Lynn Foundation, The 288

McLaren Foundation 292

Man of the People Fund 295

Marchday Charitable Fund, The 296

Marmor Charitable Trust, The Julie 299

Mattock Charitable Trust, The W T 302

Measures Charity, The James Frederick and Ethel Anne 303

Mental Health Foundation, The 305

Merchant Taylors' Consolidated Charities for the Infirm 306

Merchants House of Glasgow 307

Miller Bequest, Hugh and Mary 311

Milton Keynes Community Trust Ltd, The 312

Minet Trust, The Peter 313

Moores Family Charity Foundation, The 317

Morris Charitable Trust, The Douglas 320

Mountbatten Memorial Trust, The 322

Munro Charitable Trust, The 323

Nash Charity, The 326

Natwest Staff Samaritan Fund 330

Newstead Charity, The 334

Noel Buxton Trust, The 335

Northcott Charity Trust, The 338

Northcott Devon Foundation 338

Noswad Charity, The 341

Paget Trust, The 351

Powell Foundation, The 367

Pyke Charity Trust 372

REMEDI (Rehabilitation and Medical Research Trust) 374

Rest-Harrow Trust, The 382

Robinson Trust 4, The J C 388

Rosen Foundation, Cecil 392

Rowbotham Charitable Trust, The Christopher 393

Rowntree Foundation, Joseph 394

Rugby Football Union Charitable Fund, The 398

Said Foundation, The Karim Rida 401

Sailors' and Soldiers' Home Fund, and Leonard Lionel Bloomfield's Charity, The 401

Sainsbury Charitable Fund Ltd, The 402

Saint Sarkis Charity Trust 404

Sidbury Trust, The Second 421

Sparkes Charitable Trust, The Eric F 433

Stewart Trust, Sir Halley 437

Sykes Trust, The Charles 445

Tudor Trust, The 463

Tyne & Wear Foundation 466

Variety Club Children's Charity Limited, The 471

War on Want 479

Wates Foundation, The 481

Watson's Trust, John 482

Whitley Trust, Sheila 491

Wicksteed Village Trust, The 491

Wiltshire Community Foundation 495

Wohl Charitable Foundation, The Maurice 498

Wohl Charitable Trust, The Maurice 498

Yapp Welfare Trust, The 508

■ Disadvantaged by poverty

Funding priority

AB Charitable Trust 3

Abrahams 2nd Charitable Foundation, The Henry and Grete 5

Access 4 Trust 6

Adnams Charity, The 7

Airflow Community Ltd, The 9

Alexandra Trust 11

Alexis Trust, The 11

Alglen Ltd 11

Arbib Trust, The Annie 20

Archer Trust, The 20

Arnopa Trust, The 22

Assembled Church of Christ Trust, The 25

Atwell's Charity (Skinner's Company), Lawrence 27

BBC Children in Need Appeal, The 29

Ballinger Charitable Trust, The 32

Barnes Workhouse Fund 35

Beacon Trust 38

Bellahouston Bequest Fund 42

Beresford Trust, The 44

Betard Bequest 46

Birmingham Amenities and Welfare Trust, The 49

Black Charitable Trust, The Cyril W 51

Black Charitable Trust, Edna 51

Black Charitable Trust, Sydney 51

Black's Charity, Sir Alec 52

Blakenham's Charity Trust, Lady 53

Boots Charitable Trust 56
Brand Charitable Trust 58
Bridge Trust, The 60
Britland Charitable Trust, The 63
Brough Charitable Trust, Joseph 65
Buckingham Trust 67
Butlin Charity Trust, Bill 72
Buxton Trust, Denis 72
Cam, Charity of Ann 78
Carlton Television Trust 81
Cass's Foundation, Sir John 85
Cathedral Nursing Society Charitable Trust 85
Charity Projects 90
Chevras Ezras Nitzrochim Trust, The 91
Christian Aid 94
Christian Renewal Trust, The 94
Chronicle Cinderella Home Fund No 1, The 95
Church Urban Fund 95
Clark 1965 Charitable Trust, Stephen 98
Clarke Trust, The Thomas Edward 99
Cleveland Community Foundation 100
Clifford Charity Oxford, The 100
Clover Trust 102
Cobb Charity 103
Cole Charitable Trust, The 105
Commonweal Fund of the Trades House of Glasgow, The 108
Construction Industry Trust for Youth, The 110
Corbett's Charity, Thomas 112
Cotton Trust, The 114
Coutts Charitable Trust, The 116
Crawford Children's Charity, Michael 117
Curriers Company Charitable Fund 119
Dandeen Charitable Trust 123
Davenport's Charity Trust, Baron 124
De Yong's Charitable Trust 1984, Nicholas 128
Denne Charitable Trust 130
Desmond Charitable Trust, The Richard 131
Dibden Allotments Charity 132
Digbeth Trust Ltd, The 133
Double 'O' Charity Ltd 136
Doughty Charity Trust, The 136
du Boulay Charitable Trust, The Anthony 138
Earmark Trust, The 142
Emily Appeal Fund, The 150
Emmott Foundation Limited, The 151
Ericson Trust 152

Eventhall Family Charitable Trust, The 155
Family Trust, The 158
Fletcher Trust, Roy 165
Fleurus Trust, The 165
Fogel Charitable Trust, The Gerald 165
Fordeve Limited 167
Four Winds Trust 168
Frankel Memorial Charitable Trust, The Isaac & Freda 169
Franklin Deceased's New Second Charity, Sydney E 170
Frome Christian Fellowship 174
Fund for Human Need 175
Glasspool Trust, R L 184
Glebe Charitable Trust 185
Gluck Charitable Trust, Avraham Yitzchak 185
Grange Farm Centre Trust 191
Grant Charitable Trust, The 191
Green Foundation, The 193
Grove Charitable Trust, The 197
Grut Charitable Trust, The 198
Gurunanak 200
HACT (The Housing Association's Charitable Trust) 201
Haberdashers' Eleemosynary Charity 201
Haendler, The Nathan and Adolphe 202
Hale Trust, The 203
Hamlyn Foundation, The Helen 205
Hammerson's Charitable Trust, Sue 206
Hampstead Wells and Campden Trust 206
Hampton Fuel Allotment Charity 207
Hanley Trust (1987), The 207
Harbour Foundation Ltd, The 208
Hawthorne Charitable Trust, The 212
Held Settlement, The Gisela 215
Hertfordshire Community Trust, The 217
Hiley Trust, Joseph and Mary 219
Hillards Charitable Trust, Gay & Peter Hartley's 220
Hobbs Trust Limited, The Betty 222
Holinsworth Fund of Help, The C B and A B 224
Holmleigh Trust, The 225
Home Housing Trust 225
Hopkins, The Charity of Joseph 227

Hopkinson Educational Trust, Robert Addy 227
Hospital of God at Greatham, The 229
Humphreys Charitable Settlement, J A M 231
International Arab Women's Council Charities Fund 236
Irving Charitable Trust, The Charles 237
Isle of Dogs Community Foundation 238
JNF Charitable Trust 240
Jacobsen Foundation Limited 240
Jewish Aged Needy Pension Society, The 245
Jewish Childs' Day 245
Jubilee Outreach Yorkshire 248
Kejriwal Foundation 251
Keller Charitable Trust, Samuel 251
Kennyhill Bequest Fund 252
Kweller Charitable Trust, The Harry 259
Laing Trust, Beatrice 261
Lamb's Bequest 262
Langdale Trust 264
Lewis Family Charitable Trust, The 273
Linder Foundation, The Enid 275
Lloyd's Charities Trust 278
Lloyd's Patriotic Fund 279
(Lloyds) TSB Foundation for England and Wales 279
Localtrent Ltd 279
Lottery Sports Funds for England, Northern Ireland, Scotland and Wales 283
Lyons Charitable Trust, The 288
McCallum Bequest Fund 290
McCarthy Foundation, The John 290
MacGregor's Bequest 291
Mackintosh Foundation, The 292
Man of the People Fund 295
Manchester and Salford Medical Charities Fund 295
Marmor Charitable Trust, The Julie 299
Meath, Charity of Mary Jane, Countess of 304
Mercers' Company Educational Trust Fund, The 306
Merchant Taylors' Consolidated Charities for the Infirm 306
Merchants House of Glasgow 307
Mercury Phoenix Trust 307
Meridian Broadcasting Charitable Trust 307
Metropolitan Hospital-Sunday Fund, The 308

Mijoda Charitable Trust, The *310*

Miller Bequest, Hugh and Mary *311*

Millett Charitable Trust, The Alan and Janet *312*

Milton Keynes Community Trust Ltd, The *312*

Modiano Charitable Trust *315*

Moores Foundation, John *318*

Morgan Foundation, The Mr & Mrs J T *319*

Morrison Bequest Fund, Thomas Wharrie *320*

Munro Charitable Trust, The *323*

Music for World Development *323*

Nash Charity, The *326*

New Chasers Charitable Trust, The *332*

Newitt Fund, Richard *333*

Nichol-Young Foundation *334*

Northcott Charity Trust, The *338*

Northcott Devon Foundation *338*

Norton Foundation, The *340*

Nunburnholme Trust, The Incorporated Trustees of the *342*

Oasis Church Chadwell Heath Charitable Trust *343*

Oxfam (United Kingdom and Ireland) *348*

Paddington Charitable Estates Educational Fund *351*

Paddington Welfare Charities *351*

Paristamen Foundation, The *352*

Parivar Trust, The *353*

Pearson Foundation, The Frank *357*

Persula Foundation, The *360*

Perth's Charitable Trust, The Earl of *360*

Pick Charitable Trust, The George and Jessie *362*

Prince's Trust (now includes King George's Jubilee Trust (1935) and the Queen's Silver Jubilee Trust (1977)), The *369*

RT Trust, The *374*

Rank Xerox Trust, The *378*

Rav Chesed Trust, The *379*

Reeve's Foundation *382*

Richard III and Yorkist History Trust *384*

Robinson Trust 4, The J C *388*

Roedean School Mission Fund *390*

Rope Third Charitable Settlement, The Mrs *391*

Rowntree Charitable Trust, The Joseph *394*

Royal Gardeners' Orphan Fund, The *395*

Royal Victoria Hall Foundation, The *396*

Royle Memorial Trust, Kirstin *397*

Rozel Trust, The *397*

Rudabede *397*

Said Foundation, The Karim Rida *401*

St Katharine & Shadwell Trust *404*

Sassoon Charitable Trust, The Late Aaron D *408*

Schiff Charitable Trust, The Annie *409*

Scott Charitable Trust, The Francis C *412*

Seagram Distillers Charitable Trust *413*

Seva Trust, Rampaba Sadhu *415*

Shah Trust, The Dr N K *416*

Shipman Charitable Trust, Thomas Stanley *420*

Shuttleworth Memorial Trust, Barbara A *421*

Sidbury Trust, The Second *421*

Simon Population Trust, The *422*

Skerritt Trust *423*

Smith Trust, Metcalfe *427*

South Square Trust *430*

Sport Aid 88 Trust *434*

Stanley Foundation Limited *435*

Strangward Trust, The *439*

Street Charitable Foundation, W O *440*

Swale Charity Trust *443*

TSB Foundation for Scotland *447*

Talteg Ltd *448*

Taylor Charitable Trust, A R *449*

Tear Fund *450*

Teman Trust, The *450*

Thornton-Smith Trust, The *455*

Timson Family Charitable Trust *457*

Trust for London *461*

Trust for the Homeless *462*

Tudor Rose Ltd *463*

Turkish Women's Philanthropic Association of England *463*

Turner Charitable Settlement, The Sir Mark and Lady *464*

29th May 1961 Charity, The *465*

Tyndale Trust *466*

Tyne & Wear Foundation *466*

Tyneside Charitable Trust *466*

Van Berchem Charitable Trust, The Alec *470*

van Geest Foundation, The John and Lucille *470*

Van Norden's Charitable Foundation, Mrs Maud *471*

Variety Club Children's Charity Limited, The *471*

Veronique Charitable Trust *472*

Wakeham Trust, The *476*

War on Want *479*

Wates Foundation, The *481*

Watson's Trust, John *482*

Wedge, The *483*

Welfare Charity Establishment *485*

Westcroft Trust *486*

White Rose Children's Aid International Charity *489*

Whitehead's Charitable Trust, Sydney Dean *490*

Whitley Trust, Sheila *491*

Williams Trust, The Neville *493*

Wilson Bequest Fund, The John *495*

Wiltshire Community Foundation *495*

Wimpey Charitable Trust, The George *495*

Wix Charitable Trust, Michael and Anna *497*

Woburn 1986 Charitable Trust *498*

Woodhouse Charitable Trust, Edwin *501*

Will consider

Abbey National Charitable Trust *4*

Abel Charitable Trust *5*

Allen Trust, Mrs M H *13*

Ammco Trust, The *15*

Andrew Charitable Trust, The Prince *16*

Askew Trust, The Dorothy *25*

Astor Foundation, The *26*

Aylesfield Foundation, The *28*

Bancroft Trust, The *33*

Barbour Trust, The *33*

Barnabas Charitable Trust *34*

Bartholomew Christian Trust *36*

Beckwith Charitable Settlement, The Heather *39*

Bell Charitable Trust, John *41*

Benham Charitable Trust, Hervey *43*

Bentall Charity Trust, Rowan *44*

Berris Charitable Trust *45*

Bewley Charitable Trust, The *46*

Birtwistle Memorial Trust, The G E *50*

Blake Charitable Trust, The Morgan *53*

Brooke Benevolent Fund, William *65*

Brotherton Trust, The Charles *65*

Buckinghamshire Masonic Centenary Fund *67*

Burdall Charity, H M *69*
Camelot Foundation, The *78*
Campbell Charitable Foundation, The Ellis *79*
Carnegie Dunfermline Trust *82*
Carnegie United Kingdom Trust, The *82*
Catto Charitable Settlement, The Thomas Sivewright *86*
Challice Trust, The *87*
Company of Chartered Surveyors Charitable Trust Fund, The *108*
David Trust, The Lesley *124*
De Yong Charitable Trust, The Emma *128*
Direct Response *134*
Dorus Trust *136*
Dumbreck Charity *139*
Earley Charity, The *142*
Ebb and Flow Charitable Trust *144*
Edgar Foundation, The Gilbert and Eileen *145*
Elkes Charity Fund, The Wilfred & Elsie *147*
Emmaus Christian Foundation *150*
Epigoni Trust *152*
Essex Radio Helping Hands Trust, The *154*
Eveson Charitable Trust, The *155*
Fane Research Trust, The Edmund *159*
Ferguson Benevolent Fund Limited *161*
Fishmongers' Company's Charitable Trust *163*
Fleming Charitable Trust, The Ian *164*
Fletcher Charitable Trust, The Joyce *164*
Getty Jr General Charitable Trust, J Paul *181*
Gibson Charitable Trust, The Simon *182*
Goldsmiths' Company's Charities, The *188*
Grant-Lawson Charitable Trust, Lady Virginia *192*
Griffiths Trust, The E E and D M *196*
Groves Charitable Trust, The *197*
Handicapped Children's Aid Committee *207*
Harbinson Charitable Trust, Roderick *208*
Heath Charitable Trust *214*
Hilden Charitable Fund, The *219*
Hockerill Educational Foundation *223*
Hornsey Parochial Charities, The *228*

Hornsey Parochial Charities (Educational and Vocational Foundation), The *228*
Hudson Benevolent Trust, The Thomas *230*
Hudson Charitable Trust, The *230*
Hurst Will Trust, Arthur *231*
Innes Memorial Fund *235*
Iris Trust, The *237*
JCSCJ Charitable Trust, The *238*
Jackson Trust for Charity, The Isaac and Harriet *240*
Johnson Foundation, The *246*
Johnson Group Cleaners Charity *247*
Keeling Charitable Trust, The Petronella *251*
King Charitable Trust, The Lorna *254*
King's Fund, The *255*
Kyte Charitable Trust, The *259*
Laing Charitable Trust, The David *260*
Laing Foundation, The Christopher *260*
Laing Foundation, The Kirby *261*
Laing Foundation, The Maurice *261*
Lane Foundation, The Allen *263*
Laspen Trust *265*
Leach Fourteenth Trust, The *267*
Lewis Foundation, The John Spedan *274*
Linford Charitable Trust, The Fred *276*
Listeners, The *276*
Lloyd Charity, The S and D *278*
London Taxi Drivers' Fund for Underprivileged Children, The *280*
Luke Trust, The *286*
MacKintosh Charitable Trust, Viscount *292*
Manning Trust, Leslie & Lilian *296*
Margaret Foundation, The *297*
Marriage's Charitable Trust, Miss G M *299*
Matthews Wrightson Charity Trust *301*
Mental Health Foundation, The *305*
Milburn Charitable Trust, Frederick *310*
Minet Trust, The Peter *313*
Minge's Gift *314*
Moore Foundation, The George A *316*
Morris Charitable Trust, The Douglas *320*
NR Charitable Trust, The *325*
Nathan Charitable Trust *326*

Needham Cooper Charitable Trust, The *331*
New Court Charitable Trust *332*
New Durlston Trust, The *332*
Newby Trust Ltd *332*
Nightingale Trust, The *335*
Noah Trust, The *335*
Noel Buxton Trust, The *335*
Norman Family Charitable Trust, The *337*
Oakdale Trust, The *343*
Oldham Foundation *345*
Owen Family Trust, The *348*
Paterson Charitable Foundation, The Constance *354*
Paterson Charitable Trust, Arthur James *354*
Payne Trust, The Harry *356*
Pilgrim Trust, The *362*
Pratt Charitable Trust, The W L *367*
Prince's Trust - BRO, The *369*
Pye Christian Trust, The *371*
Pyke Charity Trust *372*
Ravenscroft Foundation, The *379*
Rest-Harrow Trust, The *382*
Robinson Brothers (Ryders Green) Ltd, Charitable Trust *388*
Rowbotham Charitable Trust, The Christopher *393*
Rowntree Foundation, Joseph *394*
Royal's Memorial Fund, Princess *396*
Sainsbury Charitable Fund Ltd, The *402*
St Christopher's Trust, The *402*
Sargeant's Charitable Trust, Mrs M E *407*
Schuster Charitable Trust, The *410*
Scott Bader Commonwealth Ltd, The *411*
Sheldon Trust, The *417*
Shelroy Charitable Trust, The *417*
Smith & Mount Trust, The Mrs *426*
Smith (Estates Charities), Henry *426*
Smith Trust, The Sydney *428*
Staples Trust *435*
Stoate Charitable Trust, The Leonard Laity *438*
Stonehouse Trust Ltd, Eric *438*
Summerfield Charitable Trust, The *442*
Summer's and I May's Charitable Settlement, The Late Misses (A N) *442*
Swann-Morton Foundation, The *444*
TSB Foundation for Northern Ireland *447*

Disaster victims

Thomson Foundation, The Sue 454

Thorpe Charity Trust, The 455

Tisbury Telegraph Trust, The 457

Tudor Trust, The 463

Van Leer Foundation UK Trust, Bernard 470

Vec Acorn Trust, The 472

Wagstaff Charitable Trust, Bob 475

Wakefield (Tower Hill, Trinity Square) Trust 476

Wallace Charity Trust, The A F 478

Weavers' Company Benevolent Fund, The 482

Wesleyan Charitable Trust, The 485

Whitecourt Charitable Trust, The 490

Wills 1961 Charitable Trust, Mr Frederick 493

Wolfson (Scotland) Trust, The Edith & Isaac 500

Woodlands Trust 501

Worshipful Company of Glass Sellers' Charity Trust, The 505

■ Disaster victims

Funding priority

Ballinger Charitable Trust, The 32

Burgess Trust, The Michael 69

Buxton Trust, Denis 72

Charity Projects 90

Cobb Charity 103

Direct Response 134

Ericson Trust 152

Fund for Human Need 175

Grant Charitable Trust, The 191

Harbinson Charitable Trust, Roderick 208

Harbour Foundation Ltd, The 208

Hiley Trust, Joseph and Mary 219

Humphreys Charitable Settlement, J A M 231

International Arab Women's Council Charities Fund 236

Kejriwal Foundation 251

Mackintosh Foundation, The 292

Music for World Development 323

Oxfam (United Kingdom and Ireland) 348

Paristamen Foundation, The 352

Swale Charity Trust 443

Swindon Charitable Trust, The Walter 445

Tear Fund 450

Tisbury Telegraph Trust, The 457

Turkish Women's Philanthropic Association of England 463

Westcroft Trust 486

Will consider

AB Charitable Trust 3

Adnams Charity, The 7

Ammco Trust, The 15

Andrew Charitable Trust, The Prince 16

Archer Trust, The 20

Askew Trust, The Dorothy 25

Astor Foundation, The 26

Bancroft Trust, The 33

Barbour Trust, The 33

Beckwith Charitable Settlement, The Heather 39

Birmingham Amenities and Welfare Trust, The 49

Birtwistle Memorial Trust, The G E 50

Blake Charitable Trust, The Morgan 53

Boots Charitable Trust 56

Brooke Benevolent Fund, William 65

Buckinghamshire Masonic Centenary Fund 67

Butlin Charity Trust, Bill 72

Camelot Foundation, The 78

Campbell Charitable Foundation, The Ellis 79

Catto Charitable Settlement, The Thomas Sivewright 86

Challice Trust, The 87

Clark 1965 Charitable Trust, Stephen 98

Clinton's Charitable Trust, Lord 100

Collier Charitable Trust, The 105

Coutts Charitable Trust, The 116

De Yong Charitable Trust, The Emma 128

Digbeth Trust Ltd, The 133

Dorus Trust 136

Dumbreck Charity 139

Early's Charitable Settlement, Richard 142

Ebb and Flow Charitable Trust 144

Edgar Foundation, The Gilbert and Eileen 145

Edgar Trust, The Gilbert 145

Elkes Charity Fund, The Wilfred & Elsie 147

Emmaus Christian Foundation 150

Epigoni Trust 152

Fletcher Charitable Trust, The Joyce 164

Fletcher Trust, Roy 165

Four Winds Trust 168

Franklin Trust, Jill 170

Gibson Charitable Trust, The Simon 182

Gladstone Charitable Trust, The E W 184

Goldsmiths' Company's Charities, The 188

Grant-Lawson Charitable Trust, Lady Virginia 192

Griffiths Trust, The E E and D M 196

Groves Charitable Trust, The 197

Hanley Trust (1987), The 207

Heath Charitable Trust 214

Held Settlement, The Gisela 215

Hertfordshire Community Trust, The 217

Hill Memorial Trust, L E 219

Hudson Benevolent Trust, The Thomas 230

Hudson Charitable Trust, The 230

Humanitarian Trust, The 230

Isle of Dogs Community Foundation 238

JCSCJ Charitable Trust, The 238

JMK Charitable Trust 239

Jarrold Trust Ltd, John 243

Keeling Charitable Trust, The Petronella 251

King Charitable Trust, The Lorna 254

Kyte Charitable Trust, The 259

Laing Charitable Trust, The David 260

Laing Foundation, The Christopher 260

Laing Foundation, The Kirby 261

Laing Foundation, The Maurice 261

Laing Trust, Beatrice 261

Laspen Trust 265

Leach Fourteenth Trust, The 267

Lee Foundation, The Edgar 269

Linford Charitable Trust, The Fred 276

Lloyd Charity, The S and D 278

Lloyd's Charities Trust 278

(Lloyds) TSB Foundation for England and Wales 279

Low & Bonar Charitable Fund, The 284

Lunn-Rockliffe Charitable Trust, Paul 286

Lyons Charitable Trust, The 288

McCarthy Foundation, The John 290

MacKintosh Charitable Trust, Viscount 292

Manning Trust, Leslie & Lilian 296

Marriage's Charitable Trust, Miss G M *299*
Milburn Charitable Trust, Frederick *310*
Milton Keynes Community Trust Ltd, The *312*
Minge's Gift *314*
Multithon Trust, The *323*
NR Charitable Trust, The *325*
Nathan Charitable Trust *326*
New Court Charitable Trust *332*
New Durlston Trust, The *332*
Newby Trust Ltd *332*
Norton Foundation, The *340*
Oakdale Trust, The *343*
Oldham Foundation *345*
Owen Family Trust, The *348*
Paget Trust, The *351*
Parivar Trust, The *353*
Payne Trust, The Harry *356*
Persula Foundation, The *360*
Pratt Charitable Trust, The W L *367*
Pye Christian Trust, The *371*
Ravenscroft Foundation, The *379*
Robinson Trust 4, The J C *388*
Rope Third Charitable Settlement, The Mrs *391*
Sainsbury Charitable Fund Ltd, The *402*
St Christopher's Trust, The *402*
Schuster Charitable Trust, The *410*
Seagram Distillers Charitable Trust *413*
Shelroy Charitable Trust, The *417*
South Square Trust *430*
Stonehouse Trust Ltd, Eric *438*
Summer's and I May's Charitable Settlement, The Late Misses (A N) *442*
Swan Mountain Trust *444*
TSB Foundation for Scotland *447*
Trust for the Homeless *462*
Van Berchem Charitable Trust, The Alec *470*
Van Leer Foundation UK Trust, Bernard *470*
Variety Club Children's Charity Limited, The *471*
Wagstaff Charitable Trust, Bob *475*
Wallace Charity Trust, The A F *478*
Wallington Missionary Mart & Auctions *478*
Wates Foundation, The *481*
Wesleyan Charitable Trust, The *485*
Whitecourt Charitable Trust, The *490*

Wills 1962 Charitable Trust, P J H *494*
Wolfe Family's Charitable Trust, The *498*

■ Doctors
see **Medical professionals, nurses & doctors**

■ Dogs – kennels & other facilities for dogs
see also **Animal facilities & services**
Funding priority
Heath Charitable Trust *214*
Kennel Club Charitable Trust, The *252*
Marchig Animal Welfare Trust *297*
Needham Cooper Charitable Trust, The *331*
Sainsbury Animal Welfare Trust, Jean *401*
Zaiger Trust, The Elizabeth and Prince *512*

Will consider
Animal Defence Trust, The *18*
Astor Foundation, The *26*
Barnby's Foundation, Lord *35*
Body Charitable Trust, Bernard Richard *55*
Butler Charitable Trust, The A S *71*
Carron Charitable Trust, The *83*
Community Trust for Greater Manchester, The *108*
Coote Animal Charity Fund, The Marjorie *111*
Corden Trust, Cyril *113*
Digby Charitable Trust, Simon *133*
Dinam Charity *134*
Dumbreck Charity *139*
Elkes Charity Fund, The Wilfred & Elsie *147*
Evetts & Robert Luff Animal Welfare Trust, Beryl *156*
Ford of Britain Trust *166*
Friends of the Animals *173*
Green Memorial Fund, The Barry *194*
Greenaway Foundation, The Sir Derek *194*
Lee Foundation, The Edgar *269*
Lowe Trust, Mrs D G *285*
MacKintosh Charitable Trust, Viscount *292*
Marriage's Charitable Trust, Miss G M *299*
Mitchell Trust *315*

Nathan Charitable Trust, Peter *326*
Norman Family Charitable Trust, The *337*
Oakdale Trust, The *343*
Peppiatt Charitable Trust, The Brian *359*
Perry Charitable Trust, Miss Frances Lucille *359*
Richard Charitable Trust, The Cliff *383*
Stevens Foundation, The June *437*
Vincent Wildlife Trust, The *473*
Walker 597 Trust, The *477*
Wyford Charitable Trust, The *507*
Wylde Memorial Charity, The Anthony and Gwendoline *507*
Wyre Animal Welfare *507*

■ Domestic Violence
see **Victims of domestic violence**

■ Drug abuse
see **Substance misuse**

■ Ecology
see also **Environment & animal sciences**
Funding priority
Bell's Charitable Trust, Lady Mary *42*
Chippindale Foundation, Sam *93*
Coates Charitable Trust 1969, Lance *103*
Cobb Charity *103*
Foreman 1980 Charitable Trust, The Russell and Mary *167*
Horn Trust, The Cuthbert *227*
Living and Waking Naturally *278*
Mattock Charitable Trust, The W T *302*
Nickerson Charitable Foundation, The Joseph *335*
Pilkington Charitable Trust, Cecil *363*
Rufford Foundation *398*
Tisbury Telegraph Trust, The *457*

Will consider
Allied Domecq Trust *13*
Arbib Foundation *20*
Astor Foundation, The *26*
Bancroft Trust, The *33*
Bentall Charity Trust, Rowan *44*

Butler Charitable Trust, The A S
71
Carnegie Dunfermline Trust 82
Clark 1965 Charitable Trust,
Stephen 98
Clutterbuck Charitable Trust,
Robert 102
Community Trust for Greater
Manchester, The 108
Countryside Trust, The 115
David Trust, The Lesley 124
D'Avigdor Goldsmid Charitable
Trust, The Sarah 125
Digby Charitable Trust, Simon
133
Direct Response 134
Earwicker Trust 142
Eaton Charitable Trust, J C J
143
Education Services 145
Glynde Place Charitable Trust
(1974), The 186
Great Britain Sasakawa
Foundation, The 193
Greenaway Foundation, The Sir
Derek 194
Hayward Foundation, The 213
Holly Hill Charitable Trust 224
Isle of Dogs Community
Foundation 238
Laing Charitable Trust, The
David 260
Lindeth Charitable Trust, The
276
MacRobert Trusts, The 294
Marchig Animal Welfare Trust
297
Measures Charity, The James
Frederick and Ethel Anne
303
Mitchell Trust 315
Oldacre Foundation, The John
345
Oldham Foundation 345
Paget Trust, The 351
Peppiatt Charitable Trust, The
Brian 359
Polden-Puckham Charitable
Foundation, The 365
Reader's Digest Trust, The 380
Royal Botanical & Horticultural
Society of Manchester and
the Northern Counties, The
395
Shaw Foundation, The Linley
416
Summerfield Charitable Trust,
The 442
Yorkshire Agricultural Society
509

■ Economic regeneration schemes

see also **Infrastructure development**

Funding priority

Baring Foundation, The 34
Coutts Charitable Trust, The
116
Ferguson Benevolent Fund
Limited 161
HACT (The Housing
Association's Charitable
Trust) 201
Homeless International 225
Hyde Charitable Trust 232
Marr-Munning Trust 299
Northern Arts 339

Will consider

Ashden Charitable Trust, The
24
Aston Charities Trust Ltd 25
Barbour Trust, The 33
Berkshire Community Trust 45
British Sugar Foundation 63
Camelot Foundation, The 78
Campden Charities, The 79
Collier Charitable Trust, The
105
Community Trust for Greater
Manchester, The 108
County Durham Foundation
115
Cripplegate Foundation 118
Digby Charitable Trust, Simon
133
Direct Response 134
Ford of Britain Trust 166
Four Lanes Trust, The 168
Great Britain Sasakawa
Foundation, The 193
Greenaway Foundation, The Sir
Derek 194
Hertfordshire Community
Trust, The 217
Humanitarian Trust, The 230
Hussey for Africans, Charity of
Rebecca 231
Isle of Dogs Community
Foundation 238
Johnson Foundation, The 246
Knott Trust, Sir James 258
Lane Foundation, The Allen
263
Lunn-Rockliffe Charitable Trust,
Paul 286
Minet Trust, The Peter 313
National Power Charitable
Trust, The 330
New Chasers Charitable Trust,
The 332
Newby Trust Ltd 332
Owen Family Trust, The 348
Paristamen Foundation, The
352

Parivar Trust, The 353
Puebla Charitable Trust
Limited, The 371
Rope Third Charitable
Settlement, The Mrs 391
Rowntree Foundation, Joseph
394
Scott Bader Commonwealth
Ltd, The 411
Summerfield Charitable Trust,
The 442
Tear Fund 450
Wakefield (Tower Hill, Trinity
Square) Trust 476
Wall Trust, Thomas 478
Whitaker Charitable Trust 489
Wills 1962 Charitable Trust,
P J H 494

■ Economic research

see **Academic subjects, sciences & research**

■ Education & training

see also **Cultural & religious teaching, English as a second or foreign language – TESL & TEFL, Literacy, Professional, specialist training, Special needs education, Textiles & upholstery, Training for community development, Training for personal development, Training for work, Vocational training**

Funding priority

AB Charitable Trust, The 3
Achiezer Association Limited 6
Aga Khan Foundation (UK) 7
Airflow Community Ltd, The 9
Aleh Charitable Foundation,
The 10
Alexander Charitable Trust,
The 10
Alexander Charitable Trust,
Mrs K L 11
All Saints Educational Trust 12
Alliance Family Foundation
Limited 13
Allsop Charitable Trust, Pat 14
Appelbe Trust, Ambrose & Ann
19
Armourers' & Brasiers' Gauntlet
Trust, The 21
Ashton Foundation, The
Norman C 24
Astor of Hever Trust, The 26
Bachad Fellowship – Friends of
Bnei Akiva 30
Barnes Workhouse Fund 35
Beacon Trust 38
Bear Mordechai Ltd 39

Bestway Foundation, The 46
Black Foundation, The Bertie 51
Blank Donations Ltd, The David 54
Bottom Charitable Trust, Harry 56
Bowland Charitable Trust, The 57
Bridgeman TRA Foundation, The Dick 60
British Sugar Foundation 63
CfBT Education Services 74
Cadbury Schweppes Foundation, The 76
Campbell Charitable Foundation, The Ellis 79
Cancer Relief Macmillan Fund 79
Careers Services Trust 81
Carron Charitable Trust, The 83
Carter Trust, The Frederick William 84
Cen Foundation, The Hyman 87
Chippindale Foundation, Sam 93
Clark Charitable Trust 98
Clark Charitable Trust, J Anthony 98
Coates Charitable Settlement, The 102
Cohen Charitable Trust, The Vivienne and Samuel 104
Company of Tobacco Pipe Makers and Tobacco Blenders Benevolent Fund 109
Crescent Trust, The 117
Curry Charitable Trust, Dennis 119
Daily Telegraph Charitable Trust 122
Daiwa Anglo-Japanese Foundation, The 122
Dandeen Charitable Trust 123
Davy Foundation, The J 126
De La Rue Charitable Trust 127
Deutsch Charitable Trust, The Andre 131
Deutsch Charitable Trust, The H & M 131
Diamond Industry Educational Charity, The 132
Djanogly Foundation, The 135
Dulverton Trust, The 139
Ebb and Flow Charitable Trust 144
Edinburgh Trust, No 2 Account 145
Elephant Jobs Charity 146
Ellis 1985 Charitable Trust, Edith M 148
Fairbairn Charitable Trust, The Esmee 157
Fairway Trust, The 158

Famos Foundation Trust 158
Fattorini Charitable Trust, James J 160
Foundation for Management Education 168
Foyle Trust, Charles Henry 169
Franklin Bequest, The Rosalind 169
Franklin Deceased's New Second Charity, Sydney E 170
Gibbs Charitable Trusts, The 181
Girdlers' Company Charitable Trust, The 184
Goodman Charitable Foundation, The Everard and Mina 188
Goodman Trust, The 189
Grahame Charitable Foundation, The 190
Greenwood Charitable Trust, The G B 195
Gross Charities Limited, M & R 197
Grosshill Charitable Trust 197
Gwent County Council Welsh Church Fund 200
Hamilton Educational Trust, Eleanor 205
Harbour Foundation Ltd, The 208
Hargreaves Trust, The Kenneth 210
Heinz Company Limited Charitable Trust, The H J 215
Held Settlement, The Gisela 215
Highcroft Charitable Trust 218
Hitachi Charitable Trust, The 222
Horne Foundation, The 228
Hornsey Parochial Charities (Educational and Vocational Foundation), The 228
IBM United Kingdom Trust 233
IPE Charitable Trust, The 233
JCA Charitable Foundation 238
James Foundation, The Catherine and Lady Grace 241
Jewish Philanthropic Association for Israel and the Middle East, The 245
Jones Trust, Cemlyn 248
Judge Charitable Foundation 249
Kahn Charitable Trust, Bernard 250
Karten Charitable Trust, The Ian 250
Kobler Trust, The 258
Kreitman Foundation 258
Kulika Charitable Trust, The 259

Kweller Charitable Trust, The Harry 259
LSA Charitable Trust 260
Landy Charitable Trust, Harry and Gertrude 263
Lanvern Foundation 265
Laski Memorial Charitable Trust, Nathan 265
Lauffer Charitable Foundation, The R & D 266
Lawley Foundation, The Edgar E 267
Leigh-Bramwell Trust 'E', P 270
Lester Trust Fund, The 271
Lewis Partnership, John 274
Lucas Charitable Trust Limited, The Joseph 286
Lunzer Charitable Trust, The Ruth & Jack 287
Lyons Charitable Trust, Sir Jack 288
Maccabi Foundation, The 290
McKenzie Trust, The Robert 292
MacRobert Trusts, The 294
Marks Foundation, The Hilda and Samuel 298
Marmor Charitable Trust, The Julie 299
Marr-Munning Trust 299
Marshall Charitable Trust, The Charlotte 300
Martin Trust, The Sir George 300
Mayfair Charities Limited 303
Medlock Charitable Trust, The 304
Mellows Charitable Settlement, The Anthony and Elizabeth 305
Mental Health Foundation, The 305
Millett Charitable Trust, The Alan and Janet 312
Modiano Charitable Trust 315
Montefiore Trust, The David 316
Moore Charitable Trust, The Horace 316
Moores Foundation, The Peter 318
Morgan Foundation, The Mr & Mrs J T 319
Muslim Hands 324
Naaman Trust, The 325
Nemoral Ltd 331
Newman Charitable Trust, Mr and Mrs F E F 334
North West Arts Board 337
Northern Dairies Educational Trust 339
Noswad Charity, The 341
Old Possums Practical Trust, The 344
Oxford Trust, The 349
PPP Healthcare Medical Trust Limited 350
Parivar Trust, The 353

Peel Medical Research Trust,
The 358
Pelech Charitable Trust, The
358
Pyke Charity Trust 372
QAS Charitable Trust 373
RVW Trust 374
Rainbow Charitable Trust 376
Rayne Foundation, The 379
Riddleston Charity of Leicester,
The Harry James 385
Robbins Trust, The Cheshire
387
Robyn Charitable Trust 389
Royal Botanical & Horticultural
Society of Manchester and
the Northern Counties, The
395
Rozel Trust, The 397
St Jude's Trust 403
Sassoon Charitable Trust, The
Late Aaron D 408
Save & Prosper Educational
Trust 408
Save & Prosper Foundation
409
Scarr-Hall Memorial Trust, The
409
Scopus Jewish Educational
Trust 411
Seva Trust, Rampaba Sadhu
415
Shah Trust, The Dr N K 416
Sherman Charitable Trust, The
Archie 419
Shine No 2 Charitable Trust,
The Barnett and Sylvia 420
Sidbury Trust, The Second 421
Simon Population Trust, The
422
Skelton Bounty, The 423
Salter Trust Ltd 424
Smith (UK) Horticultural Trust,
Stanley 428
Society of Friends of the Torah,
The 429
South Square Trust 430
Southall Charitable Trust,
Kenneth & Phyllis 431
Southall Trust, W F 432
Spoore, Merry & Rixman
Foundation, The 434
Stanley Foundation Limited
435
Stathern Chapel Close Trust,
The 436
Stewart Charitable Trust, Mary
Stephanie 437
Street Charitable Foundation,
W O 440
Swan Mountain Trust 444
TSB Foundation for the
Channel Islands 447
Tesco Charity Trust 452
Tesler Foundation, The 452
Thompson Memorial Fund, The
Edwin John 453
Thriplow Charitable Trust 456

Timson Family Charitable Trust
457
Tudor Trust, The 463
Tyndale Trust 466
United Kingdom Friends for
Further Education in Israel
468
Van Berchem Charitable Trust,
The Alec 470
Watson's Trust, John 482
Weinstock Fund, The 484
Westminster Amalgamated
Charity 487
White Rose Children's Aid
International Charity 489
Wohl Charitable Foundation,
The Maurice 498
Wohl Charitable Trust, The
Maurice 498
Wolff Charity Trust 498
Wolfson Family Charitable
Trust, The 499
Wolfson Foundation, The 499
Wolverhampton Rotary Club
Charitable Trust 500
Woodhouse Charitable Trust,
Edwin 501
Woods Charitable Foundation,
Geoffrey 502
Worms Charitable Trust, The
Freda and Della 504
Worshipful Company of
Needlemakers' Charitable
Fund 505
Yapp Welfare Trust, The 508
Yorkshire Bank Charitable
Trust, The 510
Zaiger Trust, The Elizabeth and
Prince 512

Will consider
AHJ Charitable Trust, The 3
Acacia Charitable Trust 6
Allied Domecq Trust 13
Anderson Trust, Andrew 16
Angler's Inn Trust 17
Anglo Hong Kong Trust, The
17
Anglo-German Foundation for
the Study of Industrial
Society 18
Aquarian Healing Trust 19
Aquarius Charitable
Foundation, The 19
Aquinas Trust 20
Ashby Charitable Trust, The 23
Askew Charitable Trust, The
Ian 25
Assembled Church of Christ
Trust, The 25
Assheton-Smith Charitable
Trust 25
Asthma Allergy and
Inflammation Research Trust
25
Astor's 1969 Charity, The Hon
M L 26

BBC Children in Need Appeal,
The 29
BUPA Foundation, The 29
Baring Foundation, The 34
Barnby's Foundation, Lord 35
Barnsbury Charitable Trust 35
Barton Trust, Eleanor 37
Bateman Charitable Trust, Lady
Margaret 37
Bealey Foundation, The 38
Beaverbrook Foundation, The
39
Beckwith Charitable Trust, The
Peter 40
Beckwith-Smith's Charitable
Settlement, Mrs 40
Behrens Charitable Trust, E M
40
Bentall Charity Trust, Rowan
44
Bergqvist Charitable Trust 44
Blagrave Charitable Trust, The
Herbert and Peter 52
Blakey Charitable Trust, The
Celia and Conrad 53
Blanchminster Trust, The 54
Boltons Trust, The 55
Borthwick Memorial Trust, The
Oliver 56
British Friends of Chinuch
Atzmai Trust, The 62
Brook Charitable Settlement,
R E 64
Brookhouse's Will Trust, Mr
John Charles 65
Burn Charity Trust, The J H 70
Burns Charity, The Dorothy 70
Burry Charitable Trust, The 70
Burton Charitable Trust, The
Geoffrey 71
Butler's Trust, Lord 71
Butler's Trust, Lucilla 72
CHK Charities Limited 74
Cadbury Trust (1928), The
Edward & Dorothy 76
Cardiff & Swansea Methodist
District Charitable Trust
Fund 80
Carnegie United Kingdom
Trust, The 82
Cass's Foundation, Sir John 85
Castang Charitable Trust, H
and M 85
Charity Projects 90
Childtime Trust, The 92
Christian Aid 94
Cinderford Charitable Trust,
The 96
Closehelm Ltd 101
Clutterbuck Charitable Trust,
Robert 102
Coates Charitable Trust 1969,
Lance 103
Coates Charitable Trust, The
John 103
Cohen Charity Trust, Lucy 104
Cohen Foundation, The John S
104

Condon Family Trust *109*
Cope Charitable Trust, Alfred *112*
Cymerman Trust Limited, Itzchok Meyer *120*
De Avenley Foundation, The *126*
De Rothschild 1981 Charitable Trust, The Edmund *127*
De Yong Charitable Trust, The Emma *128*
Denton Charitable Trust, The *130*
Desmond Charitable Trust, The Richard *131*
Dicken Charitable Trust, The Albert *133*
Dinam Charity *134*
Doughty Charity Trust, The *136*
D'Oyly Carte Charitable Trust, The *137*
Drapers' Charitable Fund *137*
Drayton Trust, The *138*
Dunn Charitable Trust, The Harry *140*
Earmark Trust, The *142*
Egerton of Tatton Will Trust, Lord *146*
Eling Trust *147*
Ellinson Foundation Limited *148*
Elshore Limited *149*
Family Trust, The *158*
Farmers' Company Charitable Fund, The *159*
Federation of Jewish Relief Organisations *160*
Fletcher Trust, Roy *165*
Foreman Foundation, The Carl & Eve *167*
Fry Charitable Trust, Maurice *174*
Garthgwynion Charities *179*
Gibson's Charity Trust, The Hon Mr & Mrs Clive *182*
Gilchrist Educational Trust *183*
Gillett Charitable Trust, J A *183*
Gill's Charitable Trust, Mrs M M *184*
Gold Hill Church Trust *186*
Goldberg Charitable Trust, The Lewis *186*
Goodman Trust, The S & F *189*
Gradel Foundation, The *189*
Graves Charitable Trust, J G *192*
Green Foundation, Constance *194*
Grut Charitable Trust, The *198*
Gulbenkian Foundation (Lisbon) United Kingdom Branch, Calouste *199*
HB Charitable Trust *201*
Hacking & Sons Ltd Charitable Trust, C G *201*
Hale Trust, The *203*

Hampton Fuel Allotment Charity *207*
Handicapped Children's Aid Committee *207*
Harding's Charity, William *209*
Harford Charitable Trust *209*
Harvey Charitable Trust, Gordon *211*
Hawthorne Charitable Trust, The *212*
Hewett/Driver Education Trust, The *217*
Hicks Foundation, The Sir John *218*
Hillards Charitable Trust, Gay & Peter Hartley's *220*
Hodge Foundation, The Jane *223*
Holford Trust Fund *224*
Hoover Foundation, The *226*
Horn Trust, The Cuthbert *227*
Hornby Charitable Trust, Miss D *227*
Hornton Trust, The *228*
Hughes Charitable Trust, The Geoffery C *230*
Hyde Park Place Estate Charity, The *232*
Inman Charity, The *235*
JCSCJ Charitable Trust, The *238*
Johnson Foundation, The *246*
Kalms Foundation, The Stanley *250*
Keyes Trust, The Ursula *253*
Kingsgrove Charitable Trust, The *255*
Kinnison Charitable Trust, R O *256*
Kleinwort Charitable Trust, The Ernest *257*
Knott Trust, Sir James *258*
Laing Foundation, The Christopher *260*
Laspen Trust *265*
Lavender Trust, The *267*
Leach Fourteenth Trust, The *267*
Levy Charitable Foundation, Joseph *272*
Liffe Benefit *274*
Lingwood Charitable Trust, The *276*
Lloyd's Charities Trust *278*
Localtrent Ltd *279*
Lynwood Charitable Trust, The *288*
Lyons Charitable Trust, The *288*
Lyon's Charity, John *288*
MDM Memorial Trust *289*
MacAndrew Trust, The E M *289*
McKechnie Foundation, A N *292*
McLaren Foundation *292*
McLaren Memorial Trust, The Martin *293*

Margadale Charitable Trust, Lord *297*
Marks Charitable Trust, Michael *298*
Markus Charitable Foundation, The Erich *298*
Matchan Fund Limited, The Leonard *301*
Material World Charitable Foundation Limited, The *301*
Mattock Charitable Trust, The W T *302*
Millfield House Foundation *312*
Millichope Foundation, The *312*
Morel Charitable Trust, The *318*
Morgan Crucible Company plc Charitable Trust, The *319*
Morphy Memorial Fund, Arthur *319*
Morris Charitable Trust, The Willie & Mabel *320*
Moulton Charitable Trust, The *321*
Music Sales Charitable Trust, The *324*
National Lottery Charities Board *328*
New Court Charitable Trust *332*
Newcastle's 1986 Charitable Trust, Duke of *333*
Newcomen Collett Foundation *333*
Newstead Charity, The *334*
Nidditch Foundation, The Laurie *335*
Norfolk's Family Charitable Trust, Lavinia *336*
Northcott Charity Trust, The *338*
Northern Arts *339*
Northern Electric Employee Charity Association *339*
Norton Foundation, The *340*
Nuffield Foundation *342*
Oldham Foundation *345*
Open Door Women's Trust *346*
Owen Family Trust, The *348*
Owen Trust, Margaret *348*
PDC Trust, The *349*
PJD Charitable Trust *350*
Palmer Trust, The Gerald *352*
Pascoe Charitable Trust, Alan *354*
Paul Charitable Trust, The Late Barbara May *355*
Paul Charitable Trust, Margaret Jeanne *355*
Paul Charitable Trust, Pamela Milton *355*
Paul Foundation, The *355*
Paul's Charitable Trust, R J *355*
Payne Charitable Trust, The *355*

Perry Charitable Trust, Miss
Frances Lucille *359*
Pershore Nashdom & Elmore
Trust Ltd, The *360*
Peskin Charitable Trust, The
Hazel and Leslie *360*
Phillips Charitable Foundation,
Reginald M *361*
Pitt Trust, Headley *364*
Porter Foundation *366*
Powys Welsh Church Fund *367*
Puebla Charitable Trust
Limited, The *371*
Queen Anne Street Educational
Trust Limited *373*
RT Trust, The *374*
Rackham Charitable Trust, The
Mr & Mrs Philip *375*
Radley Charitable Trust *375*
Rae Charity, H J *375*
Rainford Trust, The *376*
Rav Chesed Trust, The *379*
Reekie Trust, R A & V B *381*
Rest-Harrow Trust, The *382*
Reuter Foundation, The *382*
Richards Charity, The Clive *384*
Richmond Parish Lands Charity
384
Rivendell Trust, The *387*
Rodewald's Charitable
Settlement, Mr C A *389*
Rogers Charitable Settlement,
The Richard *390*
Rolfe Charitable Trust, The *390*
Rosen Foundation, Cecil *392*
S Group Charitable Trust *399*
Salamander Charitable Trust,
The *405*
Salters Charities *405*
Samuel Charitable Trust, M J
406
Shifrin Charitable Trust, The
Maurice and Hilda *419*
Silvester Charitable Gift Trust
422
Slater Foundation Ltd, The *424*
Solomons Charitable Trust,
David *430*
Somerfield Curtis Will Trust,
The Dorothy *430*
South East Arts Board *430*
Sumner's Trust Section 'A', Sir
John *443*
TSB Foundation for Scotland
447
Tait Charity, The Richard *448*
Taylor Charitable Trust, The B R
450
Terry Charitable Trust, Noel
Goddard *451*
Thompson Charitable Trust,
The *453*
3i Charitable Trust, The *455*
Toyota (GB) Charitable Trust,
The *459*
van Geest Foundation, The
John and Lucille *470*

Van Norden's Charitable
Foundation, Mrs Maud *471*
Vineyard Christian Fellowship
of South West *473*
Vinson Charity Trust, The 1969
473
Wakefield Trust, The *476*
Walker Trust, The *477*
Ward Blenkinsop Trust, The
480
Wates Foundation, The *481*
Welby Trust, The Barbara *484*
Whetherly's Charitable Trust,
The Hon Mrs R G A *489*
Whitehead Charitable Trust, J E
490
Whittington Charitable Trust,
The *491*
Wiggins Charity Trust, Cyril
491
Wilde Charitable Trust, The
Felicity *492*
Wills 1961 Charitable Trust,
Major Michael Thomas *494*
Wiltshire Community
Foundation *495*
Winstone Foundation, Hyman
497
Woburn 1986 Charitable Trust
498
Wychdale Limited *507*
Yapp Education and Research
Trust, The *508*
Youell Foundation Ltd, The
510

....

■ Education hardship funds

see Costs of study

....

■ Emergency & short-term housing

see also **Residential facilities & services**

Funding priority
AB Charitable Trust *3*
Aquarian Healing Trust *19*
Borthwick Memorial Trust, The
Oliver *56*
Calypso Browning Trust *78*
Charity Projects *90*
Christmas Cracker Trust *95*
County Durham Foundation
115
Curriers Company Charitable
Fund *119*
Franklin Trust, Jill *170*
Harbour Foundation Ltd, The
208
Held Settlement, The Gisela
215
Hyde Charitable Trust *232*
Kroch Foundation, The Heinz &
Anna *259*

Lacy Charity Trust, The Late Sir
Pierce *260*
Lyons Charitable Trust, The
288
Marchday Charitable Fund, The
296
Moores Foundation, John *318*
Nunburnholme Trust, The
Incorporated Trustees of the
342
Paristamen Foundation, The
352
Pick Charitable Trust, The
George and Jessie *362*
Staples Trust *435*
Swan Mountain Trust *444*
Tisbury Telegraph Trust, The
457
Trust for the Homeless *462*
Woodroffe Benton Foundation,
The *502*

Will consider
Abbey National Charitable
Trust *4*
Archer Trust, The *20*
Army Benevolent Fund, The *22*
Ashden Charitable Trust, The
24
Astor Foundation, The *26*
Baker Charitable Trust, The *30*
Barbour Trust, The *33*
Barnabas Charitable Trust *34*
Berkshire Community Trust *45*
Bilton Charity, The Percy *48*
Boots Charitable Trust *56*
Britton Charitable Trust, The J
& M *63*
Brough Charitable Trust,
Joseph *65*
Burden Trust, The *69*
Cadbury Trust (1928), The
Edward & Dorothy *76*
Campden Charities, The *79*
Chase Charity, The *91*
Chiddick Charitable Trust *92*
Cleopatra Trust *99*
Clifford Charity Oxford, The
100
Cooper Charitable Trust *111*
Coutts Charitable Trust, The
116
de Freitas Charitable Trust, The
Helen and Geoffrey *126*
Dean Refugee Trust Fund, The
Miriam *128*
Derbyshire Trust, J N *130*
Dibs Charitable Trust, The *133*
Digby Charitable Trust, Simon
133 '
Direct Response *134*
Dorus Trust *136*
Edgar Trust, The Gilbert *145*
Egerton of Tatton Will Trust,
Lord *146*
Elkes Charity Fund, The Wilfred
& Elsie *147*

Emanuel Charitable Settlement, Ralph and Muriel 150
Emmandjay Charitable Trust 150
Emmaus Christian Foundation 150
Epigoni Trust 152
Firdale Christian Trust, The 162
Follett Trust, The 166
Ford of Britain Trust 166
Garnett Charitable Trust, The 178
Gelston Charitable Trust, The 179
Greater Bristol Foundation 193
Greenaway Foundation, The Alan 194
Greenaway Foundation, The Sir Derek 194
HACT (The Housing Association's Charitable Trust) 201
Harford Charitable Trust 209
Harvey Charitable Trust, Gordon 211
Hertfordshire Community Trust, The 217
Hilden Charitable Fund, The 219
Hudson Benevolent Trust, The Thomas 230
Inverforth Charitable Trust, The 236
Isle of Dogs Community Foundation 238
Jewish Childs' Day 245
Johnson Foundation, The 246
Johnson Group Cleaners Charity 247
Keeling Charitable Trust, The Petronella 251
King Charitable Settlement, Philip 254
Laing Charitable Trust, The David 260
Laing Foundation, The Christopher 260
Laing's Charitable Trust 262
Lancaster's Trust, Bryan 263
Lane Foundation, The Allen 263
Lankelly Foundation, The 264
Lawson Charitable Trust, Raymond and Blanche 267
Leech Charity, The William 269
Lewis Partnership, John 274
Luke Trust, The 286
Lunn-Rockliffe Charitable Trust, Paul 286
McCarthy Foundation, The John 290
Mackintosh Foundation, The 292
Manning Trust, Leslie & Lilian 296
Mental Health Foundation, The 305

Morphy Memorial Fund, Arthur 319
Morris Charitable Trust, The Douglas 320
Music for World Development 323
NR Charitable Trust, The 325
New Court Charitable Trust 332
Noah Trust, The 335
Norman Family Charitable Trust, The 337
Northern Ireland Voluntary Trust 339
Norton Foundation, The 340
Oldham Foundation 345
Open Door Women's Trust 346
Pratt Charitable Trust, The W L 367
Rest-Harrow Trust, The 382
Ripley's Charitable Trust, Pat 386
Robinson Brothers (Ryders Green) Ltd, Charitable Trust 388
Rope Third Charitable Settlement, The Mrs 391
St Christopher's Trust, The 402
Saint Edmund King and Martyr Trust 402
Scott Bader Commonwealth Ltd, The 411
Seagram Distillers Charitable Trust 413
Sheldon Trust, The 417
Smith & Mount Trust, The Mrs 426
South Square Trust 430
Sparkhill Trust, The 433
Stevens Foundation, The June 437
Stoate Charitable Trust, The Leonard Laity 438
Stonehouse Trust Ltd, Eric 438
Summerfield Charitable Trust, The 442
Sussman Charitable Trust, Adrienne & Leslie 443
Sykes Trust, The Charles 445
TSB Foundation for Northern Ireland 447
Tear Fund 450
Thackray General Charitable Trust, The P & L 452
Thorpe Charity Trust, The 455
Torquay Charities, The 458
Tudor Trust, The 463
Wall Trust, Thomas 478
Wander Charitable Fund, The Dr Albert 479
Wesleyan Charitable Trust, The 485
Whesby Ltd 488
Whitaker Charitable Trust 489
Wiltshire Community Foundation 495

Woburn 1986 Charitable Trust 498
Woodlands Trust 501

....

■ Emergency appeals

see **Victims of man-made or natural disasters**

....

■ Emergency care, refugees, famine

see also **Community services**

Funding priority

Aquarian Healing Trust 19
Army Benevolent Fund, The 22
Aston Charities Trust Ltd 25
Challice Trust, The 87
Christmas Cracker Trust 95
Clark 1965 Charitable Trust, Stephen 98
David Trust, The Lesley 124
Direct Response 134
Emanuel Charitable Settlement, Ralph and Muriel 150
Franklin Trust, Jill 170
Gelston Charitable Trust, The 179
Grant Charitable Trust, The 191
Griffiths Trust, The E E and D M 196
Harbinson Charitable Trust, Roderick 208
Humphreys Charitable Settlement, J A M 231
Kroch Foundation, The Heinz & Anna 259
Lancaster's Trust, Bryan 263
Lloyd's Charities Trust 278
Marchday Charitable Fund, The 296
Mental Health Foundation, The 305
Music for World Development 323
National Power Charitable Trust, The 330
Ogilvie Charities (Deed No 1) 344
Oldham Foundation 345
Parivar Trust, The 353
Pilkington Trust, The Austin and Hope 363
Pratt Charitable Trust, The W L 367
SMB Trust, The 400
St Christopher's Trust, The 402
Seagram Distillers Charitable Trust 413
Stonehouse Trust Ltd, Eric 438
Swan Mountain Trust 444
TSB Foundation for Scotland 447

Tisbury Telegraph Trust, The 457

Toy Trust, The 459

Trust for the Homeless 462

Wates Foundation, The 481

Westcroft Trust 486

Whitaker Charitable Trust 489

Will consider

AB Charitable Trust 3

Abel Charitable Trust 5

Alexandra Trust 11

Ammco Trust, The 15

Archer Trust, The 20

Askew Trust, The Dorothy 25

Astor Foundation, The 26

Barbour Trust, The 33

Beit Trust, The 40

Berkshire Community Trust 45

BibleLands 47

Birtwistle Memorial Trust, The G E 50

Blakenham's Charity Trust, Lady 53

Bowland Charitable Trust, The 57

Brooke Benevolent Fund, William 65

Brough Charitable Trust, Joseph 65

Burdall Charity, H M 69

Burton 1960 Charitable Settlement, Audrey & Stanley 70

CLA Charitable Trust 74

Camelot Foundation, The 78

Campden Charities, The 79

Catto Charitable Settlement, The Thomas Sivewright 86

Chiddick Charitable Trust 92

Commonwealth Relations Trust 108

Community Trust for Greater Manchester, The 108

Coutts Charitable Trust, The 116

de Freitas Charitable Trust, The Helen and Geoffrey 126

Derbyshire Trust, J N 130

Digby Charitable Trust, Simon 133

Dumbreck Charity 139

Early's Charitable Settlement, Richard 142

Earwicker Trust 142

Edgar Foundation, The Gilbert and Eileen 145

Edgar Trust, The Gilbert 145

Egerton of Tatton Will Trust, Lord 146

Elkes Charity Fund, The Wilfred & Elsie 147

Emmaus Christian Foundation 150

Eventhall Family Charitable Trust, The 155

Ferguson Benevolent Fund Limited 161

Fletcher Trust, Roy 165

Fogel Charitable Trust, The Gerald 165

Follett Trust, The 166

Gardner Charitable Trust, R & J 178

Garnett Charitable Trust, The 178

Great Britain Sasakawa Foundation, The 193

Greenaway Foundation, The Sir Derek 194

Grosshill Charitable Trust 197

Hamlyn Foundation, The Paul 205

Harford Charitable Trust 209

Heath Charitable Trust 214

Humanitarian Trust, The 230

Hyde Charitable Trust 232

Ingles Charitable Trust, The 234

Isle of Dogs Community Foundation 238

JMK Charitable Trust 239

Jarrold Trust Ltd, John 243

Johnson Foundation, The 246

Johnson Group Cleaners Charity 247

Keeling Charitable Trust, The Petronella 251

King Charitable Settlement, Philip 254

Knott Trust, Sir James 258

Kyte Charitable Trust, The 259

Laing Charitable Trust, The David 260

Laing Foundation, The Christopher 260

Laing Foundation, The Kirby 261

Laing Foundation, The Maurice 261

Laing Trust, Beatrice 261

Lankelly Foundation, The 264

Leach Fourteenth Trust, The 267

Leech Charity, The William 269

Lewis Partnership, John 274

Linmardon Trust 276

Luke Trust, The 286

Lunn-Rockliffe Charitable Trust, Paul 286

Lyndhurst Settlement 287

MacKintosh Charitable Trust, Viscount 292

Mackintosh Foundation, The 292

Manning Trust, Leslie & Lilian 296

Margaret Foundation, The 297

Multithon Trust, The 323

NR Charitable Trust, The 325

Needham Cooper Charitable Trust, The 331

New Court Charitable Trust 332

Newby Trust Ltd 332

Noah Trust, The 335

Norfolk's Family Charitable Trust, Lavinia 336

Norman Family Charitable Trust, The 337

Norton Foundation, The 340

Owen Family Trust, The 348

Paget Trust, The 351

Paterson Charitable Foundation, The Constance 354

Paterson Charitable Trust, Arthur James 354

Patients' Aid Association Hospital and Medical Charities Trust 354

Payne Trust, The Harry 356

Persula Foundation, The 360

Provincial Trust for Kendal, The 370

Pye Christian Trust, The 371

Pyke Charity Trust 372

Rayner Charitable Trust, The John 380

Rest-Harrow Trust, The 382

Ripley's Charitable Trust, Pat 386

Robinson Brothers (Ryders Green) Ltd, Charitable Trust 388

Rope Third Charitable Settlement, The Mrs 391

Sainsbury Charitable Fund Ltd, The 402

Saint Edmund King and Martyr Trust 402

Sheepdrove Trust, The 417

Shepherd Family Charitable Trust, The Sir Peter 418

South Square Trust 430

Sparkhill Trust, The 433

Summer's and I May's Charitable Settlement, The Late Misses (A N) 442

Sussman Charitable Trust, Adrienne & Leslie 443

Sykes Trust, The Charles 445

TSB Foundation for Northern Ireland 447

Tear Fund 450

Thomson Foundation, The Sue 454

Tindall's Charitable Trust, Mrs R P 457

Travis Charitable Trust, Constance 460

Tudor Trust, The 463

Tyne & Wear Foundation 466

Upjohn Charitable Trust, The 469

Van Leer Foundation UK Trust, Bernard 470

Wakefield (Tower Hill, Trinity Square) Trust 476

Wakeham Trust, The 476

Webber Trust Fund, Ethel 483

Whitecourt Charitable Trust,
The *490*
Wills 1962 Charitable Trust,
P J H *494*
Wingfield's Charitable Trust,
Mrs *496*
Wolfe Family's Charitable
Trust, The *498*

....

■ Endangered habitats

see Animal facilities & services

....

■ Endangered species

see also Conservation & campaigning

Funding priority

Animal Defence Trust, The *18*
BP Conservation Programme
29
Bell's Charitable Trust, Lady
Mary *42*
Carron Charitable Trust, The
83
Coote Animal Charity Fund,
The Marjorie *111*
Friends of the Animals *173*
Haddon Charitable Trust,
William *202*
Harbinson Charitable Trust,
Roderick *208*
Kilverstone Wildlife Charitable
Trust, The *254*
Mitchell Trust *315*
Nathan Charitable Trust, Peter
326
Shepherd Conservation
Foundation, The David *418*
Tisbury Telegraph Trust, The
457
Tyler's Charitable Trust, The
Late Miss Eileen Margaret
465
Vincent Wildlife Trust, The *473*

Will consider

Ammco Trust, The *15*
Arbib Foundation *20*
Astor Foundation, The *26*
Aylesfield Foundation, The *28*
Bancroft Trust, The *33*
Barnby's Foundation, Lord *35*
Beit Trust, The *40*
Body Charitable Trust, Bernard
Richard *55*
Body Shop Foundation, The *55*
Bourne-May Charitable Trust,
The *57*
Bullough Tompson Settlement,
The *68*
Butler Charitable Trust, The A S
71
Buxton Trust, Denis *72*

Catto Charitable Settlement,
The Thomas Sivewright *86*
Coates Charitable Trust 1969,
Lance *103*
David Trust, The Lesley *124*
D'Avigdor Goldsmid Charitable
Trust, The Sarah *125*
de Freitas Charitable Trust, The
Helen and Geoffrey *126*
Digby Charitable Trust, Simon
133
Direct Response *134*
Dorus Trust *136*
Dumbreck Charity *139*
Early's Charitable Settlement,
Richard *142*
Eaton Charitable Trust, J C J
143
Edgar Foundation, The Gilbert
and Eileen *145*
Elkes Charity Fund, The Wilfred
& Elsie *147*
Epigoni Trust *152*
Fishmongers' Company's
Charitable Trust *163*
Foreman 1980 Charitable Trust,
The Russell and Mary *167*
Frazer Charities Trust, The *171*
Glynde Place Charitable Trust
(1974), The *186*
Goldsmiths' Company's
Charities, The *188*
Gough Charitable Trust, The
189
Great Britain Sasakawa
Foundation, The *193*
Greenaway Foundation, The Sir
Derek *194*
Inverforth Charitable Trust, The
236
Isle of Dogs Community
Foundation *238*
Kiln Charitable Trust, Robert
254
Laing Charitable Trust, The
David *260*
Laing Foundation, The Kirby
261
Laing Foundation, The Maurice
261
Lee Foundation, The Edgar
269
Lewis Foundation, The John
Spedan *274*
Lewis Partnership, John *274*
Lloyd Charity, The S and D *278*
Low & Bonar Charitable Fund,
The *284*
Lower Hall Charitable Trust
285
Manifold Charitable Trust, The
295
Marchig Animal Welfare Trust
297
Measures Charity, The James
Frederick and Ethel Anne
303

Mellows Charitable Settlement,
The Anthony and Elizabeth
305
Morphy Memorial Fund, Arthur
319
Norfolk's Family Charitable
Trust, Lavinia *336*
Oldham Foundation *345*
Owen Family Trust, The *348*
PF Charitable Trust *350*
Paget Trust, The *351*
Peppiatt Charitable Trust, The
Brian *359*
Pye Christian Trust, The *371*
Sargeant's Charitable Trust,
Mrs M E *407*
Schuster Charitable Trust, The
410
South Square Trust *430*
Sumner's Trust Section 'A', Sir
John *443*
Whitaker Charitable Trust *489*
Whitley Animal Protection
Trust *491*
Wingfield's Charitable Trust,
Mrs *496*
Woodlands Trust *501*

....

■ Engineering

see also Academic subjects, sciences & research

Funding priority

Gatsby Charitable Foundation,
The *179*
Hoover Foundation, The *226*
Needham Cooper Charitable
Trust, The *331*
Royal Commission for the
Exhibition of 1851 *395*
Worshipful Company of
Engineers' Charitable Trust
Fund, The *504*

Will consider

Beit Trust, The *40*
Cassel Educational Trust
(Mountbatten Memorial
Grants to Commonwealth
Students), The Sir Ernest *84*
Coutts Charitable Trust, The
116
Digby Charitable Trust, Simon
133
Dixon Charitable Trust, F E *134*
Ford of Britain Trust *166*
Holly Hill Charitable Trust *224*
Humanitarian Trust, The *230*
Owen Family Trust, The *348*

■ English as a second or foreign language – TESL & TEFL

see also Education & training

Funding priority

Allnatt Charitable Foundation, Angus *14*
Arts Council of Wales, The *23*
CfBT Education Services *74*
Carlton Television Trust *81*
St Katharine & Shadwell Trust *404*

Will consider

Campden Charities, The *79*
Collier Charitable Trust, The *105*
Curriers Company Charitable Fund *119*
Digby Charitable Trust, Simon *133*
Ford of Britain Trust *166*
Great Britain Sasakawa Foundation, The *193*
Hamlyn Foundation, The Paul *205*
Holly Hill Charitable Trust *224*
Hudson Benevolent Trust, The Thomas *230*
Isle of Dogs Community Foundation *238*
KC Charitable Trust, The *250*
Milton Keynes Community Trust Ltd, The *312*
NR Charitable Trust, The *325*
Rayner Charitable Trust, The John *380*
Rest-Harrow Trust, The *382*
Said Foundation, The Karim Rida *401*
Simon's Charity *422*
Wakefield (Tower Hill, Trinity Square) Trust *476*
Wall Trust, Thomas *478*
Wates Foundation, The *481*

■ English literature

see also Cultural heritage (of national & historical importance)

Funding priority

Cobb Charity *103*
David Trust, The Lesley *124*
Golden Charitable Trust *187*
Northern Arts *339*
St Katharine & Shadwell Trust *404*

Will consider

Astor Foundation, The *26*
Beckwith Charitable Settlement, The Heather *39*

Bulmer Charitable Trust, Becket *68*
County Durham Foundation *115*
D'Avigdor Goldsmid Charitable Trust, The Sarah *125*
Digby Charitable Trust, Simon *133*
Follett Trust, The *166*
Garnett Charitable Trust, The *178*
Granada Foundation, The *190*
Great Britain Sasakawa Foundation, The *193*
Greenaway Foundation, The Sir Derek *194*
Hudson Benevolent Trust, The Thomas *230*
Inverforth Charitable Trust, The *236*
Ireland Funds, The *237*
Laspen Trust *265*
Linford Charitable Trust, The Fred *276*
New Court Charitable Trust *332*
Oldham Foundation *345*
Owen Family Trust, The *348*
Reader's Digest Trust, The *380*
Rookes Charitable Trust, C A *390*
Summerfield Charitable Trust, The *442*
Thomson Foundation, The Sue *454*
Wakefield (Tower Hill, Trinity Square) Trust *476*

■ Entertainment professionals

see Actors & entertainment professionals

■ Environment & animal sciences

see also Agriculture, Animal breeding, Botany, Ecology, Horticulture, Natural history, Organic food production, Ornithology & zoology

Funding priority

Alexander Charitable Trust, Mrs K L *11*
Astor's 1969 Charity, The Hon M L *26*
Barnsbury Charitable Trust *35*
Bateman Charitable Trust, Lady Margaret *37*
Bergqvist Charitable Trust *44*
Burton Charitable Trust, The Geoffrey *71*
Cadbury Charitable Trust, J & L A *75*

Canine Supporters Charity, The *80*
Clark Charitable Trust, J Anthony *98*
David Trust, The Lesley *124*
De Rothschild 1981 Charitable Trust, The Edmund *127*
Dulverton Trust, The *139*
Eaton Charitable Trust, J C J *143*
Elvetham Charitable Trust, The *149*
Evans Memorial Trust, The Alan *155*
Fairbairn Charitable Trust, The Esmee *157*
Foresters' Charity Stewards UK Trust, The *167*
Fry Charitable Trust, Maurice *174*
Hamamelis Trust, The *204*
Hughes Charitable Trust, The Geoffrey C *230*
IBM United Kingdom Trust *233*
IPE Charitable Trust, The *233*
Jones Trust, Cemlyn *248*
Kinnison Charitable Trust, R O *256*
Lewis Foundation, The John Spedan *274*
Lucas Charitable Trust Limited, The Joseph *286*
Marks Charitable Trust, Michael *298*
Material World Charitable Foundation Limited, The *301*
Northern Dairies Educational Trust *339*
Paget Trust, The *351*
Panton Trust, The *352*
St John's Wood Trust, The *403*
Samuel Charitable Trust, M J *406*
Scarfe Charitable Trust, The *409*
Southall Charitable Trust, Kenneth & Phyllis *431*
Toyota (GB) Charitable Trust, The *459*
Valentine Charitable Trust, The *470*
Van Norden's Charitable Foundation, Mrs Maud *471*
Wellcome Trust, The *485*

Will consider

AHJ Charitable Trust, The *3*
Achiezer Association Limited *6*
Airflow Community Ltd, The *9*
Aleh Charitable Foundation, The *10*
Allachy Trust, The *12*
Ancaster Trust, The *16*
Anderson Trust, Andrew *16*
Angler's Inn Trust *17*

Appelbe Trust, Ambrose & Ann 19
Aquarius Charitable Foundation, The 19
Aquinas Trust 20
Askew Charitable Trust, The Ian 25
Assembled Church of Christ Trust, The 25
Astor Foundation, The 26
Astor of Hever Trust, The 26
Astor's Charitable Trust, The Hon M L 26
Barnby's Foundation, Lord 35
Barton Trust, Eleanor 37
Bealey Foundation, The 38
Beattie Charitable Trust, The James 39
Beckwith Charitable Trust, The Peter 40
Beckwith-Smith's Charitable Settlement, Mrs 40
Black Foundation, The Bertie 51
Blagrave Charitable Trust, The Herbert and Peter 52
Blakenham's Charity Trust, Lady 53
Blakey Charitable Trust, The Celia and Conrad 53
Blank Donations Ltd, The David 54
Boltons Trust, The 55
Bonham-Carter Charitable Trust, The Charlotte 55
Borthwick Memorial Trust, The Oliver 56
Bottom Charitable Trust, Harry 56
Bowland Charitable Trust, The 57
British Sugar Foundation 63
Brook Charitable Settlement, R E 64
Brookhouse's Will Trust, Mr John Charles 65
Brotherton Trust, The Charles 65
Bullough Tompson Settlement, The 68
Burn Charity Trust, The J H 70
Burns Charity, The Dorothy 70
Burry Charitable Trust, The 70
Butler's Trust, Lord 71
Butler's Trust, Lucilla 72
Buxton Trust, Denis 72
Cadbury Schweppes Foundation, The 76
Cardiff & Swansea Methodist District Charitable Trust Fund 80
Carron Charitable Trust, The 83
Carter Charitable Trust, The Leslie Mary 83
Castang Charitable Trust, H and M 85
Charity Projects 90

Childtime Trust, The 92
Christian Aid 94
Cinderford Charitable Trust, The 96
Closehelm Ltd 101
Coates Charitable Settlement, The 102
Cohen Charitable Trust, The Vivienne and Samuel 104
Cohen Charity Trust, Lucy 104
Cohen Foundation, The John S 104
Company of Tobacco Pipe Makers and Tobacco Blenders Benevolent Fund 109
Condon Family Trust 109
Conservation Foundation, The 110
Cope Charitable Trust, Alfred 112
Crescent Trust, The 117
Curry Charitable Trust, Dennis 119
Cymerman Trust Limited, Itzchok Meyer 120
Daily Telegraph Charitable Trust 122
Dandeen Charitable Trust 123
Davies Charity, The Gwendoline and Margaret 125
Davy Foundation, The J 126
De Avenley Foundation, The 126
De La Rue Charitable Trust 127
De Yong Charitable Trust, The Emma 128
Denton Charitable Trust, The 130
Desmond Charitable Trust, The Richard 131
Deutsch Charitable Trust, The Andre 131
Deutsch Charitable Trust, The H & M 131
Dicken Charitable Trust, The Albert 133
Dinam Charity 134
Djanogly Foundation, The 135
Doughty Charity Trust, The 136
D'Oyly Carte Charitable Trust, The 137
Drayton Trust, The 138
Dunn Charitable Trust, The Harry 140
Earmark Trust, The 142
Edinburgh Trust, No 2 Account 145
Egerton of Tatton Will Trust, Lord 146
Eling Trust 147
Elshore Limited 149
Family Trust, The 158
Famos Foundation Trust 158

Foreman Foundation, The Carl & Eve 167
Foyle Trust, Charles Henry 169
Franklin Bequest, The Rosalind 169
Franklin Deceased's New Second Charity, Sydney E 170
Garthgwynion Charities 179
Gibson's Charity Trust, The Hon Mr & Mrs Clive 182
Gillett Charitable Trust, J A 183
Gill's Charitable Trust, Mrs M M 184
Girdlers' Company Charitable Trust, The 184
Gold Hill Church Trust 186
Goldberg Charitable Trust, The Lewis 186
Goodman Charitable Foundation, The Everard and Mina 188
Goodman Trust, The 189
Gradel Foundation, The 189
Graves Charitable Trust, J G 192
Green Foundation, Constance 194
Greenaway Foundation, The Sir Derek 194
Gross Charities Limited, M & R 197
Grosshill Charitable Trust 197
Grut Charitable Trust, The 198
HB Charitable Trust 201
Hacking & Sons Ltd Charitable Trust, C G 201
Hamilton Educational Trust, Eleanor 205
Harbour Foundation Ltd, The 208
Hargreaves Trust, The Kenneth 210
Harvey Charitable Trust, Gordon 211
Hawthorne Charitable Trust, The 212
Heinz Company Limited Charitable Trust, The H J 215
Held Settlement, The Gisela 215
Henhurst Charitable Trust, The 216
Hillards Charitable Trust, Gay & Peter Hartley's 220
Hitachi Charitable Trust, The 222
Holford Trust Fund 224
Hoover Foundation, The 226
Hornby Charitable Trust, Miss D 227
Hornton Trust, The 228
Hudson Benevolent Trust, The Thomas 230
Inman Charity, The 235

James Foundation, The Catherine and Lady Grace *241*

KC Charitable Trust, The *250*

Karten Charitable Trust, The Ian *250*

Keyes Trust, The Ursula *253*

Kingsgrove Charitable Trust, The *255*

Kleinwort Charitable Trust, The Ernest *257*

Knott Trust, Sir James *258*

Kobler Trust, The *258*

Kreitman Foundation *258*

Kulika Charitable Trust, The *259*

Kweller Charitable Trust, The Harry *259*

Laing Charitable Trust, The David *260*

Landy Charitable Trust, Harry and Gertrude *263*

Lanvern Foundation *265*

Laski Memorial Charitable Trust, Nathan *265*

Laspen Trust *265*

Lauffer Charitable Foundation, The R & D *266*

Lavender Trust, The *267*

Lawley Foundation, The Edgar E *267*

Leach Fourteenth Trust, The *267*

Leigh-Bramwell Trust 'E', P *270*

Levy Charitable Foundation, Joseph *272*

Lewis Partnership, John *274*

Lingwood Charitable Trust, The *276*

Localtrent Ltd *279*

Lower Hall Charitable Trust *285*

Lunzer Charitable Trust, The Ruth & Jack *287*

Lynwood Charitable Trust, The *288*

Lyons Charitable Trust, The *288*

MacAndrew Trust, The E M *289*

McKechnie Foundation, A N *292*

McKenzie Trust, The Robert *292*

McLaren Foundation *292*

McLaren Memorial Trust, The Martin *293*

Marchig Animal Welfare Trust *297*

Margadale Charitable Trust, Lord *297*

Markus Charitable Foundation, The Erich *298*

Marriage's Charitable Trust, Miss G M *299*

Marr-Munning Trust *299*

Marshall Charitable Trust, The Charlotte *300*

Martin Trust, The Sir George *300*

Mayfair Charities Limited *303*

Medlock Charitable Trust, The *304*

Mellows Charitable Settlement, The Anthony and Elizabeth *305*

Millett Charitable Trust, The Alan and Janet *312*

Millichope Foundation, The *312*

Modiano Charitable Trust *315*

Montefiore Trust, The David *316*

Moore Charitable Trust, The Horace *316*

Morel Charitable Trust, The *318*

Morris Charitable Trust, The Willie & Mabel *320*

Moulton Charitable Trust, The *321*

Music Sales Charitable Trust, The *324*

Newcastle's 1986 Charitable Trust, Duke of *333*

Newman Charitable Trust, Mr and Mrs F E F *334*

Newstead Charity, The *334*

Norfolk's Family Charitable Trust, Lavinia *336*

Norman Trust, The *337*

Northcott Charity Trust, The *338*

Northern Electric Employee Charity Association *339*

Northern Ireland Voluntary Trust *339*

Old Possums Practical Trust, The *344*

Oldham Foundation *345*

Oppenheimer Charitable Trust *346*

Owen Family Trust, The *348*

Owen Trust, Margaret *348*

PDC Trust, The *349*

PJD Charitable Trust *350*

Palmer Trust, The Gerald *352*

Pascoe Charitable Trust, Alan *354*

Paul Charitable Trust, The Late Barbara May *355*

Paul Charitable Trust, Margaret Jeanne *355*

Paul Charitable Trust, Pamela Milton *355*

Paul Foundation, The *355*

Paul's Charitable Trust, R J *355*

Payne Charitable Trust, The *355*

Pelech Charitable Trust, The *358*

Perry Charitable Trust, Miss Frances Lucille *359*

Pershore Nashdom & Elmore Trust Ltd, The *360*

Peskin Charitable Trust, The Hazel and Leslie *360*

Phillips Charitable Foundation, Reginald M *361*

Pitt Trust, Headley *364*

Porter Foundation *366*

Powys Welsh Church Fund *367*

Puebla Charitable Trust Limited, The *371*

QAS Charitable Trust *373*

Quothquan Charitable Trust, The Second *373*

RT Trust, The *374*

Rackham Charitable Trust, The Mr & Mrs Philip *375*

Radley Charitable Trust *375*

Rae Charity, H J *375*

Rainford Trust, The *376*

Rav Chesed Trust, The *379*

Reekie Trust, R A & V B *381*

Reuter Foundation, The *382*

Richards Charity, The Clive *384*

Riley-Smith Charitable Trust, The F A *386*

Rivendell Trust, The *387*

Robbins Trust, The Cheshire *387*

Rodewald's Charitable Settlement, Mr C A *389*

Rogers Charitable Settlement, The Richard *390*

Rolfe Charitable Trust, The *390*

Rosen Foundation, Cecil *392*

Rowan Charitable Trust, The *393*

S Group Charitable Trust *399*

St Jude's Trust *403*

Salters Charities *405*

Save & Prosper Foundation *409*

Scarr-Hall Memorial Trust, The *409*

Seva Trust, Rampaba Sadhu *415*

Sheepdrove Trust, The *417*

Shepherd Conservation Foundation, The David *418*

Sherman Charitable Trust, The Archie *419*

Shifrin Charitable Trust, The Maurice and Hilda *419*

Sidbury Trust, The Second *421*

Silvester Charitable Gift Trust *422*

Skinners' Company Lady Neville Charity *424*

Society of Friends of the Torah, The *429*

Solomons Charitable Trust, David *430*

Somerfield Curtis Will Trust, The Dorothy *430*

Stanley Foundation Limited *435*

Stewart Charitable Trust, Mary Stephanie *437*

Swann-Morton Foundation, The *444*

Symons Charitable Trust, The Stella 446
Taylor Charitable Trust, The B R 450
Terry Charitable Trust, Noel Goddard 451
Tesco Charity Trust 452
Tesler Foundation, The 452
Tyler's Charitable Trust, The Late Miss Eileen Margaret 465
van Geest Foundation, The John and Lucille 470
Vincent Trust Fund, Eric W 473
Vineyard Christian Fellowship of South West 473
Vinson Charity Trust, The 1969 473
Vogel Charitable Trust, The Nathan 474
Wakefield Trust, The 476
Ward Blenkinsop Trust, The 480
Weinstock Fund, The 484
Welby Trust, The Barbara 484
Whetherly's Charitable Trust, The Hon Mrs R G A 489
Whitehead Charitable Trust, J E 490
Whitley Animal Protection Trust 491
Whittington Charitable Trust, The 491
Wiggins Charity Trust, Cyril 491
Wilde Charitable Trust, The Felicity 492
Winstone Foundation, Hyman 497
Woburn 1986 Charitable Trust 498
Wohl Charitable Foundation, The Maurice 498
Wohl Charitable Trust, The Maurice 498
Wolff Charity Trust 498
Wolfson Family Charitable Trust, The 499
Woodhouse Charitable Trust, Edwin 501
Woods Charitable Foundation, Geoffrey 502
Worms Charitable Trust, The Freda and Della 504
Worshipful Company of Needlemakers' Charitable Fund 505
Wychdale Limited 507
Youell Foundation Ltd, The 510
Zaiger Trust, The Elizabeth and Prince 512

Environmental issues

see also Conservation & campaigning

Funding priority

Allachy Trust, The 12
Bancroft Trust, The 33
Bell's Charitable Trust, Lady Mary 42
Coates Charitable Trust 1969, Lance 103
Cobb Charity 103
David Trust, The Lesley 124
Garnett Charitable Trust, The 178
Harbinson Charitable Trust, Roderick 208
Living and Waking Naturally 278
Mitchell Trust 315
Nathan Charitable Trust, Peter 326
Polden-Puckham Charitable Foundation, The 365
Staples Trust 435
Tisbury Telegraph Trust, The 457

Will consider

Allied Domecq Trust 13
Ammco Trust, The 15
Arbib Foundation 20
Astor Foundation, The 26
Aylesfield Foundation, The 28
Barnby's Foundation, Lord 35
Beckwith-Smith's Charitable Settlement, Mrs 40
Beit Trust, The 40
Body Shop Foundation, The 55
Bullough Tompson Settlement, The 68
Carron Charitable Trust, The 83
Community Trust for Greater Manchester, The 108
Countryside Trust, The 115
Cripplegate Foundation 118
D'Avigdor Goldsmid Charitable Trust, The Sarah 125
de Freitas Charitable Trust, The Helen and Geoffrey 126
Digby Charitable Trust, Simon 133
Direct Response 134
Dorus Trust 136
Dumbreck Charity 139
Early's Charitable Settlement, Richard 142
Earwicker Trust 142
Eaton Charitable Trust, J C J 143
Edgar Foundation, The Gilbert and Eileen 145
Education Services 145
Epigoni Trust 152
Fishmongers' Company's Charitable Trust 163

Ford of Britain Trust 166
Four Winds Trust 168
Glynde Place Charitable Trust (1974), The 186
Gough Charitable Trust, The 189
Great Britain Sasakawa Foundation, The 193
Greenaway Foundation, The Sir Derek 194
Grocers' Charity 197
Haddon Charitable Trust, William 202
Hannay Charitable Trust, The Lennox 208
Hayward Foundation, The 213
Hill Memorial Trust, L E 219
Homeless International 225
Inverforth Charitable Trust, The 236
Isle of Dogs Community Foundation 238
Jarrold Trust Ltd, John 243
Kiln Charitable Trust, Robert 254
Laing Foundation, The Christopher 260
Laing Foundation, The Maurice 261
Lane Foundation, The Allen 263
Lee Foundation, The Edgar 269
Lewis Partnership, John 274
Lloyd Charity, The S and D 278
Lloyd's Charities Trust 278
Low & Bonar Charitable Fund, The 284
Lyndhurst Settlement 287
MacKintosh Charitable Trust, Viscount 292
Marchig Animal Welfare Trust 297
Measures Charity, The James Frederick and Ethel Anne 303
Mellows Charitable Settlement, The Anthony and Elizabeth 305
Morphy Memorial Fund, Arthur 319
Needham Cooper Charitable Trust, The 331
Noah Trust, The 335
Norfolk's Family Charitable Trust, Lavinia 336
North West Arts Board 337
Oakdale Trust, The 343
Oldham Foundation 345
Owen Family Trust, The 348
PF Charitable Trust 350
Paget Trust, The 351
Peppiatt Charitable Trust, The Brian 359
Reader's Digest Trust, The 380
S Group Charitable Trust 399
Sainsbury Charitable Fund Ltd, The 402

South Square Trust *430*

Summerfield Charitable Trust, The *442*

Sumner's Trust Section 'A', Sir John *443*

Tear Fund *450*

Westcroft Trust *486*

Whitaker Charitable Trust *489*

Woodroffe Benton Foundation, The *502*

Worshipful Company of Engineers' Charitable Trust Fund, The *504*

Yorkshire Agricultural Society *509*

■ Epilepsy

Funding priority

Dahl Foundation, The Roald *122*

Franklin Trust, Jill *170*

see also Advocacy (social issues)

■ Equal opportunities (advocacy)

Funding priority

Cadbury Schweppes Foundation, The *76*

Cadbury Trust, The Barrow *76*

Community Trust for Greater Manchester, The *108*

Noah Trust, The *335*

Northern Arts *339*

Rank Xerox Trust, The *378*

Staples Trust *435*

Will consider

Abbey National Charitable Trust *4*

Abel Charitable Trust *5*

Body Shop Foundation, The *55*

Camelot Foundation, The *78*

County Durham Foundation *115*

David Trust, The Lesley *124*

Dibs Charitable Trust, The *133*

Digby Charitable Trust, Simon *133*

Follett Trust, The *166*

Hamlyn Foundation, The Paul *205*

Humanitarian Trust, The *230*

Hyde Charitable Trust *232*

Ireland Funds, The *237*

Iris Trust, The *237*

Isle of Dogs Community Foundation *238*

JCSCJ Charitable Trust, The *238*

Lane Foundation, The Allen *263*

Lankelly Foundation, The *264*

Leech Charity, The William *269*

Lyndhurst Settlement *287*

Mental Health Foundation, The *305*

New Court Charitable Trust *332*

North West Arts Board *337*

Owen Family Trust, The *348*

Payne Trust, The Harry *356*

Persula Foundation, The *360*

Rothley Trust, The *392*

Rowntree Charitable Trust, The Joseph *394*

Rowntree Foundation, Joseph *394*

Summerfield Charitable Trust, The *442*

Swan Mountain Trust *444*

Tisbury Telegraph Trust, The *457*

Wates Foundation, The *481*

Wiltshire Community Foundation *495*

Wingfield's Charitable Trust, Mrs *496*

■ Equipment for study

see Costs of study

■ Ethnic minority groups

Funding priority

European Cultural Foundation (UK Committee) *154*

Franklin Trust, Jill *170*

Garnett Charitable Trust, The *178*

HACT (The Housing Association's Charitable Trust) *201*

Mayfair Charities Limited *303*

Milton Keynes Community Trust Ltd, The *312*

Moores Foundation, John *318*

Noah Trust, The *335*

■ Evangelical

see Missionaries

■ Evangelists

Funding priority

Almond Trust, The *14*

Anderson Trust, Andrew *16*

Beacon Trust *38*

Dashe Trust, The *124*

Ebenezer Trust *144*

Emmaus Christian Foundation *150*

Griffiths Trust, The E E and D M *196*

Holford Trust Fund *224*

Kingsgrove Charitable Trust, The *255*

Kingston Religious Trust Fund, The *256*

Latham Trust, The *266*

Payne Charitable Trust, The *355*

Skinner Charitable Trust, Edward *424*

Stow Allen Trust, The *439*

Torchbearer Trust *458*

Waghorn Charitable Trust, The Albert *475*

Whiteley Trust, Norman *490*

Wills Charitable Trust, Dame Violet *494*

■ Ex-offenders & those at risk of offending

Funding priority

Alcohol Education and Research Council *9*

Butler's Trust, Lucilla *72*

Buxton Trust, Denis *72*

Cadbury Trust, The Barrow *76*

Carlton Television Trust *81*

Church Urban Fund *95*

Clifford Charity Oxford, The *100*

Coutts Charitable Trust, The *116*

Debtors' Relief Fund Charity *128*

Ericson Trust *152*

Fleurus Trust, The *165*

Franklin Trust, Jill *170*

HACT (The Housing Association's Charitable Trust) *201*

Hanley Trust (1987), The *207*

Hiley Trust, Joseph and Mary *219*

Hopkinson Educational Trust, Robert Addy *227*

JJ Charitable Trust, The *239*

Lane Foundation, The Allen *263*

Lyndhurst Settlement *287*

Norton Foundation, The *340*

Persula Foundation, The *360*

Swan Mountain Trust *444*

Truemark Trust, The *461*

Van Berchem Charitable Trust, The Alec *470*

Wates Foundation, The *481*

Weavers' Company Benevolent Fund, The *482*

Westcroft Trust *486*

Will consider

AB Charitable Trust *3*

Adnams Charity, The *7*

Alexandra Trust *11*

Ammco Trust, The *15*

Archer Trust, The 20
Ashley Foundation, The Laura 24
Astor Foundation, The 26
Atwell's Charity (Skinner's Company), Lawrence 27
Ballinger Charitable Trust, The 32
Barbour Trust, The 33
Barnabas Charitable Trust 34
Bartholomew Christian Trust 36
Beckwith Charitable Settlement, The Heather 39
Bell Charitable Trust, John 41
Blake Charitable Trust, The Morgan 53
Boots Charitable Trust 56
Camelot Foundation, The 78
Campbell Charitable Foundation, The Ellis 79
Carnegie United Kingdom Trust, The 82
Challice Trust, The 87
Charity Projects 90
Clark 1965 Charitable Trust, Stephen 98
Cole Charitable Trust, The 105
Curriers Company Charitable Fund 119
De Yong Charitable Trust, The Emma 128
Digbeth Trust Ltd, The 133
Dorus Trust 136
Ebb and Flow Charitable Trust 144
Elkes Charity Fund, The Wilfred & Elsie 147
Epigoni Trust 152
Essex Radio Helping Hands Trust, The 154
Fletcher Charitable Trust, The Joyce 164
Four Winds Trust 168
Getty Jr General Charitable Trust, J Paul 181
Gibson Charitable Trust, The Simon 182
Gladstone Charitable Trust, The E W 184
Goldsmiths' Company's Charities, The 188
Grant-Lawson Charitable Trust, Lady Virginia 192
Groves Charitable Trust, The 197
Hampstead Wells and Campden Trust 206
Harbour Foundation Ltd, The 208
Held Settlement, The Gisela 215
Hertfordshire Community Trust, The 217
Inverforth Charitable Trust, The 236
Iris Trust, The 237

Isle of Dogs Community Foundation 238
JCSCJ Charitable Trust, The 238
Jarrold Trust Ltd, John 243
Johnson Group Cleaners Charity 247
Keeling Charitable Trust, The Petronella 251
King's Fund, The 255
Laing Charitable Trust, The David 260
Laing Foundation, The Christopher 260
Laing Foundation, The Kirby 261
Laing Foundation, The Maurice 261
Laing Trust, Beatrice 261
Laspen Trust 265
Leach Fourteenth Trust, The 267
Lewis Foundation, The John Spedan 274
Linford Charitable Trust, The Fred 276
(Lloyds) TSB Foundation for England and Wales 279
Lunn-Rockliffe Charitable Trust, Paul 286
Lyndhurst Settlement 287
Lyons Charitable Trust, The 288
McCarthy Foundation, The John 290
Mackintosh Foundation, The 292
Manning Trust, Leslie & Lilian 296
Marriage's Charitable Trust, Miss G M 299
Matthews Wrightson Charity Trust 301
Mental Health Foundation, The 305
Milburn Charitable Trust, Frederick 310
Milton Keynes Community Trust Ltd, The 312
Minet Trust, The Peter 313
Moores Foundation, John 318
Music for World Development 323
NR Charitable Trust, The 325
Nathan Charitable Trust 326
New Court Charitable Trust 332
New Durlston Trust, The 332
Newby Trust Ltd 332
Norman Family Charitable Trust, The 337
Oakdale Trust, The 343
Oldham Foundation 345
Open Door Women's Trust 346
Owen Family Trust, The 348
Paristamen Foundation, The 352
Parivar Trust, The 353

Payne Trust, The Harry 356
Pye Christian Trust, The 371
Rest-Harrow Trust, The 382
Rope Third Charitable Settlement, The Mrs 391
St Christopher's Trust, The 402
Seagram Distillers Charitable Trust 413
South Square Trust 430
Staples Trust 435
Stevens Foundation, The June 437
Stonehouse Trust Ltd, Eric 438
Summerfield Charitable Trust, The 442
TSB Foundation for Northern Ireland 447
TSB Foundation for Scotland 447
Thackray General Charitable Trust, The P & L 452
Thorpe Charity Trust, The 455
Tisbury Telegraph Trust, The 457
Trust for the Homeless 462
Tudor Trust, The 463
Wagstaff Charitable Trust, Bob 475
Wakefield (Tower Hill, Trinity Square) Trust 476
Wakeham Trust, The 476
Wesleyan Charitable Trust, The 485
Whitecourt Charitable Trust, The 490
Wiltshire Community Foundation 495
Woodlands Trust 501
Woodroffe Benton Foundation, The 502
Yapp Welfare Trust, The 508

....
■ Ex-service & service people

Funding priority

Army Benevolent Fund, The 22
Balney Charitable Trust, The 32
Barnby's Foundation, Lord 35
Blott Charitable Settlement, Robert Orpwood 55
Bridgeman TRA Foundation, The Dick 60
Clutterbuck Charitable Trust, Robert 102
Corbett's Charity, Thomas 112
Edinburgh Trust, No 2 Account 145
Fraser Trust, The 170
Gray Trust, The 192
Hill Trust, The Charles Littlewood 220
McKechnie Foundation, A N 292
McLaren Foundation 292
MacRobert Trusts, The 294

Morrison Bequest Fund,
Thomas Wharrie *320*
Nash Charity, The *326*
Newcastle's 1986 Charitable
Trust, Duke of *333*
PJD Charitable Trust *350*
Sailors' and Soldiers' Home
Fund, and Leonard Lionel
Bloomfield's Charity, The
401
Summer's and I May's
Charitable Settlement, The
Late Misses (A N) *442*

■ Family planning clinic

see also **Health care**
Funding priority
GW Trust, The *176*

Will consider
Astor Foundation, The *26*
Barbour Trust, The *33*
Bottom Charitable Trust, Harry
56
CHK Charities Limited *74*
Camelot Foundation, The *78*
Catto Charitable Settlement,
The Thomas Sivewright *86*
Community Trust for Greater
Manchester, The *108*
Coutts Charitable Trust, The
116
Cripplegate Foundation *118*
Dean Refugee Trust Fund, The
Miriam *128*
Digby Charitable Trust, Simon
133
Edgar Foundation, The Gilbert
and Eileen *145*
Ferguson Benevolent Fund
Limited *161*
Foreman Foundation, The Carl
& Eve *167*
Hawley Residuary Fund, Harry
Fieldsend *212*
Isle of Dogs Community
Foundation *238*
Leech Charity, The William *269*
Milton Keynes Community
Trust Ltd, The *312*
Payne Trust, The Harry *356*
Rest-Harrow Trust, The *382*
Staples Trust *435*
Tear Fund *450*
Thompson Charitable Trust,
The *453*
Tisbury Telegraph Trust, The
457
Van Leer Foundation UK Trust,
Bernard *470*
Westcroft Trust *486*

■ Famine

see **Victims of manmade or natural disasters**

■ Fauna

see also **Conservation**
Funding priority
BP Conservation Programme
29
Barnby's Foundation, Lord *35*
Butler Charitable Trust, The A S
71
Clark Charitable Trust, J
Anthony *98*
Cobb Charity *103*
Countryside Trust, The *115*
Dulverton Trust, The *139*
GW Trust, The *176*
Garnett Charitable Trust, The
178
Haddon Charitable Trust,
William *202*
Harbinson Charitable Trust,
Roderick *208*
Kilverstone Wildlife Charitable
Trust, The *254*
Lewis Foundation, The John
Spedan *274*
Nathan Charitable Trust, Peter
326
Pike Woodlands Trust, Claude
& Margaret *362*
Shepherd Conservation
Foundation, The David *418*
Tisbury Telegraph Trust, The
457

Will consider
Ammco Trust, The *15*
Amory Charitable Trust,
Viscount *16*
Askew Charitable Trust, The
Ian *25*
Astor Foundation, The *26*
Bourne-May Charitable Trust,
The *57*
Brook Charitable Settlement,
R E *64*
Bulmer Charitable Trust, Becket
68
Burton 1960 Charitable
Settlement, Audrey &
Stanley *70*
Cadbury Trust (1928), The
Edward & Dorothy *76*
Clark 1965 Charitable Trust,
Stephen *98*
Cole Charitable Trust, The *105*
Colyer-Fergusson Charitable
Trust, The *107*
David Trust, The Lesley *124*
D'Avigdor Goldsmid Charitable
Trust, The Sarah *125*
de Freitas Charitable Trust, The
Helen and Geoffrey *126*

Digby Charitable Trust, Simon
133
Direct Response *134*
Early's Charitable Settlement,
Richard *142*
Earwicker Trust *142*
Elkes Charity Fund, The Wilfred
& Elsie *147*
Four Winds Trust *168*
Great Britain Sasakawa
Foundation, The *193*
Greenaway Foundation, The Sir
Derek *194*
Grocers' Charity *197*
Halkes Settlement, John Robert
204
Hawthorne Charitable Trust,
The *212*
Holly Hill Charitable Trust *224*
Inverforth Charitable Trust, The
236
Isle of Dogs Community
Foundation *238*
Laing Foundation, The Kirby
261
Laing Foundation, The Maurice
261
Leach Fourteenth Trust, The
267
Lee Foundation, The Edgar
269
Living and Waking Naturally
278
Lower Hall Charitable Trust
285
Marchig Animal Welfare Trust
297
Mellows Charitable Settlement,
The Anthony and Elizabeth
305
Mitchell Trust *315*
New Court Charitable Trust
332
Oakdale Trust, The *343*
Paget Trust, The *351*
Peppiatt Charitable Trust, The
Brian *359*
Persula Foundation, The *360*
Powys Welsh Church Fund *367*
Richard Charitable Trust, The
Cliff *383*
Rowbotham Charitable Trust,
The Christopher *393*
Royal Botanical & Horticultural
Society of Manchester and
the Northern Counties, The
395
Schuster Charitable Trust, The
410
Summerfield Charitable Trust,
The *442*
Sykes Trust, The Charles *445*
Symons Charitable Trust, The
Stella *446*
Terry Charitable Trust, Noel
Goddard *451*

Tyler's Charitable Trust, The
    Late Miss Eileen Margaret
    465
Unitek Foundation 469
Vincent Trust Fund, Eric W 473
Wade & Others, The Charity of
    Thomas 475
Whitaker Charitable Trust 489
Wylde Memorial Charity, The
    Anthony and Gwendoline
    507
Yorkshire Agricultural Society
    509
Young Explorers' Trust 511

■ Fees

see Bursaries & fees

■ Fellowships

see also Costs of study

Funding priority

Beit Trust, The 40
Ciba Fellowship Trust, The 95
Jeffreys Road Fund, Rees 243
Oldacre Foundation, The John
    345
Peacock Charitable Foundation,
    The Michael 356
Royal Commission for the
    Exhibition of 1851 395
South Square Trust 430
Thriplow Charitable Trust 456

Will consider

Allied Domecq Trust 13
Arkleton Trust, The 21
Ashley Foundation, The Laura
    24
Berthoud Charitable Trust,
    Patrick 45
Bulmer Charitable Trust, Becket
    68
Carlton Television Trust 81
Cooper Charitable Trust 111
Digby Charitable Trust, Simon
    133
Dixon Charitable Trust, F E 134
Earley Charity, The 142
Education Services 145
GABO Trust for Sculpture
    Conservation 175
Holly Hill Charitable Trust 224
Hudson Benevolent Trust, The
    Thomas 230
Humanitarian Trust, The 230
Ireland Funds, The 237
Leukaemia Research Fund 271
Linford Charitable Trust, The
    Fred 276
Melville Trust for Care and
    Cure of Cancer 305
Mental Health Foundation, The
    305
Owen Family Trust, The 348

Pilkington Charitable Trust,
    Cecil 363
Porcupine Trust, The 366
Radcliffe's Trust, Dr 375
Rayner Charitable Trust, The
    John 380
Rhodes Trust – Public Purposes
    Fund, The 383
Woodroffe Benton Foundation,
    The 502
Yorkshire Agricultural Society
    509

■ Festivals

see Arts activities

■ Film, video, multimedia, broadcasting

see also Arts & arts facilities

Funding priority

Arts Council of England, The
    23
Arts Council of Wales, The 23
North West Arts Board 337
Southern Arts 432
Yorkshire and Humberside Arts
    510

■ Financial services

see also Infrastructure & technical support

Funding priority

County Durham Foundation
    115
Lyndhurst Trust, The 287

Will consider

Berkshire Community Trust 45
Daily Telegraph Charitable
    Trust 122
Digby Charitable Trust, Simon
    133
Direct Response 134
HACT (The Housing
    Association's Charitable
    Trust) 201
IBM United Kingdom Trust
    233
Ireland Funds, The 237
Isle of Dogs Community
    Foundation 238
Moores Foundation, John 318
Paristamen Foundation, The
    352
Tear Fund 450
Wincott Foundation, The 496

■ Fine art

see also Arts & arts facilities

Funding priority

Arts Council of Wales, The 23
David Trust, The Lesley 124
Lynn Foundation, The 288
Mitchell Trust, Esme 315
North West Arts Board 337
Northern Arts 339
South Square Trust 430
Yorkshire and Humberside Arts
    510

Will consider

Ashley Foundation, The Laura
    24
Astor Foundation, The 26
Beckwith Charitable
    Settlement, The Heather 39
Broadley Charitable Trust, The
    64
Brooke Benevolent Fund,
    William 65
Bulmer Charitable Trust, Becket
    68
Cadbury Trust (1928), The
    Edward & Dorothy 76
Campbell Charitable
    Foundation, The Ellis 79
Campden Charities, The 79
Carnegie Dunfermline Trust 82
Carnegie United Kingdom
    Trust, The 82
Coates Charitable Trust, The
    John 103
D'Avigdor Goldsmid Charitable
    Trust, The Sarah 125
Digby Charitable Trust, Simon
    133
Edgar Foundation, The Gilbert
    and Eileen 145
Fogel Charitable Trust, The
    Gerald 165
Garnett Charitable Trust, The
    178
Granada Foundation, The 190
Great Britain Sasakawa
    Foundation, The 193
Greenaway Foundation, The Sir
    Derek 194
Gwent County Council Welsh
    Church Fund 200
Halkes Settlement, John Robert
    204
Hamlyn Foundation, The Paul
    205
Harbinson Charitable Trust,
    Roderick 208
Harding Trust, The 209
Holly Hill Charitable Trust 224
Hudson Benevolent Trust, The
    Thomas 230
Hughes Charitable Trust, The
    Geoffery C 230
Hunter Charitable Trust, The
    Claire 231
Ireland Funds, The 237

Laing Charitable Trust, The
David *260*

Lawson Charitable Trust,
Raymond and Blanche *267*

Lee Foundation, The Edgar
269

Linford Charitable Trust, The
Fred *276*

Lowenthal Charitable Trust,
The L and C *285*

Lower Hall Charitable Trust
285

Manifold Charitable Trust, The
295

Milton Keynes Community
Trust Ltd, The *312*

Music Sales Charitable Trust,
The *324*

New Court Charitable Trust
332

Noswad Charity, The *341*

Notgrove Trust, The *341*

Oldham Foundation *345*

Owen Family Trust, The *348*

PF Charitable Trust *350*

Provincial Trust for Kendal, The
370

Royal Commission for the
Exhibition of 1851 *395*

St Katharine & Shadwell Trust
404

Save & Prosper Educational
Trust *408*

Schuster Charitable Trust, The
410

Somerfield Curtis Will Trust,
The Dorothy *430*

Spooner Charitable Trust, W W
434

Strauss Charitable Trust *440*

Summerfield Charitable Trust,
The *442*

Taylor Charitable Trust, The B R
450

Turner Trust, The Douglas *464*

Wates Foundation, The *481*

Whitaker Charitable Trust *489*

Williams Charitable Trust,
Alfred *493*

....

■ First aid

see also **Health care**

Funding priority

Kroch Foundation, The Heinz &
Anna *259*

Lloyd's Charities Trust *278*

Loseley & Guildway Charitable
Trust, The *281*

Moore Foundation, The
George A *316*

Needham Cooper Charitable
Trust, The *331*

SMB Trust, The *400*

Will consider

Army Benevolent Fund, The *22*

Astor Foundation, The *26*

Barbour Trust, The *33*

Barratt Charitable Trust, The
Elaine *36*

Berkshire Community Trust *45*

BibleLands *47*

Birmingham Amenities and
Welfare Trust, The *49*

Birtwistle Memorial Trust, The
G E *50*

Bottom Charitable Trust, Harry
56

Brotherton Trust, The Charles
65

Buckinghamshire Masonic
Centenary Fund *67*

Butlin Charity Trust, Bill *72*

Cadbury Trust (1928), The
Edward & Dorothy *76*

Campden Charities, The *79*

Community Trust for Greater
Manchester, The *108*

County Durham Foundation
115

Coxen Trust Fund, Sir William
116

Dean Refugee Trust Fund, The
Miriam *128*

Denne Charitable Trust *130*

Digby Charitable Trust, Simon
133

Direct Response *134*

Dorus Trust *136*

Edgar Foundation, The Gilbert
and Eileen *145*

Edgar Trust, The Gilbert *145*

Elkes Charity Fund, The Wilfred
& Elsie *147*

Epigoni Trust *152*

Fishmongers' Company's
Charitable Trust *163*

Follett Trust, The *166*

Foreman Foundation, The Carl
& Eve *167*

Garnett's 1973 Charitable
Trust, Mrs A M *178*

Gibbins Trust, The *181*

Gladstone Charitable Trust, The
E W *184*

Grant-Lawson Charitable Trust,
Lady Virginia *192*

Greenaway Foundation, The Sir
Derek *194*

Grocers' Charity *197*

Hannay Memorial Charity,
Kathleen *208*

Hawley Residuary Fund, Harry
Fieldsend *212*

Henderson's Settlement, J R
216

Humanitarian Trust, The *230*

Innes Memorial Fund *235*

Isle of Dogs Community
Foundation *238*

Jarman Charitable Trust, The
243

Laing Charitable Trust, The
David *260*

Laing's Charitable Trust *262*

Lee Foundation, The Edgar
269

Leech Charity, The William *269*

Lloyd Charity, The S and D *278*

(Lloyds) TSB Foundation for
England and Wales *279*

London Law Trust *280*

Lowe Trust, Mrs D G *285*

Luke Trust, The *286*

Lynall Foundation, The D G
287

MacKintosh Charitable Trust,
Viscount *292*

Measures Charity, The James
Frederick and Ethel Anne
303

Middlesex County Rugby
Football Union Memorial
Fund *309*

Milburn Charitable Trust,
Frederick *310*

Milward Charity, The Edgar
313

Morris Charitable Trust, The
Douglas *320*

New Court Charitable Trust
332

Owen Family Trust, The *348*

Payne Trust, The Harry *356*

Penny in the Pound Fund
Charitable Trust *359*

Persula Foundation, The *360*

Pyke Charity Trust *372*

Ravenscroft Foundation, The
379

Rest-Harrow Trust, The *382*

Rowbotham Charitable Trust,
The Christopher *393*

Schuster Charitable Trust, The
410

Seagram Distillers Charitable
Trust *413*

Shelroy Charitable Trust, The
417

Staples Trust *435*

TSB Foundation for Northern
Ireland *447*

Tear Fund *450*

Thompson Charitable Trust,
The *453*

Tisbury Telegraph Trust, The
457

Torquay Charities, The *458*

Travis Charitable Trust,
Constance *460*

Van Leer Foundation UK Trust,
Bernard *470*

Wakefield (Tower Hill, Trinity
Square) Trust *476*

Whitaker Charitable Trust *489*

Worshipful Company of
Engineers' Charitable Trust
Fund, The *504*

Wyford Charitable Trust, The
507

Fishermen

see **Seafarers & fishermen**

Flora

see also **Conservation**

Funding priority

BP Conservation Programme 29

Barnby's Foundation, Lord 35

Butler Charitable Trust, The A S 71

Clark Charitable Trust, J Anthony 98

Cobb Charity 103

Countryside Trust, The 115

Dulverton Trust, The 139

Harbinson Charitable Trust, Roderick 208

Kilverstone Wildlife Charitable Trust, The 254

Lewis Foundation, The John Spedan 274

Lower Hall Charitable Trust 285

Nathan Charitable Trust, Peter 326

Pike Woodlands Trust, Claude & Margaret 362

Shepherd Conservation Foundation, The David 418

Will consider

Ammco Trust, The 15

Amory Charitable Trust, Viscount 16

Askew Charitable Trust, The Ian 25

Astor Foundation, The 26

Bourne-May Charitable Trust, The 57

Brook Charitable Settlement, R E 64

Bulmer Charitable Trust, Becket 68

Burton 1960 Charitable Settlement, Audrey & Stanley 70

Cadbury Trust (1928), The Edward & Dorothy 76

Clark 1965 Charitable Trust, Stephen 98

Cole Charitable Trust, The 105

Colyer-Fergusson Charitable Trust, The 107

Cripplegate Foundation 118

David Trust, The Lesley 124

D'Avigdor Goldsmid Charitable Trust, The Sarah 125

de Freitas Charitable Trust, The Helen and Geoffrey 126

Digby Charitable Trust, Simon 133

Direct Response 134

Dixon Charitable Trust, F E 134

Early's Charitable Settlement, Richard 142

Earwicker Trust 142

Elkes Charity Fund, The Wilfred & Elsie 147

Four Winds Trust 168

Garnett's 1973 Charitable Trust, Mrs A M 178

Great Britain Sasakawa Foundation, The 193

Greenaway Foundation, The Sir Derek 194

Grocers' Charity 197

Haddon Charitable Trust, William 202

Halkes Settlement, John Robert 204

Hawthorne Charitable Trust, The 212

Holly Hill Charitable Trust 224

Inverforth Charitable Trust, The 236

Isle of Dogs Community Foundation 238

JJ Charitable Trust, The 239

Laing Foundation, The Kirby 261

Laing Foundation, The Maurice 261

Leach Fourteenth Trust, The 267

Lee Foundation, The Edgar 269

Living and Waking Naturally 278

Mellows Charitable Settlement, The Anthony and Elizabeth 305

Mitchell Trust 315

New Court Charitable Trust 332

Oakdale Trust, The 343

Paget Trust, The 351

Peppiatt Charitable Trust, The Brian 359

Persula Foundation, The 360

Powys Welsh Church Fund 367

Rowbotham Charitable Trust, The Christopher 393

Royal Botanical & Horticultural Society of Manchester and the Northern Counties, The 395

Schuster Charitable Trust, The 410

Staples Trust 435

Stevens Foundation, The June 437

Summerfield Charitable Trust, The 442

Sykes Trust, The Charles 445

Symons Charitable Trust, The Stella 446

Tear Fund 450

Terry Charitable Trust, Noel Goddard 451

Tisbury Telegraph Trust, The 457

Tyler's Charitable Trust, The Late Miss Eileen Margaret 465

Unitek Foundation 469

Vincent Trust Fund, Eric W 473

Wade & Others, The Charity of Thomas 475

Whitaker Charitable Trust 489

Wylde Memorial Charity, The Anthony and Gwendoline 507

Yorkshire Agricultural Society 509

Young Explorers' Trust 511

Fostering

see **Adoption & fostering services** & see **Incare, fostered & adopted**

Friedrichs Ataxia

Funding priority

Shepherd Charitable Trust, The Sylvia and Colin 418

Gay & lesbian rights (campaigning)

see also **Campaigning (social issues)**

Funding priority

Iris Trust, The 237

Will consider

Abel Charitable Trust 5

Allachy Trust, The 12

Body Shop Foundation, The 55

Coutts Charitable Trust, The 116

Dibs Charitable Trust, The 133

Digby Charitable Trust, Simon 133

Follett Trust, The 166

Garthgwynion Charities 179

Hamlyn Foundation, The Paul 205

Isle of Dogs Community Foundation 238

Lane Foundation, The Allen 263

Leech Charity, The William 269

Lyndhurst Settlement 287

Morel Charitable Trust, The 318

National Power Charitable Trust, The 330

Noah Trust, The 335

North West Arts Board 337

Northern Ireland Voluntary Trust 339

Puebla Charitable Trust Limited, The 371

Summerfield Charitable Trust,
The 442
Tyne & Wear Foundation 466
Wakefield (Tower Hill, Trinity
Square) Trust 476
Wiltshire Community
Foundation 495
Woodhouse Charitable Trust,
Edwin 501

■ Gays & lesbians
Funding priority
Clark 1965 Charitable Trust,
Stephen 98
Clifford Charity Oxford, The
100
HACT (The Housing
Association's Charitable
Trust) 201
Iris Trust, The 237
Lane Foundation, The Allen
263

Will consider
Abel Charitable Trust 5
Barbour Trust, The 33
Boots Charitable Trust 56
Buxton Trust, Denis 72
Camelot Foundation, The 78
Carlton Television Trust 81
Carnegie United Kingdom
Trust, The 82
Charity Projects 90
Church Urban Fund 95
Cole Charitable Trust, The 105
De Yong Charitable Trust, The
Emma 128
Digbeth Trust Ltd, The 133
Ebb and Flow Charitable Trust
144
Elkes Charity Fund, The Wilfred
& Elsie 147
Ericson Trust 152
Four Winds Trust 168
Franklin Trust, Jill 170
Hanley Trust (1987), The 207
Harbour Foundation Ltd, The
208
Held Settlement, The Gisela
215
Hertfordshire Community
Trust, The 217
Hopkinson Educational Trust,
Robert Addy 227
Isle of Dogs Community
Foundation 238
King's Fund, The 255
Laing Charitable Trust, The
David 260
(Lloyds) TSB Foundation for
England and Wales 279
Lyndhurst Settlement 287
Lyons Charitable Trust, The
288
McCarthy Foundation, The
John 290

Mackintosh Foundation, The
292
Mental Health Foundation, The
305
Milton Keynes Community
Trust Ltd, The 312
Moores Foundation, John 318
Music for World Development
323
Newby Trust Ltd 332
Noah Trust, The 335
Norton Foundation, The 340
Paristamen Foundation, The
352
Parivar Trust, The 353
Persula Foundation, The 360
Summerfield Charitable Trust,
The 442
TSB Foundation for Scotland
447
Van Berchem Charitable Trust,
The Alec 470
Wakefield (Tower Hill, Trinity
Square) Trust 476
Wates Foundation, The 481
Wesleyan Charitable Trust, The
485
Westcroft Trust 486
Wiltshire Community
Foundation 495

■ General charitable
purposes
Funding priority
AB Charitable Trust 3
AFC Charitable Trust 3
AGF Charitable Trust 3
AHJ Charitable Trust, The 3
AM Charitable Trust 4
AMEC Charitable Trust 4
ATP Charitable Trust, The 4
AW Charitable Trust 4
Abraham Charitable Trust,
Keith & Freda 5
Achiezer Association Limited 6
Acorn Foundation, The 6
Adams Charitable Trust, Kate
6
Adamson Charitable Trust, The
John and Florence 7
Adint Charitable Trust, The 7
Adler Foundation, The 7
Adnams Charity, The 7
Agricola Trust, The 8
Ainsworth and Family
Benevolent Fund, Green
and Lilian F M 8
Airflow Community Ltd, The 9
Albright Charitable Trust, D G
9
Alchemy Foundation, The 9
Alecto Trust, The 10
Aleh Charitable Foundation,
The 10
Alexandra Rose Day 11

Al-Fayed Charitable
Foundation, The 11
Allen Charitable Trust, D C R
12
Allen Charitable Trust, The H B
12
Allen Charitable Trust, The Rita
12
Allen Memorial Fund, Dorothy
Gertrude 13
Amelan Charitable Trust, The
Harold 15
Amis Charitable Trust, Richard
15
Amory's Charitable Trust, Sir
John and Lady 16
Andersen Consulting
Foundation, The 16
Anderson Trust, Andrew 16
Angler's Inn Trust 17
Anglo Hong Kong Trust, The
17
Anglo-Arab Aid Ltd 17
Anne's Charities, The Princess
18
Anstruther Memorial Trust, The
Fagus 19
Appelbe Trust, Ambrose & Ann
19
Aquarius Charitable
Foundation, The 19
Aquinas Trust 20
Arbib Trust, The Annie 20
Ardwick Trust, The 20
Arihant Charitable Trust 21
Armitage Charitable Trust, G C
21
Armstrong Trust, The 21
Arno Bequest, Thomas 22
Ashcroft Charitable Trust, The
23
Ashdown Charitable
Settlement, The Lord 24
Ashley Foundation, The Laura
24
Askew Charitable Trust, The
Ian 25
Assembled Church of Christ
Trust, The 25
Astor of Hever Trust, The 26
Astor's 1969 Charity, The Hon
M L 26
Astra Foundation, The 26
Aveling Bounty, Charles and
Edith 27
Avenue Charitable Trust, The
27
AXA Equity & Law Charitable
Trust 28
BBC Children in Need Appeal,
The 29
BCH 1971 Charitable Trust 29
BUPA Foundation, The 29
Bacta Charitable Trust, The 30
Bagri Foundation 30
Bain Memorial Trust Fund, Dr
James and Dr Bozena 30

Balint Charitable Trust, Andrew 31

Balint Charitable Trust, The George 31

Ballinger Charitable Trust, The 32

Baltic Charitable Fund, The 32

Bamford Charitable Trust, The 32

Bancroft (No 2) Charitable Trust and Jenepher Gillett Trust, William P 32

Banks Educational Trust, The 33

Barbour Trust, The 33

Barclay Charitable Fund, The 33

Barclay Jewish Trust 34

Barker Foundation, David 34

Barnby's Foundation, Lord 35

Barnsbury Charitable Trust 35

Bartlett Charitable Trust, Doris and Rendell 36

Bartlett Taylor Charitable Trust 36

Bassham Charitable Trust, The Paul 37

Batchworth Trust, The 37

Bateman Charitable Trust, Lady Margaret 37

Bates Charitable Trust, The 37

Baylis (Maidenhead Advertiser) Charitable Trust, Louis 37

Beale Charitable Trust, David 38

Bealey Foundation, The 38

Bear Charitable Trust Fund, The 38

Beattie Charitable Trust, The James 39

Beaufort Charitable Trust 39

Beckwith Charitable Trust, The John 40

Beckwith Charitable Trust, The Peter 40

Beckwith-Smith's Charitable Settlement, Mrs 40

Beecham 1981 Charitable Trust, R J 40

Beecham Charitable Settlement, The Patricia 40

Bell Charitable Trust, John 41

Bell Charity, The Sylvia 41

Bellinger Donnay Trust, The 42

Belsize Charitable Trust No1 43

Benesco Charity Limited 43

Benham Charitable Settlement 43

Bergqvist Charitable Trust 44

Bernheim Charitable Trust, Andre 45

Bibby 1981 Trust, The Mason 47

Bier Charitable Settlement 47

Biggs Charitable Trust, The Ken 47

Biggs Charity, The Elizabeth Emily 48

Billmeir Charitable Trust, The 48

Bingham Trust, The 49

Bircham and Company Charitable Trust, The 49

Birchwood Trust, The 49

Birmingham Common Good Trust 49

Birmingham's Charity, Lord Mayor of 50

Bishopsdown Trust, The 51

Black Charitable Trust, Peter 51

Black Foundation, The Bertie 51

Blackford Charitable Trust, The 52

Blagrave Charitable Trust, The Herbert and Peter 52

Blake Charitable Trust, The Morgan 53

Blakemore Foundation, The 53

Blakey Charitable Trust, The Celia and Conrad 53

Blank Donations Ltd, The David 54

Blankstone Charitable Trust, The Solomon & Isobel 54

Blond Charitable Trust, Neville & Elaine 54

Bloom Charitable Trust, The Patsy 54

Blott Charitable Settlement, Robert Orpwood 55

Bluston Charitable Settlement, The 55

Boltons Trust, The 55

Bonar Charitable Trust, Andrew 55

Bonhomie United Charity Society 56

Bornstein Charitable Trust, M & S 56

Borthwick Memorial Trust, The Oliver 56

Botteley Charitable Settlement, H E & E L 56

Bottom Charitable Trust, Harry 56

Bourne Charitable Trust, The M 57

Bourne Foundation, The Anthony 57

Bowland Charitable Trust, The 57

Bowring (Charities Fund) Ltd, C T 57

Boyd Charitable Trust, The Viscountess 57

Bradford's 1981 Charitable Trust, The Seventh Earl of 58

Bradman Charitable Foundation Limited 58

Bramall Charitable Trust, The Tony 58

Bramble Charitable Trust 58

Brandt Charitable Trust, Tim 59

Branford Charitable Trust, The Jan 59

Brecher & Co Charitable Trust, The 59

Brickkiln Trust, The 59

Bridge Will Trust, The Elsie Talbot 60

Bridges Foundation, The Harold 60

Briess Family Charitable Trust 60

Brinton Foundation, Lady Mary 61

British Diabetic Association, The 61

British Humane Association 62

British Sugar Foundation 63

Brixton Estate Charitable Trust, The 63

Broackes 1993 Charitable Trust, Sir Nigel 63

Broadfield Trust 64

Brocton Trust, The 64

Brook Charitable Settlement, R E 64

Brook Charitable Trust 64

Brookhouse's Will Trust, Mr John Charles 65

Brough Charitable Trust, Joseph 65

Brown Charitable Settlement, Mrs E E 65

Brownless Charitable Trust, R S 66

Brown's Charitable Settlement, Bill 66

Brunner Third Charitable Trust, Sir Felix 66

Brunner's Charitable Trust, T B H 66

Brunner's Sons' Charitable Trust, Sir Felix 66

Brunton Charitable Trust, The Jack 66

Buccleuch Place Trust 67

Buckle Family Charitable Trust, The 67

Bulldog Trust, The 68

Bulmer Charitable Trust, The Howard 68

Bunney Reckitt Trust 68

Bunzl Charitable Foundation, G G 69

Burden's Charitable Foundation 69

Burgess Trust, The Michael 69

Burn Charity Trust, The J H 70

Burns Charity, The Dorothy 70

Burry Charitable Trust, The 70

Burton Breweries Charitable Trust, The 70

Burton Charitable Trust, The Geoffrey 71

Burton Charitable Trust, The Harriet 71

Burton Charitable Trust, R M
71
Busby Charities Fund, Sir Matt
71
Butler's Trust, Lord 71
Butler's Trust, Lucilla 72
CAF (Charities Aid Foundation)
73
CAFOD (Catholic Fund for
Overseas Development) 73
CHK Charities Limited 74
CMB Charities Limited 74
Cadbury Charitable Trust,
Richard 75
Cadbury Charitable Trust,
William Adlington 75
Cadbury Charity, C James 76
Cadbury Schweppes
Foundation, The 76
Cadbury Trust (1928), The
Edward & Dorothy 76
Cadbury Trust, A Account, The
George 77
Cadbury Trust, B Account, The
George 77
Cadell-Samworth Foundation,
The 77
Cadman Charitable Trust, The
Beatrice A V 77
Cadogan Charity, The 77
Cairns Charitable Trust, The 78
Caledonian Charitable
Foundation 78
Callingham Foundation, Roland
78
Canning Trust, The 80
Caplin Foundation, The Fay
and Robert 80
Cardiff & Swansea Methodist
District Charitable Trust
Fund 80
Carmarthenshire Welsh Church
Fund 81
Carpenter Charitable Trust 82
Carr-Ellison Charitable Trust,
The 83
Carrington Charitable Trust,
The 83
Carroll-Marx Charitable
Foundation, The 83
Carron Charitable Trust, The
83
Castang Charitable Trust, H
and M 85
Cattle Trust, The Joseph and
Annie 86
Cave Foundation, The Wilfred
and Constance 86
Challice Trust, The 87
Chamberlain Charity, June 87
Champion Foundation, The
Pamela 87
Chance Trust, Sir Hugh 87
Chandaria Foundation, The 88
Chandris Foundation, The 88
Chapman Charitable Trust 88
Chapman Charitable Trust,
John William 88

Charipot Trust 88
Charitable Fund Administered
by The Russia Company 89
Charities in Need 89
Charity Fund of the Worshipful
Company of Paviors 89
Charity Projects 90
Charterhouse Charitable Trust,
The 90
Chetwode Foundation, The 91
Chevras Ezras Nitzrochim Trust,
The 91
Chiron Trust, The 93
Christabella Charitable Trust
93
Christian Trust, The Andre 94
Churchill Christian Fellowship
Trust 95
Cinderford Charitable Trust,
The 96
City of London School
Charitable Trust, The 96
City of Westminster Charitable
Trust 96
Clapman Charitable Trust 97
Clark Charitable Trust, J
Anthony 98
Clark Charitable Trust, Hilda &
Alice 98
Clark Charitable Trust, Roger
and Sarah Bancroft 98
Clemence Charitable
Settlement, The John &
Heather 99
Cleveland Community
Foundation 100
Clifton Charitable Trust 100
Clore Foundation, The 101
Closehelm Ltd 101
Clothier Charitable Trust, The
P T & V O 101
Clothworkers' Foundation, The
101
Clover Trust 102
Clutterbuck Charitable Trust,
Robert 102
Clydpride Ltd 102
Coates Charitable Settlement,
The 102
Coates Charitable Trust 1969,
Lance 103
Cohen Charitable Foundation,
The Lucy and Henry 103
Cohen Charitable Trust, The
104
Cohen Charitable Trust, The
Andrew 104
Cohen Charitable Trust, Joseph
104
Cohen Charitable Trust, The
Vivienne and Samuel 104
Cohen Charity Trust, Lucy 104
Cohen Foundation, The Alfred
S 104
Cohen's Charitable Settlement,
The Hon L H L 105
Colline Trust Fund, Lucy Ann
105

Collins Charity, The George
Henry 106
Collinson Charitable
Settlement, R F 106
Collis Charity, Robert Hickson
106
Colman Charitable Fund Ltd,
The E Alec 106
Colman Charitable Trust, O J
106
Colman Charitable Trust, The
Timothy 107
Commonweal Fund of the
Trades House of Glasgow,
The 108
Company of Chartered
Surveyors Charitable Trust
Fund 1992, The 109
Company of Tobacco Pipe
Makers and Tobacco
Blenders Benevolent Fund
109
Condon Family Trust 109
Conrad Charitable Trust,
Neville and Carole 109
Continuation Charitable Trust,
The 110
Cooks Charity, The 111
Cooper Charitable Trust, The
111
Cooper Dean Charitable
Foundation, Alice Ellen 111
Cooper Gay Charitable Trust
111
Coote Charitable Trust,
Nicholas 111
Coote Old People's Charity
Fund, The Marjorie 112
Cope Charitable Trust, Alfred
112
Corage Charitable Trust, The
112
Corah Foundation Fund, J
Reginald 112
Coren Charitable Foundation,
The Muriel and Gershon
113
Corfield Charitable Settlement,
The Holbeche 113
Cork Charitable Trust, Sir
Kenneth 113
Corman Charitable Trust, Molly
113
Corman Charitable Trust, Ruth
and Charles 113
Cornforth 1983 Charity Trust,
Edwin 114
Cornwall Benevolent Fund, The
Duke of 114
Cornwell Charitable Trust, The
114
Coulthurst Trust, The 115
Courtauld Charitable Trust, The
Peter 115
Courtauld Trust, The Augustine
116
Cowan Foundation, The John
116

Cowley Charitable Foundation, The *116*

Cozens-Hardy Trust, The Lord *117*

Cranbury Foundation, The *117*

Cranfield Charitable Trust (1971) *117*

Crawley Warren Charitable Trust *117*

Crescent Trust, The *117*

Cripps Charitable Trust, The Violet & Milo *118*

Croft Foundation, Annie *118*

Crook Foundation, The Harry *118*

Crossfield Charitable Fund *118*

Crowson Charitable Settlement, The Derek *119*

Cruse Trust, The *119*

Curry Charitable Trust, Dennis *119*

Curry's Charitable Trust, D A *119*

Curtis Charitable Trust *119*

Cussins Foundation, The Manny *120*

Cutforth Charitable Trust, The David *120*

Cymerman Trust Limited, Itzchok Meyer *120*

DCW Trust *121*

DLM Charitable Trust, The *121*

Dacorum Community Trust *121*

Daily Telegraph Charitable Trust *122*

Dalmia Foundation, The *123*

Dana Charitable Settlement, The *123*

Dandeen Charitable Trust *123*

Daniell Charitable Trust, The Sir Peter *123*

Darell Charitable Trust *124*

Datnow Limited *124*

Davies Charitable Foundation, Richard *124*

Davies Charities Limited, J *125*

Davis Charitable Foundation, Lily & Henry *125*

Davis Charitable Settlement, Michael *125*

Davy Foundation, The J *126*

De Avenley Foundation, The *126*

De Clermont Charitable Company Limited, The *126*

De Groot Charitable Trust, Zena and Ralph *127*

De Haan Charitable Trust *127*

De La Rue Charitable Trust *127*

De Rothschild Charitable Trust, Edmund *127*

De Rothschild 1981 Charitable Trust, The Edmund *127*

De Rothschild Charitable Trust, The Leopold *127*

De Rothschild 1980 Charitable Trust, The Leopold *127*

De Vere Hunt Charitable Trust, The *128*

De Yong Charitable Trust, The Emma *128*

De Yong's Charitable Trust 1984, Nicholas *128*

Delacour, Charity of Theresa Harriet Mary *129*

Delafield Charitable Trust, The William *129*

Delfont Foundation, The *129*

Dellal Foundation, The *129*

Denton Charitable Trust, The *130*

Derby's Charitable Trust, The Right Hon The Earl of *130*

Desmond Charitable Trust, The Richard *131*

Deutsch Charitable Trust, The Andre *131*

Deutsch Charitable Trust, The H & M *131*

Devonport Charitable Trust *131*

Devonshire's Charitable Trust, The Duke of *131*

Diamond Charitable Trust, The Alan & Sheila *132*

Diana Memorial Trust, The *132*

Dibb Lupton Broomhead Charitable Trust *132*

Dicken Charitable Trust, The Albert *133*

Digbeth Trust Ltd, The *133*

Digby Charitable Trust, The Marcella and Claude *133*

Digby Charitable Trust, Simon *133*

Dinam Charity *134*

Dixon Charitable Trust, C H *134*

Dixon Trust Fund, Henry *135*

Djanogly Foundation, The *135*

Dock Charitable Fund, Otherwise Mersey Docks and Harbour Company Charitable Fund *135*

Dodd Charitable Trust, The Dudley *135*

Doidge Fund, Elsie *135*

Dolphin Charitable Trust, The *136*

Donatewell Ltd *136*

Doubleday Trust, The Garth *136*

Doughty Charity Trust, The *136*

Douglas Charitable Trust, R M *137*

Douglas Valley Evangelical Trust *137*

D'Oyly Carte Charitable Trust, The *137*

Drayton Trust, The *138*

Drexler Foundation, The George *138*

du Boulay Charitable Trust, The Anthony *138*

Duffield Foundation, The Vivien *138*

Dumbell Charitable Trust, The P B *139*

Dunecht Charity Trust *140*

Dunn Charitable Trust, The Harry *140*

Dunn Foundation, The Mrs C T M *140*

Dunn Trust, The W E *140*

Dzienisiewicz Trust, Jan *141*

ED Charitable Trust, The *141*

E D B Memorial Charitable Trust *141*

Early's Charitable Settlement, Richard *142*

Earmark Trust, The *142*

East Charitable Trust, B D *142*

Eastwood Foundation, Sir John *143*

Edinburgh Trust, No 2 Account *145*

Edwards Charity, Austin *146*

Elias Charitable Settlement, E V *146*

Elijah Trust *147*

Eling Trust *147*

Elkington Charitable Trust, The Maud *147*

Ellador Ltd *147*

Ellerman Foundation, The John *148*

Elshore Limited *149*

Elton's Charitable Settlement, Mr & Mrs *149*

Ely Charitable Trust, The Vernon N *149*

Emerton-Christie Charity *150*

Englass Charitable Trust, The *151*

Englefield Charitable Trust, The *151*

English Bowling Association Charitable Trust *151*

Enkalon Foundation *151*

Ericson Trust *152*

Esher House Charitable Trust, The *153*

Essame Charitable Trust, The Guthrie *153*

Essefian Charitable Trust, The Mihran *153*

Essex Provincial Charity Fund *154*

Essex Radio Helping Hands Trust, The *154*

Eton Action *154*

Euroclydon Trust *154*

Eventhall Family Charitable Trust, The *155*

Everard Foundation, The *155*

Eves Charitable Trust, The Douglas Heath *155*

Eyre Charitable Trust, G F *156*

FBT Charitable Fund, The *157*

FR 1978 Charitable Trust, The *157*

Fabry Trust, W F *157*

Fairbairn Trust, The Lady Mary 157
Falkner Charitable Trust, The Daniel 158
Family Foundations Trust, The 158
Family Trust, The 158
Famos Foundation Trust 158
Farmer's Trust, Samuel William 159
Farne Trust, The 159
Farr Charitable Trust, The Thomas 159
Farthing Trust, The 159
Farthing (Trust) Limited, Walter 160
Fawkes Charitable Trust, The Guy 160
Felicitas Trust, The 161
Fentham Birmingham Trust 161
Fenton Trust, The A M 161
Ferraris Charitable Trust, The 162
Fidelity UK Foundation, The 162
Fisher Foundation, The Sir John 163
Fitton Trust, The 163
Fitzmaurice Charitable Trust, The 163
Fitzwilliam Charitable Trust, The Earl 164
Fleisher Deceased, The Will of Sydney 164
Flintshire Welsh Church Fund 165
Floyd Charitable Trust, John Anthony 165
Fogwell's Charity, Sarah Wood 166
Forbes Trust, The 166
Fordeve Limited 167
Foreman Foundation, The Carl & Eve 167
Foresters' Charity Stewards UK Trust, The 167
Fourth Settlement Charity 168
Fowler Memorial Trust, The 169
Fox Memorial Trust 169
Foyle Trust, Charles Henry 169
Frampton Charitable Trust, The David 169
Frankel Memorial Charitable Trust, The Isaac & Freda 169
Franklin Bequest, The Rosalind 169
Franklin Deceased's New Second Charity, Sydney E 170
Fraser Charitable Trust, The Gordon 170
Fraser Trust, The 170
Frays Charitable Trust, The 171
Frazer Trust, Joseph Strong 171

Freedman Charitable Trust, The Louis 171
Freeman Charitable Trust, A J 171
French Charitable Trust, Charles S 171
French Foundation, The Betty 172
Freshgate Trust Foundation, The 172
Friday Charitable Trust, The 172
Friends of Biala Ltd 172
Friends of Wiznitz Limited 173
Frigenti Charitable Trust, The Nina 174
Frost Foundation, The Patrick 174
Fry Charitable Trust, Maurice 174
GMC Trust, The 175
GNC Trust 175
GRP Charitable Trust 176
GWR Community Trust 176
Gahan's Charitable Foundation, Mrs D H 176
Gale Charitable Trust, A W 176
Gale Charitable Trust, Horace and Marjorie 177
Gale Charitable Trust, R G 177
Gamma Trust 177
Garrod Memorial Charitable Trust, The John and Daisy 179
Garthgwynion Charities 179
Gee Charitable Trust, The Cecil 179
Gem Charitable Trust 179
Gemmell Bequest Fund 180
General Charity Fund, The 180
Gibson Charitable Trust, The G C 182
Gibson Charitable Trust, The Simon 182
Gibson Trust, The R F F 182
Gibson's Charitable Trust, Mrs E D 182
Gibson's Charity Trust, The Hon Mr & Mrs Clive 182
Gibson's Charity Trust, The Hon H M T 182
Gibson's Charity Trust, The Hon P N 183
Gibson's Charity Trust, The Hon W K 183
Gillett Charitable Trust, J A 183
Gill's Charitable Trust, Mrs M M 184
Gilpin Trust, The John 184
Girdlers' Company Charitable Trust, The 184
Glasser Charitable Trust, The B & P 184
Glencore Foundation for Education and Welfare 185
Gluck Charitable Trust, Avraham Yitzchak 185

Glyn Charitable Trust, The 186
Glyn Charitable Trust, James 186
Godfrey-Payton Trust, Mrs 186
Gold Hill Church Trust 186
Goldberg Charitable Trust, The Lewis 186
Goldberg Charity Trust, The Isaac 187
Golden Bottle Trust 187
Goldfinch, Charity of Fred 187
Goodacre Benevolent Fund 188
Goodisons Charitable Settlement, Sir Nicholas & Lady 188
Goodman Charitable Foundation, The Everard and Mina 188
Goodman Trust, The 189
Gosling Foundation Limited, The 189
Gradel Foundation, The 189
Gradel Trust, The Leon and Bertha 189
Graham Charity, The Mrs D M 190
Grand Metropolitan Charitable Trust, The 191
Gray Trust, The 192
Gray Trust, The Gordon 192
Green Foundation, The Charles 193
Green Foundation, Constance 194
Green, J H F 194
Greene & Co Charity Limited 195
Greenwood Charitable Trust, Naomi & Jeffrey 195
Greenwood Charity Trust, J R 195
Greibach Charitable Trust, The 196
Gresham Charitable Trust, The 196
Greystoke Trust, The 196
Grimsdale Charitable Trust 196
Gross Charities Limited, M & R 197
Grosshill Charitable Trust 197
Grove Charitable Trust, Mary Isobel 197
Groves Charitable Trust, The 197
Grumett Foundation, The David and Marie 198
Grut Charitable Trust, The 198
Guardian Foundation, The 198
Guardian Royal Exchange Charitable Trust, The 198
Gunnell Charitable Trust, The 199
Gunter Charitable Trust, The 199
Gur Trust, The 199
Gurney Foundation, The Samuel 200

Gurunanak *200*
Gwynedd County Council Welsh Church Fund *200*
HB Charitable Trust *201*
Hacking & Sons Ltd Charitable Trust, C G *201*
Hadrian Trust, The *202*
Haka Trust, The *203*
Halecat Charitable Trust, The *203*
Haley Charitable Trust, The Ethel *203*
Halifax Charitable Trust, The *204*
Hall Charitable Trust, E F & M G *204*
Hall Charity, Robert *204*
Hame Trust, The *205*
Hamilton Educational Trust, Eleanor *205*
Hamilton Trust, The *205*
Hammersmith Relief-in-Sickness Fund *206*
Hammerson Foundation, The Sue *206*
Hammerson's Charitable Trust, Sue *206*
Hampstead Wells and Campden Trust *206*
Handley Charity Trust, W A *207*
Hanley Trust (1987), The *207*
Hanover Charitable Trust, The *208*
Harbinson Charitable Trust *208*
Harbour Charitable Trust, The *208*
Harbour Foundation Ltd, The *208*
Harmony Trust, The *210*
Harris Charitable Settlement, R J *210*
Harris Charitable Trust, The John *210*
Harris Charitable Trust, The Philip & Pauline *210*
Harris Charity, The *211*
Harrisons & Crosfield Charitable Fund *211*
Hatton Charitable Trust, The Howard *212*
Hawthorne Charitable Trust, The *212*
Hay Charitable Trust, Dora *213*
Haydan Charitable Trust, The *213*
Haymills Charitable Trust *213*
Hayward Trust, The Charles *213*
Headley Trust, The *214*
Heath Charitable Trust, The Edward *214*
Heathcoat Trust *214*
Heber Percy Charitable Trust, The Mrs C S *215*
Hedley Will Trust, Percy *215*
Held Settlement, The Gisela *215*

Hennell Charitable Trust, Esther *216*
Heseltine Charitable Trust, Michael *217*
Hiam Charitable Trust, Sir Frederick *218*
Hickinbotham Charitable Trust *218*
Higgs and Hill plc Charitable Trust *218*
Hiley Trust, Joseph and Mary *219*
Hill Charitable Foundation, Herbert Charles *219*
Hill House Trust *219*
Hill Trust, The Charles Littlewood *220*
Hillards Charitable Trust, Gay & Peter Hartley's *220*
Hillcote Trust, The *220*
Hillhouse Trust, M V *220*
Hind Trust, Lady *220*
Hinton Charitable Trust, Mrs F E *221*
Hird Charitable Trust, The Thora *221*
Hobson Charitable Trust, The *222*
Hobson Charity Limited, The *222*
Hodgson Charitable Trust, Bill & May *223*
Hodgson Charitable Trust, Kenneth *223*
Holford Trust Fund *224*
Holloway Charitable Trust, The *224*
Holmes Charitable Trust, The Dorothy *224*
Holt Charitable Trust, The Douglas *225*
Holt Charitable Trust, P H *225*
Holt Trust, The Edward *225*
Homelands Charitable Trust *225*
Homfray Charitable Trust, Mary *226*
Hoover Foundation, The *226*
Horn Trust, The Cuthbert *227*
Hornby Charitable Trust, The Edward *227*
Hornby's Charitable Settlement, Mrs E G *228*
Hornton Trust, The *228*
Howarth Charity Trust, Clifford *229*
Hubert Charitable Trust, A *229*
Hudson Charitable Trust, The *230*
Hughes Charitable Trust, The Geoffery C *230*
Hugonin Family Trust, The *230*
Hull & East Riding Charitable Trust, The *230*
Humphreys Charitable Settlement, J A M *231*
Hunter Fund, The Patrick Mitchell *231*

Hunt's Trust, William *231*
Hyams Trust, The P Y N and B *232*
IB Charitable Trust, The *233*
IPE Charitable Trust, The *233*
Ibbetson Settlement, Harry *233*
Inchcape Charitable Trust Fund *234*
Inman Charity, The *235*
Innominate Trust, The *235*
International Nickel Donations Fund, The *236*
Invermark Charity *236*
JMR Charitable Trust, The *240*
JNF Charitable Trust *240*
Jackson Trust for Charity, The Isaac and Harriet *240*
Jacobs Charity, The Dorothy *240*
Jacobson Charitable Trust, The Anne & Malcolm *241*
Jacobson Charitable Trust (No 2), The Ruth & Lionel *241*
Jacobson Charitable Trust, The Yvette and Hermione *241*
James Bristol Foundation, John *241*
James Foundation, The Catherine and Lady Grace *241*
James (No 2) Charitable Foundation, The Dawn *242*
Janelaw Trust, The *242*
Janes Charitable Trust, Lois & Robert *242*
Janes Memorial Trust, Peter *243*
Jansen Charitable Trust, Peter *243*
Jarman Charitable Trust, The *243*
Jarrold Trust Ltd, John *243*
Jason Charitable Trust, The Jane *243*
Jenour Foundation, The *244*
Joels Charitable Trust, The Harold *245*
Joels Charitable Trust, The Jacob & Lena *246*
Joels Charitable Trust, The Jonathan *246*
Joels Charitable Trust, The Nicholas *246*
Johnson Charitable Settlement, Bridget Catherine *246*
Johnson Charitable Settlement, The N B *246*
Johnson Wax Limited Charitable Trust *247*
Joicey Trust, The *247*
Jones Settlement, Edward Cecil *248*
Jones Trust, Cemlyn *248*
Juno Charity Trust, The *249*
Jurgens Charitable Trust, The Anton *249*

Jusaca Charitable Trust, The 249

KC Charitable Trust, The 250

Karloff Charitable Foundation, The Boris 250

Karten Charitable Trust, The Ian 250

Kaufman Charitable Trust, The C S 251

Kaye Charitable Trust, The Henry 251

Keane Charitable Settlement, The 251

Keller Charitable Trust, Samuel 251

Kendall's Charity, William 252

Kendrew Charitable Settlement, The Florence Amelia 252

Kennedy Charitable Trust, The Mathilda & Terence 252

Kennyhill Bequest Fund 252

Kenrick Charitable Trust, Hugh 253

Kenyon Charitable Trust, The Nancy 253

Kermaville Ltd 253

Keyes Trust, The Ursula 253

Keyser Charitable Trust, C M 254

Kingsgrove Charitable Trust, The 255

Kingsmill Charitable Trust 256

Kinnison Charitable Trust, R O 256

Kirby & West Charitable Trust, The 257

Kirkham Foundation, The Graham 257

Kleinwort Benson Charitable Trust 257

Kleinwort Charitable Trust, The Ernest 257

Knightly Charitable Trust, The David 257

Knott Family Trust, The James 258

Kobler Trust, The 258

Kornberg's 1969 Charitable Settlement, Mrs Bessie 258

Kreitman Foundation 258

Kulika Charitable Trust, The 259

Kweller Charitable Trust, The Harry 259

LGT Asset Management Charitable Trust 260

Laing Foundation, The Martin 261

Lambert Charitable Trust, The 262

Landale Charitable Trust, The 263

Landy Charitable Trust, Harry and Gertrude 263

Langdale Trust 264

Langtree Trust, The 264

Lansdowne Charitable Trust, The 265

Lanvern Foundation 265

Laski Memorial Charitable Trust, Nathan 265

Laspen Trust 265

Lauchentilly Charitable Foundation 1988, The 266

Laufer Charitable Trust 266

Lauffer Charitable Foundation, The R & D 266

Laurence's Trust, Kathleen 266

Lavender Trust, The 267

Lawley Foundation, The Edgar E 267

Lawson Charitable Trust, Raymond and Blanche 267

Lawson-Beckman Charitable Trust 267

Leach Fourteenth Trust, The 267

Leathersellers' Company Charitable Fund, The 268

Lebus Charitable Trust, The 268

Lee Charitable Trust, The Arnold 269

Lee Foundation, The Edgar 269

Leeside Charitable Trust 269

Leggat Charitable Trust, Duncan 269

Lehmann Charitable Trust, The 270

Leigh Charitable Trust, Gerald 270

Leigh Charitable Trust, Kennedy 270

Leigh Foundation, The Morris 270

Leigh Trust, The 270

Leigh-Bramwell Trust 'E', P 270

Leonard Trust, The Erica 270

Lesley Lesley and Mutter Trust 271

Levein Family Charitable Trust, The 271

Levens Charitable Trust, The Leslie 272

Leverhulme Trade Charities Trust, The 272

Leverhulme's Charitable Trust, Lord 272

Levy Charitable Foundation, Joseph 272

Levy Charitable Trust, The Lawrence 273

Lewis Charitable Trust, Henry 273

Lewis Foundation, The Sir Edward 273

Lilley Benevolent Trust 275

Lilley Memorial Trust, The Thomas 275

Linbury Trust, The 275

Linder Foundation, The Enid 275

Lingwood Charitable Trust, The 276

Lipton Charitable Trust, The Ruth & Stuart 276

Lloyd Trust, The W M & B 278

Lloyd-Everett Trust, The 278

Localtrent Ltd 279

Longley Trust 280

Lovell Charitable Trust, P and M 284

Lowndes Charitable Trust, The Vanessa 285

Lucas Charitable Trust Limited, The Joseph 286

Lunzer Charitable Trust, The Ruth & Jack 287

Lynwood Charitable Trust, The 288

Lyons Charitable Trust, The 288

Lyster 1980 Charitable Trust, The Lionel 288

M D & S Charitable Trust, The 289

MDM Memorial Trust 289

MKR Charitable Trust 289

MVM Charitable Trust 289

MacAndrew Trust, The E M 289

Macaulay Family Charitable Trust 290

McCamman Trust, The Eileen 290

McCorquodale Charitable Trust, The 290

Macdonald-Buchanan Charitable Trust 291

Macfarlane Walker Trust 291

McKechnie Foundation, A N 292

McKenzie Trust, The Robert 292

McLaren Foundation 292

McLaren Memorial Trust, The Martin 293

McMorran Charitable Foundation, The Helen Isabella 293

McPhail Charitable Settlement, D D 293

MacPherson Charitable Settlement, G P S 293

MacRobert Trusts, The 294

McTurk Charitable Trust, Mary 294

Mahavir Trust 294

Major Charitable Trust, The 294

Manchester and Salford Medical Charities Fund 295

Manchester Guardian Society Charitable Trust, The 295

Mann Trustees Limited, R W 296

Manor House Charitable Trust 296

Maranatha Christian Trust 296

Margadale Charitable Trust, Lord *297*

Margulies Charitable Trust, The Stella and Alexander *297*

Marks' Charitable Settlement, J M *298*

Marks' Charitable Trust, Harry *298*

Marks Charitable Trust, Michael *298*

Markus Charitable Foundation, The Erich *298*

Marr-Munning Trust *299*

Marsh Christian Trust, The *299*

Marshall Charitable Trust, The Bob and Barbara *299*

Marshall Charitable Trust, The Charlotte *300*

Martin Charitable Trust, Mervyn *300*

Martin Trust, The Sir George *300*

Marylebone Charitable Foundation *301*

Mason Charitable Trust, The George *301*

Massey Charitable Trust, The Nancie *301*

Material World Charitable Foundation Limited, The *301*

Matthews Wrightson Charity Trust *301*

Mattock Charitable Trust, The W T *302*

Maude 1988 Charitable Trust, M F T *302*

Mauray Charitable Trust, The Violet *302*

Maxwell Foundation, The Pamela and Jack *302*

Mayfair Charities Limited *303*

Mayhew Charitable Trust, Anthony *303*

Mays-Smith Charitable Trust, The Ivona *303*

Meath, Charity of Mary Jane, Countess of *304*

Medlock Charitable Trust, The *304*

Mellows Charitable Settlement, The Anthony and Elizabeth *305*

Mercers' Charitable Foundation *306*

Messel & Co Charitable Trust, L *308*

Metro FM Pop Fund *308*

Mickel Fund *309*

Micklem Charitable Trust, The Gerald *309*

Millett Charitable Trust, The Alan and Janet *312*

Millichope Foundation, The *312*

Mishcon Charitable Trust, Victor *314*

Miskin Charitable Trust, Mary *314*

Modiano Charitable Trust *315*

Mole Charitable Trust *315*

Moncrieff Charity, D C *315*

Montagu Family Charitable Trust, The *316*

Montefiore Trust, The David *316*

Monument Trust, The *316*

Moody Charitable Trust, The *316*

Moore Charitable Trust, The Horace *316*

Morel Charitable Trust, The *318*

Morris Charitable Trust, Bernard *319*

Morris Charitable Trust, The Willie & Mabel *320*

Morrison Charitable Trust, G M *320*

Moshal Charitable Trust *321*

Moss Charitable Trust, Philip *321*

Moulton Charitable Trust, The *321*

Mount 'A' Charitable Trust *321*

Mount 'B' Charitable Trust *321*

Moxon Charitable Trust, Gweneth *322*

Murphy-Neumann Charity Company Limited *323*

Music Sales Charitable Trust, The *324*

NAM Charitable Trust *325*

NCL Charitable Trust *325*

Nagel Charitable Trust, The Willie *325*

Napier Charitable Trust, The Gordon *326*

Nash Charitable Trust, The Janet *326*

Natasha Trust, The *326*

Needham Cooper Charitable Trust, The *331*

Neighbourly Charitable Trust, The *331*

Neill Charitable Settlement, J H *331*

Nelson Memorial Trust, The Barbara *331*

Nestle Rowntree York Community Fund, Employees of *331*

Newcastle's 1986 Charitable Trust, Duke of *333*

Newhope Trust, The *333*

Newman Charitable Trust, Mr and Mrs F E F *334*

Newstead Charity, The *334*

Newton Charitable Trust *334*

Nichol-Young Foundation *334*

Norfolk and Suffolk Voluntary Health Benevolent Fund, The *336*

Norman Trust, The *337*

Normanby Charitable Trust *337*

Northcott Charity Trust, The *338*

Northern Arts *339*

Northern Electric Employee Charity Association *339*

Northfleet Lions Club Charity Trust Fund *340*

Noswal Charitable Trust, The *341*

Oak Trust, The *343*

Oakley Charitable Trust, The *343*

Oakmoor Trust, The *343*

Oasis Church Chadwell Heath Charitable Trust *343*

Ofenheim Charitable Trust, The *343*

Ogilvie Charities (Deed No 2) *344*

Old Possums Practical Trust, The *344*

Oliver Charitable Foundation, The *345*

Oppenheim Charitable Settlement, K A *346*

Oppenheimer Foundation, The Phillip *346*

Ormsby Charitable Trust, The *347*

Orr Mackintosh Foundation Limited *347*

Orrin Charitable Trust *347*

Osborne Charitable Trust, The *347*

Owen Trust, Margaret *348*

Oxfam (United Kingdom and Ireland) *348*

PAR Charitable Trust *349*

PB Charitable Trust *349*

PDC Trust, The *349*

PES Associates' Charitable Trust *350*

PF Charitable Trust *350*

PJD Charitable Trust *350*

Paddington Welfare Charities *351*

Paisner Charitable Trust, The *351*

Palmer Trust, The Gerald *352*

Parham Park Trust (1984), The *352*

Pascoe Charitable Trust, Alan *354*

Patients' Aid Association Hospital and Medical Charities Trust *354*

Paul Charitable Trust, The Late Barbara May *355*

Paul Charitable Trust, Margaret Jeanne *355*

Paul Charitable Trust, Pamela Milton *355*

Paul Foundation, The *355*

Paul's Charitable Trust, R J *355*

Payne Charitable Trust, The *355*

Peacock Charitable Trust, The
356
Peake Charitable Trust, The
Susanna 357
Pearson Charity Trust, Hon
Charles 357
Pearson Foundation, The Frank
357
Pearson plc Charitable Trust,
The 357
Pearson's 1987 Charity Trust,
Rosanna 357
Pedmore Sporting Club Trust
Fund 357
Pelech Charitable Trust, The
358
Pennycress Trust, The 359
Pen-Y-Clip Charitable Trust
359
Perry Charitable Trust, Miss
Frances Lucille 359
Pershore Nashdom & Elmore
Trust Ltd, The 360
Perth's Charitable Trust, The
Earl of 360
Peskin Charitable Trust, The
Hazel and Leslie 360
Pettit Charitable Trust 360
Peugeot Talbot Motor
Company plc Charity Trust
361
Pewterers' Charity Trust 361
Pfeffer Trust (1962), Anshel
Lord 361
Phelps Charitable Trust,
Brigadier and Mrs D V 361
Phillips Charitable Foundation,
Reginald M 361
Phillips Family Charitable Trust,
The 361
Pike Charity Settlement 362
Pilkington Charity, The C F 363
Pilkington's Charitable Trust,
Dr L H A 363
Pilozzo Charitable Trust 364
Pitt Trust, Headley 364
Plaut Charitable Trust Limited,
G S 364
Pole 1973 Charitable Trust, The
Sir Richard Carew 365
Pole Charitable Trust, Carew
365
Pollitzer Charitable Settlement,
George and Esme 366
Pollitzer's Charitable
Settlement, J S F 366
Porter Charitable Trust, John
366
Portrack Charitable Trust, The
366
Poulden Charitable Trust, The
Frank and Dorothy 366
Powys Welsh Church Fund 367
Prevezer Charitable Settlement,
S B 368
Priestman Charity Trust, Sir
John 368

Priestman Trust, S H and E C
368
Primrose Trust, The 369
Prince Foundation, The 369
Priory Foundation, The 369
Proven Family Trust, The 370
Pryor Charity, The Roland &
Kathleen 371
Pye's No 1 Charitable
Settlement, Mr and Mrs J A
372
QAS Charitable Trust 373
RT Trust, The 374
Rachel Charitable Trust 375
Rackham Charitable Trust, The
Mr & Mrs Philip 375
Rae Charity, H J 375
Randall Charitable Trust, The
Joseph and Lena 376
Rangoonwala Foundation,
ZVM 376
Rank Benevolent Trust, Joseph
377
Rank Foundation, The 377
Rapaport Charitable Trust,
Fanny 378
Ratcliff Foundation, The 378
Rathbone Charity, The
Elizabeth 378
Rav Chesed Trust, The 379
Raven Charitable Trust 379
Ravensdale Trust, The 379
Rayleigh's Charitable Trust,
Lord 379
Rayne Trust, The 380
Rayner Trust, Elizabeth 380
Reader's Digest Trust, The 380
Reckitt Charitable Trust, The
Albert 381
Reckitt Charity, Sir James 381
Red Arrows Trust, The 381
Redfern Charitable Foundation,
C A 381
Reekie Trust, R A & V B 381
Reeves Charitable Trust, The
Christopher H R 382
Rhododendron Trust, The 383
Rhondda Cynon Taff Welsh
Church Acts Fund, The 383
Richards Charity, The Clive 384
Richmond Parish Lands Charity
384
Riddleston Charity of Leicester,
The Harry James 385
Riddon Trust, The 386
Ridgmount Foundation, The
386
Rind Foundation, The 386
Ripple Effect Foundation, The
387
Ritblat Charitable Trust No 1,
The John 387
Rivendell Trust, The 387
Robbins Trust, The Cheshire
387
Robertson Charitable Trust,
The J W 388

Robinson Charitable Trust, P R
& T L 388
Robinson Trust No 3, The J C
388
Rockcliffe Charitable Trust 389
Rockwell UK Charitable Trust
389
Rodewald's Charitable
Settlement, Mr C A 389
Rogers Charitable Settlement,
The Richard 390
Rokeby Charitable Trust 390
Roland Grange Trust 390
Rolfe Charitable Trust, The 390
Roper Charitable Trust, The
D G M 391
Rosca Trust 391
Rosen Foundation, Cecil 392
Ross Charitable Trust, The 392
Rotary Club of Worthing's
Community Service Fund
392
Rothschild Foundation, The
393
Rothschild Group Charitable
Trust, The J 393
Roughley Charitable Trust, The
393
Royal Society of St George
Charitable Trust, The 396
Rubens Foundation, J B 397
Rubens Highgate Trust, The
Frank and Enid 397
Rudolf Charitable Trust, Carrie
398
Rufford Foundation 398
Russell Charitable Trust, Frank
398
Russell Charitable Trust, The
Willy 398
Russon Charitable Trust, Frank
398
SEDOS Jubilee Charity Fund
399
SEM Charitable Trust 399
SO Charitable Trust 400
Sacher Charitable Trust, The
Audrey 400
Sacher Charitable Trust, The
Michael 400
Sadagora Trust, The Ruzin 400
Saddlers Company Charitable
Fund, The 401
Sainsbury Charitable Fund, The
Alan & Babette 402
St Hilda's Trust 403
St Jude's Trust 403
Saintbury Trust, The 405
Saints and Sinners Trust
Limited, The 405
Salmon Charitable Settlement,
Harold Joseph 405
Salmon Charity, The Guy 405
Sammermar Trust, The 406
Samuel Charitable Trust, The
Basil 406
Samuel Charitable Trust, Coral
406

Samuel Charitable Trust, M J *406*

Samuel Charitable Trust, Peter *406*

Sandars Charitable Trust, The J E *407*

Sanders Charitable Settlement, G S *407*

Saranda Charitable Trust, The *407*

Sargeant's Charitable Trust, Mrs M E *407*

Save & Prosper Foundation *409*

Sayer Charity, Henry James *409*

Scarr-Hall Memorial Trust, The *409*

Schiff Charitable Trust, The Annie *409*

Schmidt-Bodner Charitable Trust, The *410*

Schroder Charity Trust *410*

Scobell Charitable Trust, The *410*

Scotbelge Charitable Trust, The *411*

Scott Charitable Trust, The Frieda *412*

Scott Charitable Will Trust, The Storrow *412*

Scott Trust, Sir James & Lady *412*

Scouloudi Foundation, The *413*

Seahorse Charitable Trust, The *413*

Sears Foundation *413*

Seccombe Charitable Trust, Leslie and Doris *414*

Second Ferndale Trust *414*

Securicor Charitable Trust, The *414*

Sedbury Trust, The *414*

Segal Charitable Trust *414*

Selig Charitable Trust, The *415*

Senna Foundation, The Ayrton *415*

Setterfield Trust, The *415*

Settlement Dated 31st March 1966 (Ref PT 865) *415*

Seva Trust, Rampaba Sadhu *415*

Sheffield Town Trust *417*

Sheldon Trust, The *417*

Shepherd Charitable Trust, The Patricia and Donald *417*

Sherman Cardiff Charitable Foundation, The Archie *418*

Sherman Charitable Trust, The Archie *419*

Sherwood Charitable Trust, Colonel J D *419*

Shifrin Charitable Trust, The Maurice and Hilda *419*

Shimpling Trust Limited, The *419*

Shine Charitable Foundation, Barnett *419*

Shine No 1 Charitable Trust, The Barnett and Sylvia *419*

Shipman Charitable Trust, Thomas Stanley *420*

Shippam Trust, Bassil *420*

Shuttleworth Memorial Trust, Barbara A *421*

Sidbury Trust, The Second *421*

Sieff Charitable Trust, The David and Jennifer *421*

Sieff Charitable Trust, The Lily & Marcus *421*

Silman Charitable Trust, The Julius *421*

Silvester Charitable Gift Trust *422*

Simpson Foundation, The *422*

Simpson Settlement, Miss D B *422*

Sinclair Charitable Trust, The Huntly & Margery *423*

Sinclair Henderson Trust, A *423*

Singer Foundation *423*

Slater Foundation, The John *424*

Slaughter Charitable Trust, The Ernest William *425*

Slavin Charitable Foundation, The Josephine & Barry *425*

Sloane Street Trust, The *425*

Smiley Charitable Trust, The Andrew *425*

Smiley's Second Charity Trust, Mrs *425*

Smith Charitable Settlement, The N *426*

Smith Charitable Trust, The *426*

Smith General Charitable Trust, The Stanley *427*

Smith (Haltwhistle & District) Charitable Trust, The *427*

Smith Memorial Trust, The Albert & Florence *427*

Smith Trust Fund, The Griffith *427*

Sobell Foundation, The *428*

Sobell Welsh People's Charitable Association, Michael *429*

Society of Friends of the Torah, The *429*

Solev Co Limited *429*

Solomon Family Charitable Trust, The *429*

Solomons Charitable Trust, David *430*

Solway Sound Charitable Trust *430*

Somerfield Curtis Will Trust, The Dorothy *430*

Songdale Limited *430*

Southall Trust, W F *432*

Spencer Hart Charitable Trust, The *433*

Spencer Trust, The Jessie *433*

Stanhope-Palmer Charity *435*

Stanley Foundation Limited *435*

Stansfield Charitable Trust *435*

Starkie Bence Charitable Trust *436*

Steel Charitable Trust, The *436*

Stephenson Charitable Trust Fund *436*

Stephenson (Decd), Will Trust of Edgar John Henry *436*

Stewart Charitable Trust, George *437*

Stewart Charitable Trust, Mary Stephanie *437*

Still Waters Charitable Trust *438*

Stokes Trust, F C *438*

Storey Family Charitable Trust, The Samuel *439*

Strasser Foundation, The *439*

Strathspey Charitable Trust, The *440*

Streeter Charitable Settlement, David James *440*

Strudwick Charitable Trust, The Roy *441*

Studd Charitable Trust *441*

Sudborough Foundation, The *441*

Sugar Foundation, The Alan *441*

Sugden-Wilson's Charitable Trust, Mrs Gabrielle Mary *441*

Summerfield Charitable Trust, The *442*

Sumray Charitable Trust, The *443*

Sunley Charitable Foundation, The Bernard *443*

Susman Charitable Trust, The Ann *443*

Swan Trust *444*

Swaziland Charitable Trust *444*

Sweett Charitable Trust, The Barbara *445*

Swindon Charitable Trust, The Walter *445*

Swinstead Charitable Trust, The *445*

Swire 1989 Charitable Trust, John *445*

Sykes Charitable Trust, The Hugh & Ruby *445*

Sykes Trust, The *445*

TG No 1 Charitable Trust *447*

TUUT Charitable Trust, The *448*

Talbot House Trust, The *448*

Tangent Charitable Trust *448*

Tankel Charitable Trust, Alfred *449*

Tankel Charitable Trust, Gerald *449*

Tanner Charitable Settlement, The Joan *449*

Tavener Charitable Trust, Mrs K M *449*

Taverne Trust, The *449*
Taylor Charitable Trust, A R *449*
Taylor Charitable Trust, The B R *450*
Taylor Fund, A P *450*
Taylor Trust, C B & H H *450*
Terry Charitable Trust, Noel Goddard *451*
Tesco Charity Trust *452*
Tesler Foundation, The *452*
Thames Wharf Charity, The *452*
Thatcher Charitable Trust, The Margaret *452*
Tho Memorial Foundation, Loke Wan *452*
Thompson Family Charitable Trust, The *453*
Thomson Corporation Charitable Trust, The *453*
Thoresby Charitable Trust *454*
Thornton Charitable Settlement, The Ruth *454*
Thornton Foundation, The *455*
Thwaite Charitable Trust, The Daniel *456*
Thyne Trust, William *456*
Tillotson Charitable Trust, G L *457*
Tindle Family Charity, The *457*
Tolkien Trust, The *458*
Tollemache (Buckminster) Charitable Trust *458*
Tomchei Torah Charitable Trust *458*
Tompkins Foundation, The *458*
Tory Family Foundation, The *459*
Towry Law Charitable Trust, The *459*
Tranmer Charitable Trust, Annie *460*
Triodos Foundation *460*
Troughton's Charity Trust, Mrs S H *461*
Tryst Settlement, The *462*
Tucker Charitable Settlement, The Roy *462*
Tufton Charitable Trust, The *463*
Turner Charitable Trust, The R D *464*
Turner Trust, The Douglas *464*
Turner Trust, G J W *464*
29th May 1961 Charity, The *465*
Tyneside Charitable Trust *466*
Ullmann Trust, The *467*
Uxbridge Charitable Trust *469*
van Geest Foundation, The John and Lucille *470*
Van Heemstra's Charitable Trust, Baroness *470*
Van Norden's Charitable Foundation, Mrs Maud *471*
Vandervell Foundation *471*
Vardy Foundation, The *471*

Variety Club Children's Charity Limited, The *471*
Vec Acorn Trust, The *472*
Vendquot Ltd *472*
Verdon-Smith Family Charitable Settlement, The *472*
Vineyard Christian Fellowship of South West *473*
Vinson Charity Trust, The 1969 *473*
Vodafone Group Charitable Trust, The *474*
Vogel Charitable Trust, The Nathan *474*
Wade Foundation *475*
Wainwright Charity, The Scurrah *475*
Wakefield Trust, The *476*
of Wales Charities, The Prince *477*
Wales' Charities Trust, The Princess of *477*
Waley-Cohen Charitable Trust, Robert & Felicity *477*
Wall Charitable Trust, The *478*
Wallace Charity Trust, The A F *478*
Wallis Charitable Trust, The Francis *479*
Walton Charitable Trust, The *479*
Warbeck Fund Limited *480*
Ward Blenkinsop Trust, The *480*
Ward Charitable Trust, The George *480*
Warwick Trust, The *480*
Waterhouse Charitable Trust, Mrs *480*
Waters 1989 Charity Trust, The Roger *481*
Watkinson Charity Trust, May *481*
Webb Charitable Trust, The Denis George *483*
Webber Trust Fund, Ethel *483*
Webster Charitable Trust, William *483*
Weinberg Foundation, The *483*
Weinstein Foundation, The *484*
Weinstock Fund, The *484*
Weintrop Charity, The Alfred and Beatrice *484*
Welton Foundation, The *485*
West Glamorgan Welsh Church Fund, The *486*
West London Synagogue Charitable Fund *486*
Western Foils Charitable Trust *487*
Westminster Foundation, The *487*
Weston Bampfylde Trust, The *488*

Weston Foundation, Garfield *488*
Westward Trust, The *488*
Whetherly's Charitable Trust, The Hon Mrs R G A *489*
Whitbread 1988 Charitable Trust, The *489*
Whitbread Charitable Trust, Samuel *489*
Whitbread Charitable Trust, The Simon *489*
Whitehead Charitable Trust, J E *490*
Whittington Charitable Trust, The *491*
Wiggins Charity Trust, Cyril *491*
Wightwick Charitable Trust, The Gladys *492*
Wilde Charitable Trust, The Felicity *492*
Will Charitable Trust, The *492*
Willan Charitable Trust, The *492*
Willcox Trust, The Ronald *492*
Williamson Trust *493*
Willis Charitable Trust, R H *493*
Wills 1965 Charitable Trust, The H D H *494*
Wills Charitable Trust, Dame Violet *494*
Wills Will Trust 1965, Dame Violet *494*
Wimpey Charitable Trust, The George *495*
Wine Charitable Trust, The J L *496*
Winegarten Charitable Trust, Benjamin *496*
Winham Foundation, The Francis *497*
Wise Charitable Trust, The James *497*
Woburn 1986 Charitable Trust *498*
Wohl Charitable Foundation, The Maurice *498*
Wohl Charitable Trust, The Maurice *498*
Wolff Charity Trust *498*
Wolfson Charitable Trust, The Aviezer *499*
Wolfson Charitable Trust, The Charles *499*
Wolfson Family Charitable Trust, The *499*
Wood Bequest Fund, James *500*
Wood Charitable Foundation, The Louise *501*
Wood Charity, The Phyllis E *501*
Woodhead Charitable Trust, Michael *501*
Woodlands Trust *501*
Woods Charitable Foundation, Geoffrey *502*

Woodward Charitable Trust, The 502

Wootton Grange Charitable Trust, The 503

Workman Trust, The 503

Worms Charitable Trust, The Freda and Della 504

Worshipful Company of Builders Merchants 504

Worshipful Company of Cutlers, The 504

Worshipful Company of Feltmakers of London Charitable Foundation, The 505

Worshipful Company of Innholders General Charity Fund 505

Worshipful Company of Launderers Benevolent Trust Fund, The 505

Worshipful Company of Needlemakers' Charitable Fund 505

Worshipful Company of Turners, The 506

Wragge & Co Charitable Trust, The 506

Wright Deceased Trust, John William 506

Wychdale Limited 507

Wylde Memorial Charity, The Anthony and Gwendoline 507

Wyvill Charitable Trust, The 507

Yablon Family Charity Company Limited, The 508

Yardley Great Trust 508

Yardy Charitable Trust, The Dennis Alan 509

York Common Good Trust 509

Youell Foundation Ltd, The 510

Young Charitable Settlement, The John 510

Youth Appeal for Eastern Europe 511

Zaiger Trust, The Elizabeth and Prince 512

Ziff Charitable Foundation, I A 512

Zochonis Charitable Trust, The 512

■ Governesses

see Teachers & governesses

■ Gurdwaras

see Temples, gurdwaras

■ Haemophilia

see Blood disorders & haemophilia

■ Handicapped

see Disabled people (physical, sensory, learning impairments)

■ Head & other injuries

Funding priority

Blagrave Charitable Trust, The Herbert and Peter 52

Dahl Foundation, The Roald 122

D'Avigdor Goldsmid Charitable Trust, The Sarah 125

Lewis Family Charitable Trust 273

Nash Charity, The 326

Rugby Football Union Charitable Fund, The 398

Solway Sound Charitable Trust 430

■ Health care

see also Acute health care, Aftercare, Alternative health care, Counselling (health), Dentistry, Family planning clinic, First aid, Hospice at home, Nursing service, Primary health care, Respite care, care for carers, Support, self help groups, Well woman clinics

Funding priority

Aga Khan Foundation (UK) 7

Alexander Charitable Trust, Mrs K L 11

Alliance Family Foundation Limited 13

Allied Dunbar Charitable Trust Limited, The 13

Allied Dunbar Staff Charity Fund 13

Allsop Charitable Trust, Pat 14

Aquinas Trust 20

Artemis Charitable Trust, The 22

Arthritis and Rheumatism Council for Research in Great Britain and the Commonwealth, The 22

Askew Charitable Trust, The Ian 25

Assembled Church of Christ Trust, The 25

Astor of Hever Trust, The 26

Avins Trustees, The John 28

Bailey Charitable Trust, Veta 30

Ball Charitable Trust, The Bruce 31

Bealey Foundation, The 38

Beauland Ltd 39

Beckwith Charitable Trust, The Peter 40

Beckwith-Smith's Charitable Settlement, Mrs 40

Birmingham District Nursing Charitable Trust 49

Black Charitable Trust, Edna 51

Black Charitable Trust, Sydney 51

Blakey Charitable Trust, The Celia and Conrad 53

Boltons Trust, The 55

British Sugar Foundation 63

Brook Charitable Settlement, R E 64

Burns Charity, The Dorothy 70

Burry Charitable Trust, The 70

Cadbury Schweppes Foundation, The 76

Cancer Relief Macmillan Fund 79

Carron Charitable Trust, The 83

Carter Trust, The Frederick William 84

Cathedral Nursing Society Charitable Trust 85

Charities Fund 89

Child Growth Foundation 92

Chownes Foundation, The 93

Christian Renewal Trust, The 94

Christmas Cracker Trust 95

Cinderford Charitable Trust, The 96

Clark Charitable Trust, J Anthony 98

Clark Charitable Trust, Elizabeth 98

Cloudesley's Charity/School Parents & Friends Association, Richard 102

Coates Charitable Settlement, The 102

Cohen Charitable Trust, The Vivienne and Samuel 104

Cole Charitable Trust, The 105

Commonwealth Relations Trust 108

Condon Family Trust 109

Corbett's Charity, Thomas 112

Corden Trust, Cyril 113

Cotton Trust, The 114

Coxen Trust Fund, Sir William 116

Crawford Children's Charity, Michael 117

Crescent Trust, The 117

Dahl Foundation, The Roald 122

Delmar Charitable Trust 129

Derbyshire Trust, J N *130*
Desmond Charitable Trust, The Richard *131*
Devon Association for the Blind *131*
Djanogly Foundation, The *135*
Doughty Charity Trust, The *136*
D'Oyly Carte Charitable Trust, The *137*
Dunn Charitable Trust, The Harry *140*
Earmark Trust, The *142*
Eling Trust *147*
Ellerman Foundation, The John *148*
Elvetham Charitable Trust, The *149*
Family Trust, The *158*
Flanagan Leukaemia Fund, Bud *164*
Franklin Trust, Jill *170*
Frazer Charities Trust, The *171*
Frognal Trust *174*
Fry Charitable Trust, Maurice *174*
GW Trust, The *176*
Gatsby Charitable Foundation, The *179*
Gibson's Charity Trust, The Hon Mr & Mrs Clive *182*
Girdlers' Company Charitable Trust, The *184*
Good Neighbours Trust, The *188*
Goodman Charitable Foundation, The Everard and Mina *188*
Goodman Trust, The *189*
Gradel Foundation, The *189*
Gray Charitable Trust, R B *192*
Green Foundation, Constance *194*
Greenwood Charitable Trust, The G B *195*
Grut Charitable Trust, The *198*
Haemophilia Society, The *202*
Harbour Foundation Ltd, The *208*
Hartley Memorial Trust, The N & P *211*
Heinz Company Limited Charitable Trust, The H J *215*
Held Settlement, The Gisela *215*
Hill Memorial Trust, L E *219*
Hitachi Charitable Trust, The *222*
Hornton Trust, The *228*
IPE Charitable Trust, The *233*
Jewish Philanthropic Association for Israel and the Middle East, The *245*
Jones Trust, Cemlyn *248*
Jubilee Outreach Yorkshire *248*

Kendall Leukaemia Fund, Kay *252*
Keyes Trust, The Ursula *253*
Keymer Trust, The Ronald and Mary *253*
King Charitable Trust, The Lorna *254*
Kinnison Charitable Trust, R O *256*
Kobler Trust, The *258*
Kreitman Foundation *258*
Lambourne Memorial Trust, The Emma *262*
Landy Charitable Trust, Harry and Gertrude *263*
Langley Charitable Trust, The *264*
Lanvern Foundation *265*
Lauffer Charitable Foundation, The R & D *266*
Lavender Trust, The *267*
Levy Charitable Foundation, Joseph *272*
Liebes Charitable Trust, The Martha Bud *274*
Liffe Benefit *274*
Low & Bonar Charitable Fund, The *284*
Lucas Charitable Trust Limited, The Joseph *286*
MacAndrew Trust, The E M *289*
Mackintosh Foundation, The *292*
McLaren Memorial Trust, The Martin *293*
MacRobert Trusts, The *294*
Margadale Charitable Trust, Lord *297*
Marmor Charitable Trust, The Julie *299*
Medical Aid Trust *304*
Medlock Charitable Trust, The *304*
Merchants House of Glasgow *307*
Mercury Phoenix Trust *307*
Migraine Trust, The *310*
Millichope Foundation, The *312*
Minet Trust, The Peter *313*
Moore Charitable Trust, The Horace *316*
Morgan Crucible Company plc Charitable Trust, The *319*
Moulton Charitable Trust, The *321*
Muslim Hands *324*
National Kidney Research Fund Limited, The *328*
National Power Charitable Trust, The *330*
Newstead Charity, The *334*
Northcott Devon Foundation *338*
Northern Dairies Educational Trust *339*

Northern Electric Employee Charity Association *339*
Norton Foundation, The *340*
Oliver Trust, Kate Wilson *345*
Oppenheimer Charitable Trust *346*
PDC Trust, The *349*
PJD Charitable Trust *350*
Palmer Trust, The Gerald *352*
Pascoe Charitable Trust, Alan *354*
Paul Foundation, The *355*
Pershore Nashdom & Elmore Trust Ltd, The *360*
Personal Assurance Charitable Trust *360*
Peskin Charitable Trust, The Hazel and Leslie *360*
Pick Charitable Trust, The George and Jessie *362*
Pilkington Trust, The Austin and Hope *363*
Pitman Charitable Trust, The John *364*
Powys Welsh Church Fund *367*
Proctor Charitable Trust, The Albert Edward *370*
QAS Charitable Trust *373*
Rank Xerox Trust, The *378*
Rayne Foundation, The *379*
Rayner Charitable Trust, The John *380*
Reekie Trust, R A & V B *381*
Richards Charity, The Violet M *384*
Rivendell Trust, The *387*
Robbins Trust, The Cheshire *387*
Rosen Foundation, Cecil *392*
Rozel Trust, The *397*
Seedfield Trust, The *414*
Sherman Charitable Trust, The Archie *419*
Shifrin Charitable Trust, The Maurice and Hilda *419*
Sidbury Trust, The Second *421*
Salter Trust Ltd *424*
Smith Foundation, The Leslie *427*
Southon Charitable Trust, The *432*
Street Charitable Foundation, W O *440*
Stroke Association, The *441*
Swale Charity Trust *443*
Swan Mountain Trust *444*
Taylor Charitable Trust, The B R *450*
Tesco Charity Trust *452*
Ulverscroft Foundation, The *468*
Valentine Charitable Trust, The *470*
van Geest Foundation, The John and Lucille *470*
War on Want *479*
Watson Foundation, The Bertie *482*

Wesleyan Charitable Trust, The 485

West & Others, Charity of John 486

Westminster Amalgamated Charity 487

White Rose Children's Aid International Charity 489

Whitley Trust, Sheila 491

Whittington Charitable Trust, The 491

Wilde Charitable Trust, The Felicity 492

Wohl Charitable Foundation, The Maurice 498

Wohl Charitable Trust, The Maurice 498

Wolfson Family Charitable Trust, The 499

Wolfson Foundation, The 499

Woodcote Trust, The 501

Woolf Charitable Trust, The 502

Will consider

AHJ Charitable Trust, The 3

Achiezer Association Limited 6

Airflow Community Ltd, The 9

Aleh Charitable Foundation, The 10

Alexis Trust, The 11

Ancaster Trust, The 16

Anderson Trust, Andrew 16

Angler's Inn Trust 17

Appelbe Trust, Ambrose & Ann 19

Aquarian Healing Trust 19

Aquarius Charitable Foundation, The 19

Askew Trust, The Dorothy 25

Assheton-Smith Charitable Trust 25

Asthma Allergy and Inflammation Research Trust 25

Astor Foundation, The 26

Astor's 1969 Charity, The Hon M L 26

BBC Children in Need Appeal, The 29

BUPA Foundation, The 29

Baring Foundation, The 34

Barnby's Foundation, Lord 35

Barnes Workhouse Fund 35

Barnsbury Charitable Trust 35

Bateman Charitable Trust, Lady Margaret 37

Beattie Charitable Trust, The James 39

Bellahouston Bequest Fund 42

Bergqvist Charitable Trust 44

Bilton Charity, The Percy 48

Black Foundation, The Bertie 51

Blagrave Charitable Trust, The Herbert and Peter 52

Blake Charitable Trust, The Hubert 53

Blakenham's Charity Trust, Lady 53

Blank Donations Ltd, The David 54

Boots Charitable Trust 56

Borthwick Memorial Trust, The Oliver 56

Bowland Charitable Trust, The 57

Brand Trust, The 59

Brookhouse's Will Trust, Mr John Charles 65

Buckingham Trust 67

Burden Trust, The 69

Burn Charity Trust, The J H 70

Burton Charitable Trust, The Geoffrey 71

Butler's Trust, Lord 71

Butler's Trust, Lucilla 72

Cadbury Trust (1928), The Edward & Dorothy 76

Cardiff & Swansea Methodist District Charitable Trust Fund 80

Castang Charitable Trust, H and M 85

Challice Trust, The 87

Charity Projects 90

Chiddick Charitable Trust 92

Chrimes Family Charitable Trust, The 93

Christian Aid 94

Closehelm Ltd 101

Clutterbuck Charitable Trust, Robert 102

Coates Charitable Trust 1969, Lance 103

Cohen Charity Trust, Lucy 104

Collinson Charitable Trust, The Norman 106

Company of Tobacco Pipe Makers and Tobacco Blenders Benevolent Fund 109

Cope Charitable Trust, Alfred 112

Curry Charitable Trust, Dennis 119

Cymerman Trust Limited, Itzchok Meyer 120

Daily Telegraph Charitable Trust 122

Dandeen Charitable Trust 123

Davies Charity, The Gwendoline and Margaret 125

Davy Foundation, The J 126

De Avenley Foundation, The 126

De La Rue Charitable Trust 127

De Rothschild 1981 Charitable Trust, The Edmund 127

De Yong Charitable Trust, The Emma 128

Denby Charitable Foundation, The 130

Denne Charitable Trust 130

Denton Charitable Trust, The 130

Deutsch Charitable Trust, The Andre 131

Deutsch Charitable Trust, The H & M 131

Dicken Charitable Trust, The Albert 133

Dinam Charity 134

Drapers' Charitable Fund 137

Drayton Trust, The 138

Edinburgh Trust, No 2 Account 145

Egerton of Tatton Will Trust, Lord 146

Elshore Limited 149

Emanuel Charitable Settlement, Ralph and Muriel 150

Esperanza Charitable Trust, The 153

Famos Foundation Trust 158

Fane Research Trust, The Edmund 159

Federation of Jewish Relief Organisations 160

Fletcher Trust, Roy 165

Ford of Britain Trust 166

Foyle Trust, Charles Henry 169

Franklin Bequest, The Rosalind 169

Franklin Deceased's New Second Charity, Sydney E 170

Friarsgate Trust 172

Frome Christian Fellowship 174

Galinski Charitable Trust 177

Gardner Charitable Trust, R & J 178

Garthgwynion Charities 179

Gillett Charitable Trust, J A 183

Gill's Charitable Trust, Mrs M M 184

Gold Hill Church Trust 186

Goldberg Charitable Trust, The Lewis 186

Golders Green Foundation 187

Goodman Trust, The S & F 189

Graves Charitable Trust, J G 192

Greenaway Foundation, The Sir Derek 194

Gross Charities Limited, M & R 197

Grosshill Charitable Trust 197

HB Charitable Trust 201

Hacking & Sons Ltd Charitable Trust, C G 201

Hamilton Educational Trust, Eleanor 205

Hampstead Wells and Campden Trust 206

Hargreaves Trust, The Kenneth 210

Harvey Charitable Trust, Gordon *211*

Hawthorne Charitable Trust, The *212*

Higgs Charitable Trust, The *218*

Hillards Charitable Trust, Gay & Peter Hartley's *220*

Holford Trust Fund *224*

Hoover Foundation, The *226*

Horn Trust, The Cuthbert *227*

Hornby Charitable Trust, Miss D *227*

Hudson Benevolent Trust, The Thomas *230*

Hughes Charitable Trust, The Geoffery C *230*

Hussey for Africans, Charity of Rebecca *231*

Hyde Park Place Estate Charity, The *232*

Inman Charity, The *235*

International Arab Women's Council Charities Fund *236*

Inverforth Charitable Trust, The *236*

Irving Charitable Trust, The Charles *237*

JCSCJ Charitable Trust, The *238*

James Foundation, The Catherine and Lady Grace *241*

Jarrold Trust Ltd, John *243*

Jewish Childs' Day *245*

Johnson Foundation, The *246*

Johnson Foundation, The Beth *247*

KC Charitable Trust, The *250*

Karten Charitable Trust, The Ian *250*

King Charitable Settlement, Philip *254*

King's Fund, The *255*

Kingsgrove Charitable Trust, The *255*

Kleinwort Charitable Trust, The Ernest *257*

Knott Trust, Sir James *258*

Kulika Charitable Trust, The *259*

Kweller Charitable Trust, The Harry *259*

Laing Foundation, The Christopher *260*

Laski Memorial Charitable Trust, Nathan *265*

Laspen Trust *265*

Lass Charities Limited, Rachel and Jack *265*

Lawley Foundation, The Edgar E *267*

Leigh-Bramwell Trust 'E', P *270*

Lewis Family Charitable Trust, The *273*

Lewis Partnership, John *274*

Lingwood Charitable Trust, The *276*

Livesley 1992 Charitable Trust, Mrs C M *277*

Localtrent Ltd *279*

Lunzer Charitable Trust, The Ruth & Jack *287*

Lynwood Charitable Trust, The *288*

Lyons Charitable Trust, The *288*

Lyons Charitable Trust, Sir Jack *288*

MDM Memorial Trust *289*

McCallum Bequest Fund *290*

McKechnie Foundation, A N *292*

McKenzie Trust, The Robert *292*

McLaren Foundation *292*

Man of the People Fund *295*

Margaret Foundation, The *297*

Marks Charitable Trust, Michael *298*

Marks Foundation, The Hilda and Samuel *298*

Markus Charitable Foundation, The Erich *298*

Marriage's Charitable Trust, Miss G M *299*

Marr-Munning Trust *299*

Marshall Charitable Trust, The Charlotte *300*

Martin Trust, The Sir George *300*

Matchan Fund Limited, The Leonard *301*

Material World Charitable Foundation Limited, The *301*

Mattock Charitable Trust, The W T *302*

Mayfair Charities Limited *303*

Meath, Charity of Mary Jane, Countess of *304*

Mellows Charitable Settlement, The Anthony and Elizabeth *305*

Middlesex County Rugby Football Union Memorial Fund *309*

Milburn Charitable Trust, Frederick *310*

Millett Charitable Trust, The Alan and Janet *312*

Modiano Charitable Trust *315*

Montefiore Trust, The David *316*

Moore Stephens Charitable Foundation, The *317*

Morel Charitable Trust, The *318*

Morphy Memorial Fund, Arthur *319*

Morris Charitable Trust, The Willie & Mabel *320*

Music Sales Charitable Trust, The *324*

NR Charitable Trust, The *325*

National Lottery Charities Board *328*

Newcastle's 1986 Charitable Trust, Duke of *333*

Newman Charitable Trust, Mr and Mrs F E F *334*

Nidditch Foundation, The Laurie *335*

Norfolk's Family Charitable Trust, Lavinia *336*

North West Arts Board *337*

Northcott Charity Trust, The *338*

Northern Arts *339*

Northern Ireland Voluntary Trust *339*

Nuffield Foundation *342*

Old Possums Practical Trust, The *344*

Owen Family Trust, The *348*

Owen Trust, Margaret *348*

PF Charitable Trust *350*

Paristamen Foundation, The *352*

Paterson Charitable Foundation, The Constance *354*

Paterson Charitable Trust, Arthur James *354*

Patients' Aid Association Hospital and Medical Charities Trust *354*

Paul Charitable Trust, The Late Barbara May *355*

Paul Charitable Trust, Margaret Jeanne *355*

Paul Charitable Trust, Pamela Milton *355*

Paul's Charitable Trust, R J *355*

Payne Charitable Trust, The *355*

Pelech Charitable Trust, The *358*

Perry Charitable Trust, Miss Frances Lucille *359*

Phillips Charitable Foundation, Reginald M *361*

Pilkington Charitable Trust, Cecil *363*

Pitt Trust, Headley *364*

Porter Foundation *366*

Prendergast Charitable Trust, The Simone *368*

Puebla Charitable Trust Limited, The *371*

Quothquan Charitable Trust, The Second *373*

RT Trust, The *374*

Rackham Charitable Trust, The Mr & Mrs Philip *375*

Radley Charitable Trust *375*

Rae Charity, H J *375*

Rainford Trust, The *376*

Rav Chesed Trust, The *379*

Rest-Harrow Trust, The *382*

Reuter Foundation, The *382*

Rich Charities, S & J *383*

Richard Charitable Trust, The
  Cliff *383*
Richards Charity, The Clive *384*
Richmond Parish Lands Charity
  384
Rodewald's Charitable
  Settlement, Mr C A *389*
Rogers Charitable Settlement,
  The Richard *390*
Rokeby Charitable Trust *390*
Rolfe Charitable Trust, The *390*
Rookes Charitable Trust, C A
  390
Rowan Charitable Trust, The
  393
S Group Charitable Trust *399*
Said Foundation, The Karim
  Rida *401*
St Jude's Trust *403*
Salters Charities *405*
Samuel Charitable Trust, M J
  406
Save & Prosper Foundation
  409
Scarr-Hall Memorial Trust, The
  409
Scott Charitable Trust, The
  Francis C *412*
Seva Trust, Rampaba Sadhu
  415
Silvester Charitable Gift Trust
  422
Skinners' Company Lady Neville
  Charity *424*
Smith Trust, Metcalfe *427*
Society of Friends of the Torah,
  The *429*
Solomons Charitable Trust,
  David *430*
Somerfield Curtis Will Trust,
  The Dorothy *430*
Stanley Foundation Limited
  435
Stewart Charitable Trust, Mary
  Stephanie *437*
Sumner's Trust Section 'A', Sir
  John *443*
Swann-Morton Foundation,
  The *444*
Symons Charitable Trust, The
  Stella *446*
TSB Foundation for Scotland
  447
TSB Foundation for the
  Channel Islands *447*
Tait Charity, The Richard *448*
Templeton Goodwill Trust *451*
Terry Charitable Trust, Noel
  Goddard *451*
Tesler Foundation, The *452*
3i Charitable Trust, The *455*
Toler Foundation, The *457*
Toyota (GB) Charitable Trust,
  The *459*
Upjohn Charitable Trust, The
  469
Van Norden's Charitable
  Foundation, Mrs Maud *471*

Vincent Trust Fund, Eric W *473*
Vineyard Christian Fellowship
  of South West *473*
Vinson Charity Trust, The 1969
  473
Vogel Charitable Trust, The
  Nathan *474*
Wagstaff Charitable Trust, Bob
  475
Wakefield Trust, The *476*
Walker Trust, The *477*
Wander Charitable Fund, The
  Dr Albert *479*
Ward Blenkinsop Trust, The
  480
Weinstock Fund, The *484*
Welby Trust, The Barbara *484*
Whetherly's Charitable Trust,
  The Hon Mrs R G A *489*
Whitehead Charitable Trust, J E
  490
Wiggins Charity Trust, Cyril
  491
Wills 1961 Charitable Trust,
  Major Michael Thomas *494*
Wiltshire Community
  Foundation *495*
Wingate Foundation, The
  Harold Hyam *496*
Winstone Foundation, Hyman
  497
Woburn 1986 Charitable Trust
  498
Wolfe Family's Charitable
  Trust, The *498*
Wolff Charity Trust *498*
Woodhouse Charitable Trust,
  Edwin *501*
Woods Charitable Foundation,
  Geoffrey *502*
Worms Charitable Trust, The
  Freda and Della *504*
Worshipful Company of
  Founders Charities, The *505*
Worshipful Company of
  Needlemakers' Charitable
  Fund *505*
Wychdale Limited *507*
Youell Foundation Ltd, The
  510
Zaiger Trust, The Elizabeth and
  Prince *512*

....

■ Health economics

see **Medical studies &
research**

....

■ Health education

see also **Campaigning
(health)**

Funding priority

Allied Dunbar Charitable Trust
  Limited, The *13*
British Heart Foundation *62*

Cloudesley's Charity/School
  Parents & Friends
  Association, Richard *102*
Foreman Foundation, The Carl
  & Eve *167*
Humphreys Charitable
  Settlement, J A M *231*
Mercury Phoenix Trust *307*
Paristamen Foundation, The
  352
Simon Population Trust, The
  422
Stroke Association, The *441*
Tisbury Telegraph Trust, The
  457

Will consider

Ammco Trust, The *15*
Astor Foundation, The *26*
Bancroft Trust, The *33*
Barbour Trust, The *33*
Beckwith Charitable
  Settlement, The Heather *39*
Berkshire Community Trust *45*
Brooke Benevolent Fund,
  William *65*
Charities Fund *89*
Clinton's Charitable Trust, Lord
  100
County Durham Foundation
  115
Coutts Charitable Trust, The
  116
Digby Charitable Trust, Simon
  133
Dorus Trust *136*
Eaton Charitable Trust, J C J
  143
Edgar Foundation, The Gilbert
  and Eileen *145*
Elkes Charity Fund, The Wilfred
  & Elsie *147*
Emanuel Charitable Settlement,
  Ralph and Muriel *150*
Epigoni Trust *152*
Erycinus Charitable Trust *153*
Follett Trust, The *166*
GW Trust, The *176*
Gray Charitable Trust, R B *192*
Great Britain Sasakawa
  Foundation, The *193*
Greenaway Foundation, The Sir
  Derek *194*
Grocers' Charity *197*
Grundy Foundation, The
  Stanley *198*
Isle of Dogs Community
  Foundation *238*
Kroch Foundation, The Heinz &
  Anna *259*
Laing Charitable Trust, The
  David *260*
Laing Foundation, The Maurice
  261
Lankelly Foundation, The *264*
Lawson Charitable Trust,
  Raymond and Blanche *267*

Leech Charity, The William 269
Lewis Partnership, John 274
Lloyd's Charities Trust 278
Mental Health Foundation, The 305
Minet Trust, The Peter 313
Needham Cooper Charitable Trust, The 331
Noswad Charity, The 341
Owen Family Trust, The 348
Paterson Charitable Foundation, The Constance 354
Paterson Charitable Trust, Arthur James 354
Payne Trust, The Harry 356
Purey-Cust Trust, The 371
Reader's Digest Trust, The 380
Schuster Charitable Trust, The 410
Skelton Bounty, The 423
South Square Trust 430
Stewart Trust, Sir Halley 437
TSB Foundation for Northern Ireland 447
Travis Charitable Trust, Constance 460
Wakeham Trust, The 476
Webber Trust Fund, Ethel 483
Wills 1962 Charitable Trust, P J H 494
Wiltshire Community Foundation 495
Woolton Charitable Trust, The 503
Worshipful Company of Engineers' Charitable Trust Fund, The 504

■ Health facilities & buildings

see also **Ambulances & mobile units, Convalescent homes, Hospices, Hospitals, Medical centres, Nursing homes, Rehabilitation centres**

Funding priority

Aga Khan Foundation (UK) 7
Alexander Charitable Trust, Mrs K L 11
Alliance Family Foundation Limited 13
Allied Dunbar Staff Charity Fund 13
Allsop Charitable Trust, Pat 14
Aquinas Trust 20
Assembled Church of Christ Trust, The 25
Astor of Hever Trust, The 26
Avins Trustees, The John 28
Baronets Trust, The 35
Bealey Foundation, The 38
Beauland Ltd 39
Beckwith Charitable Trust, The Peter 40

Beckwith-Smith's Charitable Settlement, Mrs 40
Birmingham Amenities and Welfare Trust, The 49
Birmingham District Nursing Charitable Trust 49
Black Charitable Trust, Edna 51
Black Charitable Trust, Sydney 51
Black's Charity, Sir Alec 52
Blakey Charitable Trust, The Celia and Conrad 53
Boltons Trust, The 55
Bridge Trust, The 60
British Heart Foundation 62
British Sugar Foundation 63
Brook Charitable Settlement, R E 64
Burns Charity, The Dorothy 70
Burry Charitable Trust, The 70
Cadbury Schweppes Foundation, The 76
Cancer Relief Macmillan Fund 79
Carron Charitable Trust, The 83
Carter Trust, The Frederick William 84
Charities Fund 89
Christian Renewal Trust, The 94
Christmas Cracker Trust 95
Cinderford Charitable Trust, The 96
City Parochial Foundation 96
Clark Charitable Trust, J Anthony 98
Cloudesley's Charity/School Parents & Friends Association, Richard 102
Coates Charitable Settlement, The 102
Cohen Charitable Trust, The Vivienne and Samuel 104
Cohen Charity Trust, Lucy 104
Condon Family Trust 109
Cotton Trust, The 114
Crawford Children's Charity, Michael 117
Crescent Trust, The 117
Cripps Foundation 118
Delmar Charitable Trust 129
Desmond Charitable Trust, The Richard 131
Devon Association for the Blind 131
Djanogly Foundation, The 135
Doughty Charity Trust, The 136
D'Oyly Carte Charitable Trust, The 137
Dunn Charitable Trust, The Harry 140
Eling Trust 147
Elvetham Charitable Trust, The 149
Family Trust, The 158

Frazer Charities Trust, The 171
Fry Charitable Trust, Maurice 174
Gibson's Charity Trust, The Hon Mr & Mrs Clive 182
Girdlers' Company Charitable Trust, The 184
Good Neighbours Trust, The 188
Goodman Charitable Foundation, The Everard and Mina 188
Goodman Trust, The 189
Gradel Foundation, The 189
Green Foundation, Constance 194
Greenwood Charitable Trust, The G B 195
Harbour Foundation Ltd, The 208
Heinz Company Limited Charitable Trust, The H J 215
Held Settlement, The Gisela 215
Hitachi Charitable Trust, The 222
Hornton Trust, The 228
Hudson Charitable Trust, The 230
Hutchinson Charitable Trust, E B 232
IPE Charitable Trust, The 233
Jewish Philanthropic Association for Israel and the Middle East, The 245
Jones Trust, Cemlyn 248
Jubilee Outreach Yorkshire 248
Keyes Trust, The Ursula 253
King Charitable Trust, The Lorna 254
Kinnison Charitable Trust, R O 256
Kobler Trust, The 258
Kreitman Foundation 258
Landy Charitable Trust, Harry and Gertrude 263
Langley Charitable Trust, The 264
Lanvern Foundation 265
Lauffer Charitable Foundation, The R & D 266
Lavender Trust, The 267
Levy Charitable Foundation, Joseph 272
Liffe Benefit 274
Lloyd's Charities Trust 278
Low & Bonar Charitable Fund, The 284
Lucas Charitable Trust Limited, The Joseph 286
MacAndrew Trust, The E M 289
MacRobert Trusts, The 294
Marmor Charitable Trust, The Julie 299

Measures Charity, The James Frederick and Ethel Anne *303*

Medical Aid Trust *304*

Medlock Charitable Trust, The *304*

Mercury Phoenix Trust *307*

Millichope Foundation, The *312*

Moore Charitable Trust, The Horace *316*

Morgan Crucible Company plc Charitable Trust, The *319*

Moulton Charitable Trust, The *321*

Muslim Hands *324*

National Power Charitable Trust, The *330*

Newstead Charity, The *334*

Nidditch Foundation, The Laurie *335*

Northern Dairies Educational Trust *339*

Northern Electric Employee Charity Association *339*

Norton Foundation, The *340*

Oliver Trust, Kate Wilson *345*

Oppenheimer Charitable Trust *346*

PDC Trust, The *349*

PJD Charitable Trust *350*

Palmer Trust, The Gerald *352*

Pascoe Charitable Trust, Alan *354*

Paul Foundation, The *355*

Pershore Nashdom & Elmore Trust Ltd, The *360*

Personal Assurance Charitable Trust *360*

Peskin Charitable Trust, The Hazel and Leslie *360*

Pick Charitable Trust, The George and Jessie *362*

Pilkington Trust, The Austin and Hope *363*

Pitman Charitable Trust, The John *364*

Proctor Charitable Trust, The Albert Edward *370*

QAS Charitable Trust *373*

Rayne Foundation, The *379*

Rayner Charitable Trust, The John *380*

Reekie Trust, R A & V B *381*

Richards Charity, The Violet M *384*

Robbins Trust, The Cheshire *387*

Rodewald's Charitable Settlement, Mr C A *389*

Rozel Trust, The *397*

Sailors' and Soldiers' Home Fund, and Leonard Lionel Bloomfield's Charity, The *401*

Sherman Charitable Trust, The Archie *419*

Shifrin Charitable Trust, The Maurice and Hilda *419*

Sidbury Trust, The Second *421*

Salter Trust Ltd *424*

Street Charitable Foundation, W O *440*

Sykes Trust, The Charles *445*

Taylor Charitable Trust, The B R *450*

Tesco Charity Trust *452*

Valentine Charitable Trust, The *470*

van Geest Foundation, The John and Lucille *470*

Watson Foundation, The Bertie *482*

Wesleyan Charitable Trust, The *485*

Westminster Amalgamated Charity *487*

White Rose Children's Aid International Charity *489*

Whitley Trust, Sheila *491*

Whittington Charitable Trust, The *491*

Wilde Charitable Trust, The Felicity *492*

Wohl Charitable Foundation, The Maurice *498*

Wohl Charitable Trust, The Maurice *498*

Wolfson Family Charitable Trust, The *499*

Wolfson Foundation, The *499*

Woodcote Trust, The *501*

Woodhouse Charitable Trust, Edwin *501*

Woolf Charitable Trust, The *502*

Wylde Memorial Charity, The Anthony and Gwendoline *507*

Will consider

AHJ Charitable Trust, The *3*

Achiezer Association Limited *6*

Airflow Community Ltd, The *9*

Aleh Charitable Foundation, The *10*

Alexis Trust, The *11*

Anderson Trust, Andrew *16*

Angler's Inn Trust *17*

Appelbe Trust, Ambrose & Ann *19*

Aquarian Healing Trust *19*

Aquarius Charitable Foundation, The *19*

Askew Charitable Trust, The Ian *25*

Askew Trust, The Dorothy *25*

Assheton-Smith Charitable Trust *25*

Asthma Allergy and Inflammation Research Trust *25*

Astor Foundation, The *26*

Astor's 1969 Charity, The Hon M L *26*

BBC Children in Need Appeal, The *29*

BUPA Foundation, The *29*

Barnby's Foundation, Lord *35*

Barnes Workhouse Fund *35*

Barnsbury Charitable Trust *35*

Bateman Charitable Trust, Lady Margaret *37*

Beattie Charitable Trust, The James *39*

Bergqvist Charitable Trust *44*

Berris Charitable Trust *45*

Bilton Charity, The Percy *48*

Black Foundation, The Bertie *51*

Blagrave Charitable Trust, The Herbert and Peter *52*

Blake Charitable Trust, The Hubert *53*

Blakenham's Charity Trust, Lady *53*

Blank Donations Ltd, The David *54*

Boots Charitable Trust *56*

Borthwick Memorial Trust, The Oliver *56*

Bottom Charitable Trust, Harry *56*

Bowland Charitable Trust, The *57*

Brookhouse's Will Trust, Mr John Charles *65*

Buckingham Trust *67*

Burn Charity Trust, The J H *70*

Burton Charitable Trust, The Geoffrey *71*

Butler's Trust, Lord *71*

Butler's Trust, Lucilla *72*

Cadbury Trust (1928), The Edward & Dorothy *76*

Cardiff & Swansea Methodist District Charitable Trust Fund *80*

Castang Charitable Trust, H and M *85*

Charity Projects *90*

Chrimes Family Charitable Trust, The *93*

Christian Aid *94*

Closehelm Ltd *101*

Clutterbuck Charitable Trust, Robert *102*

Coates Charitable Trust 1969, Lance *103*

Collinson Charitable Trust, The Norman *106*

Company of Tobacco Pipe Makers and Tobacco Blenders Benevolent Fund *109*

Cope Charitable Trust, Alfred *112*

Curry Charitable Trust, Dennis *119*

Cymerman Trust Limited, Itzchok Meyer *120*

Daily Telegraph Charitable Trust *122*

Dandeen Charitable Trust *123*

Davies Charity, The Gwendoline and Margaret *125*

De Avenley Foundation, The *126*

De Rothschild 1981 Charitable Trust, The Edmund *127*

De Yong Charitable Trust, The Emma *128*

Denton Charitable Trust, The *130*

Deutsch Charitable Trust, The Andre *131*

Deutsch Charitable Trust, The H & M *131*

Dicken Charitable Trust, The Albert *133*

Dinam Charity *134*

Drapers' Charitable Fund *137*

Drayton Trust, The *138*

Dunhill Medical Trust, The *140*

Earley Charity, The *142*

Earmark Trust, The *142*

Edinburgh Trust, No 2 Account *145*

Elkes Charity Fund, The Wilfred & Elsie *147*

Elshore Limited *149*

Elton John Aids Foundation, The *149*

Esperanza Charitable Trust, The *153*

Famos Foundation Trust *158*

Fane Research Trust, The Edmund *159*

Federation of Jewish Relief Organisations *160*

Fletcher Trust, Roy *165*

Follett Trust, The *166*

Foreman Foundation, The Carl & Eve *167*

Foyle Trust, Charles Henry *169*

Franklin Bequest, The Rosalind *169*

Friarsgate Trust *172*

Frome Christian Fellowship *174*

Galinski Charitable Trust *177*

Gardner Charitable Trust, R & J *178*

Garthgwynion Charities *179*

Gibbins Trust, The *181*

Gillett Charitable Trust, J A *183*

Gill's Charitable Trust, Mrs M M *184*

Gold Hill Church Trust *186*

Goldberg Charitable Trust, The Lewis *186*

Golders Green Foundation *187*

Goodman Trust, The S & F *189*

Greenaway Foundation, The Sir Derek *194*

Gross Charities Limited, M & R *197*

Grosshill Charitable Trust *197*

Grundy Foundation, The Stanley *198*

Grut Charitable Trust, The *198*

HB Charitable Trust *201*

Hacking & Sons Ltd Charitable Trust, C G *201*

Halkes Settlement, John Robert *204*

Hamilton Educational Trust, Eleanor *205*

Hampstead Wells and Campden Trust *206*

Hargreaves Trust, The Kenneth *210*

Hawley Residuary Fund, Harry Fieldsend *212*

Hawthorne Charitable Trust, The *212*

Higgs Charitable Trust, The *218*

Hillards Charitable Trust, Gay & Peter Hartley's *220*

Holford Trust Fund *224*

Hoover Foundation, The *226*

Horn Trust, The Cuthbert *227*

Hornby Charitable Trust, Miss D *227*

Hudson Benevolent Trust, The Thomas *230*

Hughes Charitable Trust, The Geoffery C *230*

Hussey for Africans, Charity of Rebecca *231*

Hyde Park Place Estate Charity, The *232*

Innes Memorial Fund *235*

International Arab Women's Council Charities Fund *236*

Inverforth Charitable Trust, The *236*

Irving Charitable Trust, The Charles *237*

JCSCJ Charitable Trust, The *238*

James Foundation, The Catherine and Lady Grace *241*

Jarrold Trust Ltd, John *243*

Jewish Childs' Day *245*

Johnson Foundation, The *246*

Johnson Foundation, The Beth *247*

KC Charitable Trust, The *250*

Karten Charitable Trust, The Ian *250*

King Charitable Settlement, Philip *254*

Kingsgrove Charitable Trust, The *255*

Kleinwort Charitable Trust, The Ernest *257*

Knott Trust, Sir James *258*

Kulika Charitable Trust, The *259*

Kweller Charitable Trust, The Harry *259*

Laing Foundation, The Christopher *260*

Laing's Charitable Trust *262*

Lambourne Memorial Trust, The Emma *262*

Laski Memorial Charitable Trust, Nathan *265*

Laspen Trust *265*

Lass Charities Limited, Rachel and Jack *265*

Lawley Foundation, The Edgar E *267*

Leigh-Bramwell Trust 'E', P *270*

Lewis Family Charitable Trust, The *273*

Lewis Partnership, John *274*

Lingwood Charitable Trust, The *276*

Livesley 1992 Charitable Trust, Mrs C M *277*

Localtrent Ltd *279*

Loseley & Guildway Charitable Trust, The *281*

Lunzer Charitable Trust, The Ruth & Jack *287*

Lynwood Charitable Trust, The *288*

Lyons Charitable Trust, The *288*

Lyons Charitable Trust, Sir Jack *288*

MDM Memorial Trust *289*

McKechnie Foundation, A N *292*

McKenzie Trust, The Robert *292*

Mackintosh Foundation, The *292*

McLaren Foundation *292*

McLaren Memorial Trust, The Martin *293*

Man of the People Fund *295*

Margadale Charitable Trust, Lord *297*

Margaret Foundation, The *297*

Marks Charitable Trust, Michael *298*

Marks Foundation, The Hilda and Samuel *298*

Markus Charitable Foundation, The Erich *298*

Marriage's Charitable Trust, Miss G M *299*

Marr-Munning Trust *299*

Marshall Charitable Trust, Charlotte *300*

Martin Trust, The Sir George *300*

Matchan Fund Limited, The Leonard *301*

Material World Charitable Foundation Limited, The *301*

Mattock Charitable Trust, The W T *302*

Mayfair Charities Limited *303*

Meath, Charity of Mary Jane, Countess of *304*

Merchants House of Glasgow *307*

Millett Charitable Trust, The Alan and Janet *312*

Minet Trust, The Peter *313*

Modiano Charitable Trust *315*

Montefiore Trust, The David *316*

Moore Stephens Charitable Foundation, The *317*

Morel Charitable Trust, The *318*

Morphy Memorial Fund, Arthur *319*

Morris Charitable Trust, The Willie & Mabel *320*

Music Sales Charitable Trust, The *324*

NR Charitable Trust, The *325*

National Lottery Charities Board *328*

Newcastle's 1986 Charitable Trust, Duke of *333*

Newman Charitable Trust, Mr and Mrs F E F *334*

Norfolk's Family Charitable Trust, Lavinia *336*

North West Arts Board *337*

Northcott Charity Trust, The *338*

Northern Arts *339*

Northern Ireland Voluntary Trust *339*

Nuffield Foundation *342*

Old Possums Practical Trust, The *344*

Owen Trust, Margaret *348*

PF Charitable Trust *350*

Paristamen Foundation, The *352*

Paterson Charitable Foundation, The Constance *354*

Paterson Charitable Trust, Arthur James *354*

Patients' Aid Association Hospital and Medical Charities Trust *354*

Paul Charitable Trust, The Late Barbara May *355*

Paul Charitable Trust, Margaret Jeanne *355*

Paul Charitable Trust, Pamela Milton *355*

Payne Charitable Trust, The *355*

Pelech Charitable Trust, The *358*

Perry Charitable Trust, Miss Frances Lucille *359*

Phillips Charitable Foundation, Reginald M *361*

Pilkington Charitable Trust, Cecil *363*

Pitt Trust, Headley *364*

Porter Foundation *366*

Powys Welsh Church Fund *367*

Puebla Charitable Trust Limited, The *371*

RT Trust, The *374*

Rackham Charitable Trust, The Mr & Mrs Philip *375*

Radley Charitable Trust *375*

Rae Charity, H J *375*

Rainford Trust, The *376*

Rav Chesed Trust, The *379*

Reuter Foundation, The *382*

Rich Charities, S & J *383*

Richard Charitable Trust, The Cliff *383*

Richards Charity, The Clive *384*

Richmond Parish Lands Charity *384*

Rivendell Trust, The *387*

Rogers Charitable Settlement, The Richard *390*

Rokeby Charitable Trust *390*

Rolfe Charitable Trust, The *390*

Rosen Foundation, Cecil *392*

Rowan Charitable Trust, The *393*

S Group Charitable Trust *399*

Said Foundation, The Karim Rida *401*

St Jude's Trust *403*

Salters Charities *405*

Samuel Charitable Trust, M J *406*

Sargeant's Charitable Trust, Mrs M E *407*

Save & Prosper Foundation *409*

Scarr-Hall Memorial Trust, The *409*

Scott Charitable Trust, The Francis C *412*

Seedfield Trust, The *414*

Seva Trust, Rampaba Sadhu *415*

Silvester Charitable Gift Trust *422*

Skinners' Company Lady Neville Charity *424*

Smith (Estates Charities), Henry *426*

Society of Friends of the Torah, The *429*

Solomons Charitable Trust, David *430*

Somerfield Curtis Will Trust, The Dorothy *430*

Stanley Foundation Limited *435*

Stewart Charitable Trust, Mary Stephanie *437*

Sumner's Trust Section 'A', Sir John *443*

Swann-Morton Foundation, The *444*

Symons Charitable Trust, The Stella *446*

TSB Foundation for the Channel Islands *447*

Terry Charitable Trust, Noel Goddard *451*

Tesler Foundation, The *452*

3i Charitable Trust, The *455*

Toler Foundation, The *457*

Toyota (GB) Charitable Trust, The *459*

Upjohn Charitable Trust, The *469*

Van Norden's Charitable Foundation, Mrs Maud *471*

Vincent Trust Fund, Eric W *473*

Vineyard Christian Fellowship of South West *473*

Vinson Charity Trust, The 1969 *473*

Vogel Charitable Trust, The Nathan *474*

Wagstaff Charitable Trust, Bob *475*

Wakefield Trust, The *476*

Walker Trust, The *477*

Wander Charitable Fund, The Dr Albert *479*

War on Want *479*

Ward Blenkinsop Trust, The *480*

Weinstock Fund, The *484*

Welby Trust, The Barbara *484*

Whetherly's Charitable Trust, The Hon Mrs R G A *489*

Whitehead Charitable Trust, J E *490*

Wiggins Charity Trust, Cyril *491*

Wills 1961 Charitable Trust, Major Michael Thomas *494*

Wills 1962 Charitable Trust, P J H *494*

Wingate Foundation, The Harold Hyam *496*

Winstone Foundation, Hyman *497*

Woburn 1986 Charitable Trust *498*

Wolfe Family's Charitable Trust, The *498*

Wolff Charity Trust *498*

Woods Charitable Foundation, Geoffrey *502*

Worms Charitable Trust, The Freda and Della *504*

Worshipful Company of Founders Charities, The *505*

Worshipful Company of Needlemakers' Charitable Fund *505*

Wychdale Limited *507*

Youell Foundation Ltd, The *510*

Zaiger Trust, The Elizabeth and Prince *512*

■ Health issues

see also **Campaigning (health)**

Funding priority

Allied Dunbar Charitable Trust Limited, The *13*
Cloudesley's Charity/School Parents & Friends Association, Richard *102*
Heritage of London Trust, The *216*
Hutchinson Charitable Trust, E B *232*
Kroch Foundation, The Heinz & Anna *259*
Paristamen Foundation, The *352*

Will consider

Ammco Trust, The *15*
Astor Foundation, The *26*
Bancroft Trust, The *33*
Barbour Trust, The *33*
Beckwith Charitable Settlement, The Heather *39*
Berkshire Community Trust *45*
Charities Fund *89*
Clinton's Charitable Trust, Lord *100*
County Durham Foundation *115*
Coutts Charitable Trust, The *116*
Denne Charitable Trust *130*
Digby Charitable Trust, Simon *133*
Dorus Trust *136*
Eaton Charitable Trust, J C J *143*
Edgar Foundation, The Gilbert and Eileen *145*
Elkes Charity Fund, The Wilfred & Elsie *147*
Epigoni Trust *152*
Erycinus Charitable Trust *153*
Follett Trust, The *166*
Foreman Foundation, The Carl & Eve *167*
Gray Charitable Trust, R B *192*
Great Britain Sasakawa Foundation, The *193*
Greenaway Foundation, The Sir Derek *194*
Grocers' Charity *197*
Hunter Charitable Trust, The Claire *231*
Isle of Dogs Community Foundation *238*
Leech Charity, The William *269*
Lloyd's Charities Trust *278*
MacKintosh Charitable Trust, Viscount *292*
Mental Health Foundation, The *305*
Minet Trust, The Peter *313*
National Waterways Restoration & Development

Fund of the Inland Waterways Association, The *330*
Needham Cooper Charitable Trust, The *331*
Owen Family Trust, The *348*
Payne Trust, The Harry *356*
Persula Foundation, The *360*
Purey-Cust Trust, The *371*
Reader's Digest Trust, The *380*
South Square Trust *430*
Stewart Trust, Sir Halley *437*
Summer's and I May's Charitable Settlement, The Late Misses (A N) *442*
Tear Fund *450*
Tisbury Telegraph Trust, The *457*
Travis Charitable Trust, Constance *460*
Wakeham Trust, The *476*
Webber Trust Fund, Ethel *483*

■ Health professional bodies

see also **Professional bodies**

Funding priority

Astor Foundation, The *26*
Cooper Charitable Trust *111*
Fogel Charitable Trust, The Gerald *165*
Lynall Foundation, The D G *287*

Will consider

Barbour Trust, The *33*
Boots Charitable Trust *56*
Cottingham Charitable Trust, Mrs Diana Mary *114*
Denne Charitable Trust *130*
Digby Charitable Trust, Simon *133*
Edgar Foundation, The Gilbert and Eileen *145*
Franklin Trust, Jill *170*
Great Britain Sasakawa Foundation, The *193*
Humanitarian Trust, The *230*
Leech Charity, The William *269*
London Law Trust *280*
Newby Trust Ltd *332*
Norwich Church of England Young Men's Society *340*
Persula Foundation, The *360*
Robinson Brothers (Ryders Green) Ltd, Charitable Trust *388*
Summer's and I May's Charitable Settlement, The Late Misses (A N) *442*
Wakefield (Tower Hill, Trinity Square) Trust *476*
Webber Trust Fund, Ethel *483*
Whesby Ltd *488*

Whitaker Charitable Trust *489*
Woolton Charitable Trust, The *503*

■ Health promotion

see also **Campaigning (health)**

Funding priority

Kroch Foundation, The Heinz & Anna *259*
Meridian Broadcasting Charitable Trust *307*
Noah Trust, The *335*
Paristamen Foundation, The *352*
Purey-Cust Trust, The *371*
SMB Trust, The *400*

Will consider

Ammco Trust, The *15*
Astor Foundation, The *26*
Bancroft Trust, The *33*
Barbour Trust, The *33*
Berkshire Community Trust *45*
Brooke Benevolent Fund, William *65*
Charities Fund *89*
Clinton's Charitable Trust, Lord *100*
Cloudesley's Charity/School Parents & Friends Association, Richard *102*
County Durham Foundation *115*
Coutts Charitable Trust, The *116*
Digby Charitable Trust, Simon *133*
Dorus Trust *136*
Eaton Charitable Trust, J C J *143*
Edgar Foundation, The Gilbert and Eileen *145*
Elkes Charity Fund, The Wilfred & Elsie *147*
Epigoni Trust *152*
Erycinus Charitable Trust *153*
Follett Trust, The *166*
Foreman Foundation, The Carl & Eve *167*
Gray Charitable Trust, R B *192*
Great Britain Sasakawa Foundation, The *193*
Greenaway Foundation, The Sir Derek *194*
Grocers' Charity *197*
Isle of Dogs Community Foundation *238*
Lankelly Foundation, The *264*
Leech Charity, The William *269*
Lloyd's Charities Trust *278*
MacKintosh Charitable Trust, Viscount *292*
Mental Health Foundation, The *305*
Minet Trust, The Peter *313*

Needham Cooper Charitable
Trust, The *331*
Owen Family Trust, The *348*
Payne Trust, The Harry *356*
Reader's Digest Trust, The *380*
Skelton Bounty, The *423*
Stewart Trust, Sir Halley *437*
TSB Foundation for Northern
Ireland *447*
Tisbury Telegraph Trust, The
457
Travis Charitable Trust,
Constance *460*
Wakeham Trust, The *476*
Wills 1962 Charitable Trust,
P J H *494*

■ Health related
volunteer schemes
see also Advocacy (health)
Funding priority
Bilton Charity, The Percy *48*
Seagram Distillers Charitable
Trust *413*
Tudor Trust, The *463*

Will consider
Andrew Charitable Trust, The
Prince *16*
Astor Foundation, The *26*
Barbour Trust, The *33*
Beckwith Charitable
Settlement, The Heather *39*
Boots Charitable Trust *56*
Brough Charitable Trust,
Joseph *65*
Camelot Foundation, The *78*
Charities Fund *89*
Coutts Charitable Trust, The
116
Cripplegate Foundation *118*
Digby Charitable Trust, Simon
133
Dorus Trust *136*
Epigoni Trust *152*
Franklin Trust, Jill *170*
Great Britain Sasakawa
Foundation, The *193*
Greenaway Foundation, The Sir
Derek *194*
Hudson Benevolent Trust, The
Thomas *230*
Isle of Dogs Community
Foundation *238*
Leech Charity, The William *269*
Lloyd's Charities Trust *278*
London Law Trust *280*
MacKintosh Charitable Trust,
Viscount *292*
Mercury Phoenix Trust *307*
Minet Trust, The Peter *313*
Needham Cooper Charitable
Trust, The *331*
Owen Family Trust, The *348*
Persula Foundation, The *360*

Sheldon Trust, The *417*
Smith & Mount Trust, The Mrs
426
Summerfield Charitable Trust,
The *442*
Swan Mountain Trust *444*
Wakefield (Tower Hill, Trinity
Square) Trust *476*
Wakeham Trust, The *476*
Whitaker Charitable Trust *489*
Wiltshire Community
Foundation *495*
Woodlands Trust *501*

■ Hearing loss
Funding priority
Baker Charitable Trust, The *30*
Corbett's Charity, Thomas *112*
Debtors' Relief Fund Charity
128
Elkes Charity Fund, The Wilfred
& Elsie *147*
Ferguson Benevolent Fund
Limited *161*
Gray Trust, The *192*
HB Charitable Trust *201*
Harbinson Charitable Trust,
Roderick *208*
Lamb's Bequest *262*
MacKintosh Charitable Trust,
Viscount *292*
Man of the People Fund *295*
Meridian Broadcasting
Charitable Trust *307*
Oldham Foundation *345*
Paget Trust, The *351*
Rest-Harrow Trust, The *382*
Rosen Foundation, Cecil *392*
Swan Mountain Trust *444*

■ Heart disease
Funding priority
British Heart Foundation *62*
Prophit, Charity of James
Maxwell Grant *370*

■ Heritage
see also Conservation &
campaigning
Funding priority
Bancroft Trust, The *33*
Barnby's Foundation, Lord *35*
Campbell Charitable
Foundation, The Ellis *79*
Cobb Charity *103*
Countryside Trust, The *115*
David Trust, The Lesley *124*
Essex Heritage Trust *153*
Friends of Friendless Churches,
The *173*
Historic Churches Preservation
Trust, The *221*

Lower Hall Charitable Trust
285
Mellows Charitable Settlement,
The Anthony and Elizabeth
305
Mitchell Trust *315*
Nathan Charitable Trust, Peter
326
Shepherd Conservation
Foundation, The David *418*

Will consider
Alec-Smith Charitable Trust,
R A *10*
Allied Domecq Trust *13*
Ammco Trust, The *15*
Astor Foundation, The *26*
Avenal *27*
Beckwith-Smith's Charitable
Settlement, Mrs *40*
Benham Charitable Trust,
Hervey *43*
Bullough Tompson Settlement,
The *68*
Carron Charitable Trust, The
83
Coates Charitable Trust 1969,
Lance *103*
Company of Chartered
Surveyors Charitable Trust
Fund, The *108*
Cripplegate Foundation *118*
D'Avigdor Goldsmid Charitable
Trust, The Sarah *125*
de Freitas Charitable Trust, The
Helen and Geoffrey *126*
Digby Charitable Trust, Simon
133
Direct Response *134*
Dumbreck Charity *139*
Early's Charitable Settlement,
Richard *142*
Edgar Foundation, The Gilbert
and Eileen *145*
Elkes Charity Fund, The Wilfred
& Elsie *147*
Fishmongers' Company's
Charitable Trust *163*
Ford of Britain Trust *166*
Four Winds Trust *168*
Glynde Place Charitable Trust
(1974), The *186*
Goldsmiths' Company's
Charities, The *188*
Great Britain Sasakawa
Foundation, The *193*
Greenaway Foundation, The Sir
Derek *194*
Grocers' Charity *197*
Haddon Charitable Trust,
William *202*
Halkes Settlement, John Robert
204
Hannay Charitable Trust, The
Lennox *208*
Inverforth Charitable Trust, The
236

Isle of Dogs Community Foundation *238*
Jarrold Trust Ltd, John *243*
Johnson Foundation, The *246*
Laing Foundation, The Christopher *260*
Leche Trust, The *268*
Lee Foundation, The Edgar *269*
Leech Charity, The William *269*
Linford Charitable Trust, The Fred *276*
Lloyd Charity, The S and D *278*
Lloyd's Charities Trust *278*
Low & Bonar Charitable Fund, The *284*
Lyndhurst Settlement *287*
MacKintosh Charitable Trust, Viscount *292*
Measures Charity, The James Frederick and Ethel Anne *303*
Morphy Memorial Fund, Arthur *319*
Needham Cooper Charitable Trust, The *331*
Norfolk's Family Charitable Trust, Lavinia *336*
Oldham Foundation *345*
Owen Family Trust, The *348*
PF Charitable Trust *350*
Paget Trust, The *351*
Peppiatt Charitable Trust, The Brian *359*
Prendergast Charitable Trust, The Simone *368*
Radcliffe's Trust, Dr *375*
Royal Commission for the Exhibition of 1851 *395*
S Group Charitable Trust *399*
Schuster Charitable Trust, The *410*
Seagram Distillers Charitable Trust *413*
South Square Trust *430*
Stoate Charitable Trust, The Leonard Laity *438*
Strauss Charitable Trust *440*
Summerfield Charitable Trust, The *442*
Sumner's Trust Section 'A', Sir John *443*
Tisbury Telegraph Trust, The *457*
Toyota (GB) Charitable Trust, The *459*
Whitaker Charitable Trust *489*
Wood Charity, The Phyllis E *501*
Woodroffe Benton Foundation, The *502*
Worshipful Company of Engineers' Charitable Trust Fund, The *504*
Wylde Memorial Charity, The Anthony and Gwendoline *507*

■ **Higher education**
see Tertiary & higher education

■ **Historic buildings**
see also Conservation
Funding priority
Alec-Smith Charitable Trust, R A *10*
Askew Charitable Trust, The Ian *25*
Barnby's Foundation, Lord *35*
Brook Charitable Settlement, R E *64*
Chase Charity, The *91*
Cripps Foundation *118*
David Trust, The Lesley *124*
Gwent County Council Welsh Church Fund *200*
Hawthorne Charitable Trust, The *212*
Ireland Funds, The *237*
Lower Hall Charitable Trust *285*
MacKintosh Charitable Trust, Viscount *292*
Mellows Charitable Settlement, The Anthony and Elizabeth *305*
Mitchell Trust, Esme *315*
Powys Welsh Church Fund *367*
Terry Charitable Trust, Noel Goddard *451*

Will consider
Ammco Trust, The *15*
Astor Foundation, The *26*
Balney Charitable Trust, The *32*
Bancroft Trust, The *33*
Barbour Trust, The *33*
Barrie Charitable Trust, The Misses *36*
Beit Trust, The *40*
Bellahouston Bequest Fund *42*
Broadley Charitable Trust, The *64*
Butlin Charity Trust, Bill *72*
Cadbury Trust (1928), The Edward & Dorothy *76*
Clark 1965 Charitable Trust, Stephen *98*
Coates Charitable Trust, The John *103*
Colyer-Fergusson Charitable Trust, The *107*
Company of Chartered Surveyors Charitable Trust Fund, The *108*
Cripplegate Foundation *118*
D'Avigdor Goldsmid Charitable Trust, The Sarah *125*
de Freitas Charitable Trust, The Helen and Geoffrey *126*

Digby Charitable Trust, Simon *133*
Direct Response *134*
Dixon Charitable Trust, F E *134*
Dumbreck Charity *139*
Early's Charitable Settlement, Richard *142*
Edgar Foundation, The Gilbert and Eileen *145*
Fishmongers' Company's Charitable Trust *163*
Fletcher Trust, Roy *165*
Franklin Trust, Jill *170*
Garnett's 1973 Charitable Trust, Mrs A M *178*
Getty Jr General Charitable Trust, J Paul *181*
Glynde Place Charitable Trust (1974), The *186*
Goldsmiths' Company's Charities, The *188*
Greenaway Foundation, The Sir Derek *194*
Grocers' Charity *197*
Haddon Charitable Trust, William *202*
Halkes Settlement, John Robert *204*
Holly Hill Charitable Trust *224*
Idlewild Trust, The *234*
Inverforth Charitable Trust, The *236*
Isle of Dogs Community Foundation *238*
Jarrold Trust Ltd, John *243*
Kiln Charitable Trust, Robert *254*
Lankelly Foundation, The *264*
Lawson Charitable Trust, Raymond and Blanche *267*
Leach Fourteenth Trust, The *267*
Leche Trust, The *268*
Lee Foundation, The Edgar *269*
Leech Charity, The William *269*
Lloyd's Charities Trust *278*
Low & Bonar Charitable Fund, The *284*
Lyndhurst Settlement *287*
Mitchell Trust *315*
NR Charitable Trust, The *325*
New Court Charitable Trust *332*
Owen Family Trust, The *348*
Persula Foundation, The *360*
Pilkington Trust, The Austin and Hope *363*
Prince's Trust - BRO, The *369*
Provincial Trust for Kendal, The *370*
Rookes Charitable Trust, C A *390*
Rowbotham Charitable Trust, The Christopher *393*
Royal Commission for the Exhibition of 1851 *395*

Schuster Charitable Trust, The 410

Seagram Distillers Charitable Trust 413

Shepherd Charitable Trust, The Sylvia and Colin 418

South Square Trust 430

Stevens Foundation, The June 437

Strauss Charitable Trust 440

Summerfield Charitable Trust, The 442

Sykes Trust, The Charles 445

Symons Charitable Trust, The Stella 446

Tisbury Telegraph Trust, The 457

Unitek Foundation 469

Vincent Trust Fund, Eric W 473

Worshipful Company of Engineers' Charitable Trust Fund, The 504

Wylde Memorial Charity, The Anthony and Gwendoline 507

■ HIV & AIDS

Funding priority

Archer Trust, The 20

Elton John Aids Foundation, The 149

Hill Memorial Trust, L E 219

Lyndhurst Settlement 287

Mackintosh Foundation, The 292

Melville Trust for Care and Cure of Cancer 305

Mercury Phoenix Trust 307

Moores Foundation, John 318

NR Charitable Trust, The 325

Wates Foundation, The 481

■ Holiday accommodation

see also Residential facilities & services

Funding priority

Blakenham's Charity Trust, Lady 53

Four Winds Trust 168

GW Trust, The 176

Harvey Charitable Trust, Gordon 211

Hudson Benevolent Trust, The Thomas 230

Hyde Charitable Trust 232

Roedean School Mission Fund 390

Will consider

AB Charitable Trust 3

Ammco Trust, The 15

Anstey Charitable Settlement, J C W 18

Aquarius Charitable Foundation, The 19

Archer Trust, The 20

Army Benevolent Fund, The 22

Astor Foundation, The 26

Barbour Trust, The 33

Bilton Charity, The Percy 48

Birtwistle Memorial Trust, The G E 50

Blake Charitable Trust, The Hubert 53

Boots Charitable Trust 56

Borthwick Memorial Trust, The Oliver 56

Brotherton Trust, The Charles 65

Burden Trust, The 69

Butlin Charity Trust, Bill 72

CLA Charitable Trust 74

Cadbury Trust (1928), The Edward & Dorothy 76

Camelot Foundation, The 78

Campden Charities, The 79

Challice Trust, The 87

Charities Fund 89

Charity Projects 90

Chase Charity, The 91

County Durham Foundation 115

Coutts Charitable Trust, The 116

D'Avigdor Goldsmid Charitable Trust, The Sarah 125

Derbyshire Trust, J N 130

Dibs Charitable Trust, The 133

Digby Charitable Trust, Simon 133

Edgar Trust, The Gilbert 145

Egerton of Tatton Will Trust, Lord 146

Elkes Charity Fund, The Wilfred & Elsie 147

Emmandjay Charitable Trust 150

Ferguson Benevolent Fund Limited 161

Gluckstein Charitable Settlement, The Penelope 185

Grant-Lawson Charitable Trust, Lady Virginia 192

Harford Charitable Trust 209

Held Settlement, The Gisela 215

JDM Charitable Trust 239

Jewish Childs' Day 245

Laing Charitable Trust, The David 260

Leadbeater Trust, The Alfred 268

Lewis Partnership, John 274

Lyons Charitable Trust, The 288

Marchday Charitable Fund, The 296

Marriage's Charitable Trust, Miss G M 299

Milburn Charitable Trust, Frederick 310

Moore Foundation, The George A 316

Morphy Memorial Fund, Arthur 319

Needham Cooper Charitable Trust, The 331

Northern Ireland Voluntary Trust 339

Norton Foundation, The 340

Oldham Foundation 345

Provincial Trust for Kendal, The 370

Rest-Harrow Trust, The 382

Rowbotham Charitable Trust, The Christopher 393

Seagram Distillers Charitable Trust 413

South Square Trust 430

Sykes Trust, The Charles 445

TSB Foundation for Northern Ireland 447

Truemark Trust, The 461

Unitek Foundation 469

Wall Trust, Thomas 478

Wander Charitable Fund, The Dr Albert 479

Weir Foundation, The James 484

Wesleyan Charitable Trust, The 485

Whesby Ltd 488

Whitaker Charitable Trust 489

Woburn 1986 Charitable Trust 498

Wolfe Family's Charitable Trust, The 498

■ Holiday playschemes

see Playschemes

■ Holidays & outings

see also Community services

Funding priority

Army Benevolent Fund, The 22

Aston Charities Trust Ltd 25

Astor Foundation, The 26

Beckwith Charitable Settlement, The Heather 39

Blakenham's Charity Trust, Lady 53

Challice Trust, The 87

Chronicle Cinderella Home Fund No 1, The 95

Clipsham Charitable Settlement, R E 101

County Durham Foundation 115

Egerton of Tatton Will Trust, Lord 146

Four Winds Trust 168

Gluckstein Charitable
Settlement, The Penelope
185
Harford Charitable Trust *209*
Hudson Benevolent Trust, The
Thomas *230*
Ingles Charitable Trust, The
234
Johnson Group Cleaners
Charity *247*
Marchday Charitable Fund, The
296
Moores Family Charity
Foundation, The *317*
Ogilvie Charities (Deed No 2)
344
Robinson Trust 4, The J C *388*
Roedean School Mission Fund
390
SMB Trust, The *400*
Wade & Others, The Charity of
Thomas *475*
Wakeham Trust, The *476*

Will consider
AB Charitable Trust *3*
Ammco Trust, The *15*
Amory Charitable Trust,
Viscount *16*
Anstey Charitable Settlement,
J C W *18*
Aquarius Charitable
Foundation, The *19*
Archer Trust, The *20*
Askew Trust, The Dorothy *25*
Avon Trust, The *28*
Aylesfield Foundation, The *28*
Barbour Trust, The *33*
Barratt Charitable Trust, The
Elaine *36*
Berkshire Community Trust *45*
Betard Bequest *46*
Birtwistle Memorial Trust, The
G E *50*
Bisgood's Charitable Trust, Miss
Jeanne *50*
Blanchminster Trust, The *54*
Boots Charitable Trust *56*
Bowland Charitable Trust, The
57
Bridge Trust, The *60*
Brighton & Hove Charitable
Youth Trust *60*
Brotherton Trust, The Charles
65
Buckinghamshire Masonic
Centenary Fund *67*
Burdall Charity, H M *69*
Burton 1960 Charitable
Settlement, Audrey &
Stanley *70*
Butlin Charity Trust, Bill *72*
Cadbury Charitable Trust
(Incorporated), Edward *75*
Camelot Foundation, The *78*
Campden Charities, The *79*
Carnegie Dunfermline Trust *82*

Chapman Foundation *88*
Chiddick Charitable Trust *92*
Chrimes Family Charitable
Trust, The *93*
Clark 1965 Charitable Trust,
Stephen *98*
Cleopatra Trust *99*
Cloudesley's Charity/School
Parents & Friends
Association, Richard *102*
Community Trust for Greater
Manchester, The *108*
Coutts Charitable Trust, The
116
Curzon Charitable Trust, The
Wallace *120*
Davies Charity, The
Gwendoline and Margaret
125
de Freitas Charitable Trust, The
Helen and Geoffrey *126*
Debtors' Relief Fund Charity
128
Derbyshire Trust, J N *130*
Digby Charitable Trust, Simon
133
Dorus Trust *136*
Dumbreck Charity *139*
Ebb and Flow Charitable Trust
144
Edgar Foundation, The Gilbert
and Eileen *145*
Edgar Trust, The Gilbert *145*
Elkes Charity Fund, The Wilfred
& Elsie *147*
Emmandjay Charitable Trust
150
Emmaus Christian Foundation
150
Epigoni Trust *152*
Ferguson Benevolent Fund
Limited *161*
Fletcher Charitable Trust, The
Joyce *164*
Fletcher Trust, Roy *165*
Four Lanes Trust, The *168*
Franklin Trust, Jill *170*
GW Trust, The *176*
Gelston Charitable Trust, The
179
Gibbins Trust, The *181*
Grant-Lawson Charitable Trust,
Lady Virginia *192*
Grocers' Charity *197*
Grosshill Charitable Trust *197*
Grundy Foundation, The
Stanley *198*
Haberdashers' Eleemosynary
Charity *201*
Halkes Settlement, John Robert
204
Hertfordshire Community
Trust, The *217*
Homfray Trust, The *226*
Humanitarian Trust, The *230*
Hyde Charitable Trust *232*
Isle of Dogs Community
Foundation *238*

JDM Charitable Trust *239*
Jarman Charitable Trust, The
243
Johnson Foundation, The *246*
Knott Trust, Sir James *258*
Kyte Charitable Trust, The *259*
Laing Charitable Trust, The
David *260*
Lankelly Foundation, The *264*
Lawson Charitable Trust,
Raymond and Blanche *267*
Leach Fourteenth Trust, The
267
Lee Foundation, The Edgar
269
Lewis Partnership, John *274*
Lloyd's Charities Trust *278*
(Lloyds) TSB Foundation for
England and Wales *279*
London Taxi Drivers' Fund for
Underprivileged Children,
The *280*
Lunn-Rockliffe Charitable Trust,
Paul *286*
Lynall Foundation, The D G
287
Mackintosh Foundation, The
292
Margaret Foundation, The *297*
Measures Charity, The James
Frederick and Ethel Anne
303
Middlesex County Rugby
Football Union Memorial
Fund *309*
Milburn Charitable Trust,
Frederick *310*
Milton Keynes Community
Trust Ltd, The *312*
Minet Trust, The Peter *313*
Music for World Development
323
NR Charitable Trust, The *325*
National Power Charitable
Trust, The *330*
Needham Cooper Charitable
Trust, The *331*
New Chasers Charitable Trust,
The *332*
Newby Trust Ltd *332*
Norfolk's Family Charitable
Trust, Lavinia *336*
Norman Family Charitable
Trust, The *337*
Northcott Devon Foundation
338
Norton Foundation, The *340*
Oldham Foundation *345*
Owen Family Trust, The *348*
PF Charitable Trust *350*
Paget Trust, The *351*
Parivar Trust, The *353*
Paterson Charitable
Foundation, The Constance
354
Paterson Charitable Trust,
Arthur James *354*
Payne Trust, The Harry *356*

Persula Foundation, The *360*

Porter Foundation *366*

Powell Foundation, The *367*

Pratt Charitable Trust, The W L *367*

Provincial Trust for Kendal, The *370*

Ravenscroft Foundation, The *379*

Rayner Charitable Trust, The John *380*

Reader's Digest Trust, The *380*

Rest-Harrow Trust, The *382*

Richard Charitable Trust, The Cliff *383*

Ripley's Charitable Trust, Pat *386*

Robinson Brothers (Ryders Green) Ltd, Charitable Trust *388*

Rookes Charitable Trust, C A *390*

Rope Third Charitable Settlement, The Mrs *391*

Rowbotham Charitable Trust, The Christopher *393*

Sainsbury Charitable Fund Ltd, The *402*

Saint Edmund King and Martyr Trust *402*

Seagram Distillers Charitable Trust *413*

Shelroy Charitable Trust, The *417*

Shepherd Family Charitable Trust, The Sir Peter *418*

Skelton Bounty, The *423*

South Square Trust *430*

Sparkhill Trust, The *433*

Stevens Foundation, The June *437*

Stoate Charitable Trust, The Leonard Laity *438*

Sussman Charitable Trust, Adrienne & Leslie *443*

Swan Mountain Trust *444*

Sykes Trust, The Charles *445*

TSB Foundation for Northern Ireland *447*

Thomson Foundation, The Sue *454*

Tisbury Telegraph Trust, The *457*

Torquay Charities, The *458*

Towler Charity Trust, The Fred *459*

Truemark Trust, The *461*

Van Berchem Charitable Trust, The Alec *470*

Victoria & Johnson Memorial Trust, Queen *472*

Wakefield (Tower Hill, Trinity Square) Trust *476*

Wall Trust, Thomas *478*

Wates Foundation, The *481*

Watson Foundation, The Bertie *482*

Wedge, The *483*

Weir Foundation, The James *484*

Wesleyan Charitable Trust, The *485*

Westcroft Trust *486*

Whitecourt Charitable Trust, The *490*

Wingate Foundation, The Harold Hyam *496*

Wolfe Family's Charitable Trust, The *498*

Women Caring Trust, The *500*

Worshipful Company of Glass Sellers' Charity Trust, The *505*

Wylde Memorial Charity, The Anthony and Gwendoline *507*

Yorkshire Bank Charitable Trust, The *510*

....

■ Homeless

Funding priority

AB Charitable Trust *3*

Adnams Charity, The *7*

Alexandra Trust *11*

Baker Charitable Trust, The *30*

Ballinger Charitable Trust, The *32*

Borthwick Memorial Trust, The Oliver *56*

Calypso Browning Trust *78*

Carlton Television Trust *81*

Charity Projects *90*

Christmas Cracker Trust *95*

Church Urban Fund *95*

Clifford Charity Oxford, The *100*

Cole Charitable Trust, The *105*

Construction Industry Trust for Youth, The *110*

Coutts Charitable Trust, The *116*

Curriers Company Charitable Fund *119*

Debtors' Relief Fund Charity *128*

Ebb and Flow Charitable Trust *144*

Edgar Trust, The Gilbert *145*

Franklin Trust, Jill *170*

HACT (The Housing Association's Charitable Trust) *201*

Hampstead Wells and Campden Trust *206*

Hanley Trust (1987), The *207*

Harbour Foundation Ltd, The *208*

Heath Charitable Trust *214*

Held Settlement, The Gisela *215*

Help the Homeless *215*

Hertfordshire Community Trust, The *217*

Hiley Trust, Joseph and Mary *219*

Hussey for Africans, Charity of Rebecca *231*

Irving Charitable Trust, The Charles *237*

Isle of Dogs Community Foundation *238*

King's Fund, The *255*

Laing Trust, Beatrice *261*

Lamb's Bequest *262*

Lane Foundation, The Allen *263*

Lloyd's Charities Trust *278*

(Lloyds) TSB Foundation for England and Wales *279*

Lyons Charitable Trust, The *288*

MacGregor's Bequest *291*

Mackintosh Foundation, The *292*

Marchday Charitable Fund, The *296*

Moores Family Charity Foundation, The *317*

Moores Foundation, John *318*

Music for World Development *323*

Norton Foundation, The *340*

Paristamen Foundation, The *352*

Persula Foundation, The *360*

Pryor Charitable Trust, The John *370*

Rogers Charitable Settlement, The Richard *390*

Rope Third Charitable Settlement, The Mrs *391*

Scott Bader Commonwealth Ltd, The *411*

Seva Trust, Rampaba Sadhu *415*

South Square Trust *430*

Swindon Charitable Trust, The Walter *445*

TSB Foundation for Scotland *447*

Tisbury Telegraph Trust, The *457*

Toy Trust, The *459*

Trust for the Homeless *462*

Tudor Trust, The *463*

Van Berchem Charitable Trust, The Alec *470*

Wates Foundation, The *481*

Wiltshire Community Foundation *495*

Will consider

Abbey National Charitable Trust *4*

Abel Charitable Trust *5*

Ammco Trust, The *15*

Andrew Charitable Trust, The Prince *16*

Archer Trust, The *20*

Askew Trust, The Dorothy *25*

Astor Foundation, The *26*

Atwell's Charity (Skinner's Company), Lawrence *27*

Barbour Trust, The *33*

Barnabas Charitable Trust *34*

Barratt Charitable Trust, The Elaine *36*

Bartholomew Christian Trust *36*

Beckwith Charitable Settlement, The Heather *39*

Birtwistle Memorial Trust, The G E *50*

Blake Charitable Trust, The Morgan *53*

Boots Charitable Trust *56*

Bridge Trust, The *60*

Brotherton Trust, The Charles *65*

Butlin Charity Trust, Bill *72*

Cadbury Charitable Trust (Incorporated), Edward *75*

Camelot Foundation, The *78*

Campbell Charitable Foundation, The Ellis *79*

Carter Charitable Trust, The Leslie Mary *83*

Catto Charitable Settlement, The Thomas Sivewright *86*

Challice Trust, The *87*

Clark 1965 Charitable Trust, Stephen *98*

David Trust, The Lesley *124*

De Yong Charitable Trust, The Emma *128*

Digbeth Trust Ltd, The *133*

Direct Response *134*

Dorus Trust *136*

Dumbreck Charity *139*

Earley Charity, The *142*

Earwicker Trust *142*

Edgar Foundation, The Gilbert and Eileen *145*

Elkes Charity Fund, The Wilfred & Elsie *147*

Emmaus Christian Foundation *150*

Epigoni Trust *152*

Ericson Trust *152*

Essex Radio Helping Hands Trust, The *154*

Eveson Charitable Trust, The *155*

Fletcher Charitable Trust, The Joyce *164*

Fletcher Trust, Roy *165*

Four Winds Trust *168*

Getty Jr General Charitable Trust, J Paul *181*

Gibson Charitable Trust, The Simon *182*

Gladstone Charitable Trust, The E W *184*

Goldsmiths' Company's Charities, The *188*

Grant-Lawson Charitable Trust, Lady Virginia *192*

Greater Bristol Foundation *193*

Groves Charitable Trust, The *197*

Hilden Charitable Fund, The *219*

Hill Memorial Trust, L E *219*

Hopkinson Educational Trust, Robert Addy *227*

Ibbett Trust, The *233*

Iris Trust, The *237*

JCSCJ Charitable Trust, The *238*

Johnson Foundation, The *246*

Keeling Charitable Trust, The Petronella *251*

King Charitable Trust, The Lorna *254*

Laing Charitable Trust, The David *260*

Laing Foundation, The Christopher *260*

Laing Foundation, The Kirby *261*

Laing Foundation, The Maurice *261*

Laing's Charitable Trust *262*

Laspen Trust *265*

Leach Fourteenth Trust, The *267*

Linford Charitable Trust, The Fred *276*

Lloyd Charity, The S and D *278*

Low & Bonar Charitable Fund, The *284*

Luke Trust, The *286*

Lunn-Rockliffe Charitable Trust, Paul *286*

Lyndhurst Settlement *287*

McCarthy Foundation, The John *290*

MacKintosh Charitable Trust, Viscount *292*

Manning Trust, Leslie & Lilian *296*

Marriage's Charitable Trust, Miss G M *299*

Mental Health Foundation, The *305*

Metropolitan Hospital-Sunday Fund, The *308*

Milburn Charitable Trust, Frederick *310*

Milton Keynes Community Trust Ltd, The *312*

Minet Trust, The Peter *313*

Minge's Gift *314*

Morris Charitable Trust, The Douglas *320*

Multithon Trust, The *323*

NR Charitable Trust, The *325*

Nathan Charitable Trust *326*

Needham Cooper Charitable Trust, The *331*

New Court Charitable Trust *332*

New Durlston Trust, The *332*

Newby Trust Ltd *332*

Noah Trust, The *335*

Norman Family Charitable Trust, The *337*

Oakdale Trust, The *343*

Owen Family Trust, The *348*

Paget Trust, The *351*

Parivar Trust, The *353*

Payne Trust, The Harry *356*

Pratt Charitable Trust, The W L *367*

Pye Christian Trust, The *371*

Pyke Charity Trust *372*

Rest-Harrow Trust, The *382*

Robinson Brothers (Ryders Green) Ltd, Charitable Trust *388*

Robinson Trust 4, The J C *388*

Rowntree Foundation, Joseph *394*

Sainsbury Charitable Fund Ltd, The *402*

St Christopher's Trust, The *402*

Sargeant's Charitable Trust, Mrs M E *407*

Schuster Charitable Trust, The *410*

Seagram Distillers Charitable Trust *413*

Sheldon Trust, The *417*

Smith & Mount Trust, The Mrs *426*

South Yorkshire Community Foundation *431*

Staples Trust *435*

Stoate Charitable Trust, The Leonard Laity *438*

Stonehouse Trust Ltd, Eric *438*

Summerfield Charitable Trust, The *442*

Summer's and I May's Charitable Settlement, The Late Misses (A N) *442*

Swan Mountain Trust *444*

Swann-Morton Foundation, The *444*

TSB Foundation for Northern Ireland *447*

Tear Fund *450*

Thackray General Charitable Trust, The P & L *452*

Thorpe Charity Trust, The *455*

Van Leer Foundation UK Trust, Bernard *470*

Variety Club Children's Charity Limited, The *471*

Vec Acorn Trust, The *472*

Wagstaff Charitable Trust, Bob *475*

Wakefield (Tower Hill, Trinity Square) Trust *476*

Wakeham Trust, The *476*

Weir Foundation, The James *484*

Wesleyan Charitable Trust, The *485*

Westcroft Trust *486*

Whitecourt Charitable Trust, The *490*

Wix Charitable Trust, Michael and Anna *497*
Wolfe Family's Charitable Trust, The *498*
Woodlands Trust *501*
Woodroffe Benton Foundation, The *502*

■ Horses – stables & other facilities for horses

see also **Animal facilities & services**

Funding priority
Barnby's Foundation, Lord *35*
Coote Animal Charity Fund, The Marjorie *111*
Heath Charitable Trust *214*
Sainsbury Animal Welfare Trust, Jean *401*

Will consider
Ammco Trust, The *15*
Animal Defence Trust, The *18*
Arbib Foundation *20*
Astor Foundation, The *26*
Body Charitable Trust, Bernard Richard *55*
Butler Charitable Trust, The A S *71*
CLA Charitable Trust *74*
Carron Charitable Trust, The *83*
Community Trust for Greater Manchester, The *108*
Corden Trust, Cyril *113*
Digby Charitable Trust, Simon *133*
Dinam Charity *134*
Dumbreck Charity *139*
Elkes Charity Fund, The Wilfred & Elsie *147*
Evetts & Robert Luff Animal Welfare Trust, Beryl *156*
Ford of Britain Trust *166*
Friends of the Animals *173*
Green Memorial Fund, The Barry *194*
Greenaway Foundation, The Sir Derek *194*
Hunter Charitable Trust, The Claire *231*
Isle of Dogs Community Foundation *238*
Laing Charitable Trust, The David *260*
Lee Foundation, The Edgar *269*
Lowe Trust, Mrs D G *285*
Marchig Animal Welfare Trust *297*
Marriage's Charitable Trust, Miss G M *299*
Nathan Charitable Trust, Peter *326*

Norman Family Charitable Trust, The *337*
PF Charitable Trust *350*
Perry Charitable Trust, Miss Frances Lucille *359*
Stevens Foundation, The June *437*
Sumner's Trust Section 'A', Sir John *443*
Vincent Wildlife Trust, The *473*
Walker 597 Trust, The *477*
Whitaker Charitable Trust *489*
Wylde Memorial Charity, The Anthony and Gwendoline *507*
Wyre Animal Welfare *507*
Zaiger Trust, The Elizabeth and Prince *512*

■ Horticulture

see also **Environment & animal sciences**

Funding priority
Coates Charitable Trust 1969, Lance *103*
Cobb Charity *103*
LSA Charitable Trust *260*
Lower Hall Charitable Trust *285*
MacRobert Trusts, The *294*
Needham Cooper Charitable Trust, The *331*
Pilkington Charitable Trust, Cecil *363*
Royal Botanical & Horticultural Society of Manchester and the Northern Counties, The *395*
Royal Gardeners' Orphan Fund, The *395*
Smith (UK) Horticultural Trust, Stanley *428*
Yorkshire Agricultural Society *509*

Will consider
Allied Domecq Trust *13*
Ashley Foundation, The Laura *24*
Astor Foundation, The *26*
Barrie Charitable Trust, The Misses *36*
Bentall Charity Trust, Rowan *44*
CLA Charitable Trust *74*
Carnegie Dunfermline Trust *82*
Chippindale Foundation, Sam *93*
Clutterbuck Charitable Trust, Robert *102*
Company of Chartered Surveyors Charitable Trust Fund, The *108*
Digby Charitable Trust, Simon *133*

Eaton Charitable Trust, J C J *143*
Goldsmiths' Company's Charities, The *188*
Great Britain Sasakawa Foundation, The *193*
Greenaway Foundation, The Sir Derek *194*
Hayward Foundation, The *213*
Horn Trust, The Cuthbert *227*
Hunter Charitable Trust, The Claire *231*
Idlewild Trust, The *234*
Isle of Dogs Community Foundation *238*
Lee Foundation, The Edgar *269*
Lloyd Charity, The S and D *278*
Mattock Charitable Trust, The W T *302*
Measures Charity, The James Frederick and Ethel Anne *303*
NR Charitable Trust, The *325*
Oldham Foundation *345*
Paget Trust, The *351*
Parkinson Agricultural Trust, The Frank *353*
Pilgrim Trust, The *362*
Reader's Digest Trust, The *380*
Sainsbury Charitable Fund Ltd, The *402*
Shaw Foundation, The Linley *416*
Summerfield Charitable Trust, The *442*
Sumner's Trust Section 'A', Sir John *443*
Tear Fund *450*
Woodlands Trust *501*

■ Hospice at home

see also **Health care**

Funding priority
Allied Dunbar Charitable Trust Limited, The *13*
Cancer Relief Macmillan Fund *79*
Coutts Charitable Trust, The *116*
Davis Charitable Trust, Wilfrid Bruce *126*
Edgar Trust, The Gilbert *145*
Heath Charitable Trust *214*
Hudson Charitable Trust, The *230*
Kroch Foundation, The Heinz & Anna *259*
Lacy Charity Trust, The Late Sir Pierce *260*
Lawson Charitable Trust, Raymond and Blanche *267*
Lloyd's Charities Trust *278*
Loseley & Guildway Charitable Trust, The *281*

MacKintosh Charitable Trust, Viscount *292*

Manning Trust, Leslie & Lilian *296*

Pratt Charitable Trust, The W L *367*

Pryor Charitable Trust, The John *370*

Rowbotham Charitable Trust, The Christopher *393*

Royal Theatrical Fund, The *396*

SMB Trust, The *400*

Sheepdrove Trust, The *417*

Stonehouse Trust Ltd, Eric *438*

Will consider

AB Charitable Trust *3*

Abbey National Charitable Trust *4*

Allen Trust, Mrs M H *13*

Ammco Trust, The *15*

Andrew Charitable Trust, The Prince *16*

Andrew Convalescent Trust, The Frederick *17*

Anstey Charitable Settlement, J C W *18*

Archer Trust, The *20*

Army Benevolent Fund, The *22*

Astor Foundation, The *26*

Avon Trust, The *28*

Bancroft Trust, The *33*

Barbour Trust, The *33*

Barratt Charitable Trust, The Elaine *36*

Beckwith Charitable Settlement, The Heather *39*

Berkshire Community Trust *45*

Berris Charitable Trust *45*

Birmingham Amenities and Welfare Trust, The *49*

Birtwistle Memorial Trust, The G E *50*

Bottom Charitable Trust, Harry *56*

Bourne-May Charitable Trust, The *57*

British Dietetic Association General and Education Trust Fund, The *61*

Britton Charitable Trust, The J & M *63*

Brooke Benevolent Fund, William *65*

Brotherton Trust, The Charles *65*

Buckinghamshire Masonic Centenary Fund *67*

Bullough Tompson Settlement, The *68*

Burdall Charity, H M *69*

Butlin Charity Trust, Bill *72*

Cadbury Trust (1928), The Edward & Dorothy *76*

Camelot Foundation, The *78*

Campden Charities, The *79*

Cathedral Nursing Society Charitable Trust *85*

Clarke Charitable Settlement, The *99*

Cleopatra Trust *99*

Clinton's Charitable Trust, Lord *100*

Collier Charitable Trust, The *105*

Community Trust for Greater Manchester, The *108*

Cottingham Charitable Trust, Mrs Diana Mary *114*

Denne Charitable Trust *130*

Digby Charitable Trust, Simon *133*

Dorus Trust *136*

Dumbreck Charity *139*

Dunhill Medical Trust, The *140*

Earley Charity, The *142*

Early's Charitable Settlement, Richard *142*

Edgar Foundation, The Gilbert and Eileen *145*

Elkes Charity Fund, The Wilfred & Elsie *147*

Emmaus Christian Foundation *150*

Epigoni Trust *152*

Eventhall Family Charitable Trust, The *155*

Ferguson Benevolent Fund Limited *161*

Fogel Charitable Trust, The Gerald *165*

Follett Trust, The *166*

Foreman Foundation, The Carl & Eve *167*

Fortune Trust, The *167*

Franklin Trust, Jill *170*

Gardner Charitable Trust, R & J *178*

Gibbins Trust, The *181*

Gladstone Charitable Trust, The E W *184*

Gluckstein Charitable Settlement, The Penelope *185*

Goldsmiths' Company's Charities, The *188*

Good Neighbours Trust, The *188*

Graham Charitable Trust, Reginald *190*

Grant Foundation, The Raymond *191*

Grant-Lawson Charitable Trust, Lady Virginia *192*

Gray Charitable Trust, R B *192*

Greenaway Foundation, The Alan *194*

Greenaway Foundation, The Sir Derek *194*

Grocers' Charity *197*

Grundy Foundation, The Stanley *198*

Hawley Residuary Fund, Harry Fieldsend *212*

Hertfordshire Community Trust, The *217*

Hill Memorial Trust, L E *219*

Holly Hill Charitable Trust *224*

Humanitarian Trust, The *230*

Innes Memorial Fund *235*

Isle of Dogs Community Foundation *238*

JDM Charitable Trust *239*

Jarman Charitable Trust, The *243*

Kiln Charitable Trust, Robert *254*

Laing Charitable Trust, The David *260*

Laing Trust, Beatrice *261*

Laing's Charitable Trust *262*

Leach Fourteenth Trust, The *267*

Lee Foundation, The Edgar *269*

Leech Charity, The William *269*

Linford Charitable Trust, The Fred *276*

Lloyd Charity, The S and D *278*

(Lloyds) TSB Foundation for England and Wales *279*

London Law Trust *280*

Lynall Foundation, The D G *287*

Mackintosh Foundation, The *292*

Marchday Charitable Fund, The *296*

Merchants House of Glasgow *307*

Mercury Phoenix Trust *307*

Milburn Charitable Trust, Frederick *310*

Milward Charity, The Edgar *313*

Moore Foundation, The George A *316*

Morris Charitable Trust, The Douglas *320*

Multithon Trust, The *323*

Music for World Development *323*

Natwest Staff Samaritan Fund *330*

Needham Cooper Charitable Trust, The *331*

New Court Charitable Trust *332*

Noswad Charity, The *341*

Oakdale Trust, The *343*

Owen Family Trust, The *348*

Paget Trust, The *351*

Payne Trust, The Harry *356*

Persula Foundation, The *360*

Prendergast Charitable Trust, The Simone *368*

Pye Christian Trust, The *371*

Pyke Charity Trust *372*

Rest-Harrow Trust, The *382*

Rothley Trust, The *392*

St Christopher's Trust, The *402*

Schuster Charitable Trust, The *410*

Seagram Distillers Charitable Trust *413*

Shelroy Charitable Trust, The *417*

Simon's Charity *422*

Skelton Bounty, The *423*

South Square Trust *430*

Summerfield Charitable Trust, The *442*

Sussman Charitable Trust, Adrienne & Leslie *443*

TSB Foundation for Northern Ireland *447*

Tear Fund *450*

Thackray General Charitable Trust, The P & L *452*

Thomson Foundation, The Sue *454*

Tindall's Charitable Trust, Mrs R P *457*

Torquay Charities, The *458*

Travis Charitable Trust, Constance *460*

Truemark Trust, The *461*

Turner Trust, The Douglas *464*

Van Neste Foundation, The *471*

Victoria & Johnson Memorial Trust, Queen *472*

Wakefield (Tower Hill, Trinity Square) Trust *476*

Wakeham Trust, The *476*

Wall Trust, Thomas *478*

Westcroft Trust *486*

Whesby Ltd *488*

Whitaker Charitable Trust *489*

Wills 1962 Charitable Trust, P J H *494*

Woodlands Trust *501*

....

■ **Hospices**

see also **Health facilities & buildings**

Funding priority

Allied Dunbar Charitable Trust Limited, The *13*

Ammco Trust, The *15*

Assheton-Smith Charitable Trust *25*

Astor Foundation, The *26*

Avon Trust, The *28*

Berris Charitable Trust *45*

Coutts Charitable Trust, The *116*

De La Rue Charitable Trust *127*

Edgar Trust, The Gilbert *145*

Emanuel Charitable Settlement, Ralph and Muriel *150*

Fogel Charitable Trust, The Gerald *165*

Heath Charitable Trust *214*

Hill Memorial Trust, L E *219*

Inman Charity, The *235*

Jarman Charitable Trust, The *243*

Lacy Charity Trust, The Late Sir Pierce *260*

Leech Charity, The William *269*

MacKintosh Charitable Trust, Viscount *292*

Mellows Charitable Settlement, The Anthony and Elizabeth *305*

Mercury Phoenix Trust *307*

Natwest Staff Samaritan Fund *330*

Needham Cooper Charitable Trust, The *331*

Noswad Charity, The *341*

Pratt Charitable Trust, The W L *367*

Prestwich Charitable Trust, The Douglas P *368*

Pryor Charitable Trust, The John *370*

Roberts Charitable Trust, F G *388*

Rocket Club Benevolent Fund, The *389*

SMB Trust, The *400*

Sheepdrove Trust, The *417*

Stonehouse Trust Ltd, Eric *438*

Toy Trust, The *459*

Will consider

AB Charitable Trust *3*

Andrew Charitable Trust, The Prince *16*

Anstey Charitable Settlement, J C W *18*

Archer Trust, The *20*

Army Benevolent Fund, The *22*

Balney Charitable Trust, The *32*

Bancroft Trust, The *33*

Barbour Trust, The *33*

Barratt Charitable Trust, The Elaine *36*

Beckwith Charitable Settlement, The Heather *39*

Behrens Charitable Trust, E M *40*

Beit Trust, The *40*

Berkshire Community Trust *45*

Birtwistle Memorial Trust, The G E *50*

Britton Charitable Trust, The J & M *63*

Brooke Benevolent Fund, William *65*

Brotherton Trust, The Charles *65*

Brough Charitable Trust, Joseph *65*

Buckinghamshire Masonic Centenary Fund *67*

Bullough Tompson Settlement, The *68*

Burdall Charity, H M *69*

Butlin Charity Trust, Bill *72*

Cadbury Trust (1928), The Edward & Dorothy *76*

Camelot Foundation, The *78*

Catto Charitable Settlement, The Thomas Sivewright *86*

Challice Trust, The *87*

Chiddick Charitable Trust *92*

Clarke Charitable Settlement, The *99*

Cleopatra Trust *99*

Clinton's Charitable Trust, Lord *100*

Coates Charitable Trust, The John *103*

Collier Charitable Trust, The *105*

Colyer-Fergusson Charitable Trust, The *107*

Community Trust for Greater Manchester, The *108*

Company of Chartered Surveyors Charitable Trust Fund, The *108*

Cooper Charitable Trust *111*

Corbett's Charity, Thomas *112*

Cottingham Charitable Trust, Mrs Diana Mary *114*

Denne Charitable Trust *130*

Derbyshire Trust, J N *130*

Digby Charitable Trust, Simon *133*

Dorus Trust *136*

Dumbreck Charity *139*

Early's Charitable Settlement, Richard *142*

Egerton of Tatton Will Trust, Lord *146*

Elkes Charity Fund, The Wilfred & Elsie *147*

Emmandjay Charitable Trust *150*

Epigoni Trust *152*

Eventhall Family Charitable Trust, The *155*

Eveson Charitable Trust, The *155*

Fishmongers' Company's Charitable Trust *163*

Ford of Britain Trust *166*

Fortune Trust, The *167*

Franklin Deceased's New Second Charity, Sydney E *170*

Gladstone Charitable Trust, The E W *184*

Glynde Place Charitable Trust (1974), The *186*

Goldsmiths' Company's Charities, The *188*

Good Neighbours Trust, The *188*

Grant-Lawson Charitable Trust, Lady Virginia *192*

Graves Charitable Trust, J G *192*

Gray Charitable Trust, R B *192*

Greenaway Foundation, The Alan *194*

Greenaway Foundation, The Sir
   Derek *194*
Grundy Foundation, The
   Stanley *198*
Halkes Settlement, John Robert
   204
Hannay Charitable Trust, The
   Lennox *208*
Hannay Memorial Charity,
   Kathleen *208*
Harford Charitable Trust *209*
Harvey Charitable Trust,
   Gordon *211*
Haywood Charitable Trust *214*
Henderson's Settlement, J R
   216
Holly Hill Charitable Trust *224*
Humanitarian Trust, The *230*
Ibbett Trust, The *233*
Isle of Dogs Community
   Foundation *238*
JDM Charitable Trust *239*
JHL Trust, The *239*
JMK Charitable Trust *239*
Johnson Group Cleaners
   Charity *247*
Keeling Charitable Trust, The
   Petronella *251*
Kiln Charitable Trust, Robert
   254
Laing Charitable Trust, The
   David *260*
Laing Foundation, The Kirby
   261
Laing Foundation, The Maurice
   261
Laing Trust, Beatrice *261*
Lawson Charitable Trust,
   Raymond and Blanche *267*
Leadbeater Trust, The Alfred
   268
Lee Foundation, The Edgar
   269
Linmardon Trust *276*
Lloyd Charity, The S and D *278*
(Lloyds) TSB Foundation for
   England and Wales *279*
London Law Trust *280*
Lowe Trust, Mrs D G *285*
Lynall Foundation, The D G
   287
Marchday Charitable Fund, The
   296
Metropolitan Hospital-Sunday
   Fund, The *308*
Middlesex County Rugby
   Football Union Memorial
   Fund *309*
Milburn Charitable Trust,
   Frederick *310*
Milward Charity, The Edgar
   313
Minet Trust, The Peter *313*
Moores Foundation, John *318*
Morris Charitable Trust, The
   Douglas *320*
Mountbatten Trust, The
   Edwina *322*

Music for World Development
   323
Newby Trust Ltd *332*
Norman Family Charitable
   Trust, The *337*
Oakdale Trust, The *343*
Owen Family Trust, The *348*
Paget Trust, The *351*
Paul's Charitable Trust, R J *355*
Payne Trust, The Harry *356*
Penny in the Pound Fund
   Charitable Trust *359*
Peppiatt Charitable Trust, The
   Brian *359*
Persula Foundation, The *360*
Prendergast Charitable Trust,
   The Simone *368*
Pye Christian Trust, The *371*
Pyke Charity Trust *372*
Robinson Trust 4, The J C *388*
Rookes Charitable Trust, C A
   390
Rothley Trust, The *392*
Royal's Memorial Fund,
   Princess *396*
Sargeant's Charitable Trust,
   Mrs M E *407*
Schuster Charitable Trust, The
   410
Shelroy Charitable Trust, The
   417
Shepherd Charitable Trust, The
   Sylvia and Colin *418*
Simon's Charity *422*
Skelton Bounty, The *423*
Smith (Estates Charities), Henry
   426
Sportsman's Aid Charity Ltd,
   The *434*
Stoate Charitable Trust, The
   Leonard Laity *438*
Summerfield Charitable Trust,
   The *442*
Summer's and I May's
   Charitable Settlement, The
   Late Misses (A N) *442*
Sussman Charitable Trust,
   Adrienne & Leslie *443*
TSB Foundation for Northern
   Ireland *447*
TSB Foundation for Scotland
   447
Templeton Goodwill Trust *451*
Tindall's Charitable Trust, Mrs
   R P *457*
Tisbury Telegraph Trust, The
   457
Travis Charitable Trust,
   Constance *460*
Turner Trust, The Douglas *464*
Van Berchem Charitable Trust,
   The Alec *470*
Victoria & Johnson Memorial
   Trust, Queen *472*
Wall Trust, Thomas *478*
Watson Foundation, The Bertie
   482
Webber Trust Fund, Ethel *483*

Weir Foundation, The James
   484
Whesby Ltd *488*
Whitaker Charitable Trust *489*
Wingfield's Charitable Trust,
   Mrs *496*
Woodroffe Benton Foundation,
   The *502*
Woolton Charitable Trust, The
   503
Wylde Memorial Charity, The
   Anthony and Gwendoline
   507

....
■ **Hospitals**
see also **Health facilities &
buildings**
Funding priority
Baronets Trust, The *35*
Bull Charitable Trust, Henry
   Robert *68*
Burn Charity Trust, The J H *70*
Cancer Relief Macmillan Fund
   79
Cohen Charity Trust, Lucy *104*
Cooper Charitable Trust *111*
Corbett's Charity, Thomas *112*
Coxen Trust Fund, Sir William
   116
Dahl Foundation, The Roald
   122
Davy Foundation, The J *126*
Fogel Charitable Trust, The
   Gerald *165*
Franklin Deceased's New
   Second Charity, Sydney E
   170
Harvey Charitable Trust,
   Gordon *211*
Hutchinson Charitable Trust,
   E B *232*
Lacy Charity Trust, The Late Sir
   Pierce *260*
Needham Cooper Charitable
   Trust, The *331*
Paul's Charitable Trust, R J *355*
Rich Charities, S & J *383*
Rickman Trust, Muriel Edith
   385
Sassoon Charitable Trust, The
   Late Aaron D *408*
Stonehouse Trust Ltd, Eric *438*
Ulverscroft Foundation, The
   468

Will consider
Anstey Charitable Settlement,
   J C W *18*
Army Benevolent Fund, The *22*
Astor Foundation, The *26*
Bancroft Trust, The *33*
Beckwith Charitable
   Settlement, The Heather *39*
Beit Trust, The *40*
Bentall Charity Trust, Rowan
   44

Birtwistle Memorial Trust, The
  G E 50
Britton Charitable Trust, The J
  & M 63
Broadley Charitable Trust, The
  64
Brotherton Trust, The Charles
  65
Buckinghamshire Masonic
  Centenary Fund 67
Bullough Tompson Settlement,
  The 68
Catto Charitable Settlement,
  The Thomas Sivewright 86
Challice Trust, The 87
Children's Research Fund, The
  92
Clarke Charitable Settlement,
  The 99
Company of Chartered
  Surveyors Charitable Trust
  Fund, The 108
Dean Refugee Trust Fund, The
  Miriam 128
Derbyshire Trust, J N 130
Digby Charitable Trust, Simon
  133
Direct Response 134
Dorus Trust 136
Dumbreck Charity 139
Edgar Trust, The Gilbert 145
Elkes Charity Fund, The Wilfred
  & Elsie 147
Emmandjay Charitable Trust
  150
Epigoni Trust 152
Eveson Charitable Trust, The
  155
Fishmongers' Company's
  Charitable Trust 163
Fleming Charitable Trust, The
  Ian 164
Glynde Place Charitable Trust
  (1974), The 186
Goldsmiths' Company's
  Charities, The 188
Good Neighbours Trust, The
  188
Greenaway Foundation, The Sir
  Derek 194
Grocers' Charity 197
Halkes Settlement, John Robert
  204
Hannay Charitable Trust, The
  Lennox 208
Henderson's Settlement, J R
  216
Humanitarian Trust, The 230
Ibbett Trust, The 233
Inman Charity, The 235
JDM Charitable Trust 239
JHL Trust, The 239
JMK Charitable Trust 239
Kiln Charitable Trust, Robert
  254
Laing Charitable Trust, The
  David 260

Lawson Charitable Trust,
  Raymond and Blanche 267
Leadbeater Trust, The Alfred
  268
Lee Foundation, The Edgar
  269
Leech Charity, The William 269
Leukaemia Research Fund 271
London Law Trust 280
Lowe Trust, Mrs D G 285
MacKintosh Charitable Trust,
  Viscount 292
Mellows Charitable Settlement,
  The Anthony and Elizabeth
  305
Mercury Phoenix Trust 307
Milward Charity, The Edgar
  313
Minet Trust, The Peter 313
Natwest Staff Samaritan Fund
  330
Newby Trust Ltd 332
Owen Family Trust, The 348
Parivar Trust, The 353
Penny in the Pound Fund
  Charitable Trust 359
Peppiatt Charitable Trust, The
  Brian 359
Pratt Charitable Trust, The W L
  367
Pyke Charity Trust 372
Ravenscroft Foundation, The
  379
SMB Trust, The 400
Schuster Charitable Trust, The
  410
Shelroy Charitable Trust, The
  417
Smith (Estates Charities), Henry
  426
Sportsman's Aid Charity Ltd,
  The 434
Summer's and I May's
  Charitable Settlement, The
  Late Misses (A N) 442
Sussman Charitable Trust,
  Adrienne & Leslie 443
Sykes Trust, The Charles 445
Thompson Charitable Trust,
  The 453
Tisbury Telegraph Trust, The
  457
Travis Charitable Trust,
  Constance 460
Webber Trust Fund, Ethel 483
Wylde Memorial Charity, The
  Anthony and Gwendoline
  507

Army Benevolent Fund, The 22
Borthwick Memorial Trust, The
  Oliver 56
Calypso Browning Trust 78
Charity Projects 90
Curriers Company Charitable
  Fund 119
HACT (The Housing
  Association's Charitable
  Trust) 201
Held Settlement, The Gisela
  215
Hudson Benevolent Trust, The
  Thomas 230
Humphreys Charitable
  Settlement, J A M 231
Hyde Charitable Trust 232
Lyons Charitable Trust, The
  288
Pick Charitable Trust, The
  George and Jessie 362
Swan Mountain Trust 444
Trust for the Homeless 462
Woodroffe Benton Foundation,
  The 502

Will consider

Abbey National Charitable
  Trust 4
Abel Charitable Trust 5
Alexis Trust, The 11
Anstey Charitable Settlement,
  J C W 18
Aquarius Charitable
  Foundation, The 19
Archer Trust, The 20
Ashden Charitable Trust, The
  24
Astor Foundation, The 26
Avon Trust, The 28
Baker Charitable Trust, The 30
Barbour Trust, The 33
Barratt Charitable Trust, The
  Elaine 36
Berkshire Community Trust 45
Bilton Charity, The Percy 48
Boots Charitable Trust 56
Britton Charitable Trust, The J
  & M 63
Brotherton Trust, The Charles
  65
Brough Charitable Trust,
  Joseph 65
Burdall Charity, H M 69
Burden Trust, The 69
Butlin Charity Trust, Bill 72
Cadbury Trust (1928), The
  Edward & Dorothy 76
Camelot Foundation, The 78
Campden Charities, The 79
Cazalet Charitable Trust, The
  Raymond 87
Chase Charity, The 91
Chiddick Charitable Trust 92
Christmas Cracker Trust 95
Cleopatra Trust 99

....

■ Hostels

see also **Residential facilities
& services**

Funding priority

AB Charitable Trust 3
Allied Dunbar Charitable Trust
  Limited, The 13

Clifford Charity Oxford, The 100

Company of Chartered Surveyors Charitable Trust Fund, The 108

County Durham Foundation 115

Coutts Charitable Trust, The 116

de Freitas Charitable Trust, The Helen and Geoffrey 126

Derbyshire Trust, J N 130

Dibs Charitable Trust, The 133

Digby Charitable Trust, Simon 133

Ebb and Flow Charitable Trust 144

Edgar Foundation, The Gilbert and Eileen 145

Edgar Trust, The Gilbert 145

Egerton of Tatton Will Trust, Lord 146

Elkes Charity Fund, The Wilfred & Elsie 147

Emmandjay Charitable Trust 150

Epigoni Trust 152

Ferguson Benevolent Fund Limited 161

Fishmongers' Company's Charitable Trust 163

Ford of Britain Trust 166

Frognal Trust 174

Greater Bristol Foundation 193

Harford Charitable Trust 209

Harvey Charitable Trust, Gordon 211

Heath Charitable Trust 214

Hilden Charitable Fund, The 219

Inverforth Charitable Trust, The 236

Isle of Dogs Community Foundation 238

JDM Charitable Trust 239

Johnson Foundation, The 246

Laing Charitable Trust, The David 260

Laing Foundation, The Christopher 260

Lane Foundation, The Allen 263

Lankelly Foundation, The 264

Leadbeater Trust, The Alfred 268

Leech Charity, The William 269

Lewis Partnership, John 274

Linmardon Trust 276

Luke Trust, The 286

Mackintosh Foundation, The 292

Manning Trust, Leslie & Lilian 296

Marchday Charitable Fund, The 296

Marriage's Charitable Trust, Miss G M 299

Mental Health Foundation, The 305

Milburn Charitable Trust, Frederick 310

Moore Foundation, The George A 316

Moores Foundation, John 318

Morphy Memorial Fund, Arthur 319

NR Charitable Trust, The 325

New Court Charitable Trust 332

Norman Family Charitable Trust, The 337

Northern Ireland Voluntary Trust 339

Norton Foundation, The 340

Oldham Foundation 345

Open Door Women's Trust 346

Owen Family Trust, The 348

PF Charitable Trust 350

Pratt Charitable Trust, The W L 367

Pryor Charitable Trust, The John 370

Rest-Harrow Trust, The 382

Robinson Brothers (Ryders Green) Ltd, Charitable Trust 388

Rope Third Charitable Settlement, The Mrs 391

Rothley Trust, The 392

St Christopher's Trust, The 402

Scott Bader Commonwealth Ltd, The 411

Seagram Distillers Charitable Trust 413

Sheldon Trust, The 417

Smith & Mount Trust, The Mrs 426

South Square Trust 430

Sparkhill Trust, The 433

Stevens Foundation, The June 437

Stoate Charitable Trust, The Leonard Laity 438

Stonehouse Trust Ltd, Eric 438

Sykes Trust, The Charles 445

TSB Foundation for Northern Ireland 447

Tisbury Telegraph Trust, The 457

Travis Charitable Trust, Constance 460

Truemark Trust, The 461

Tudor Trust, The 463

Unitek Foundation 469

Wander Charitable Fund, The Dr Albert 479

Wesleyan Charitable Trust, The 485

Whesby Ltd 488

Woburn 1986 Charitable Trust 498

Wolfe Family's Charitable Trust, The 498

Woodlands Trust 501

■ Housing

see Residential facilities & services

■ Housing associations

see also Residential facilities & services

Funding priority

HACT (The Housing Association's Charitable Trust) 201

Hyde Charitable Trust 232

Will consider

AB Charitable Trust 3

Abbey National Charitable Trust 4

Amory Charitable Trust, Viscount 16

Army Benevolent Fund, The 22

Astor Foundation, The 26

Barbour Trust, The 33

Bilton Charity, The Percy 48

Boots Charitable Trust 56

Borthwick Memorial Trust, The Oliver 56

Brough Charitable Trust, Joseph 65

Burden Trust, The 69

Camelot Foundation, The 78

Campden Charities, The 79

Challice Trust, The 87

Charity Projects 90

Chase Charity, The 91

Clark 1965 Charitable Trust, Stephen 98

Company of Chartered Surveyors Charitable Trust Fund, The 108

County Durham Foundation 115

Coutts Charitable Trust, The 116

Curriers Company Charitable Fund 119

David Trust, The Lesley 124

de Freitas Charitable Trust, The Helen and Geoffrey 126

Derbyshire Trust, J N 130

Digby Charitable Trust, Simon 133

Direct Response 134

Dumbreck Charity 139

Edgar Foundation, The Gilbert and Eileen 145

Edgar Trust, The Gilbert 145

Emanuel Charitable Settlement, Ralph and Muriel 150

Emmandjay Charitable Trust 150

Ferguson Benevolent Fund Limited 161

Fishmongers' Company's Charitable Trust 163

Ford of Britain Trust *166*
Frognal Trust *174*
GW Trust, The *176*
Harford Charitable Trust *209*
Harvey Charitable Trust,
    Gordon *211*
Held Settlement, The Gisela
    215
Hudson Benevolent Trust, The
    Thomas *230*
Kroch Foundation, The Heinz &
    Anna *259*
Laing Charitable Trust, The
    David *260*
Laing Foundation, The
    Christopher *260*
Laing's Charitable Trust *262*
Lankelly Foundation, The *264*
Leech Charity, The William *269*
Lewis Partnership, John *274*
Licensed Trade Charities Trust,
    The *274*
Lyons Charitable Trust, The
    288
Mackintosh Foundation, The
    292
Marchday Charitable Fund, The
    296
Mental Health Foundation, The
    305
Music for World Development
    323
NR Charitable Trust, The *325*
Natwest Staff Samaritan Fund
    330
New Court Charitable Trust
    332
Newby Trust Ltd *332*
Norman Family Charitable
    Trust, The *337*
North British Hotel Trust *337*
Norton Foundation, The *340*
PF Charitable Trust *350*
Pryor Charitable Trust, The
    John *370*
Rest-Harrow Trust, The *382*
Rothley Trust, The *392*
Rowntree Foundation, Joseph
    394
Sparkhill Trust, The *433*
Summerfield Charitable Trust,
    The *442*
Swan Mountain Trust *444*
Sykes Trust, The Charles *445*
Tisbury Telegraph Trust, The
    457
Torquay Charities, The *458*
Trust for the Homeless *462*
Tudor Trust, The *463*
Wesleyan Charitable Trust, The
    485
Woburn 1986 Charitable Trust
    498

■ Human resources
see **Personnel & human resource services**

■ Human rights
see **Campaigning (social issues)**

■ Immigrants
Funding priority
Buxton Trust, Denis *72*
Cobb Charity *103*
Ericson Trust *152*
Fogel Charitable Trust, The
    Gerald *165*
Franklin Trust, Jill *170*
HACT (The Housing
    Association's Charitable
    Trust) *201*
Isle of Dogs Community
    Foundation *238*
King's Fund, The *255*
Lane Foundation, The Allen
    263
Lyndhurst Settlement *287*
Moores Family Charity
    Foundation, The *317*
Rowntree Charitable Trust, The
    Joseph *394*
Tisbury Telegraph Trust, The
    457
Trust for London *461*
Welfare Charity Establishment
    485

Will consider
AB Charitable Trust *3*
Alexandra Trust *11*
Barbour Trust, The *33*
Blake Charitable Trust, The
    Morgan *53*
Butlin Charity Trust, Bill *72*
Camelot Foundation, The *78*
Carlton Television Trust *81*
Carnegie United Kingdom
    Trust, The *82*
Charity Projects *90*
Church Urban Fund *95*
Cole Charitable Trust, The *105*
Coutts Charitable Trust, The
    116
De Yong Charitable Trust, The
    Emma *128*
Digbeth Trust Ltd, The *133*
Ebb and Flow Charitable Trust
    144
Edgar Foundation, The Gilbert
    and Eileen *145*
Elkes Charity Fund, The Wilfred
    & Elsie *147*
Four Winds Trust *168*
Goldsmiths' Company's
    Charities, The *188*

Grant-Lawson Charitable Trust,
    Lady Virginia *192*
Groves Charitable Trust, The
    197
Hampstead Wells and
    Campden Trust *206*
Hanley Trust (1987), The *207*
Harbour Foundation Ltd, The
    208
Held Settlement, The Gisela
    215
Hertfordshire Community
    Trust, The *217*
Hopkinson Educational Trust,
    Robert Addy *227*
Humanitarian Trust, The *230*
Iris Trust, The *237*
JCSCJ Charitable Trust, The
    238
Keeling Charitable Trust, The
    Petronella *251*
Laing Charitable Trust, The
    David *260*
Laing Foundation, The
    Christopher *260*
Laing Foundation, The Kirby
    261
Laing Foundation, The Maurice
    261
Laing Trust, Beatrice *261*
Lloyd Charity, The S and D *278*
(Lloyds) TSB Foundation for
    England and Wales *279*
Lyons Charitable Trust, The
    288
McCarthy Foundation, The
    John *290*
Mackintosh Foundation, The
    292
Mental Health Foundation, The
    305
Milton Keynes Community
    Trust Ltd, The *312*
Minet Trust, The Peter *313*
Moores Foundation, John *318*
Music for World Development
    323
Nathan Charitable Trust *326*
New Court Charitable Trust
    332
New Durlston Trust, The *332*
Newby Trust Ltd *332*
Noah Trust, The *335*
Noel Buxton Trust, The *335*
Paristamen Foundation, The
    352
Parivar Trust, The *353*
Payne Trust, The Harry *356*
Persula Foundation, The *360*
Pye Christian Trust, The *371*
Rope Third Charitable
    Settlement, The Mrs *391*
St Christopher's Trust, The *402*
Seagram Distillers Charitable
    Trust *413*
South Square Trust *430*
Summerfield Charitable Trust,
    The *442*

Swan Mountain Trust *444*
TSB Foundation for Scotland *447*
Trust for the Homeless *462*
Tudor Trust, The *463*
Van Berchem Charitable Trust, The Alec *470*
Van Leer Foundation UK Trust, Bernard *470*
Variety Club Children's Charity Limited, The *471*
Wakefield (Tower Hill, Trinity Square) Trust *476*
Wakeham Trust, The *476*
Wates Foundation, The *481*
Wesleyan Charitable Trust, The *485*
Westcroft Trust *486*
Whitecourt Charitable Trust, The *490*
Woodlands Trust *501*
Worshipful Company of Glass Sellers' Charity Trust, The *505*

■ In care, fostered & adopted

Funding priority

Access 4 Trust *6*
Ballard Charitable Trust, The Stanton *32*
Ballinger Charitable Trust, The *32*
Clipsham Charitable Settlement, R E *101*
Fogel Charitable Trust, The Gerald *165*
Four Winds Trust *168*
Gluckstein Charitable Settlement, The Penelope *185*
Hiley Trust, Joseph and Mary *219*
Humphreys Charitable Settlement, J A M *231*
Lynall Foundation, The D G *287*
Marmor Charitable Trust, The Julie *299*
Melchett Children's Trust, The Violet *305*
Muslim Hands *324*
Nidditch Foundation, The Laurie *335*
Sassoon Charitable Trust, The Late Aaron D *408*
Variety Club Children's Charity Limited, The *471*

Will consider

Ashley Foundation, The Laura *24*
Astor Foundation, The *26*
Barnabas Charitable Trust *34*
Beckwith Charitable Settlement, The Heather *39*
Blackburn Trust, The *51*
Cadbury Charitable Trust (Incorporated), Edward *75*
Carlton Television Trust *81*
Cobb Charity *103*
Curzon Charitable Trust, The Wallace *120*
Ferguson Benevolent Fund Limited *161*
Fishmongers' Company's Charitable Trust *163*
Frognal Trust *174*
Garnett's 1973 Charitable Trust, Mrs A M *178*
Griffiths Trust, The E E and D M *196*
Handicapped Children's Aid Committee *207*
Harford Charitable Trust *209*
Hudson Benevolent Trust, The Thomas *230*
JDM Charitable Trust *239*
Kyte Charitable Trust, The *259*
Laing Charitable Trust, The David *260*
Lane Foundation, The Allen *263*
London Taxi Drivers' Fund for Underprivileged Children, The *280*
Mental Health Foundation, The *305*
Milburn Charitable Trust, Frederick *310*
Milward Charity, The Edgar *313*
Newby Trust Ltd *332*
Noel Buxton Trust, The *335*
Norman Family Charitable Trust, The *337*
Payne Trust, The Harry *356*
Pyke Charity Trust *372*
Reeve's Foundation *382*
Riddleston Charity of Leicester, The Harry James *385*
Robinson Brothers (Ryders Green) Ltd, Charitable Trust *388*
Sargeant's Charitable Trust, Mrs M E *407*
South Square Trust *430*
Southover Manor General Education Trust Ltd *433*
Thomson Foundation, The Sue *454*
Van Leer Foundation UK Trust, Bernard *470*
Yardy Charitable Trust, The Dennis Alan *509*

■ Income support & maintenance

see also Community services

Funding priority

Airflow Community Ltd, The *9*
Alglen Ltd *11*
Alliance Family Foundation Limited *13*
Aquarian Healing Trust *19*
Army Benevolent Fund, The *22*
Ashton Foundation, The Norman C *24*
Beacon Trust *38*
Bear Mordechai Ltd *39*
Beauland Ltd *39*
Belljoe Tzedoko Ltd *42*
Blakenham's Charity Trust, Lady *53*
Blank Donations Ltd, The David *54*
Brushmill Ltd *66*
Buckingham Trust *67*
Carter Trust, The Frederick William *84*
Cen Foundation, The Hyman *87*
Childtime Trust, The *92*
Christian Renewal Trust, The *94*
Clark Charitable Trust *98*
Closehelm Ltd *101*
Cope Charitable Trust, Alfred *112*
Crawford Children's Charity, Michael *117*
Curriers Company Charitable Fund *119*
Dahl Foundation, The Roald *122*
Dandeen Charitable Trust *123*
Desmond Charitable Trust, The Richard *131*
Elanore Ltd *146*
Elephant Jobs Charity *146*
Eling Trust *147*
Elton John Aids Foundation, The *149*
Family Trust, The *158*
Flanagan Leukaemia Fund, Bud *164*
Franklin Deceased's New Second Charity, Sydney E *170*
Fund for Human Need *175*
Grahame Charitable Foundation, The *190*
Grosshill Charitable Trust *197*
Grove Charitable Trust, The *197*
Harbour Foundation Ltd, The *208*
Harding's Charity, William *209*
Highcroft Charitable Trust *218*
JCA Charitable Foundation *238*
Jubilee Outreach Yorkshire *248*

Kahn Charitable Trust, Bernard *250*
Kweller Charitable Trust, The Harry *259*
Liebes Charitable Trust, The Martha Bud *274*
Lloyd's Charities Trust *278*
Localtrent Ltd *279*
Marchday Charitable Fund, The *296*
Mercury Phoenix Trust *307*
Millett Charitable Trust, The Alan and Janet *312*
Modiano Charitable Trust *315*
Morgan Foundation, The Mr & Mrs J T *319*
Muslim Hands *324*
Nunburnholme Trust, The Incorporated Trustees of the *342*
Palmer Trust, The Gerald *352*
Pick Charitable Trust, The George and Jessie *362*
QAS Charitable Trust *373*
Robbins Trust, The Cheshire *387*
Rope Third Charitable Settlement, The Mrs *391*
Royal Theatrical Fund, The *396*
Rudabede *397*
Seedfield Trust, The *414*
Shah Trust, The Dr N K *416*
Sidbury Trust, The Second *421*
Society of Friends of the Torah, The *429*
Stanley Foundation Limited *435*
Stathern Chapel Close Trust, The *436*
Trenance Charitable Trust *460*
Tudor Rose Ltd *463*
Tyndale Trust *466*
Veronique Charitable Trust *472*
Vineyard Christian Fellowship of South West *473*
White Rose Children's Aid International Charity *489*
Woods Charitable Foundation, Geoffrey *502*

Will consider

Access 4 Trust *6*
Betard Bequest *46*
Bisgood Trust, The *50*
Bisgood's Charitable Trust, Miss Jeanne *50*
Bowland Charitable Trust, The *57*
Brand Charitable Trust *58*
Brooke Benevolent Fund, William *65*
CLA Charitable Trust *74*
Cathedral Nursing Society Charitable Trust *85*
Challice Trust, The *87*
Chiddick Charitable Trust *92*

County Durham Foundation *115*
Coutts Charitable Trust, The *116*
Debtors' Relief Fund Charity *128*
Digby Charitable Trust, Simon *133*
Dumbreck Charity *139*
Egerton of Tatton Will Trust, Lord *146*
Elkes Charity Fund, The Wilfred & Elsie *147*
Fletcher Trust, Roy *165*
Gelston Charitable Trust, The *179*
Greenaway Foundation, The Sir Derek *194*
Haberdashers' Eleemosynary Charity *201*
Harford Charitable Trust *209*
Hertfordshire Community Trust, The *217*
Kroch Foundation, The Heinz & Anna *259*
Laing Foundation, The Christopher *260*
Lankelly Foundation, The *264*
Leech Charity, The William *269*
Lewis Partnership, John *274*
Lloyd's Patriotic Fund *279*
Mackintosh Foundation, The *292*
Margaret Foundation, The *297*
National Power Charitable Trust, The *330*
Needham Cooper Charitable Trust, The *331*
Newby Trust Ltd *332*
Norton Foundation, The *340*
Paterson Charitable Foundation, The Constance *354*
Paterson Charitable Trust, Arthur James *354*
Ripley's Charitable Trust, Pat *386*
Salamander Charitable Trust, The *405*
Shepherd Family Charitable Trust, The Sir Peter *418*
Sparkhill Trust, The *433*
Swan Mountain Trust *444*
Talteg Ltd *448*
Wates Foundation, The *481*
Wiltshire Community Foundation *495*

....

■ Independent schools

see also **Schools & colleges**

Funding priority
Beit Trust, The *40*
Catholic Education Service for England and Wales *86*
Christmas Cracker Trust *95*

Hussey for Africans, Charity of Rebecca *231*
Whitehead Charitable Trust, J E *490*

Will consider
Ammco Trust, The *15*
Archer Trust, The *20*
Arts Council of Wales, The *23*
Betton's Charity (Educational), Mr Thomas *46*
BibleLands *47*
British Schools and Universities Foundation (Inc) *62*
Bullough Tompson Settlement, The *68*
Carlton Television Trust *81*
Cazalet Charitable Trust, The Raymond *87*
Community Trust for Greater Manchester, The *108*
Curzon Charitable Trust, The Wallace *120*
Derbyshire Trust, J N *130*
Digby Charitable Trust, Simon *133*
Edgar Trust, The Gilbert *145*
Four Winds Trust *168*
Glynde Place Charitable Trust (1974), The *186*
Goldsmiths' Company's Charities, The *188*
Great Britain Sasakawa Foundation, The *193*
Henderson's Settlement, J R *216*
Hillards Charitable Trust, Gay & Peter Hartley's *220*
Hudson Benevolent Trust, The Thomas *230*
Ingles Charitable Trust, The *234*
Ireland Funds, The *237*
Lee Foundation, The Edgar *269*
Lewis Foundation, The John Spedan *274*
Licensed Trade Charities Trust, The *274*
Littler Foundation, The Emile *277*
Lloyd's Charities Trust *278*
Measures Charity, The James Frederick and Ethel Anne *303*
Milward Charity, The Edgar *313*
Montefiore Trust, The David *316*
Moore Foundation, The George A *316*
Morphy Memorial Fund, Arthur *319*
Newcomen Collett Foundation *333*
Notgrove Trust, The *341*
Owen Family Trust, The *348*

Provincial Trust for Kendal, The
370
Pyke Charity Trust 372
Rothley Trust, The 392
Salters Charities 405
Van Leer Foundation UK Trust,
Bernard 470

see also **Advocacy (social
issues)**

··

■ **Individual rights
(advocacy)**
Funding priority
Cadbury Trust, The Barrow 76
HACT (The Housing
Association's Charitable
Trust) 201
Kroch Foundation, The Heinz &
Anna 259
Lyndhurst Settlement 287
Mental Health Foundation, The
305
Northern Arts 339
Staples Trust 435
Swan Mountain Trust 444

Will consider
Body Shop Foundation, The 55
Cadbury Schweppes
Foundation, The 76
Campden Charities, The 79
County Durham Foundation
115
Cripplegate Foundation 118
David Trust, The Lesley 124
Dibs Charitable Trust, The 133
Digby Charitable Trust, Simon
133
Follett Trust, The 166
Gelston Charitable Trust, The
179
Goldsmiths' Company's
Charities, The 188
Hamlyn Foundation, The Paul
205
Harford Charitable Trust 209
Humanitarian Trust, The 230
Ireland Funds, The 237
JCSCJ Charitable Trust, The
238
Lankelly Foundation, The 264
New Court Charitable Trust
332
Newby Trust Ltd 332
Noah Trust, The 335
North West Arts Board 337
Open Door Women's Trust 346
Owen Family Trust, The 348
Payne Trust, The Harry 356
Persula Foundation, The 360
Polden-Puckham Charitable
Foundation, The 365
Rothley Trust, The 392
Rowntree Foundation, Joseph
394

Saint Sarkis Charity Trust 404
Summerfield Charitable Trust,
The 442
Tear Fund 450
Tisbury Telegraph Trust, The
457
Wates Foundation, The 481
Wiltshire Community
Foundation 495

··

■ **Information
technology &
computers**
see also **Infrastructure &
technical support**
Funding priority
County Durham Foundation
115
Homeless International 225
IBM United Kingdom Trust
233

Will consider
Aston Charities Trust Ltd 25
Berkshire Community Trust 45
Camelot Foundation, The 78
Collier Charitable Trust, The
105
Daily Telegraph Charitable
Trust 122
Digby Charitable Trust, Simon
133
Direct Response 134
Egerton of Tatton Will Trust,
Lord 146
Ford of Britain Trust 166
Four Lanes Trust, The 168
Great Britain Sasakawa
Foundation, The 193
Iris Trust, The 237
Isle of Dogs Community
Foundation 238
Jarrold Trust Ltd, John 243
Laing Foundation, The
Christopher 260
Licensed Trade Charities Trust,
The 274
Skelton Bounty, The 423
Tear Fund 450

··

■ **Infrastructure &
technical support**
see also **Building services,
Financial services,
Information technology &
computers, Legal services,
Management services,
Personnel & human
resource services, Publishing
& printing, Recruitment
services**

Funding priority
Edinburgh Trust, No 2 Account
145
Pitman Charitable Trust, The
John 364

Will consider
AHJ Charitable Trust, The 3
Achiezer Association Limited 6
Airflow Community Ltd, The 9
Ajahma Charitable Trust, The
9
Aleh Charitable Foundation,
The 10
Allachy Trust, The 12
Anderson Trust, Andrew 16
Angler's Inn Trust 17
Anglo Hong Kong Trust, The
17
Appelbe Trust, Ambrose & Ann
19
Aquarius Charitable
Foundation, The 19
Aquinas Trust 20
Askew Charitable Trust, The
Ian 25
Assembled Church of Christ
Trust, The 25
Assheton-Smith Charitable
Trust 25
Astor of Hever Trust, The 26
Astor's 1969 Charity, The Hon
M L 26
Baring Foundation, The 34
Barnby's Foundation, Lord 35
Barnsbury Charitable Trust 35
Barton Trust, Eleanor 37
Bateman Charitable Trust, Lady
Margaret 37
Bealey Foundation, The 38
Beckwith Charitable Trust, The
Peter 40
Beckwith-Smith's Charitable
Settlement, Mrs 40
Bergqvist Charitable Trust 44
Black Foundation, The Bertie
51
Blagrave Charitable Trust, The
Herbert and Peter 52
Blakenham's Charity Trust,
Lady 53
Blakey Charitable Trust, The
Celia and Conrad 53
Blank Donations Ltd, The David
54
Boltons Trust, The 55
Borthwick Memorial Trust, The
Oliver 56
Bottom Charitable Trust, Harry
56
Bowland Charitable Trust, The
57
British Sugar Foundation 63
Brook Charitable Settlement,
R E 64
Brookhouse's Will Trust, Mr
John Charles 65
Burn Charity Trust, The J H 70

Burns Charity, The Dorothy 70
Burry Charitable Trust, The 70
Burton Charitable Trust, The Geoffrey 71
Butler's Trust, Lord 71
Butler's Trust, Lucilla 72
Cadbury Schweppes Foundation, The 76
Cardiff & Swansea Methodist District Charitable Trust Fund 80
Carron Charitable Trust, The 83
Castang Charitable Trust, H and M 85
Charity Projects 90
Christian Aid 94
Christmas Cracker Trust 95
Cinderford Charitable Trust, The 96
Clark Charitable Trust, J Anthony 98
Closehelm Ltd 101
Clutterbuck Charitable Trust, Robert 102
Coates Charitable Settlement, The 102
Coates Charitable Trust 1969, Lance 103
Cohen Charitable Trust, The Vivienne and Samuel 104
Cohen Charity Trust, Lucy 104
Comino Foundation 107
Company of Tobacco Pipe Makers and Tobacco Blenders Benevolent Fund 109
Condon Family Trust 109
Cope Charitable Trust, Alfred 112
Crescent Trust, The 117
Curry Charitable Trust, Dennis 119
Cymerman Trust Limited, Itzchok Meyer 120
Dandeen Charitable Trust 123
Davy Foundation, The J 126
De Avenley Foundation, The 126
De La Rue Charitable Trust 127
De Rothschild 1981 Charitable Trust, The Edmund 127
De Yong Charitable Trust, The Emma 128
Delmar Charitable Trust 129
Denton Charitable Trust, The 130
Desmond Charitable Trust, The Richard 131
Deutsch Charitable Trust, The Andre 131
Deutsch Charitable Trust, The H & M 131
Dicken Charitable Trust, The Albert 133
Dinam Charity 134
Djanogly Foundation, The 135

Doughty Charity Trust, The 136
D'Oyly Carte Charitable Trust, The 137
Drayton Trust, The 138
Dulverton Trust, The 139
Dunn Charitable Trust, The Harry 140
Earmark Trust, The 142
Eling Trust 147
Elshore Limited 149
Family Trust, The 158
Famos Foundation Trust 158
Foreman Foundation, The Carl & Eve 167
Foyle Trust, Charles Henry 169
Franklin Bequest, The Rosalind 169
Franklin Deceased's New Second Charity, Sydney E 170
Fry Charitable Trust, Maurice 174
Garthgwynion Charities 179
Gibson's Charity Trust, The Hon Mr & Mrs Clive 182
Gillett Charitable Trust, J A 183
Gill's Charitable Trust, Mrs M M 184
Girdlers' Company Charitable Trust, The 184
Gold Hill Church Trust 186
Goldberg Charitable Trust, The Lewis 186
Goodman Charitable Foundation, The Everard and Mina 188
Goodman Trust, The 189
Gradel Foundation, The 189
Green Foundation, Constance 194
Gross Charities Limited, M & R 197
Grosshill Charitable Trust 197
Grut Charitable Trust, The 198
HB Charitable Trust 201
Hacking & Sons Ltd Charitable Trust, C G 201
Hamilton Educational Trust, Eleanor 205
Harbour Foundation Ltd, The 208
Harvey Charitable Trust, Gordon 211
Hawthorne Charitable Trust, The 212
Heinz Company Limited Charitable Trust, The H J 215
Held Settlement, The Gisela 215
Hillards Charitable Trust, Gay & Peter Hartley's 220
Holford Trust Fund 224
Hoover Foundation, The 226
Horn Trust, The Cuthbert 227

Hornby Charitable Trust, Miss D 227
Hornton Trust, The 228
Hughes Charitable Trust, The Geoffery C 230
IPE Charitable Trust, The 233
Inman Charity, The 235
James Foundation, The Catherine and Lady Grace 241
Jones Trust, Cemlyn 248
KC Charitable Trust, The 250
Karten Charitable Trust, The Ian 250
Keyes Trust, The Ursula 253
Kingsgrove Charitable Trust, The 255
Kinnison Charitable Trust, R O 256
Kleinwort Charitable Trust, The Ernest 257
Knott Trust, Sir James 258
Kobler Trust, The 258
Kreitman Foundation 258
Kulika Charitable Trust, The 259
Kweller Charitable Trust, The Harry 259
Landy Charitable Trust, Harry and Gertrude 263
Lanvern Foundation 265
Laski Memorial Charitable Trust, Nathan 265
Laspen Trust 265
Lauffer Charitable Foundation, The R & D 266
Lavender Trust, The 267
Lawley Foundation, The Edgar E 267
Leigh-Bramwell Trust 'E', P 270
Levy Charitable Foundation, Joseph 272
Liffe Benefit 274
Lingwood Charitable Trust, The 276
(Lloyds) TSB Foundation for England and Wales 279
Localtrent Ltd 279
Lucas Charitable Trust Limited, The Joseph 286
Lunzer Charitable Trust, The Ruth & Jack 287
Lynwood Charitable Trust, The 288
Lyons Charitable Trust, The 288
MDM Memorial Trust 289
MacAndrew Trust, The E M 289
McKechnie Foundation, A N 292
McKenzie Trust, The Robert 292
McLaren Foundation 292
McLaren Memorial Trust, The Martin 293
MacRobert Trusts, The 294

Margadale Charitable Trust, Lord *297*

Marks Charitable Trust, Michael *298*

Markus Charitable Foundation, The Erich *298*

Marr-Munning Trust *299*

Marshall Charitable Trust, The Charlotte *300*

Martin Trust, The Sir George *300*

Material World Charitable Foundation Limited, The *301*

Mattock Charitable Trust, The W T *302*

Mayfair Charities Limited *303*

Medlock Charitable Trust, The *304*

Mellows Charitable Settlement, The Anthony and Elizabeth *305*

Millett Charitable Trust, The Alan and Janet *312*

Millfield House Foundation *312*

Millichope Foundation, The *312*

Modiano Charitable Trust *315*

Montefiore Trust, The David *316*

Moore Charitable Trust, The Horace *316*

Morel Charitable Trust, The *318*

Morgan Crucible Company plc Charitable Trust, The *319*

Morris Charitable Trust, The Willie & Mabel *320*

Moulton Charitable Trust, The *321*

Music Sales Charitable Trust, The *324*

National Lottery Charities Board *328*

National Power Charitable Trust, The *330*

Newcastle's 1986 Charitable Trust, Duke of *333*

Newman Charitable Trust, Mr and Mrs F E F *334*

Newstead Charity, The *334*

Northcott Charity Trust, The *338*

Northern Electric Employee Charity Association *339*

Northern Ireland Voluntary Trust *339*

Old Possums Practical Trust, The *344*

Oppenheimer Charitable Trust *346*

Owen Trust, Margaret *348*

PDC Trust, The *349*

PJD Charitable Trust *350*

Palmer Trust, The Gerald *352*

Pascoe Charitable Trust, Alan *354*

Paul Charitable Trust, The Late Barbara May *355*

Paul Charitable Trust, Margaret Jeanne *355*

Paul Charitable Trust, Pamela Milton *355*

Paul Foundation, The *355*

Paul's Charitable Trust, R J *355*

Payne Charitable Trust, The *355*

Pelech Charitable Trust, The *358*

Perry Charitable Trust, Miss Frances Lucille *359*

Pershore Nashdom & Elmore Trust Ltd, The *360*

Peskin Charitable Trust, The Hazel and Leslie *360*

Phillips Charitable Foundation, Reginald M *361*

Pitt Trust, Headley *364*

Powys Welsh Church Fund *367*

Puebla Charitable Trust Limited, The *371*

QAS Charitable Trust *373*

Quothquan Charitable Trust, The Second *373*

RT Trust, The *374*

Rackham Charitable Trust, The Mr & Mrs Philip *375*

Radley Charitable Trust *375*

Rae Charity, H J *375*

Rav Chesed Trust, The *379*

Reekie Trust, R A & V B *381*

Richards Charity, The Clive *384*

Rivendell Trust, The *387*

Robbins Trust, The Cheshire *387*

Rodewald's Charitable Settlement, Mr C A *389*

Rogers Charitable Settlement, The Richard *390*

Rolfe Charitable Trust, The *390*

Rosen Foundation, Cecil *392*

S Group Charitable Trust *399*

St Jude's Trust *403*

Samuel Charitable Trust, M J *406*

Save & Prosper Foundation *409*

Scarr-Hall Memorial Trust, The *409*

Seva Trust, Rampaba Sadhu *415*

Sherman Charitable Trust, The Archie *419*

Shifrin Charitable Trust, The Maurice and Hilda *419*

Sidbury Trust, The Second *421*

Silvester Charitable Gift Trust *422*

Society of Friends of the Torah, The *429*

Solomons Charitable Trust, David *430*

Somerfield Curtis Will Trust, The Dorothy *430*

Stanley Foundation Limited *435*

Stewart Charitable Trust, Mary Stephanie *437*

Symons Charitable Trust, The Stella *446*

Taylor Charitable Trust, The B R *450*

Terry Charitable Trust, Noel Goddard *451*

Tesco Charity Trust *452*

Tesler Foundation, The *452*

van Geest Foundation, The John and Lucille *470*

Van Norden's Charitable Foundation, Mrs Maud *471*

Vineyard Christian Fellowship of South West *473*

Vinson Charity Trust, The 1969 *473*

Vogel Charitable Trust, The Nathan *474*

Wakefield Trust, The *476*

Ward Blenkinsop Trust, The *480*

Weinstock Fund, The *484*

West Midlands Regional Arts Board *486*

Whetherly's Charitable Trust, The Hon Mrs R G A *489*

Whitehead Charitable Trust, J E *490*

Whittington Charitable Trust, The *491*

Wiggins Charity Trust, Cyril *491*

Wilde Charitable Trust, The Felicity *492*

Williams Charitable Trust, Alfred *493*

Wiltshire Community Foundation *495*

Woburn 1986 Charitable Trust *498*

Wohl Charitable Foundation, The Maurice *498*

Wohl Charitable Trust, The Maurice *498*

Wolff Charity Trust *498*

Wolfson Family Charitable Trust, The *499*

Woods Charitable Foundation, Geoffrey *502*

Worms Charitable Trust, The Freda and Della *504*

Worshipful Company of Needlemakers' Charitable Fund *505*

Wychdale Limited *507*

Youell Foundation Ltd, The *510*

Zaiger Trust, The Elizabeth and Prince *512*

■ Infrastructure development

see also **Community businesses, Community development, Economic regeneration schemes, Job creation, Small enterprises, Support to voluntary & community organisations, Support to volunteers, Tourism**

Funding priority

Aga Khan Foundation (UK) *7*
Ajahma Charitable Trust, The *9*
Arkleton Trust, The *21*
CLA Charitable Trust *74*
Charity Projects *90*
Clark 1965 Charitable Trust, Stephen *98*
Comino Foundation *107*
Ellis 1985 Charitable Trust, Edith M *148*
Kulika Charitable Trust, The *259*
Millfield House Foundation *312*
Noah Trust, The *335*
Pitman Charitable Trust, The John *364*
Riddleston Charity of Leicester, The Harry James *385*
Riley-Smith Charitable Trust, The F A *386*
Rowan Charitable Trust, The *393*
Tudor Trust, The *463*
Vinson Charity Trust, The 1969 *473*

Will consider

AHJ Charitable Trust, The *3*
Achiezer Association Limited *6*
Airflow Community Ltd, The *9*
Aleh Charitable Foundation, The *10*
Allachy Trust, The *12*
Anderson Trust, Andrew *16*
Angler's Inn Trust *17*
Anglo Hong Kong Trust, The *17*
Appelbe Trust, Ambrose & Ann *19*
Aquarius Charitable Foundation, The *19*
Aquinas Trust *20*
Askew Charitable Trust, The Ian *25*
Assembled Church of Christ Trust, The *25*
Assheton-Smith Charitable Trust *25*
Astor of Hever Trust, The *26*
Astor's 1969 Charity, The Hon M L *26*
Barbour Trust, The *33*

Barnby's Foundation Appointed Fund, Lord *35*
Barnby's Foundation, Lord *35*
Barnsbury Charitable Trust *35*
Barton Trust, Eleanor *37*
Bateman Charitable Trust, Lady Margaret *37*
Bealey Foundation, The *38*
Beattie Charitable Trust, The James *39*
Beckwith Charitable Trust, The Peter *40*
Beckwith-Smith's Charitable Settlement, Mrs *40*
Bergqvist Charitable Trust *44*
Black Foundation, The Bertie *51*
Blagrave Charitable Trust, The Herbert and Peter *52*
Blakenham's Charity Trust, Lady *53*
Blakey Charitable Trust, The Celia and Conrad *53*
Blank Donations Ltd, The David *54*
Boltons Trust, The *55*
Boots Charitable Trust *56*
Borthwick Memorial Trust, The Oliver *56*
Bottom Charitable Trust, Harry *56*
Bowland Charitable Trust, The *57*
Brook Charitable Settlement, R E *64*
Brookhouse's Will Trust, Mr John Charles *65*
Burn Charity Trust, The J H *70*
Burns Charity, The Dorothy *70*
Burry Charitable Trust, The *70*
Burton Charitable Trust, The Geoffrey *71*
Butler's Trust, Lord *71*
Butler's Trust, Lucilla *72*
Cadbury Schweppes Foundation, The *76*
Cadbury Trust (1928), The Edward & Dorothy *76*
Cardiff & Swansea Methodist District Charitable Trust Fund *80*
Carnegie United Kingdom Trust, The *82*
Carron Charitable Trust, The *83*
Castang Charitable Trust, H and M *85*
Christian Aid *94*
Christmas Cracker Trust *95*
Cinderford Charitable Trust, The *96*
Clark Charitable Trust, J Anthony *98*
Closehelm Ltd *101*
Clutterbuck Charitable Trust, Robert *102*
Coates Charitable Settlement, The *102*

Coates Charitable Trust 1969, Lance *103*
Cohen Charitable Trust, The Vivienne and Samuel *104*
Cohen Charity Trust, Lucy *104*
Company of Tobacco Pipe Makers and Tobacco Blenders Benevolent Fund *109*
Condon Family Trust *109*
Cope Charitable Trust, Alfred *112*
Crescent Trust, The *117*
Curry Charitable Trust, Dennis *119*
Cymerman Trust Limited, Itzchok Meyer *120*
Daily Telegraph Charitable Trust *122*
Dandeen Charitable Trust *123*
Davy Foundation, The J *126*
De Avenley Foundation, The *126*
De La Rue Charitable Trust *127*
De Rothschild 1981 Charitable Trust, The Edmund *127*
De Yong Charitable Trust, The Emma *128*
Delmar Charitable Trust *129*
Denton Charitable Trust, The *130*
Desmond Charitable Trust, The Richard *131*
Deutsch Charitable Trust, The Andre *131*
Deutsch Charitable Trust, The H & M *131*
Dicken Charitable Trust, The Albert *133*
Dinam Charity *134*
Djanogly Foundation, The *135*
Doughty Charity Trust, The *136*
D'Oyly Carte Charitable Trust, The *137*
Drayton Trust, The *138*
Dulverton Trust, The *139*
Dunn Charitable Trust, The Harry *140*
Earmark Trust, The *142*
Edinburgh Trust, No 2 Account *145*
Egerton of Tatton Will Trust, Lord *146*
Eling Trust *147*
Elshore Limited *149*
Family Trust, The *158*
Famos Foundation Trust *158*
Foreman Foundation, The Carl & Eve *167*
Foyle Trust, Charles Henry *169*
Franklin Bequest, The Rosalind *169*
Franklin Deceased's New Second Charity, Sydney E *170*

Fry Charitable Trust, Maurice *174*
Garthgwynion Charities *179*
Gibson's Charity Trust, The Hon Mr & Mrs Clive *182*
Gillett Charitable Trust, J A *183*
Gill's Charitable Trust, Mrs M M *184*
Girdlers' Company Charitable Trust, The *184*
Gold Hill Church Trust *186*
Goldberg Charitable Trust, The Lewis *186*
Goodman Charitable Foundation, The Everard and Mina *188*
Goodman Trust, The *189*
Gradel Foundation, The *189*
Green Foundation, Constance *194*
Greenaway Foundation, The Sir Derek *194*
Gross Charities Limited, M & R *197*
Grosshill Charitable Trust *197*
Growth Building Trust, The *198*
Grut Charitable Trust, The *198*
HB Charitable Trust *201*
Hacking & Sons Ltd Charitable Trust, C G *201*
Hamilton Educational Trust, Eleanor *205*
Hampstead Wells and Campden Trust *206*
Harbour Foundation Ltd, The *208*
Harvey Charitable Trust, Gordon *211*
Hawthorne Charitable Trust, The *212*
Heinz Company Limited Charitable Trust, The H J *215*
Held Settlement, The Gisela *215*
Hillards Charitable Trust, Gay & Peter Hartley's *220*
Holford Trust Fund *224*
Hoover Foundation, The *226*
Horn Trust, The Cuthbert *227*
Hornby Charitable Trust, Miss D *227*
Hornton Trust, The *228*
Houblon-Norman Fund *229*
Hughes Charitable Trust, The Geoffery C *230*
IPE Charitable Trust, The *233*
Inman Charity, The *235*
Ireland Fund of Great Britain, The *237*
James Foundation, The Catherine and Lady Grace *241*
Jones Trust, Cemlyn *248*
Jubilee Outreach Yorkshire *248*

KC Charitable Trust, The *250*
Karten Charitable Trust, The Ian *250*
Keyes Trust, The Ursula *253*
Kingsgrove Charitable Trust, The *255*
Kinnison Charitable Trust, R O *256*
Kleinwort Charitable Trust, The Ernest *257*
Kobler Trust, The *258*
Kreitman Foundation *258*
Kweller Charitable Trust, The Harry *259*
Laing Foundation, The Christopher *260*
Laing's Charitable Trust *262*
Landy Charitable Trust, Harry and Gertrude *263*
Lanvern Foundation *265*
Laski Memorial Charitable Trust, Nathan *265*
Laspen Trust *265*
Lauffer Charitable Foundation, The R & D *266*
Lavender Trust, The *267*
Lawley Foundation, The Edgar E *267*
Leigh-Bramwell Trust 'E', P *270*
Levy Charitable Foundation, Joseph *272*
Lewis Foundation, The John Spedan *274*
Lewis Partnership, John *274*
Liffe Benefit *274*
Lingwood Charitable Trust, The *276*
(Lloyds) TSB Foundation for England and Wales *279*
Localtrent Ltd *279*
Lucas Charitable Trust Limited, The Joseph *286*
Lunzer Charitable Trust, The Ruth & Jack *287*
Lynwood Charitable Trust, The *288*
Lyons Charitable Trust, The *288*
MDM Memorial Trust *289*
MacAndrew Trust, The E M *289*
McKechnie Foundation, A N *292*
McKenzie Trust, The Robert *292*
McLaren Foundation *292*
McLaren Memorial Trust, The Martin *293*
MacRobert Trusts, The *294*
Margadale Charitable Trust, Lord *297*
Marks Charitable Trust, Michael *298*
Markus Charitable Foundation, The Erich *298*
Marshall Charitable Trust, The Charlotte *300*

Martin Trust, The Sir George *300*
Material World Charitable Foundation Limited, The *301*
Mattock Charitable Trust, The W T *302*
Mayfair Charities Limited *303*
Medlock Charitable Trust, The *304*
Mellows Charitable Settlement, The Anthony and Elizabeth *305*
Millennium Commission *311*
Millett Charitable Trust, The Alan and Janet *312*
Millichope Foundation, The *312*
Modiano Charitable Trust *315*
Montefiore Trust, The David *316*
Moore Charitable Trust, The Horace *316*
Morel Charitable Trust, The *318*
Morgan Crucible Company plc Charitable Trust, The *319*
Morris Charitable Trust, The Willie & Mabel *320*
Moulton Charitable Trust, The *321*
Music for World Development *323*
Music Sales Charitable Trust, The *324*
National Lottery Charities Board *328*
Newcastle's 1986 Charitable Trust, Duke of *333*
Newman Charitable Trust, Mr and Mrs F E F *334*
Newstead Charity, The *334*
Northcott Charity Trust, The *338*
Northern Arts *339*
Northern Electric Employee Charity Association *339*
Old Possums Practical Trust, The *344*
Oppenheimer Charitable Trust *346*
Owen Trust, Margaret *348*
PDC Trust, The *349*
PJD Charitable Trust *350*
Palmer Trust, The Gerald *352*
Pascoe Charitable Trust, Alan *354*
Paul Charitable Trust, The Late Barbara May *355*
Paul Charitable Trust, Margaret Jeanne *355*
Paul Charitable Trust, Pamela Milton *355*
Paul Foundation, The *355*
Paul's Charitable Trust, R J *355*
Payne Charitable Trust, The *355*

Pelech Charitable Trust, The
358
Perry Charitable Trust, Miss
Frances Lucille 359
Pershore Nashdom & Elmore
Trust Ltd, The 360
Peskin Charitable Trust, The
Hazel and Leslie 360
Phillips Charitable Foundation,
Reginald M 361
Pitt Trust, Headley 364
Powys Welsh Church Fund 367
QAS Charitable Trust 373
Quothquan Charitable Trust,
The Second 373
RT Trust, The 374
Rackham Charitable Trust, The
Mr & Mrs Philip 375
Radley Charitable Trust 375
Rae Charity, H J 375
Rav Chesed Trust, The 379
Reekie Trust, R A & V B 381
Richard Charitable Trust, The
Cliff 383
Richards Charity, The Clive 384
Richmond Parish Lands Charity
384
Ripley's Charitable Trust, Pat
386
Rivendell Trust, The 387
Robbins Trust, The Cheshire
387
Rodewald's Charitable
Settlement, Mr C A 389
Rogers Charitable Settlement,
The Richard 390
Rolfe Charitable Trust, The 390
Rope Third Charitable
Settlement, The Mrs 391
Rosen Foundation, Cecil 392
S Group Charitable Trust 399
St Jude's Trust 403
Samuel Charitable Trust, M J
406
Save & Prosper Foundation
409
Scarr-Hall Memorial Trust, The
409
Seva Trust, Rampaba Sadhu
415
Sherman Charitable Trust, The
Archie 419
Shifrin Charitable Trust, The
Maurice and Hilda 419
Sidbury Trust, The Second 421
Silvester Charitable Gift Trust
422
Skinners' Company Lady Neville
Charity 424
Society of Friends of the Torah,
The 429
Solomons Charitable Trust,
David 430
Somerfield Curtis Will Trust,
The Dorothy 430
Stanley Foundation Limited
435

Stewart Charitable Trust, Mary
Stephanie 437
Symons Charitable Trust, The
Stella 446
TSB Foundation for Scotland
447
Taylor Charitable Trust, The B R
450
Terry Charitable Trust, Noel
Goddard 451
Tesco Charity Trust 452
Tesler Foundation, The 452
van Geest Foundation, The
John and Lucille 470
Van Norden's Charitable
Foundation, Mrs Maud 471
Vineyard Christian Fellowship
of South West 473
Vogel Charitable Trust, The
Nathan 474
Wakefield Trust, The 476
Ward Blenkinsop Trust, The
480
Weinstock Fund, The 484
Westminster Amalgamated
Charity 487
Whetherly's Charitable Trust,
The Hon Mrs R G A 489
Whitehead Charitable Trust, J E
490
Whittington Charitable Trust,
The 491
Wiggins Charity Trust, Cyril
491
Wilde Charitable Trust, The
Felicity 492
Wiltshire Community
Foundation 495
Woburn 1986 Charitable Trust
498
Wohl Charitable Foundation,
The Maurice 498
Wohl Charitable Trust, The
Maurice 498
Wolff Charity Trust 498
Wolfson Family Charitable
Trust, The 499
Woodhouse Charitable Trust,
Edwin 501
Woods Charitable Foundation,
Geoffrey 502
Worms Charitable Trust, The
Freda and Della 504
Worshipful Company of
Needlemakers' Charitable
Fund 505
Wychdale Limited 507
Youell Foundation Ltd, The
510
Zaiger Trust, The Elizabeth and
Prince 512

■ Interfaith

see Ethnic minority groups

■ International relations

see Advocacy (social issues)

■ International rights of the individual (campaigning)

see also Campaigning
(social issues)

Funding priority
Direct Response 134
Lyndhurst Settlement 287
National Power Charitable
Trust, The 330
Staples Trust 435

Will consider
AB Charitable Trust 3
Allachy Trust, The 12
Bell's Charitable Trust, Lady
Mary 42
Body Shop Foundation, The 55
Clark 1965 Charitable Trust,
Stephen 98
Coutts Charitable Trust, The
116
Dibs Charitable Trust, The 133
Digby Charitable Trust, Simon
133
Early's Charitable Settlement,
Richard 142
Emanuel Charitable Settlement,
Ralph and Muriel 150
Emmaus Christian Foundation
150
Fogel Charitable Trust, The
Gerald 165
Follett Trust, The 166
Garthgwynion Charities 179
Gelston Charitable Trust, The
179
Hamlyn Foundation, The Paul
205
Harford Charitable Trust 209
Hilden Charitable Fund, The
219
JCSCJ Charitable Trust, The
238
Kroch Foundation, The Heinz &
Anna 259
Laing Foundation, The
Christopher 260
Leech Charity, The William 269
Morel Charitable Trust, The
318
Music for World Development
323
New Court Charitable Trust
332
Noah Trust, The 335
North West Arts Board 337
Northern Ireland Voluntary
Trust 339
Oldham Foundation 345
Open Door Women's Trust 346

Payne Trust, The Harry 356
Persula Foundation, The 360
Polden-Puckham Charitable
Foundation, The 365
Puebla Charitable Trust
Limited, The 371
Rest-Harrow Trust, The 382
Rope Third Charitable
Settlement, The Mrs 391
Symons Charitable Trust, The
Stella 446
Tear Fund 450
Tisbury Telegraph Trust, The
457

■ **Islam**
see **Muslims**

■ **Jainism**
see **Buddhists & Jainists**

■ **Jews**
Funding priority
Acacia Charitable Trust 6
Achiezer Association Limited 6
Alglen Ltd 11
Bachad Fellowship – Friends of
Bnei Akiva 30
Barclay Jewish Trust 34
Beauland Ltd 39
Beecham Charitable
Settlement, The Patricia 40
Belljoe Tzedoko Ltd 42
Black Charitable Trust, Peter
51
Blond Charitable Trust, Neville
& Elaine 54
Bloom Foundation, Abraham
Algy 54
Bornstein Charitable Trust, M &
S 56
Bourne Charitable Trust, The M
57
British Friends of Chinuch
Atzmai Trust, The 62
Brown Charitable Settlement,
Mrs E E 65
Brushmill Ltd 66
Cen Foundation, The Hyman
87
Closehelm Ltd 101
Cohen and William Leech
Foundation, Sebag 103
Cohen Charitable Trust, Joseph
104
Cohen Charity Trust, Lucy 104
Cohen's Charitable Settlement,
The Hon L H L 105
Conrad Charitable Trust,
Neville and Carole 109
Cooper Charitable Trust 111
Cymerman Trust Limited,
Itzchok Meyer 120

Davies Charities Limited, J 125
Davis Charitable Foundation,
Lily & Henry 125
Deutsch Charitable Trust, The
H & M 131
Doughty Charity Trust, The
136
Elanore Ltd 146
Elias Charitable Settlement, E V
146
Ellador Ltd 147
Family Foundations Trust, The
158
Federation of Jewish Relief
Organisations 160
Fogel Charitable Trust, The
Gerald 165
Forbesville Limited 166
Fordeve Limited 167
Franklin Deceased's New
Second Charity, Sydney E
170
Gee Charitable Trust, The Cecil
179
Gelston Charitable Trust, The
179
Greenwood Charitable Trust,
Naomi & Jeffrey 195
Gross Charities Limited, M & R
197
Grosshill Charitable Trust 197
Grove Charitable Trust, The
197
Haendler, The Nathan and
Adolphe 202
Hanover Charitable Trust, The
208
Highcroft Charitable Trust 218
JCA Charitable Foundation 238
JL Charity Trust, The 239
JMK Charitable Trust 239
JNF Charitable Trust 240
Jacobs Charity, The Dorothy
240
Jewish Aged Needy Pension
Society, The 245
Jewish Childs' Day 245
Joseph Charitable Trust, J E
248
Kahn Charitable Trust, Bernard
250
Kalms Foundation, The Stanley
250
Lambert Charitable Trust, The
262
Layton Charity Trust, The Julian
267
Leeside Charitable Trust 269
Lipton Charitable Trust, The
Ruth & Stuart 276
Localtrent Ltd 279
M D & S Charitable Trust, The
289
Maccabi Foundation, The 290
Margulies Charitable Trust, The
Stella and Alexander 297
Marks' Charitable Settlement,
J M 298

Marks' Charitable Trust, Harry
298
Mayfair Charities Limited 303
Mole Charitable Trust 315
Moshal Charitable Trust 321
Nelson Memorial Trust, The
Barbara 331
Porter Foundation 366
Rav Chesed Trust, The 379
Rubens Highgate Trust, The
Frank and Enid 397
Sadagora Trust, The Ruzin 400
Sassoon Charitable Trust, The
Late Aaron D 408
Schiff Charitable Trust, The
Annie 409
Scopus Jewish Educational
Trust 411
Slavin Charitable Foundation,
The Josephine & Barry 425
Songdale Limited 430
Talteg Ltd 448
Tesler Foundation, The 452
Tomchei Torah Charitable Trust
458
Vendquot Ltd 472
Vogel Charitable Trust, The
Nathan 474
Waley-Cohen Charitable Trust,
Robert & Felicity 477
Weintrop Charity, The Alfred
and Beatrice 484
Wingate Foundation, The
Harold Hyam 496
Wolfson Charitable Trust, The
Aviezer 499
Wychdale Limited 507

■ **Job creation**
see also **Infrastructure
development**
Funding priority
Coutts Charitable Trust, The
116
Homeless International 225
Hyde Charitable Trust 232

Will consider
Ashden Charitable Trust, The
24
Aston Charities Trust Ltd 25
Barbour Trust, The 33
BibleLands 47
Blake Charitable Trust, The
Hubert 53
British Sugar Foundation 63
Brotherton Trust, The Charles
65
CHK Charities Limited 74
CLA Charitable Trust 74
Camelot Foundation, The 78
Campden Charities, The 79
Clifford Charity Oxford, The
100
Collier Charitable Trust, The
105

Community Trust for Greater Manchester, The *108*
County Durham Foundation *115*
Debtors' Relief Fund Charity *128*
Digby Charitable Trust, Simon *133*
Ford of Britain Trust *166*
Franklin Trust, Jill *170*
Goldsmiths' Company's Charities, The *188*
Graves Charitable Trust, J G *192*
Great Britain Sasakawa Foundation, The *193*
Greenaway Foundation, The Sir Derek *194*
Harford Charitable Trust *209*
Humanitarian Trust, The *230*
Hussey for Africans, Charity of Rebecca *231*
Ireland Funds, The *237*
Isle of Dogs Community Foundation *238*
Knott Trust, Sir James *258*
Lane Foundation, The Allen *263*
Leech Charity, The William *269*
Lloyd's Charities Trust *278*
London Law Trust *280*
Marr-Munning Trust *299*
Milton Keynes Community Trust Ltd, The *312*
Minet Trust, The Peter *313*
National Power Charitable Trust, The *330*
Notgrove Trust, The *341*
Open Door Women's Trust *346*
Owen Family Trust, The *348*
Parivar Trust, The *353*
Pratt Charitable Trust, The W L *367*
Puebla Charitable Trust Limited, The *371*
Rope Third Charitable Settlement, The Mrs *391*
Sainsbury Charitable Fund Ltd, The *402*
Scott Bader Commonwealth Ltd, The *411*
Skelton Bounty, The *423*
Summerfield Charitable Trust, The *442*
Sykes Trust, The Charles *445*
TSB Foundation for Northern Ireland *447*
Tear Fund *450*
Thomson Foundation, The Sue *454*
Wakefield (Tower Hill, Trinity Square) Trust *476*
Wall Trust, Thomas *478*
Whesby Ltd *488*
Whitaker Charitable Trust *489*
Woodlands Trust *501*

....

■ Junior schools
see also Schools & colleges

Funding priority
Catholic Education Service for England and Wales *86*
Clark Charitable Trust, J Anthony *98*
Dulverton Trust, The *139*
Hillards Charitable Trust, Gay & Peter Hartley's *220*
Humphreys Charitable Settlement, J A M *231*
Hussey for Africans, Charity of Rebecca *231*
Newman's Charity, John *334*
St Katharine & Shadwell Trust *404*

Will consider
Archer Trust, The *20*
Arts Council of Wales, The *23*
BBC Children in Need Appeal, The *29*
BibleLands *47*
Boots Charitable Trust *56*
Buckinghamshire Masonic Centenary Fund *67*
Bulmer Charitable Trust, Becket *68*
Campbell Charitable Foundation, The Ellis *79*
Carlton Television Trust *81*
Carnegie Dunfermline Trust *82*
Clifford Charity Oxford, The *100*
Commonwealth Relations Trust *108*
Cripplegate Foundation *118*
Curriers Company Charitable Fund *119*
Derbyshire Trust, J N *130*
Dibden Allotments Charity *132*
Digby Charitable Trust, Simon *133*
Dixon Charitable Trust, F E *134*
Ebb and Flow Charitable Trust *144*
Elkes Charity Fund, The Wilfred & Elsie *147*
Emmandjay Charitable Trust *150*
Ferguson Benevolent Fund Limited *161*
Four Lanes Trust, The *168*
Four Winds Trust *168*
Goldsmiths' Company's Charities, The *188*
Great Britain Sasakawa Foundation, The *193*
Hamlyn Foundation, The Paul *205*
Holly Hill Charitable Trust *224*
Howard Charitable Trust, John & Ruth *229*
Hudson Benevolent Trust, The Thomas *230*

Ingles Charitable Trust, The *234*
Ireland Funds, The *237*
Isle of Dogs Community Foundation *238*
JMK Charitable Trust *239*
Jewish Childs' Day *245*
Leonard Trust, The Mark *271*
Lewis Foundation, The John Spedan *274*
Linmardon Trust *276*
Littler Foundation, The Emile *277*
Marriage's Charitable Trust, Miss G M *299*
Milward Charity, The Edgar *313*
Montefiore Trust, The David *316*
Newby Trust Ltd *332*
Newcomen Collett Foundation *333*
Norman, The Educational Foundation of Alderman John *337*
Oldham Foundation *345*
Owen Family Trust, The *348*
Provincial Trust for Kendal, The *370*
Pyke Charity Trust *372*
Rhodes Trust – Public Purposes Fund, The *383*
Salters Charities *405*
Sheepdrove Trust, The *417*
Simon's Charity *422*
Skelton Bounty, The *423*
Sport Aid 88 Trust *434*
Summerfield Charitable Trust, The *442*
Torquay Charities, The *458*
Travis Charitable Trust, Constance *460*
Upjohn Charitable Trust, The *469*
Wakefield (Tower Hill, Trinity Square) Trust *476*
Wates Foundation, The *481*
Whitehead Charitable Trust, J E *490*
Woolmen's Company Charitable Trust, The *503*
Wylde Memorial Charity, The Anthony and Gwendoline *507*
Yorkshire Agricultural Society *509*

....

■ Kennels
see Dogs – kennels & other facilities for dogs

■ Kidney disease

Funding priority

National Kidney Research Fund
Limited, The *328*

■ Lakes

see also Conservation

Funding priority

Clark Charitable Trust, J
Anthony *98*
Dulverton Trust, The *139*
GW Trust, The *176*
Mitchell Trust *315*
Pilkington Trust, The Austin
and Hope *363*

Will consider

Ammco Trust, The *15*
Askew Charitable Trust, The
Ian *25*
Astor Foundation, The *26*
Barnby's Foundation, Lord *35*
Brook Charitable Settlement,
R E *64*
CLA Charitable Trust *74*
Clark 1965 Charitable Trust,
Stephen *98*
Community Trust for Greater
Manchester, The *108*
David Trust, The Lesley *124*
de Freitas Charitable Trust, The
Helen and Geoffrey *126*
Digby Charitable Trust, Simon
133
Direct Response *134*
Dixon Charitable Trust, F E *134*
Early's Charitable Settlement,
Richard *142*
Earwicker Trust *142*
Elkes Charity Fund, The Wilfred
& Elsie *147*
Fishmongers' Company's
Charitable Trust *163*
Four Winds Trust *168*
Getty Jr General Charitable
Trust, J Paul *181*
Greenaway Foundation, The Sir
Derek *194*
Haddon Charitable Trust,
William *202*
Halkes Settlement, John Robert
204
Harbinson Charitable Trust,
Roderick *208*
Hawthorne Charitable Trust,
The *212*
Holly Hill Charitable Trust *224*
Isle of Dogs Community
Foundation *238*
Kilverstone Wildlife Charitable
Trust, The *254*
Lawson Charitable Trust,
Raymond and Blanche *267*
Leach Fourteenth Trust, The
267

Lee Foundation, The Edgar
269
Lewis Foundation, The John
Spedan *274*
Living and Waking Naturally
278
Mellows Charitable Settlement,
The Anthony and Elizabeth
305
Paget Trust, The *351*
Persula Foundation, The *360*
Powys Welsh Church Fund *367*
Prince's Trust - BRO, The *369*
Richard Charitable Trust, The
Cliff *383*
Rowbotham Charitable Trust,
The Christopher *393*
Shepherd Charitable Trust, The
Sylvia and Colin *418*
Stevens Foundation, The June
437
Summerfield Charitable Trust,
The *442*
Symons Charitable Trust, The
Stella *446*
Terry Charitable Trust, Noel
Goddard *451*
Tisbury Telegraph Trust, The
457
Vincent Trust Fund, Eric W *473*
Wade & Others, The Charity of
Thomas *475*
Whitaker Charitable Trust *489*
Worshipful Company of
Engineers' Charitable Trust
Fund, The *504*
Wylde Memorial Charity, The
Anthony and Gwendoline
507
Yorkshire Agricultural Society
509
Young Explorers' Trust *511*

■ Landscapes

see also Conservation

Funding priority

Bancroft Trust, The *33*
Barnby's Foundation, Lord *35*
Cathedral Amenities Fund, The
85
Clark Charitable Trust, J
Anthony *98*
Cobb Charity *103*
Countryside Trust, The *115*
Dulverton Trust, The *139*
McLaren Foundation *292*
Mitchell Trust, Esme *315*
Northcott Charitable Trust *338*
Paget Trust, The *351*
Pilkington Trust, The Austin
and Hope *363*
Shepherd Conservation
Foundation, The David *418*

Smith (UK) Horticultural Trust,
Stanley *428*
Wade & Others, The Charity of
Thomas *475*

Will consider

Ammco Trust, The *15*
Askew Charitable Trust, The
Ian *25*
Astor Foundation, The *26*
Balney Charitable Trust, The
32
Bourne-May Charitable Trust,
The *57*
Brook Charitable Settlement,
R E *64*
CLA Charitable Trust *74*
Clark 1965 Charitable Trust,
Stephen *98*
Coates Charitable Trust, The
John *103*
Community Trust for Greater
Manchester, The *108*
David Trust, The Lesley *124*
de Freitas Charitable Trust, The
Helen and Geoffrey *126*
Digby Charitable Trust, Simon
133
Direct Response *134*
Dixon Charitable Trust, F E *134*
Dumbreck Charity *139*
Early's Charitable Settlement,
Richard *142*
Earwicker Trust *142*
Elkes Charity Fund, The Wilfred
& Elsie *147*
Feeney Charitable Bequest, The
John *161*
Four Winds Trust *168*
Garnett's 1973 Charitable
Trust, Mrs A M *178*
Getty Jr General Charitable
Trust, J Paul *181*
Greenaway Foundation, The Sir
Derek *194*
Grocers' Charity *197*
Haddon Charitable Trust,
William *202*
Halkes Settlement, John Robert
204
Harbinson Charitable Trust,
Roderick *208*
Hawthorne Charitable Trust,
The *212*
Holly Hill Charitable Trust *224*
Idlewild Trust, The *234*
Ireland Funds, The *237*
Isle of Dogs Community
Foundation *238*
Kilverstone Wildlife Charitable
Trust, The *254*
Lawson Charitable Trust,
Raymond and Blanche *267*
Leach Fourteenth Trust, The
267
Lee Foundation, The Edgar
269

Lewis Foundation, The John Spedan *274*
Living and Waking Naturally *278*
Lower Hall Charitable Trust *285*
Lyndhurst Settlement *287*
Mellows Charitable Settlement, The Anthony and Elizabeth *305*
Mitchell Trust *315*
Peppiatt Charitable Trust, The Brian *359*
Persula Foundation, The *360*
Powys Welsh Church Fund *367*
Prince's Trust - BRO, The *369*
Richard Charitable Trust, The Cliff *383*
Rowbotham Charitable Trust, The Christopher *393*
Royal Commission for the Exhibition of 1851 *395*
Shepherd Charitable Trust, The Sylvia and Colin *418*
Sobell Welsh People's Charitable Association, Michael *429*
Stevens Foundation, The June *437*
Summerfield Charitable Trust, The *442*
Symons Charitable Trust, The Stella *446*
Terry Charitable Trust, Noel Goddard *451*
Tisbury Telegraph Trust, The *457*
Vincent Trust Fund, Eric W *473*
Whitaker Charitable Trust *489*
Woodroffe Benton Foundation, The *502*
Worshipful Company of Engineers' Charitable Trust Fund, The *504*
Wylde Memorial Charity, The Anthony and Gwendoline *507*
Yorkshire Agricultural Society *509*
Young Explorers' Trust *511*

■ Language schools

see also Schools & colleges

Funding priority
Christmas Cracker Trust *95*
Clark Charitable Trust, J Anthony *98*
Dulverton Trust, The *139*
Great Britain Sasakawa Foundation, The *193*

Will consider
Boots Charitable Trust *56*
Bulmer Charitable Trust, Becket *68*
Carlton Television Trust *81*

Digby Charitable Trust, Simon *133*
Direct Response *134*
Edgar Trust, The Gilbert *145*
Hillards Charitable Trust, Gay & Peter Hartley's *220*
Hudson Benevolent Trust, The Thomas *230*
Ireland Funds, The *237*
Isle of Dogs Community Foundation *238*
Littler Foundation, The Emile *277*
Montefiore Trust, The David *316*
Newcomen Collett Foundation *333*
St Katharine & Shadwell Trust *404*
Salters Charities *405*
Wakefield (Tower Hill, Trinity Square) Trust *476*
Whitehead Charitable Trust, J E *490*

■ Law centres

see also Advice & information (social issues)

Funding priority
County Durham Foundation *115*
Wilde Sapte Charitable Trust, The *492*

Will consider
Astor Foundation, The *26*
Berkshire Community Trust *45*
Camelot Foundation, The *78*
Clark 1965 Charitable Trust, Stephen *98*
Coutts Charitable Trust, The *116*
David Trust, The Lesley *124*
Dibs Charitable Trust, The *133*
Digby Charitable Trust, Simon *133*
Gelston Charitable Trust, The *179*
Hyde Charitable Trust *232*
Ireland Funds, The *237*
Isle of Dogs Community Foundation *238*
Knott Trust, Sir James *258*
Lankelly Foundation, The *264*
Leech Charity, The William *269*
Mental Health Foundation, The *305*
NR Charitable Trust, The *325*
Needham Cooper Charitable Trust, The *331*
New Court Charitable Trust *332*
Newby Trust Ltd *332*
Noah Trust, The *335*
Payne Trust, The Harry *356*
Persula Foundation, The *360*

Rest-Harrow Trust, The *382*
Rope Third Charitable Settlement, The Mrs *391*
Rothley Trust, The *392*
Saint Sarkis Charity Trust *404*
Swan Mountain Trust *444*
Tisbury Telegraph Trust, The *457*
Travis Charitable Trust, Constance *460*
Tudor Trust, The *463*
Wiltshire Community Foundation *495*

■ Leadership training

see Training for personal development

■ Learning difficulties

see Disabled people (physical, sensory, learning impairments)

■ Legal services

see also Infrastructure & technical support

Funding priority
International Bar Association Educational Trust *236*

Will consider
Berkshire Community Trust *45*
Campden Charities, The *79*
County Durham Foundation *115*
Daily Telegraph Charitable Trust *122*
Digby Charitable Trust, Simon *133*
Direct Response *134*
Goldsmiths' Company's Charities, The *188*
IBM United Kingdom Trust *233*
Ireland Funds, The *237*
Iris Trust, The *237*
Isle of Dogs Community Foundation *238*
Jarrold Trust Ltd, John *243*
Lane Foundation, The Allen *263*
Paristamen Foundation, The *352*
Tear Fund *450*

■ Leprosy

Funding priority
St Francis Leprosy Guild *402*
Westcroft Trust *486*

■ Lesbian rights

see Gay & lesbian rights

■ Libraries & museums

see also Community facilities

Funding priority

Aldwyns Trust, The 10
Arbib Foundation 20
Beit Trust, The 40
Carnegie United Kingdom Trust, The 82
Cobb Charity 103
Crescent Trust, The 117
Daiwa Anglo-Japanese Foundation, The 122
David Trust, The Lesley 124
Gilpin Trust, The John 184
Grange Farm Centre Trust 191
Gwent County Council Welsh Church Fund 200
Ireland Funds, The 237
Lower Hall Charitable Trust 285
Mitchell Trust, Esme 315
North West Arts Board 337
Northern Arts 339
Reekie Trust, R A & V B 381
South Square Trust 430
Ulverscroft Foundation, The 468
Wolfson Foundation, The 499
Woolf Charitable Trust, The 502
Worshipful Company of Engineers' Charitable Trust Fund, The 504
Yorkshire and Humberside Arts 510

Will consider

Abbey National Charitable Trust 4
Amory Charitable Trust, Viscount 16
Angler's Inn Trust 17
Aquarius Charitable Foundation, The 19
Arts Council of Wales, The 23
Astor Foundation, The 26
Astor of Hever Trust, The 26
Barbour Trust, The 33
Beckwith Charitable Settlement, The Heather 39
Beit Trust, The 40
Bowland Charitable Trust, The 57
Brand Trust, The 59
Bridge Trust, The 60
Broadley Charitable Trust, The 64
Bullough Tompson Settlement, The 68

Bulmer Charitable Trust, Becket 68
Butler's Trust, Lord 71
Cadbury Charitable Trust (Incorporated), Edward 75
Cadbury Trust (1928), The Edward & Dorothy 76
Campbell Charitable Foundation, The Ellis 79
Carnegie Dunfermline Trust 82
Carnegie United Kingdom Trust, The 82
Catto Charitable Settlement, The Thomas Sivewright 86
Challice Trust, The 87
Chase Charity, The 91
Christmas Cracker Trust 95
Clark 1965 Charitable Trust, Stephen 98
Clutterbuck Charitable Trust, Robert 102
Coates Charitable Trust, The John 103
Cobb Charity 103
Colyer-Fergusson Charitable Trust, The 107
Commonwealth Relations Trust 108
Community Trust for Greater Manchester, The 108
D'Avigdor Goldsmid Charitable Trust, The Sarah 125
de Freitas Charitable Trust, The Helen and Geoffrey 126
Digby Charitable Trust, Simon 133
Direct Response 134
Dixon Charitable Trust, F E 134
Dulverton Trust, The 139
Dumbreck Charity 139
Early's Charitable Settlement, Richard 142
Edgar Foundation, The Gilbert and Eileen 145
Education Services 145
Emmandjay Charitable Trust 150
Eventhall Family Charitable Trust, The 155
Feeney Charitable Bequest, The John 161
Finzi Charitable Trust, Gerald 162
Fishmongers' Company's Charitable Trust 163
Fogel Charitable Trust, The Gerald 165
Follett Trust, The 166
Ford of Britain Trust 166
Four Lanes Trust, The 168
Franklin Trust, Jill 170
Frognal Trust 174
Garnett Charitable Trust, The 178
Granada Foundation, The 190
Grange Farm Centre Trust 191
Great Britain Sasakawa Foundation, The 193

Greenaway Foundation, The Sir Derek 194
Grocers' Charity 197
Halkes Settlement, John Robert 204
Hamlyn Foundation, The Paul 205
Harbinson Charitable Trust, Roderick 208
Harford Charitable Trust 209
Hillards Charitable Trust, Gay & Peter Hartley's 220
Holly Hill Charitable Trust 224
Howard Charitable Trust, John & Ruth 229
Hudson Benevolent Trust, The Thomas 230
Hughes Charitable Trust, The Geoffery C 230
Humanitarian Trust, The 230
Hunter Charitable Trust, The Claire 231
Hussey for Africans, Charity of Rebecca 231
Inverforth Charitable Trust, The 236
Ireland Funds, The 237
Isle of Dogs Community Foundation 238
Kiln Charitable Trust, Robert 254
Knott Trust, Sir James 258
Kroch Foundation, The Heinz & Anna 259
Laing Charitable Trust, The David 260
Lankelly Foundation, The 264
Leach Fourteenth Trust, The 267
Leche Trust, The 268
Lee Foundation, The Edgar 269
Linford Charitable Trust, The Fred 276
Littler Foundation, The Emile 277
Lloyd's Charities Trust 278
(Lloyds) TSB Foundation for England and Wales 279
Lowenthal Charitable Trust, The L and C 285
Lyndhurst Settlement 287
Lynn Foundation, The 288
MacKintosh Charitable Trust, Viscount 292
Manifold Charitable Trust, The 295
Marriage's Charitable Trust, Miss G M 299
Moore Foundation, The George A 316
Morel Charitable Trust, The 318
Music Sales Charitable Trust, The 324
New Court Charitable Trust 332
Newby Trust Ltd 332

Norfolk's Family Charitable Trust, Lavinia 336
Norman Family Charitable Trust, The 337
North West Arts Board 337
Oldham Foundation 345
Owen Family Trust, The 348
PF Charitable Trust 350
Persula Foundation, The 360
Pilkington Trust, The Austin and Hope 363
Porter Foundation 366
Provincial Trust for Kendal, The 370
Radcliffe's Trust, Dr 375
Rayner Charitable Trust, The John 380
Reekie Trust, R A & V B 381
Rest-Harrow Trust, The 382
Rookes Charitable Trust, C A 390
Royal Commission for the Exhibition of 1851 395
St Katharine & Shadwell Trust 404
Save & Prosper Educational Trust 408
Schuster Charitable Trust, The 410
Sheepdrove Trust, The 417
Shepherd Family Charitable Trust, The Sir Peter 418
Sobell Welsh People's Charitable Association, Michael 429
Somerfield Curtis Will Trust, The Dorothy 430
South Square Trust 430
Southern Arts 432
Spoore, Merry & Rixman Foundation, The 434
Stevens Foundation, The June 437
Strauss Charitable Trust 440
Summerfield Charitable Trust, The 442
Sussman Charitable Trust, Adrienne & Leslie 443
Symons Charitable Trust, The Stella 446
TSB Foundation for Scotland 447
Taylor Charitable Trust, The B R 450
Tisbury Telegraph Trust, The 457
Torquay Charities, The 458
Turner Trust, The Douglas 464
Wagstaff Charitable Trust, Bob 475
Walker Trust, The 477
Wall Trust, Thomas 478
Wander Charitable Fund, The Dr Albert 479
Wates Foundation, The 481
Wingate Foundation, The Harold Hyam 496

Woolmen's Company Charitable Trust, The 503
Wylde Memorial Charity, The Anthony and Gwendoline 507

■ Literacy
see also Education & training
Funding priority
Dahl Foundation, The Roald 122
JJ Charitable Trust, The 239
Marriage's Charitable Trust, Miss G M 299

■ Literature
see also Arts & arts facilities
Funding priority
Arts Council of England, The 23
Arts Council of Wales, The 23
David Trust, The Lesley 124
Delius Trust, The 129
Duncan Literary Fund, Ronald 139
Golden Charitable Trust 187
North West Arts Board 337
Northern Arts 339
Yorkshire and Humberside Arts 510

Will consider
Astor Foundation, The 26
Beckwith Charitable Settlement, The Heather 39
Brooke Benevolent Fund, William 65
Bulmer Charitable Trust, Becket 68
Campden Charities, The 79
Carnegie Dunfermline Trust 82
Carnegie United Kingdom Trust, The 82
Coates Charitable Trust, The John 103
Cripplegate Foundation 118
D'Avigdor Goldsmid Charitable Trust, The Sarah 125
Digby Charitable Trust, Simon 133
Early's Charitable Settlement, Richard 142
Follett Trust, The 166
Garnett Charitable Trust, The 178
Granada Foundation, The 190
Great Britain Sasakawa Foundation, The 193
Greenaway Foundation, The Sir Derek 194
Halkes Settlement, John Robert 204

Hamlyn Foundation, The Paul 205
Harding Trust, The 209
Holly Hill Charitable Trust 224
Howard Charitable Trust, John & Ruth 229
Hudson Benevolent Trust, The Thomas 230
Hughes Charitable Trust, The Geoffery C 230
Ireland Funds, The 237
Laing Charitable Trust, The David 260
Laing Foundation, The Christopher 260
Lee Foundation, The Edgar 269
Linford Charitable Trust, The Fred 276
Milton Keynes Community Trust Ltd, The 312
Music Sales Charitable Trust, The 324
New Court Charitable Trust 332
Oldham Foundation 345
Owen Family Trust, The 348
Provincial Trust for Kendal, The 370
St Katharine & Shadwell Trust 404
Snipe Charitable Trust 428
Somerfield Curtis Will Trust, The Dorothy 430
South Square Trust 430
Summerfield Charitable Trust, The 442
Taylor Charitable Trust, The B R 450
Thomson Foundation, The Sue 454
Wates Foundation, The 481
Whitaker Charitable Trust 489
Worshipful Company of Engineers' Charitable Trust Fund, The 504

■ Live arts
see Combined arts

■ Management services
see also Infrastructure & technical support
Funding priority
County Durham Foundation 115
Homeless International 225
IBM United Kingdom Trust 233

Will consider

Berkshire Community Trust 45
Camelot Foundation, The 78
Daily Telegraph Charitable
Trust 122
Digby Charitable Trust, Simon
133
Direct Response 134
HACT (The Housing
Association's Charitable
Trust) 201
Ireland Funds, The 237
Iris Trust, The 237
Isle of Dogs Community
Foundation 238
Lane Foundation, The Allen
263
Licensed Trade Charities Trust,
. The 274
Paristamen Foundation, The
352
Skelton Bounty, The 423
Tear Fund 450
Wiltshire Community
Foundation 495

■ Man-made disasters

see Victims of manmade or
natural disasters

■ Meals provision

see also Community
services

Funding priority

AB Charitable Trust, The 3
Alexandra Trust 11
Aquarian Healing Trust 19
Christmas Cracker Trust 95
County Durham Foundation
115
Eventhall Family Charitable
Trust, The 155
Grant Charitable Trust, The
191
Harding's Charity, William 209
Merchant Taylors' Consolidated
Charities for the Infirm 306
Royal Theatrical Fund, The 396
SMB Trust, The 400

Will consider

AB Charitable Trust 3
Alexis Trust, The 11
Amory Charitable Trust,
Viscount 16
Aquarius Charitable
Foundation, The 19
Barratt Charitable Trust, The
Elaine 36
Berkshire Community Trust 45
Betard Bequest 46
BibleLands 47
Bisgood Trust, The 50

Bisgood's Charitable Trust, Miss
Jeanne 50
Blakenham's Charity Trust,
Lady 53
Boots Charitable Trust 56
Bowland Charitable Trust, The
57
Brotherton Trust, The Charles
65
Burdall Charity, H M 69
CLA Charitable Trust 74
Camelot Foundation, The 78
Cloudesley's Charity/School
Parents & Friends
Association, Richard 102
Community Trust for Greater
Manchester, The 108
Coutts Charitable Trust, The
116
Curriers Company Charitable
Fund 119
Curzon Charitable Trust, The
Wallace 120
Debtors' Relief Fund Charity
128
Derbyshire Trust, J N 130
Digby Charitable Trust, Simon
133
Dumbreck Charity 139
Egerton of Tatton Will Trust,
Lord 146
Elkes Charity Fund, The Wilfred
& Elsie 147
Fletcher Trust, Roy 165
Gibbins Trust, The 181
Greenaway Foundation, The Sir
Derek 194
Grocers' Charity 197
Grosshill Charitable Trust 197
Haberdashers' Eleemosynary
Charity 201
Harbinson Charitable Trust,
Roderick 208
Harford Charitable Trust 209
Hartley Memorial Trust, The N
& P 211
Henderson's Settlement, J R
216
Hertfordshire Community
Trust, The 217
Homfray Trust, The 226
Hudson Benevolent Trust, The
Thomas 230
Hyde Charitable Trust 232
Isle of Dogs Community
Foundation 238
Johnson Foundation, The 246
Knott Trust, Sir James 258
Kroch Foundation, The Heinz &
Anna 259
Kyte Charitable Trust, The 259
Laing Foundation, The
Christopher 260
Lancaster's Trust, Bryan 263
Lankelly Foundation, The 264
Leech Charity, The William 269
Lewis Partnership, John 274
Lloyd's Charities Trust 278

Lowe Trust, Mrs D G 285
Mackintosh Foundation, The
292
Marchday Charitable Fund, The
296
Margaret Foundation, The 297
Mercury Phoenix Trust 307
Moore Foundation, The
George A 316
NR Charitable Trust, The 325
National Power Charitable
Trust, The 330
New Court Charitable Trust
332
Newby Trust Ltd 332
Norton Foundation, The 340
Parivar Trust, The 353
Paterson Charitable
Foundation, The Constance
354
Paterson Charitable Trust,
Arthur James 354
Patients' Aid Association
Hospital and Medical
Charities Trust 354
Payne Trust, The Harry 356
Persula Foundation, The 360
Porter Foundation 366
Powell Foundation, The 367
Rayner Charitable Trust, The
John 380
Rope Third Charitable
Settlement, The Mrs 391
Rowbotham Charitable Trust,
The Christopher 393
Saint Edmund King and Martyr
Trust 402
Shepherd Family Charitable
Trust, The Sir Peter 418
Skelton Bounty, The 423
Sparkhill Trust, The 433
Sussman Charitable Trust,
Adrienne & Leslie 443
TSB Foundation for Northern
Ireland 447
Tear Fund 450
Thackray General Charitable
Trust, The P & L 452
Towler Charity Trust, The Fred
459
Trust for the Homeless 462
Tyne & Wear Foundation 466
Wates Foundation, The 481
Wesleyan Charitable Trust, The
485
Whitaker Charitable Trust 489
Wingate Foundation, The
Harold Hyam 496

■ Media

see Film, video, multimedia,
broadcasting

■ Medical centres

see also **Health facilities & buildings**

Funding priority

Cooper Charitable Trust *111*

Coxen Trust Fund, Sir William *116*

Lacy Charity Trust, The Late Sir Pierce *260*

Pryor Charitable Trust, The John *370*

Rickman Trust, Muriel Edith *385*

Will consider

Ammco Trust, The *15*

Anstey Charitable Settlement, J C W *18*

Army Benevolent Fund, The *22*

Astor Foundation, The *26*

Bancroft Trust, The *33*

Barrie Charitable Trust, The Misses *36*

Beit Trust, The *40*

BibleLands *47*

Birtwistle Memorial Trust, The G E *50*

Britton Charitable Trust, The J & M *63*

Brooke Benevolent Fund, William *65*

Brotherton Trust, The Charles *65*

Cancer Relief Macmillan Fund *79*

Challice Trust, The *87*

Corbett's Charity, Thomas *112*

Dahl Foundation, The Roald *122*

Dean Refugee Trust Fund, The Miriam *128*

Denne Charitable Trust *130*

Derbyshire Trust, J N *130*

Digby Charitable Trust, Simon *133*

Direct Response *134*

Dorus Trust *136*

Dumbreck Charity *139*

Elkes Charity Fund, The Wilfred & Elsie *147*

Epigoni Trust *152*

Fishmongers' Company's Charitable Trust *163*

Fortune Trust, The *167*

Franklin Deceased's New Second Charity, Sydney E *170*

Good Neighbours Trust, The *188*

Greenaway Foundation, The Sir Derek *194*

Harvey Charitable Trust, Gordon *211*

Haywood Charitable Trust *214*

Ibbett Trust, The *233*

Inman Charity, The *235*

Isle of Dogs Community Foundation *238*

JHL Trust, The *239*

Leech Charity, The William *269*

Leukaemia Research Fund *271*

Lloyd Charity, The S and D *278*

London Law Trust *280*

MacKintosh Charitable Trust, Viscount *292*

Mellows Charitable Settlement, The Anthony and Elizabeth *305*

Metropolitan Hospital-Sunday Fund, The *308*

Middlesex County Rugby Football Union Memorial Fund *309*

Minet Trust, The Peter *313*

Natwest Staff Samaritan Fund *330*

Needham Cooper Charitable Trust, The *331*

Norman Family Charitable Trust, The *337*

Paul's Charitable Trust, R J *355*

Payne Trust, The Harry *356*

Penny in the Pound Fund Charitable Trust *359*

Peppiatt Charitable Trust, The Brian *359*

SMB Trust, The *400*

Schuster Charitable Trust, The *410*

Shelroy Charitable Trust, The *417*

Smith (Estates Charities), Henry *426*

Sportsman's Aid Charity Ltd, The *434*

Stonehouse Trust Ltd, Eric *438*

Thompson Charitable Trust, The *453*

Tisbury Telegraph Trust, The *457*

Travis Charitable Trust, Constance *460*

■ Medical professionals, nurses & doctors

Funding priority

Cathedral Nursing Society Charitable Trust *85*

Charities Fund *89*

Kennel Club Charitable Trust, The *252*

PPP Healthcare Medical Trust Limited *350*

■ Medical studies & research

see also **Cancer research, MS research, Ophthalmology**

Funding priority

Acacia Charitable Trust *6*

Action Research *6*

Aga Khan Foundation (UK) *7*

Alcohol Education and Research Council *9*

Alexander Charitable Trust, Mrs K L *11*

Alliance Family Foundation Limited *13*

Aquinas Trust *20*

Askew Charitable Trust, The Ian *25*

Astor of Hever Trust, The *26*

Avins Trustees, The John *28*

Balney Charitable Trust, The *32*

Bealey Foundation, The *38*

Beauland Ltd *39*

Beckwith Charitable Trust, The Peter *40*

Beckwith-Smith's Charitable Settlement, Mrs *40*

Bergqvist Charitable Trust *44*

Birmingham District Nursing Charitable Trust *49*

Blagrave Charitable Trust, The Herbert and Peter *52*

Blakenham's Charity Trust, Lady *53*

Blakey Charitable Trust, The Celia and Conrad *53*

Boltons Trust, The *55*

Bottom Charitable Trust, Harry *56*

Breast Cancer Research Trust, The *59*

British Council for Prevention of Blindness *61*

British Diabetic Association, The *61*

British Heart Foundation *62*

British Sugar Foundation *63*

Brook Charitable Settlement, R E *64*

Burn Charity Trust, The J H *70*

Burns Charity, The Dorothy *70*

Burry Charitable Trust, The *70*

Cadbury Schweppes Foundation, The *76*

Carron Charitable Trust, The *83*

Carter Trust, The Frederick William *84*

Castang Charitable Trust, H and M *85*

Catto Charitable Settlement, The Thomas Sivewright *86*

Charities Fund *89*

Cinderford Charitable Trust, The *96*

Clark Charitable Trust, J Anthony *98*

Clifford Charity Oxford, The *100*

Cohen Charitable Trust, The Vivienne and Samuel *104*

Condon Family Trust *109*

Cooper Charitable Trust *111*

Cotton Trust, The *114*

Crawford Children's Charity, Michael *117*

Crescent Trust, The *117*

D'Avigdor Goldsmid Charitable Trust, The Sarah *125*

Delmar Charitable Trust *129*

Denton Charitable Trust, The *130*

Derbyshire Trust, J N *130*

Devon Association for the Blind *131*

Djanogly Foundation, The *135*

D'Oyly Carte Charitable Trust, The *137*

Dunhill Medical Trust, The *140*

Dunn Charitable Trust, The Harry *140*

Eastwood Memorial Trust, Sybil *143*

Edgar Trust, The Gilbert *145*

Eling Trust *147*

Elkes Charity Fund, The Wilfred & Elsie *147*

Ellerman Foundation, The John *148*

Elvetham Charitable Trust, The *149*

Emmandjay Charitable Trust *150*

Eranda Foundation, The *152*

Fane Research Trust, The Edmund *159*

Flanagan Leukaemia Fund, Bud *164*

Frazer Charities Trust, The *171*

Frost Charitable Trust, T F C *174*

Fry Charitable Trust, Maurice *174*

Garnett's 1973 Charitable Trust, Mrs A M *178*

Garthgwynion Charities *179*

General Nursing Council for England and Wales Trust, The *180*

Gibson's Charity Trust, The Hon Mr & Mrs Clive *182*

Girdlers' Company Charitable Trust, The *184*

Golders Green Foundation *187*

Goodman Charitable Foundation, The Everard and Mina *188*

Goodman Trust, The *189*

Gradel Foundation, The *189*

Grant Foundation, The Raymond *191*

Green Foundation, Constance *194*

Greenwood Charitable Trust, The G B *195*

Grundy Foundation, The Stanley *198*

Gwent County Council Welsh Church Fund *200*

Haemophilia Society, The *202*

Hamamelis Trust, The *204*

Hannay Memorial Charity, Kathleen *208*

Harbinson Charitable Trust, Roderick *208*

Hargreaves Trust, The Kenneth *210*

Harris Charitable Trust, The Philip & Pauline *210*

Hartnett Charitable Trust, The *211*

Hawthorne Charitable Trust, The *212*

Heinz Company Limited Charitable Trust, The H J *215*

Higgs Charitable Trust, The *218*

Hitachi Charitable Trust, The *222*

Hodge Charitable Trust, The Sir Julian *223*

Hoover Foundation, The *226*

Hornton Trust, The *228*

Hudson Benevolent Trust, The Thomas *230*

Hutchinson Charitable Trust, E B *232*

IPE Charitable Trust, The *233*

Jones Trust, Cemlyn *248*

KC Charitable Trust, The *250*

Kendall Leukaemia Fund, Kay *252*

Keyes Trust, The Ursula *253*

King Charitable Trust, The Lorna *254*

Kings Medical Research Trust, The *255*

Kinnison Charitable Trust, R O *256*

Kobler Trust, The *258*

Kreitman Foundation *258*

Landy Charitable Trust, Harry and Gertrude *263*

Lanvern Foundation *265*

Lauffer Charitable Foundation, The R & D *266*

Lawley Foundation, The Edgar E *267*

Lee Foundation, The Edgar *269*

Levy Charitable Foundation, Joseph *272*

Lewis Family Charitable Trust *273*

Liffe Benefit *274*

Linmardon Trust *276*

Lloyd's Charities Trust *278*

London Law Trust *280*

Low & Bonar Charitable Fund, The *284*

Lucas Charitable Trust Limited, The Joseph *286*

Lyons Charitable Trust, The *288*

MacAndrew Trust, The E M *289*

McKechnie Foundation, A N *292*

Mackintosh Foundation, The *292*

MacRobert Trusts, The *294*

Margaret Foundation, The *297*

Marriage's Charitable Trust, Miss G M *299*

Mattock Charitable Trust, The W T *302*

Medlock Charitable Trust, The *304*

Mellows Charitable Settlement, The Anthony and Elizabeth *305*

Mental Health Foundation, The *305*

Migraine Trust, The *310*

Millichope Foundation, The *312*

Moore Charitable Trust, The Horace *316*

Morgan Crucible Company plc Charitable Trust, The *319*

Morris Charitable Trust, The Willie & Mabel *320*

Moulton Charitable Trust, The *321*

Mountbatten Memorial Trust, The *322*

NR Charitable Trust, The *325*

National Kidney Research Fund Limited, The *328*

National Power Charitable Trust, The *330*

Newman Foundation, The Frances and Augustus *334*

Newstead Charity, The *334*

Nidditch Foundation, The Laurie *335*

Noah Trust, The *335*

Northern Dairies Educational Trust *339*

Northern Electric Employee Charity Association *339*

Nuffield Foundation *342*

Nuffield Provincial Hospitals Trust *342*

Oliver Trust, Kate Wilson *345*

Oppenheimer Charitable Trust *346*

Owen Family Trust, The *348*

PPP Healthcare Medical Trust Limited *350*

Palmer Trust, The Gerald *352*

Pascoe Charitable Trust, Alan *354*

Paterson Charitable Foundation, The Constance *354*

Paterson Charitable Trust, Arthur James *354*

Paul Charitable Trust, The Late Barbara May *355*
Paul Charitable Trust, Margaret Jeanne *355*
Paul Charitable Trust, Pamela Milton *355*
Paul Foundation, The *355*
Peel Medical Research Trust, The *358*
Peskin Charitable Trust, The Hazel and Leslie *360*
Phillips Charitable Foundation, Reginald M *361*
Pick Charitable Trust, The George and Jessie *362*
Pilkington Trust, The Austin and Hope *363*
Powys Welsh Church Fund *367*
Proctor Charitable Trust, The Albert Edward *370*
Psoriasis Association Research Fund (1968), The *371*
Pye Christian Trust, The *371*
QAS Charitable Trust *373*
RED Trust, The *374*
REMEDI (Rehabilitation and Medical Research Trust) *374*
Rayne Foundation, The *379*
Rayner Charitable Trust, The John *380*
Reekie Trust, R A & V B *381*
Richards Charity, The Violet M *384*
Rickman Trust, Muriel Edith *385*
Ripley's Charitable Trust, Pat *386*
Robbins Trust, The Cheshire *387*
Robinson Brothers (Ryders Green) Ltd, Charitable Trust *388*
Rolfe Charitable Trust, The *390*
Rosen Foundation, Cecil *392*
Rosenbaum Golden Trust, Teresa *392*
SMB Trust, The *400*
Samuel Fund, The Camillla *406*
Sanity *407*
Sargeant's Charitable Trust, Mrs M E *407*
Scarfe Charitable Trust, The *409*
Scott of Yews Trust, Sir Samuel *412*
Sherman Charitable Trust, The Archie *419*
Shifrin Charitable Trust, The Maurice and Hilda *419*
Sidbury Trust, The Second *421*
Simon Population Trust, The *422*
Salter Trust Ltd *424*
Southon Charitable Trust, The *432*
Stonehouse Trust Ltd, Eric *438*
Street Charitable Foundation, W O *440*

Summer's and I May's Charitable Settlement, The Late Misses (A N) *442*
Swale Charity Trust *443*
Szeben Peto Foundation, The *446*
TSB Foundation for the Channel Islands *447*
Taylor Charitable Trust, The B R *450*
Tenovus – Scotland *451*
Thorn Charitable Trust, The Sir Jules *454*
Toy Trust, The *459*
Turner Charitable Settlement, The Sir Mark and Lady *464*
Ulverscroft Foundation, The *468*
Valentine Charitable Trust, The *470*
van Geest Foundation, The John and Lucille *470*
Walker Trust, The *477*
Warburg's Voluntary Settlement, Sir Siegmund *480*
Ward Blenkinsop Trust, The *480*
Wellcome Trust, The *485*
Wesleyan Charitable Trust, The *485*
Westcroft Trust *486*
White Rose Children's Aid International Charity *489*
Whittington Charitable Trust, The *491*
Wilde Charitable Trust, The Felicity *492*
Wohl Charitable Foundation, The Maurice *498*
Wohl Charitable Trust, The Maurice *498*
Wolfson Family Charitable Trust, The *499*
Wolfson Foundation, The *499*
Woodcote Trust, The *501*
Woolf Charitable Trust, The *502*
Woolton Charitable Trust, The *503*

Will consider
AHJ Charitable Trust, The *3*
Achiezer Association Limited *6*
Airflow Community Ltd, The *9*
Aleh Charitable Foundation, The *10*
Allsop Charitable Trust, Pat *14*
Anderson Trust, Andrew *16*
Andrew Charitable Trust, The Prince *16*
Angler's Inn Trust *17*
Appelbe Trust, Ambrose & Ann *19*
Aquarius Charitable Foundation, The *19*
Askew Trust, The Dorothy *25*

Assembled Church of Christ Trust, The *25*
Assheton-Smith Charitable Trust *25*
Astor Foundation, The *26*
Astor's 1969 Charity, The Hon M L *26*
BUPA Foundation, The *29*
Balint Charitable Trust, Paul *31*
Barbour Trust, The *33*
Barnby's Foundation, Lord *35*
Barnsbury Charitable Trust *35*
Barrie Charitable Trust, The Misses *36*
Bateman Charitable Trust, Lady Margaret *37*
Beattie Charitable Trust, The James *39*
Beckwith Charitable Settlement, The Heather *39*
Bellahouston Bequest Fund *42*
Belmont Trust, The *42*
Billingsgate Christian Mission Charitable Trust *48*
Birtwistle Memorial Trust, The G E *50*
Black Foundation, The Bertie *51*
Blake Charitable Trust, The Hubert *53*
Blank Donations Ltd, The David *54*
Boots Charitable Trust *56*
Borthwick Memorial Trust, The Oliver *56*
Bowland Charitable Trust, The *57*
Britton Charitable Trust, The J & M *63*
Brookhouse's Will Trust, Mr John Charles *65*
Brotherton Trust, The Charles *65*
Burden Trust, The *69*
Burton Charitable Trust, The Geoffrey *71*
Butler's Trust, Lord *71*
Butler's Trust, Lucilla *72*
Cadbury Trust (1928), The Edward & Dorothy *76*
Cardiff & Swansea Methodist District Charitable Trust Fund *80*
Cazalet Charitable Trust, The Raymond *87*
Charity Projects *90*
Chiddick Charitable Trust *92*
Chrimes Family Charitable Trust, The *93*
Christian Aid *94*
Christian Renewal Trust, The *94*
Closehelm Ltd *101*
Clutterbuck Charitable Trust, Robert *102*
Coates Charitable Settlement, The *102*

Coates Charitable Trust 1969, Lance *103*
Cohen Charity Trust, Lucy *104*
Collinson Charitable Trust, The Norman *106*
Company of Tobacco Pipe Makers and Tobacco Blenders Benevolent Fund *109*
Cope Charitable Trust, Alfred *112*
Curry Charitable Trust, Dennis *119*
Cymerman Trust Limited, Itzchok Meyer *120*
Daily Telegraph Charitable Trust *122*
Dandeen Charitable Trust *123*
Davies Charity, The Gwendoline and Margaret *125*
Davy Foundation, The J *126*
De Avenley Foundation, The *126*
De La Rue Charitable Trust *127*
De Rothschild 1981 Charitable Trust, The Edmund *127*
De Yong Charitable Trust, The Emma *128*
Denne Charitable Trust *130*
Desmond Charitable Trust, The Richard *131*
Deutsch Charitable Trust, The Andre *131*
Deutsch Charitable Trust, The H & M *131*
Dicken Charitable Trust, The Albert *133*
Dinam Charity *134*
Doughty Charity Trust, The *136*
Drapers' Charitable Fund *137*
Drayton Trust, The *138*
Dumbreck Charity *139*
Edinburgh Trust, No 2 Account *145*
Education Services *145*
Egerton of Tatton Will Trust, Lord *146*
Elshore Limited *149*
Emanuel Charitable Settlement, Ralph and Muriel *150*
Erycinus Charitable Trust *153*
Esperanza Charitable Trust, The *153*
Eveson Charitable Trust, The *155*
Family Trust, The *158*
Famos Foundation Trust *158*
Federation of Jewish Relief Organisations *160*
Ferguson Benevolent Fund Limited *161*
Fishmongers' Company's Charitable Trust *163*
Fletcher Trust, Roy *165*
Follett Trust, The *166*

Foreman Foundation, The Carl & Eve *167*
Foyle Trust, Charles Henry *169*
Franklin Bequest, The Rosalind *169*
Franklin Deceased's New Second Charity, Sydney E *170*
Frome Christian Fellowship *174*
Galinski Charitable Trust *177*
Gardner Charitable Trust, R & J *178*
Gibbins Trust, The *181*
Gillett Charitable Trust, J A *183*
Gill's Charitable Trust, Mrs M M *184*
Gold Hill Church Trust *186*
Goldberg Charitable Trust, The Lewis *186*
Graham Charitable Trust, Reginald *190*
Grand Charity (of Freemasons under the United Grand Lodge of England), The *190*
Greenaway Foundation, The Alan *194*
Greenaway Foundation, The Sir Derek *194*
Grimley Charity, The *196*
Gross Charities Limited, M & R *197*
Grosshill Charitable Trust *197*
Grut Charitable Trust, The *198*
Hacking & Sons Ltd Charitable Trust, C G *201*
Hamilton Educational Trust, Eleanor *205*
Hammerson's Charitable Trust, Sue *206*
Handicapped Children's Aid Committee *207*
Harbour Foundation Ltd, The *208*
Hartley Memorial Trust, The N & P *211*
Harvey Charitable Trust, Gordon *211*
Hawley Residuary Fund, Harry Fieldsend *212*
Hayward Foundation, The *213*
Held Settlement, The Gisela *215*
Hillards Charitable Trust, Gay & Peter Hartley's *220*
Hodge Foundation, The Jane *223*
Holford Trust Fund *224*
Holly Hill Charitable Trust *224*
Horn Trust, The Cuthbert *227*
Hughes Charitable Trust, The Geoffery C *230*
Hyde Park Place Estate Charity, The *232*
Inman Charity, The *235*
Innes Memorial Fund *235*

Inverforth Charitable Trust, The *236*
Irving Charitable Trust, The Charles *237*
JCSCJ Charitable Trust, The *238*
JHL Trust, The *239*
JMK Charitable Trust *239*
Jacobs Charitable Trust, The J P *240*
James Foundation, The Catherine and Lady Grace *241*
Jarrold Trust Ltd, John *243*
Jewish Philanthropic Association for Israel and the Middle East, The *245*
Johnson Foundation, The *246*
Jubilee Outreach Yorkshire *248*
Karten Charitable Trust, The Ian *250*
Keeling Charitable Trust, The Petronella *251*
King Charitable Settlement, Philip *254*
Kingsgrove Charitable Trust, The *255*
Kleinwort Charitable Trust, The Ernest *257*
Knott Trust, Sir James *258*
Kulika Charitable Trust, The *259*
Kweller Charitable Trust, The Harry *259*
Laing Foundation, The Christopher *260*
Laing Foundation, The Kirby *261*
Laing Trust, Beatrice *261*
Laing's Charitable Trust *262*
Lambourne Memorial Trust, The Emma *262*
Langley Charitable Trust, The *264*
Laski Memorial Charitable Trust, Nathan *265*
Laspen Trust *265*
Lass Charities Limited, Rachel and Jack *265*
Lavender Trust, The *267*
Leach Fourteenth Trust, The *267*
Leadbeater Trust, The Alfred *268*
Leech Charity, The William *269*
Leigh-Bramwell Trust 'E', P *270*
Lewis Family Charitable Trust, The *273*
Lewis Partnership, John *274*
Lingwood Charitable Trust, The *276*
Livesley 1992 Charitable Trust, Mrs C M *277*
Lloyd Charity, The S and D *278*
Localtrent Ltd *279*
Loseley & Guildway Charitable Trust, The *281*

Lunzer Charitable Trust, The Ruth & Jack 287

Lynwood Charitable Trust, The 288

Lyons Charitable Trust, Sir Jack 288

MDM Memorial Trust 289

McKenzie Trust, The Robert 292

McLaren Foundation 292

McLaren Memorial Trust, The Martin 293

Margadale Charitable Trust, Lord 297

Marks Charitable Trust, Michael 298

Marks Foundation, The Hilda and Samuel 298

Markus Charitable Foundation, The Erich 298

Marr-Munning Trust 299

Marshall Charitable Trust, The Charlotte 300

Martin Trust, The Sir George 300

Matchan Fund Limited, The Leonard 301

Material World Charitable Foundation Limited, The 301

Mayfair Charities Limited 303

Medical Aid Trust 304

Middlesex County Rugby Football Union Memorial Fund 309

Milburn Charitable Trust, Frederick 310

Millett Charitable Trust, The Alan and Janet 312

Modiano Charitable Trust 315

Montefiore Trust, The David 316

Moore Stephens Charitable Foundation, The 317

Morel Charitable Trust, The 318

Morphy Memorial Fund, Arthur 319

Morris Charitable Trust, The Douglas 320

Multithon Trust, The 323

Music for World Development 323

Music Sales Charitable Trust, The 324

Muslim Hands 324

National Lottery Charities Board 328

New Court Charitable Trust 332

Newcastle's 1986 Charitable Trust, Duke of 333

Newman Charitable Trust, Mr and Mrs F E F 334

Norfolk's Family Charitable Trust, Lavinia 336

North British Hotel Trust 337

Northcott Charity Trust, The 338

Northern Ireland Voluntary Trust 339

Old Possums Practical Trust, The 344

PDC Trust, The 349

PF Charitable Trust 350

PJD Charitable Trust 350

Paristamen Foundation, The 352

Patients' Aid Association Hospital and Medical Charities Trust 354

Paul's Charitable Trust, R J 355

Payne Charitable Trust, The 355

Pelech Charitable Trust, The 358

Perry Charitable Trust, Miss Frances Lucille 359

Pershore Nashdom & Elmore Trust Ltd, The 360

Personal Assurance Charitable Trust 360

Pilkington Charitable Trust, Cecil 363

Pitt Trust, Headley 364

Porter Foundation 366

Prendergast Charitable Trust, The Simone 368

RT Trust, The 374

Rackham Charitable Trust, The Mr & Mrs Philip 375

Radley Charitable Trust 375

Rae Charity, H J 375

Rainford Trust, The 376

Rav Chesed Trust, The 379

Rest-Harrow Trust, The 382

Reuter Foundation, The 382

Rich Charities, S & J 383

Richard Charitable Trust, The Cliff 383

Richards Charity, The Clive 384

Rivendell Trust, The 387

Rodewald's Charitable Settlement, Mr C A 389

Rogers Charitable Settlement, The Richard 390

Rokeby Charitable Trust 390

Rozel Trust, The 397

Said Foundation, The Karim Rida 401

St Christopher's Trust, The 402

St Jude's Trust 403

Salters Charities 405

Samuel Charitable Trust, M J 406

Save & Prosper Foundation 409

Scarr-Hall Memorial Trust, The 409

Seedfield Trust, The 414

Seva Trust, Rampaba Sadhu 415

Shepherd Charitable Trust, The Sylvia and Colin 418

Simon's Charity 422

Smith (Estates Charities), Henry 426

Society of Friends of the Torah, The 429

Solomons Charitable Trust, David 430

Somerfield Curtis Will Trust, The Dorothy 430

Stanley Foundation Limited 435

Stewart Charitable Trust, Mary Stephanie 437

Sumner's Trust Section 'A', Sir John 443

Sussman Charitable Trust, Adrienne & Leslie 443

Swann-Morton Foundation, The 444

Symons Charitable Trust, The Stella 446

TSB Foundation for Scotland 447

Tait Charity, The Richard 448

Templeton Goodwill Trust 451

Terry Charitable Trust, Noel Goddard 451

Tesco Charity Trust 452

Tesler Foundation, The 452

Thompson Charitable Trust, The 453

3i Charitable Trust, The 455

Toler Foundation, The 457

Toyota (GB) Charitable Trust, The 459

Travis Charitable Trust, Constance 460

Turner Trust, The Douglas 464

Upjohn Charitable Trust, The 469

Van Norden's Charitable Foundation, Mrs Maud 471

Vineyard Christian Fellowship of South West 473

Vinson Charity Trust, The 1969 473

Vogel Charitable Trust, The Nathan 474

Wagstaff Charitable Trust, Bob 475

Wakefield Trust, The 476

Wander Charitable Fund, The Dr Albert 479

Weinstock Fund, The 484

Weir Foundation, The James 484

Welby Trust, The Barbara 484

Whesby Ltd 488

Whitehead Charitable Trust, J E 490

Wiggins Charity Trust, Cyril 491

Wills 1961 Charitable Trust, Major Michael Thomas 494

Wills 1962 Charitable Trust, P J H 494

Wingate Foundation, The Harold Hyam 496

Winstone Foundation, Hyman
497
Woburn 1986 Charitable Trust
498
Wolff Charity Trust *498*
Woodhouse Charitable Trust,
Edwin *501*
Woods Charitable Foundation,
Geoffrey *502*
Worms Charitable Trust, The
Freda and Della *504*
Worshipful Company of
Founders Charities, The *505*
Worshipful Company of
Needlemakers' Charitable
Fund *505*
Wychdale Limited *507*
Yapp Education and Research
Trust, The *508*
Youell Foundation Ltd, The
510
Zaiger Trust, The Elizabeth and
Prince *512*

■ **Medicine**

see also **Academic subjects,
sciences & research**

Funding priority
Asthma Allergy and
Inflammation Research Trust
25
Cancer Relief Macmillan Fund
79
Holly Hill Charitable Trust *224*
Nidditch Foundation, The
Laurie *335*
Nuffield Foundation *342*
PPP Healthcare Medical Trust
Limited *350*
Palmer Trust, The Gerald *352*
Peel Medical Research Trust,
The *358*
Richards Charity, The Violet M
384
Royal Commission for the
Exhibition of 1851 *395*
Thomson Charitable Trust, The
Arthur *453*

■ **Memorials &
monuments**

see also **Conservation**

Funding priority
Alec-Smith Charitable Trust,
R A *10*
Clark Charitable Trust, J
Anthony *98*
Dulverton Trust, The *139*
Mitchell Trust, Esme *315*

Will consider
Ammco Trust, The *15*
Askew Charitable Trust, The
Ian *25*

Astor Foundation, The *26*
Bancroft Trust, The *33*
Barnby's Foundation, Lord *35*
Broadley Charitable Trust, The
64
Brook Charitable Settlement,
R E *64*
Coates Charitable Trust, The
John *103*
Cripplegate Foundation *118*
David Trust, The Lesley *124*
D'Avigdor Goldsmid Charitable
Trust, The Sarah *125*
de Freitas Charitable Trust, The
Helen and Geoffrey *126*
Digby Charitable Trust, Simon
133
Direct Response *134*
Dixon Charitable Trust, F E *134*
Early's Charitable Settlement,
Richard *142*
GABO Trust for Sculpture
Conservation *175*
Getty Jr General Charitable
Trust, J Paul *181*
Goldsmiths' Company's
Charities, The *188*
Greenaway Foundation, The Sir
Derek *194*
Grocers' Charity *197*
Halkes Settlement, John Robert
204
Hawthorne Charitable Trust,
The *212*
Idlewild Trust, The *234*
Ireland Funds, The *237*
Isle of Dogs Community
Foundation *238*
Lawson Charitable Trust,
Raymond and Blanche *267*
Leach Fourteenth Trust, The
267
Leche Trust, The *268*
Lee Foundation, The Edgar
269
Linford Charitable Trust, The
Fred *276*
MacKintosh Charitable Trust,
Viscount *292*
Mellows Charitable Settlement,
The Anthony and Elizabeth
305
Owen Family Trust, The *348*
Persula Foundation, The *360*
Powys Welsh Church Fund *367*
Prince's Trust - BRO, The *369*
Radcliffe's Trust, Dr *375*
Rowbotham Charitable Trust,
The Christopher *393*
Royal Commission for the
Exhibition of 1851 *395*
Schuster Charitable Trust, The
410
Shepherd Charitable Trust, The
Sylvia and Colin *418*
South Square Trust *430*
Summerfield Charitable Trust,
The *442*

Symons Charitable Trust, The
Stella *446*
Terry Charitable Trust, Noel
Goddard *451*
Unitek Foundation *469*
Vincent Trust Fund, Eric W *473*
Worshipful Company of
Engineers' Charitable Trust
Fund, The *504*
Wylde Memorial Charity, The
Anthony and Gwendoline
507

■ **Mental health**

see **Mental illness**

■ **Mental illness**

Funding priority
Archer Trust, The *20*
Askew Charitable Trust, The
Ian *25*
Ball Charitable Trust, The Bruce
31
British Council for Prevention
of Blindness *61*
Chownes Foundation, The *93*
Commonwealth Relations Trust
108
Ebb and Flow Charitable Trust
144
Ericson Trust *152*
Ferguson Benevolent Fund
Limited *161*
Franklin Trust, Jill *170*
Gatsby Charitable Foundation,
The *179*
Gray Charitable Trust, R B *192*
Hanley Trust (1987), The *207*
Hannay Memorial Charity,
Kathleen *208*
Hartnett Charitable Trust, The
211
Holmes Foundation, Godfrey
224
Lane Foundation, The Allen
263
(Lloyds) TSB Foundation for
England and Wales *279*
McLaren Memorial Trust, The
Martin *293*
Mental Health Foundation, The
305
Meridian Broadcasting
Charitable Trust *307*
Powell Foundation, The *367*
Rosen Foundation, Cecil *392*
Sanity *407*
Shuttleworth Memorial Trust,
Barbara A *421*
Smith & Mount Trust, The Mrs
426
Swan Mountain Trust *444*
Tudor Trust, The *463*

Wagstaff Charitable Trust, Bob
475
Watson Foundation, The Bertie
482

■ Mentally handicapped
see **Disabled people (physical, sensory, learning impairments)**

■ Methodists
Funding priority
Aid to the Church in Need
(United Kingdom) 8
Askew Trust, The Dorothy 25
Avon Trust, The 28
Brough Charitable Trust,
Joseph 65
Cardiff & Swansea Methodist
District Charitable Trust
Fund 80
Chesters Settlement for
Methodist Church Purposes,
Mr H G 91
David Trust, The Lesley 124
Ferguson Benevolent Fund
Limited 161
Gibbs Charitable Trusts, The
181
Halkes Settlement, John Robert
204
Pye Christian Trust, The 371
Rutland Historic Churches
Preservation Trust 399
Stoate Charitable Trust, The
Leonard Laity 438
Wright Deceased Trust, John
William 506

■ Missionaries, evangelicals
see also **Advancement of religion**
Funding priority
Aid to the Church in Need
(United Kingdom) 8
Alexis Trust, The 11
Almond Trust, The 14
Anderson Trust, Andrew 16
Barleycorn Trust, The 34
Bartholomew Christian Trust
36
Birchwood Trust, The 49
Black Charitable Trust, The
Cyril W 51
Black Charitable Trust, Edna
51
Candap Trust, The 80
Church Urban Fund 95
Collier Charitable Trust, The
105

Dibdin Foundation, Thomas
Peter 132
Dicken Charitable Trust, The
Albert 133
Drummond Trust, The 138
Emmaus Christian Foundation
150
Firdale Christian Trust, The 162
Firtree Trust, The 163
Gelston Charitable Trust, The
179
Griffiths Trust, The E E and
D M 196
Groves Charitable Trust, The
197
Growth Building Trust, The
198
Hame Trust, The 205
Holford Trust Fund 224
James Charitable Trust, John
241
James Trust, The 242
Jerusalem Trust 244
Kingsgrove Charitable Trust,
The 255
Laing Foundation, The Maurice
261
Laing Trust, Beatrice 261
Laing Trust, The J W 261
Lavender Trust, The 267
Lunn-Rockliffe Charitable Trust,
Paul 286
Marshall Charitable Trust, The
299
Milward Charity, The Edgar
313
NR Charitable Trust, The 325
Ogle Trust, The 344
Owen Family Trust, The 348
Payne Charitable Trust, The
355
Pye Christian Trust, The 371
Richard Charitable Trust, The
Cliff 383
Riddell Charitable Trust, R G
385
Rozel Trust, The 397
SMB Trust, The 400
Skinner Charitable Trust,
Edward 424
Stewardship Trust Ripon, The
437
Stow Allen Trust, The 439
Tikva Trust, The 456
Tisbury Telegraph Trust, The
457
Tunstall Charitable Trust 463
Waghorn Charitable Trust, The
Albert 475
Whitecourt Charitable Trust,
The 490
Whiteley Trust, Norman 490
Wiggins Charity Trust, Cyril
491

Will consider
Appleton Trust, The 19
Archer Trust, The 20
Astor Foundation, The 26
Britland Charitable Trust, The
63
Brooke Benevolent Fund,
William 65
Burden Trust, The 69
Cadbury Charitable Trust
(Incorporated), Edward 75
Clarke Charitable Settlement,
The 99
David Trust, The Lesley 124
Debtors' Relief Fund Charity
128
Digby Charitable Trust, Simon
133
Ebenezer Family Trust 144
Feed the Minds 160
Fulham Cross Christian Mission
175
Greenaway Foundation, The Sir
Derek 194
Halkes Settlement, John Robert
204
Hannay Memorial Charity,
Kathleen 208
Hudson Benevolent Trust, The
Thomas 230
Hussey for Africans, Charity of
Rebecca 231
Ibbett Trust, The 233
Kingston Religious Trust Fund,
The 256
Laing Charitable Trust, The
David 260
Laing Foundation, The Kirby
261
Laspen Trust 265
Latham Trust, The 266
Leech Charity, The William 269
Linford Charitable Trust, The
Fred 276
Littler Foundation, The Emile
277
Lloyd Charity, The S and D 278
New Durlston Trust, The 332
Nightingale Trust, The 335
Norwich Church of England
Young Men's Society 340
Paristamen Foundation, The
352
Rainbow Charitable Trust 376
St Christopher's Trust, The 402
Saint Edmund King and Martyr
Trust 402
Sharon Trust, The 416
Shelroy Charitable Trust, The
417
Shone Memorial Trust, J A 420
Sparkhill Trust, The 433
Stonehouse Trust Ltd, Eric 438
Summer's and I May's
Charitable Settlement, The
Late Misses (A N) 442
Tear Fund 450
Thorpe Charity Trust, The 455

Tindall's Charitable Trust, Mrs
R P *457*
Trust for the Homeless *462*
United Society for Christian
Literature *468*
Wagstaff Charitable Trust, Bob
475
Wallington Missionary Mart &
Auctions *478*
Wates Charitable Trust, John
481
Webber Trust Fund, Ethel *483*
Williams Trust, James *493*

■ **Mobile units**

see Ambulances & mobile
units

■ **Monuments**

see Memorials &
monuments

■ **Mosques**

see also Religious buildings

Will consider

Beckwith-Smith's Charitable
Settlement, Mrs *40*
Chesters Settlement for
Methodist Church Purposes,
Mr H G *91*
Digby Charitable Trust, Simon
133
Greenaway Foundation, The Sir
Derek *194*
Hillards Charitable Trust, Gay &
Peter Hartley's *220*
Hussey for Africans, Charity of
Rebecca *231*
Moore Charitable Trust, The
Horace *316*

■ **Mothers**

see Parents & children

■ **Motor neurone
disease**

Funding priority

Archer Trust, The *20*
Patrick Charitable Trust, The
354
Woodroffe Benton Foundation,
The *502*

■ **MS research**

see also Medical studies &
research

Funding priority

Ammco Trust, The *15*
Ashby Charitable Trust, The *23*
Assheton-Smith Charitable
Trust *25*
Edgar Trust, The Gilbert *145*
Fogel Charitable Trust, The
Gerald *165*
Garthgwynion Charities *179*
Gilley Charitable Trust, The L &
R *183*
Heath Charitable Trust *214*
Holmes Foundation, Godfrey
224
Kroch Foundation, The Heinz &
Anna *259*
Multiple Sclerosis Society of
Great Britain & Northern
Ireland *322*
Pryor Charitable Trust, The
John *370*
Tisbury Telegraph Trust, The
457
Woodroffe Benton Foundation,
The *502*

Will consider

Action Research *6*
Anstey Charitable Settlement,
J C W *18*
Archer Trust, The *20*
Astor Foundation, The *26*
Avenal *27*
Balney Charitable Trust, The
32
Bancroft Trust, The *33*
Barbour Trust, The *33*
Beckwith Charitable
Settlement, The Heather *39*
Buckinghamshire Masonic
Centenary Fund *67*
Cadbury Trust (1928), The
Edward & Dorothy *76*
Clarke Charitable Settlement,
The *99*
Clinton's Charitable Trust, Lord
100
Coates Charitable Trust, The
John *103*
Coutts Charitable Trust, The
116
Digby Charitable Trust, Simon
133
Dorus Trust *136*
Early's Charitable Settlement,
Richard *142*
Edgar Foundation, The Gilbert
and Eileen *145*
Education Services *145*
Emmandjay Charitable Trust
150
Emmaus Christian Foundation
150
Epigoni Trust *152*

Eventhall Family Charitable
Trust, The *155*
Gladstone Charitable Trust, The
E W *184*
Gluckstein Charitable
Settlement, The Penelope
185
Glynde Place Charitable Trust
(1974), The *186*
Grant Foundation, The
Raymond *191*
Gray Charitable Trust, R B *192*
Great Britain Sasakawa
Foundation, The *193*
Greenaway Foundation, The Sir
Derek *194*
HB Charitable Trust *201*
Haywood Charitable Trust *214*
Hornby Charitable Trust, Miss
D *227*
Hunter Charitable Trust, The
Claire *231*
Kyte Charitable Trust, The *259*
Lawson Charitable Trust,
Raymond and Blanche *267*
Lee Foundation, The Edgar
269
Leech Charity, The William *269*
Linmardon Trust *276*
London Law Trust *280*
Lowe Trust, Mrs D G *285*
Lowenthal Charitable Trust,
The L and C *285*
Lynall Foundation, The D G
287
MacKintosh Charitable Trust,
Viscount *292*
Mackintosh Foundation, The
292
Manning Trust, Leslie & Lilian
296
Milburn Charitable Trust,
Frederick *310*
Needham Cooper Charitable
Trust, The *331*
New Court Charitable Trust
332
Newby Trust Ltd *332*
Norman Family Charitable
Trust, The *337*
Noswad Charity, The *341*
Owen Family Trust, The *348*
Peppiatt Charitable Trust, The
Brian *359*
Persula Foundation, The *360*
Pratt Charitable Trust, The W L
367
REMEDI (Rehabilitation and
Medical Research Trust) *374*
Rest-Harrow Trust, The *382*
Schuster Charitable Trust, The
410
South Square Trust *430*
Summer's and I May's
Charitable Settlement, The
Late Misses (A N) *442*
Sussman Charitable Trust,
Adrienne & Leslie *443*

Sykes Trust, The Charles *445*
Toy Trust, The *459*
Travis Charitable Trust, Constance *460*
Webber Trust Fund, Ethel *483*
Wellcome Trust, The *485*
Wingfield's Charitable Trust, Mrs *496*
Wolfe Family's Charitable Trust, The *498*
Woolton Charitable Trust, The *503*
Worshipful Company of Engineers' Charitable Trust Fund, The *504*

■ Multifaith

see **Advancement of religion**

■ Multimedia

see **Film, video, multimedia, broadcasting**

■ Multiple sclerosis

Funding priority

Holmes Foundation, Godfrey *224*
Multiple Sclerosis Society of Great Britain & Northern Ireland *322*

■ Muscular dystrophy

Funding priority

Patrick Charitable Trust, The *354*

■ Museums

see **Libraries & Museums**

■ Music

see also **Arts & arts facilities**

Funding priority

Allnatt Charitable Foundation, Angus *14*
Arts Council of England, The *23*
Arts Council of Wales, The *23*
Blakey Charitable Trust, The Celia and Conrad *53*
Blay Trust, The Robert *54*
Classic FM Charitable Trust, The *99*
Cohen Foundation, The John S *104*
Courtauld Trust for the Advancement of Music, The *116*

Delius Trust, The *129*
Elmchurch Trust, The *148*
Finzi Charitable Trust, Gerald *162*
Fletcher Charitable Trust, The Joyce *164*
Gardner Memorial Trust, The Samuel *178*
Harding Trust, The *209*
Harewood's Charitable Settlement, Lord *209*
Heseltine Charitable Trust, Michael *217*
Hinrichsen Foundation, The *221*
Hudson Benevolent Trust, The Thomas *230*
Hunter Charitable Trust, The Claire *231*
Lower Hall Charitable Trust *285*
Ludgate Trust, The *286*
Lynn Foundation, The *288*
Merchants House of Glasgow *307*
Music Sales Charitable Trust, The *324*
Needham Cooper Charitable Trust, The *331*
North West Arts Board *337*
Northern Arts *339*
Noswad Charity, The *341*
Paragon Concert Society *352*
RVW Trust *374*
Radcliffe's Trust, Dr *375*
Somerfield Curtis Will Trust, The Dorothy *430*
South Square Trust *430*
Taylor Charitable Trust, The B R *450*
Tillett Trust, The *456*
Tutton Charitable Trust, Miss S M *465*
Wates Charitable Trust, John *481*
Yorkshire and Humberside Arts *510*

Will consider

Astor Foundation, The *26*
Beckwith Charitable Settlement, The Heather *39*
Beit Trust, The *40*
Belmont Trust, The *42*
Bridge Trust, The *60*
Britton Charitable Trust, The J & M *63*
Broadley Charitable Trust, The *64*
Brooke Benevolent Fund, William *65*
Bulmer Charitable Trust, Becket *68*
Cadbury Trust (1928), The Edward & Dorothy *76*
Campden Charities, The *79*
Carnegie Dunfermline Trust *82*

Carnegie United Kingdom Trust, The *82*
Coates Charitable Trust, The John *103*
Colyer-Fergusson Charitable Trust, The *107*
Cripplegate Foundation *118*
D'Avigdor Goldsmid Charitable Trust, The Sarah *125*
Debtors' Relief Fund Charity *128*
Digby Charitable Trust, Simon *133*
Dixon Charitable Trust, F E *134*
Dumbreck Charity *139*
Early's Charitable Settlement, Richard *142*
Edgar Foundation, The Gilbert and Eileen *145*
Fogel Charitable Trust, The Gerald *165*
Follett Trust, The *166*
Granada Foundation, The *190*
Great Britain Sasakawa Foundation, The *193*
Greenaway Foundation, The Sir Derek *194*
Grundy Foundation, The Stanley *198*
Halkes Settlement, John Robert *204*
Hamlyn Foundation, The Paul *205*
Harbinson Charitable Trust, Roderick *208*
Henderson's Settlement, J R *216*
Holly Hill Charitable Trust *224*
Howard Charitable Trust, John & Ruth *229*
Hughes Charitable Trust, The Geoffery C *230*
Inverforth Charitable Trust, The *236*
Ireland Funds, The *237*
JMK Charitable Trust *239*
Laing Charitable Trust, The David *260*
Laing Foundation, The Christopher *260*
Leche Trust, The *268*
Lee Foundation, The Edgar *269*
Lewis Foundation, The John Spedan *274*
Liebes Charitable Trust, The Martha Bud *274*
Linford Charitable Trust, The Fred *276*
Mackintosh Foundation, The *292*
Milton Keynes Community Trust Ltd, The *312*
Mitchell Trust, Esme *315*
Music Libraries Trust, The *323*
New Court Charitable Trust *332*
Notgrove Trust, The *341*

Oldham Foundation *345*
Owen Family Trust, The *348*
PF Charitable Trust *350*
Provincial Trust for Kendal, The *370*
Reader's Digest Trust, The *380*
Rookes Charitable Trust, C A *390*
Royal Commission for the Exhibition of 1851 *395*
St Katharine & Shadwell Trust *404*
Sheepdrove Trust, The *417*
Sobell Welsh People's Charitable Association, Michael *429*
Strauss Charitable Trust *440*
Summerfield Charitable Trust, The *442*
Summer's and I May's Charitable Settlement, The Late Misses (A N) *442*
Thomson Foundation, The Sue *454*
Turner Trust, The Douglas *464*
Wakefield (Tower Hill, Trinity Square) Trust *476*
Walker Trust, The *477*
Wander Charitable Fund, The Dr Albert *479*
Wates Foundation, The *481*
Whitaker Charitable Trust *489*
Williams Charitable Trust, Alfred *493*
Woodlands Trust *501*

■ Music education
see Education & training

■ Musicians
Funding priority
Burden Trust, The *69*
Hannay Memorial Charity, Kathleen *208*
Liebes Charitable Trust, The Martha Bud *274*
RVW Trust *374*

■ Muslims
Funding priority
Muslim Hands *324*

■ Natural disasters
see Victims of man-made or natural disasters

■ Natural history
see also Environment & animal sciences
Funding priority
Clutterbuck Charitable Trust, Robert *102*
Cobb Charity *103*

Will consider
Allied Domecq Trust *13*
Ashley Foundation, The Laura *24*
Astor Foundation, The *26*
Butler Charitable Trust, The A S *71*
Carnegie Dunfermline Trust *82*
Chippindale Foundation, Sam *93*
Coates Charitable Trust 1969, Lance *103*
Community Trust for Greater Manchester, The *108*
David Trust, The Lesley *124*
D'Avigdor Goldsmid Charitable Trust, The Sarah *125*
Digby Charitable Trust, Simon *133*
Direct Response *134*
GW Trust, The *176*
Glynde Place Charitable Trust (1974), The *186*
Goldsmiths' Company's Charities, The *188*
Great Britain Sasakawa Foundation, The *193*
Greenaway Foundation, The Sir Derek *194*
Horn Trust, The Cuthbert *227*
Idlewild Trust, The *234*
Isle of Dogs Community Foundation *238*
Living and Waking Naturally *278*
Lloyd Charity, The S and D *278*
Lloyd's Charities Trust *278*
MacRobert Trusts, The *294*
Mattock Charitable Trust, The W T *302*
Measures Charity, The James Frederick and Ethel Anne *303*
Mitchell Trust *315*
Nathan Charitable Trust, Peter *326*
Oldham Foundation *345*
Paget Trust, The *351*
Peppiatt Charitable Trust, The Brian *359*
Pilgrim Trust, The *362*
Pilkington Charitable Trust, Cecil *363*
Reader's Digest Trust, The *380*
Shaw Foundation, The Linley *416*

Tisbury Telegraph Trust, The *457*
Whitaker Charitable Trust *489*
Young Explorers' Trust *511*

■ Nature reserves
see also Conservation
Funding priority
Barnby's Foundation, Lord *35*
Clark Charitable Trust, J Anthony *98*
Cobb Charity *103*
Dulverton Trust, The *139*
Four Winds Trust *168*
GW Trust, The *176*
Haddon Charitable Trust, William *202*
Harbinson Charitable Trust, Roderick *208*
Living and Waking Naturally *278*
Mitchell Trust *315*
Mitchell Trust, Esme *315*
Nathan Charitable Trust, Peter *326*
Persula Foundation, The *360*
Pilkington Trust, The Austin and Hope *363*
Tisbury Telegraph Trust, The *457*
Tyler's Charitable Trust, The Late Miss Eileen Margaret *465*
Yorkshire Field Studies Trust *510*

Will consider
Ammco Trust, The *15*
Askew Charitable Trust, The Ian *25*
Astor Foundation, The *26*
BP Conservation Programme *29*
Balney Charitable Trust, The *32*
Barbour Trust, The *33*
Beit Trust, The *40*
Bourne-May Charitable Trust, The *57*
Broadley Charitable Trust, The *64*
Brook Charitable Settlement, R E *64*
Bulmer Charitable Trust, Becket *68*
Burton 1960 Charitable Settlement, Audrey & Stanley *70*
Butler Charitable Trust, The A S *71*
Cadbury Trust (1928), The Edward & Dorothy *76*
Clark 1965 Charitable Trust, Stephen *98*
Coates Charitable Trust, The John *103*

Cole Charitable Trust, The *105*
Colyer-Fergusson Charitable Trust, The *107*
Community Trust for Greater Manchester, The *108*
Countryside Trust, The *115*
Cripplegate Foundation *118*
David Trust, The Lesley *124*
D'Avigdor Goldsmid Charitable Trust, The Sarah *125*
de Freitas Charitable Trust, The Helen and Geoffrey *126*
Digby Charitable Trust, Simon *133*
Direct Response *134*
Early's Charitable Settlement, Richard *142*
Earwicker Trust *142*
Edgar Foundation, The Gilbert and Eileen *145*
Elkes Charity Fund, The Wilfred & Elsie *147*
Feeney Charitable Bequest, The John *161*
Fishmongers' Company's Charitable Trust *163*
Garnett's 1973 Charitable Trust, Mrs A M *178*
Glynde Place Charitable Trust (1974), The *186*
Great Britain Sasakawa Foundation, The *193*
Greenaway Foundation, The Sir Derek *194*
Grocers' Charity *197*
Halkes Settlement, John Robert *204*
Hannay Charitable Trust, The Lennox *208*
Hawthorne Charitable Trust, The *212*
Holly Hill Charitable Trust *224*
Isle of Dogs Community Foundation *238*
JJ Charitable Trust, The *239*
Jarrold Trust Ltd, John *243*
Kiln Charitable Trust, Robert *254*
Kilverstone Wildlife Charitable Trust, The *254*
Laing Foundation, The Kirby *261*
Laing Foundation, The Maurice *261*
Lankelly Foundation, The *264*
Lawson Charitable Trust, Raymond and Blanche *267*
Leach Fourteenth Trust, The *267*
Lee Foundation, The Edgar *269*
Lewis Foundation, The John Spedan *274*
Lewis Partnership, John *274*
Lowe Trust, Mrs D G *285*
Lower Hall Charitable Trust *285*
Lyndhurst Settlement *287*

MacKintosh Charitable Trust, Viscount *292*
Marchday Charitable Fund, The *296*
Marchig Animal Welfare Trust *297*
Mellows Charitable Settlement, The Anthony and Elizabeth *305*
Minet Trust, The Peter *313*
NR Charitable Trust, The *325*
Needham Cooper Charitable Trust, The *331*
New Court Charitable Trust *332*
Owen Family Trust, The *348*
Paget Trust, The *351*
Peppiatt Charitable Trust, The Brian *359*
Powys Welsh Church Fund *367*
Prince's Trust - BRO, The *369*
Pye Christian Trust, The *371*
Pyke Charity Trust *372*
Ravenscroft Foundation, The *379*
Reader's Digest Trust, The *380*
Richard Charitable Trust, The Cliff *383*
Rowbotham Charitable Trust, The Christopher *393*
Sargeant's Charitable Trust, Mrs M E *407*
Schuster Charitable Trust, The *410*
Sobell Welsh People's Charitable Association, Michael *429*
South Square Trust *430*
Staples Trust *435*
Stevens Foundation, The June *437*
Stoate Charitable Trust, The Leonard Laity *438*
Summerfield Charitable Trust, The *442*
Sykes Trust, The Charles *445*
Symons Charitable Trust, The Stella *446*
Terry Charitable Trust, Noel Goddard *451*
Unitek Foundation *469*
Vincent Trust Fund, Eric W *473*
Wade & Others, The Charity of Thomas *475*
Webber Trust Fund, Ethel *483*
Whitaker Charitable Trust *489*
Woodroffe Benton Foundation, The *502*
Wylde Memorial Charity, The Anthony and Gwendoline *507*
Yorkshire Agricultural Society *509*
Yorkshire Bank Charitable Trust, The *510*
Young Explorers' Trust *511*

▪ Needy

see **Disadvantaged by poverty**

▪ Nuclear energy, nuclear power

see also **Conservation & campaigning**

Will consider

Barnby's Foundation, Lord *35*
Beckwith-Smith's Charitable Settlement, Mrs *40*
Carron Charitable Trust, The *83*
Coates Charitable Trust 1969, Lance *103*
Digby Charitable Trust, Simon *133*
Early's Charitable Settlement, Richard *142*
Edgar Foundation, The Gilbert and Eileen *145*
Greenaway Foundation, The Sir Derek *194*
Lane Foundation, The Allen *263*
Living and Waking Naturally *278*
Mellows Charitable Settlement, The Anthony and Elizabeth *305*
Morphy Memorial Fund, Arthur *319*
North West Arts Board *337*
Polden-Puckham Charitable Foundation, The *365*
S Group Charitable Trust *399*
Summerfield Charitable Trust, The *442*
Tisbury Telegraph Trust, The *457*
Worshipful Company of Engineers' Charitable Trust Fund, The *504*

▪ Nurses

see **Medical professionals, nurses & doctors**

▪ Nursing homes

see also **Health facilities & buildings**

Funding priority

Assheton-Smith Charitable Trust *25*
Bilton Charity, The Percy *48*
Cohen Charity Trust, Lucy *104*
Fogel Charitable Trust, The Gerald *165*
Frognal Trust *174*
Heath Charitable Trust *214*

Lacy Charity Trust, The Late Sir Pierce *260*
SMB Trust, The *400*
Stonehouse Trust Ltd, Eric *438*

Will consider
AB Charitable Trust *3*
Ammco Trust, The *15*
Andrew Charitable Trust, The Prince *16*
Anstey Charitable Settlement, J C W *18*
Army Benevolent Fund, The *22*
Astor Foundation, The *26*
Bancroft Trust, The *33*
Barbour Trust, The *33*
Barratt Charitable Trust, The Elaine *36*
Birtwistle Memorial Trust, The G E *50*
Britton Charitable Trust, The J & M *63*
Brotherton Trust, The Charles *65*
Bullough Tompson Settlement, The *68*
Catto Charitable Settlement, The Thomas Sivewright *86*
Chase Charity, The *91*
Collier Charitable Trust, The *105*
Corbett's Charity, Thomas *112*
Dean Refugee Trust Fund, The Miriam *128*
Denne Charitable Trust *130*
Digby Charitable Trust, Simon *133*
Dorus Trust *136*
Dumbreck Charity *139*
Edgar Trust, The Gilbert *145*
Elkes Charity Fund, The Wilfred & Elsie *147*
Epigoni Trust *152*
Fleming Charitable Trust, The Ian *164*
Fortune Trust, The *167*
Franklin Deceased's New Second Charity, Sydney E *170*
Goldsmiths' Company's Charities, The *188*
Good Neighbours Trust, The *188*
Grant-Lawson Charitable Trust, Lady Virginia *192*
Greenaway Foundation, The Sir Derek *194*
Harvey Charitable Trust, Gordon *211*
Henderson's Settlement, J R *216*
Homfray Trust, The *226*
Inman Charity, The *235*
Isle of Dogs Community Foundation *238*
JDM Charitable Trust *239*
JHL Trust, The *239*

Jarman Charitable Trust, The *243*
Lankelly Foundation, The *264*
Leech Charity, The William *269*
Licensed Trade Charities Trust, The *274*
(Lloyds) TSB Foundation for England and Wales *279*
Luke Trust, The *286*
MacKintosh Charitable Trust, Viscount *292*
Mellows Charitable Settlement, The Anthony and Elizabeth *305*
Metropolitan Hospital-Sunday Fund, The *308*
Milburn Charitable Trust, Frederick *310*
Milward Charity, The Edgar *313*
Minet Trust, The Peter *313*
Natwest Staff Samaritan Fund *330*
Needham Cooper Charitable Trust, The *331*
Noswad Charity, The *341*
Owen Family Trust, The *348*
Paget Trust, The *351*
Paul's Charitable Trust, R J *355*
Payne Trust, The Harry *356*
Royal's Memorial Fund, Princess *396*
Schuster Charitable Trust, The *410*
Shelroy Charitable Trust, The *417*
Smith (Estates Charities), Henry *426*
Tisbury Telegraph Trust, The *457*
Travis Charitable Trust, Constance *460*
Van Neste Foundation, The *471*
Woodroffe Benton Foundation, The *502*
Wylde Memorial Charity, The Anthony and Gwendoline *507*

....

■ Nursing service
see also Health care
Funding priority
Birmingham Amenities and Welfare Trust, The *49*
Burn Charity Trust, The J H *70*
Cancer Relief Macmillan Fund *79*
Dahl Foundation, The Roald *122*
Davis Charitable Trust, Wilfrid Bruce *126*
Edgar Trust, The Gilbert *145*
General Nursing Council for England and Wales Trust, The *180*

Heath Charitable Trust *214*
Lloyd's Charities Trust *278*
Loseley & Guildway Charitable Trust, The *281*
National Waterways Restoration & Development Fund of the Inland Waterways Association, The *330*
SMB Trust, The *400*

Will consider
AB Charitable Trust *3*
Army Benevolent Fund, The *22*
Astor Foundation, The *26*
Avon Trust, The *28*
Balint Charitable Trust, Paul *31*
Bancroft Trust, The *33*
Beckwith Charitable Settlement, The Heather *39*
Berkshire Community Trust *45*
Birtwistle Memorial Trust, The G E *50*
Bottom Charitable Trust, Harry *56*
Britton Charitable Trust, The J & M *63*
Brotherton Trust, The Charles *65*
Burdall Charity, H M *69*
Camelot Foundation, The *78*
Cathedral Nursing Society Charitable Trust *85*
Cleopatra Trust *99*
Commonwealth Relations Trust *108*
Coutts Charitable Trust, The *116*
Coxen Trust Fund, Sir William *116*
Curzon Charitable Trust, The Wallace *120*
Dean Refugee Trust Fund, The Miriam *128*
Digby Charitable Trust, Simon *133*
Direct Response *134*
Dorus Trust *136*
Dumbreck Charity *139*
Edgar Foundation, The Gilbert and Eileen *145*
Elkes Charity Fund, The Wilfred & Elsie *147*
Emmandjay Charitable Trust *150*
Emmaus Christian Foundation *150*
Epigoni Trust *152*
Fogel Charitable Trust, The Gerald *165*
Follett Trust, The *166*
Foreman Foundation, The Carl & Eve *167*
Fortune Trust, The *167*
Gibbins Trust, The *181*
Gladstone Charitable Trust, The E W *184*

Goldsmiths' Company's
Charities, The *188*
Good Neighbours Trust, The
188
Grant Foundation, The
Raymond *191*
Grant-Lawson Charitable Trust,
Lady Virginia *192*
Gray Charitable Trust, R B *192*
Greenaway Foundation, The
Alan *194*
Greenaway Foundation, The Sir
Derek *194*
Grocers' Charity *197*
Hawley Residuary Fund, Harry
Fieldsend *212*
Homfray Trust, The *226*
Innes Memorial Fund *235*
Isle of Dogs Community
Foundation *238*
JDM Charitable Trust *239*
JHL Trust, The *239*
Lawson Charitable Trust,
Raymond and Blanche *267*
Lee Foundation, The Edgar
269
Leech Charity, The William *269*
Licensed Trade Charities Trust,
The *274*
Lloyd Charity, The S and D *278*
London Law Trust *280*
Lynall Foundation, The D G
287
MacKintosh Charitable Trust,
Viscount *292*
Mackintosh Foundation, The
292
Merchants House of Glasgow
307
Mercury Phoenix Trust *307*
Milburn Charitable Trust,
Frederick *310*
Milward Charity, The Edgar
313
Moore Foundation, The
George A *316*
Mountbatten Trust, The
Edwina *322*
Multithon Trust, The *323*
Music for World Development
323
Needham Cooper Charitable
Trust, The *331*
New Court Charitable Trust
332
North British Hotel Trust *337*
Norwich Church of England
Young Men's Society *340*
Noswad Charity, The *341*
Oakdale Trust, The *343*
Owen Family Trust, The *348*
Payne Trust, The Harry *356*
Pratt Charitable Trust, The W L
367
Ravenscroft Foundation, The
379
Saint Edmund King and Martyr
Trust *402*

Salamander Charitable Trust,
The *405*
Shelroy Charitable Trust, The
417
Simon's Charity *422*
Skelton Bounty, The *423*
South Square Trust *430*
Stonehouse Trust Ltd, Eric *438*
Sussman Charitable Trust,
Adrienne & Leslie *443*
Thompson Charitable Trust,
The *453*
Torquay Charities, The *458*
Turner Trust, The Douglas *464*
Victoria & Johnson Memorial
Trust, Queen *472*
Westcroft Trust *486*

....

■ Older people
Funding priority

AB Charitable Trust *3*
Ainsworth and Family
Benevolent Fund, Green
and Lilian F M *8*
Alexandra Rose Day *11*
Alexis Trust, The *11*
Arbib Trust, The Annie *20*
Assembled Church of Christ
Trust, The *25*
Assheton-Smith Charitable
Trust *25*
Austin of Longbridge Will
Trust, The Rt Hon Herbert,
Baron *27*
Baker Charitable Trust, The *30*
Balint Charitable Trust, Paul *31*
Barleycorn Trust, The *34*
Barratt Charitable Trust, The
Elaine *36*
Bateman Charitable Trust, Lady
Margaret *37*
Bentall Charity Trust, Rowan
44
Beresford Trust, The *44*
Betard Bequest *46*
Bibby 1981 Trust, The Mason
47
Bilton Charity, The Percy *48*
Birmingham Amenities and
Welfare Trust, The *49*
Bisgood Trust, The *50*
Bisgood's Charitable Trust, Miss
Jeanne *50*
Black Charitable Trust, The
Cyril W *51*
Black Charitable Trust, Edna
51
Black Charitable Trust, Sydney
51
Blackman Foundation, Isabel
52
Blagrave Charitable Trust, The
Herbert and Peter *52*
Blakenham's Charity Trust,
Lady *53*

Blott Charitable Settlement,
Robert Orpwood *55*
Bonhomie United Charity
Society *56*
Borthwick Memorial Trust, The
Oliver *56*
Bottom Charitable Trust, Harry
56
Bridge Trust, The *60*
Buccleuch Place Trust *67*
Buckingham Trust *67*
Burdall Charity, H M *69*
Butlin Charity Trust, Bill *72*
Cadbury Charitable Trust,
Richard *75*
Cam, Charity of Ann *78*
Cathedral Nursing Society
Charitable Trust *85*
Challice Trust, The *87*
Charity Projects *90*
Chase Charity, The *91*
Childwick Trust, The *93*
Christian Renewal Trust, The
94
Clover Trust *102*
Cobb Charity *103*
Cohen and William Leech
Foundation, Sebag *103*
Collins Charity, The George
Henry *106*
Collinson Charitable Trust, The
Norman *106*
Commonweal Fund of the
Trades House of Glasgow,
The *108*
Coote Old People's Charity
Fund, The Marjorie *112*
Cope Charitable Trust, Alfred
112
Corbett's Charity, Thomas *112*
Davenport's Charity Trust,
Baron *124*
Derbyshire Trust, J N *130*
Dibden Allotments Charity *132*
Djanogly Foundation, The *135*
Doughty Charity Trust, The
136
Dumbreck Charity *139*
Dunhill Medical Trust, The *140*
Earley Charity, The *142*
Eaton Fund for Artists, Nurses
and Gentlewomen *144*
Edgar Trust, The Gilbert *145*
Emerton-Christie Charity *150*
Englass Charitable Trust, The
151
Eventhall Family Charitable
Trust, The *155*
Eveson Charitable Trust, The
155
Family Trust, The *158*
Fogel Charitable Trust, The
Gerald *165*
Foresters' Charity Stewards UK
Trust, The *167*
Friarsgate Trust *172*
Frognal Trust *174*
GW Trust, The *176*

Gale Charitable Trust, A W *176*
Gatsby Charitable Foundation, The *179*
Gilley Charitable Trust, The L & R *183*
Gold Hill Church Trust *186*
Golders Green Foundation *187*
Grand Charity (of Freemasons under the United Grand Lodge of England), The *190*
Grange Farm Centre Trust *191*
Gray Trust, The *192*
Grimley Charity, The *196*
HACT (The Housing Association's Charitable Trust) *201*
HB Charitable Trust *201*
Hall Charitable Trust, E F & M G *204*
Hamlyn Foundation, The Helen *205*
Harding's Charity, William *209*
Harford Charitable Trust *209*
Hartley Memorial Trust, The N & P *211*
Hawthorne Charitable Trust, The *212*
Hertfordshire Community Trust, The *217*
Historic Churches Preservation Trust, The *221*
Hobbs Trust Limited, The Betty *222*
Homfray Trust, The *226*
Hopkins, The Charity of Joseph *227*
Horn Trust, The Cuthbert *227*
Hornby Charitable Trust, Miss D *227*
Hussey Trust, The *232*
Ibbett Trust, The *233*
Inman Charity, The *235*
Isle of Dogs Community Foundation *238*
Jacobsen Foundation Limited *240*
Jacobson Charitable Trust, The Yvette and Hermione *241*
Jewish Aged Needy Pension Society, The *245*
Johnson Foundation, The Beth *247*
Keller Charitable Trust, Samuel *251*
Kingston Old People's Home Fund for Ileostomists, The *256*
Kleinwort Charitable Trust, The Ernest *257*
Langdale Trust *264*
Lankelly Foundation, The *264*
Lawley Foundation, The Edgar E *267*
Lewis Family Charitable Trust, The *273*
Lloyd's Patriotic Fund *279*
(Lloyds) TSB Foundation for England and Wales *279*

Luke Trust, The *286*
Lynn Foundation, The *288*
McCarthy Foundation, The John *290*
McLaren Foundation *292*
Man of the People Fund *295*
Margadale Charitable Trust, Lord *297*
Merchant Taylors' Consolidated Charities for the Infirm *306*
Merchants House of Glasgow *307*
Metropolitan Hospital-Sunday Fund, The *308*
Mid Moss Charitable Trust, The *309*
Minet Trust, The Peter *313*
Moore Charitable Trust, The Horace *316*
Moores Family Charity Foundation, The *317*
Morrison Bequest Fund, Thomas Wharrie *320*
Murphy-Neumann Charity Company Limited *323*
Nash Charity, The *326*
Needham Cooper Charitable Trust, The *331*
Nidditch Foundation, The Laurie *335*
Ogilvie Charities (Deed No 2) *344*
Open Door Women's Trust *346*
Oppenheimer Charitable Trust *346*
Ormsby Charitable Trust, The *347*
PJD Charitable Trust *350*
Park Hill Trust, The *353*
Paul Charitable Trust, The Late Barbara May *355*
Paul Charitable Trust, Margaret Jeanne *355*
Paul Charitable Trust, Pamela Milton *355*
Pearson Foundation, The Frank *357*
Persula Foundation, The *360*
Pitt Trust, Headley *364*
Powell Foundation, The *367*
Prestwich Charitable Trust, The Douglas P *368*
Priestman Trust, S H and E C *368*
Proctor Charitable Trust, The Albert Edward *370*
REMEDI (Rehabilitation and Medical Research Trust) *374*
Rae Charity, H J *375*
Rangoonwala Foundation, ZVM *376*
Rayne Foundation, The *379*
Richards Charity, The Violet M *384*
Rickard Animals' Charity, Miss Maria Susan *385*
Rickard Cats' Charity, Miss Maria Susan *385*

Ridgmount Foundation, The *386*
Roberts Charitable Trust, F G *388*
Rocket Club Benevolent Fund, The *389*
Rosca Trust *391*
Royal Theatrical Fund, The *396*
Royal's Memorial Fund, Princess *396*
Shelroy Charitable Trust, The *417*
Skerritt Trust *423*
Slater Foundation Ltd, The *424*
Salter Trust Ltd *424*
Slaughter Charitable Trust, The Ernest William *425*
Smith (Estates Charities), Henry *426*
Smith Foundation, The Leslie *427*
Southon Charitable Trust, The *432*
Spalding Trust *433*
Sparkes Charitable Trust, The Eric F *433*
Stewart Trust, Sir Halley *437*
Street Charitable Foundation, W O *440*
Sugden-Wilson's Charitable Trust, Mrs Gabrielle Mary *441*
Swindon Charitable Trust, The Walter *445*
Sykes Trust, The Charles *445*
Thornton-Smith Trust, The *455*
Timson Family Charitable Trust *457*
Trust for London *461*
Turkish Women's Philanthropic Association of England *463*
Turner Charitable Settlement, The Sir Mark and Lady *464*
29th May 1961 Charity, The *465*
van Geest Foundation, The John and Lucille *470*
Van Neste Foundation, The *471*
Van Norden's Charitable Foundation, Mrs Maud *471*
Veronique Charitable Trust *472*
Vodafone Group Charitable Trust, The *474*
Wakeham Trust, The *476*
Wates Foundation, The *481*
Weinberg Foundation, The *483*
Weinstock Fund, The *484*
Whitley Trust, Sheila *491*
Williams Trust, The Neville *493*
Wilson Bequest Fund, The John *495*
Wiltshire Community Foundation *495*
Winham Foundation, The Francis *497*

Wix Charitable Trust, Michael and Anna *497*

Woburn 1986 Charitable Trust *498*

Wohl Charitable Foundation, The Maurice *498*

Wohl Charitable Trust, The Maurice *498*

Woodhouse Charitable Trust, Edwin *501*

Woodroffe Benton Foundation, The *502*

Workman Trust, The *503*

Yapp Welfare Trust, The *508*

Will consider

AHJ Charitable Trust, The *3*

Abrahams 2nd Charitable Foundation, The Henry and Grete *5*

Access 4 Trust *6*

Adnams Charity, The *7*

Allen Trust, Mrs M H *13*

Almshouse Association, The *14*

Ammco Trust, The *15*

Andrew Convalescent Trust, The Frederick *17*

Anstey Charitable Settlement, J C W *18*

Aquinas Trust *20*

Arts Council of Wales, The *23*

Astor Foundation, The *26*

Avenal *27*

BBC Children in Need Appeal, The *29*

Ballard Charitable Trust, The Stanton *32*

Ballinger Charitable Trust, The *32*

Beckwith Charitable Settlement, The Heather *39*

Behrens Charitable Trust, E M *40*

Beit Trust, The *40*

Bell Charitable Trust, John *41*

Benlian Trust, The *44*

Bergqvist Charitable Trust *44*

Betteshanger Charitable Trust *46*

Birtwistle Memorial Trust, The G E *50*

Bowland Charitable Trust, The *57*

Bramall Charitable Trust, The Tony *58*

Breast Cancer Research Trust, The *59*

British Dietetic Association General and Education Trust Fund, The *61*

Brook Charitable Trust *64*

Brotherton Trust, The Charles *65*

Buckinghamshire Masonic Centenary Fund *67*

Bulmer Charitable Trust, Becket *68*

Butler's Trust, Lord *71*

Butler's Trust, Lucilla *72*

Carnegie United Kingdom Trust, The *82*

Cazalet Charitable Trust, The Raymond *87*

Chandris Foundation, The *88*

Children's Research Fund, The *92*

Chownes Foundation, The *93*

Clinton's Charitable Trust, Lord *100*

Colt Foundation, The *107*

Condon Family Trust *109*

Coxen Trust Fund, Sir William *116*

Crawford Children's Charity, Michael *117*

Dacorum Community Trust *121*

Dahl Foundation, The Roald *122*

Dashe Trust, The *124*

David Trust, The Lesley *124*

De Yong Charitable Trust, The Emma *128*

De Yong's Charitable Trust 1984, Nicholas *128*

Dean Refugee Trust Fund, The Miriam *128*

Delius Trust, The *129*

Delmar Charitable Trust *129*

Denne Charitable Trust *130*

Denton Charitable Trust, The *130*

Desmond Charitable Trust, The Richard *131*

Digby Charitable Trust, Simon *133*

Dinam Charity *134*

Early's Charitable Settlement, Richard *142*

Egerton of Tatton Will Trust, Lord *146*

Emily Appeal Fund, The *150*

Fletcher Charitable Trust, The Joyce *164*

Franklin Deceased's New Second Charity, Sydney E *170*

French Charitable Trust, Charles S *171*

Gannochy Trust, The *177*

Garbacz Charitable Trust, The Bernard & Vera *178*

Gibson's Charity Trust, The Hon Mr & Mrs Clive *182*

Gill's Charitable Trust, Mrs M M *184*

Goodman Charitable Foundation, The Everard and Mina *188*

Granada Foundation, The *190*

Grant-Lawson Charitable Trust, Lady Virginia *192*

Greater Bristol Foundation *193*

Grocers' Charity *197*

Hanley Trust (1987), The *207*

Harding Trust, The *209*

Hinrichsen Foundation, The *221*

Hopkinson Educational Trust, Robert Addy *227*

Horne Foundation, The *228*

Hudson Charitable Trust, The *230*

Hurst Will Trust, Arthur *231*

Hutchinson Charitable Trust, E B *232*

Iris Trust, The *237*

Jackson Trust for Charity, The Isaac and Harriet *240*

Laing Charitable Trust, The David *260*

Lambourne Memorial Trust, The Emma *262*

Lane Foundation, The Allen *263*

Lee Foundation, The Edgar *269*

Levy Charitable Foundation, Joseph *272*

Lewis Foundation, The John Spedan *274*

Licensed Trade Charities Trust, The *274*

Littler Foundation, The Emile *277*

London Law Trust *280*

Lowenthal Charitable Trust, The L and C *285*

Lowndes Charitable Trust, The Vanessa *285*

Lunn-Rockliffe Charitable Trust, Paul *286*

Lyons Charitable Trust, The *288*

Lyon's Charity, John *288*

MacAndrew Trust, The E M *289*

McDougall Trust, The *291*

Marmor Charitable Trust, The Julie *299*

Material World Charitable Foundation Limited, The *301*

Maxwell Law Scholarship Trust, The Alexander *303*

Mellows Charitable Settlement, The Anthony and Elizabeth *305*

Mijoda Charitable Trust, The *310*

Milward Charity, The Edgar *313*

Minge's Gift *314*

Montefiore Trust, The David *316*

Moore Foundation, The George A *316*

Morgan Crucible Company plc Charitable Trust, The *319*

Mount Everest Foundation, The *321*

Music Sales Charitable Trust, The *324*

Nathan Charitable Trust *326*

New Durlston Trust, The *332*
Newby Trust Ltd *332*
Newcastle Children's Mission & Institute *333*
Newitt Fund, Richard *333*
Norman Family Charitable Trust, The *337*
Northcott Devon Foundation *338*
Oakdale Trust, The *343*
Oldham Foundation *345*
Oxford Trust, The *349*
Paget Trust, The *351*
Paragon Concert Society *352*
Pascoe Charitable Trust, Alan *354*
Peppiatt Charitable Trust, The Brian *359*
Pettit Charitable Trust *360*
Rank Benevolent Fund, Joseph *376*
Rayner Charitable Trust, The John *380*
Rest-Harrow Trust, The *382*
Robyn Charitable Trust *389*
Rokeby Charitable Trust *390*
Rolfe Charitable Trust, The *390*
Rookes Charitable Trust, C A *390*
Rothschild Group Charitable Trust, The J *393*
Rowntree Foundation, Joseph *394*
Said Foundation, The Karim Rida *401*
Sailors' and Soldiers' Home Fund, and Leonard Lionel Bloomfield's Charity, The *401*
St Hilda's Trust *403*
Sargeant's Charitable Trust, Mrs M E *407*
Scott Charitable Trust, The Francis C *412*
Seagram Distillers Charitable Trust *413*
Sharon Trust, The *416*
Shepherd Charitable Trust, The Sylvia and Colin *418*
Shepherd Family Charitable Trust, The Sir Peter *418*
Shuttleworth Memorial Trust, Barbara A *421*
Silvester Charitable Gift Trust *422*
South Square Trust *430*
Southdown Trust *432*
Spooner Charitable Trust, W W *434*
Stewards' Charitable Trust, The *437*
Summerfield Charitable Trust, The *442*
Thompson Memorial Fund, The Edwin John *453*
Thwaite Charitable Trust, The Daniel *456*

Travis Charitable Trust, Constance *460*
Van Berchem Charitable Trust, The Alec *470*
Vincent Trust Fund, Eric W *473*
Wall Trust, Thomas *478*
Wallington Missionary Mart & Auctions *478*
Wills 1961 Charitable Trust, Mr Frederick *493*
Wimpey Charitable Trust, The George *495*
Wincott Foundation, The *496*
Wingate Foundation, The Harold Hyam *496*
Woodhead Charitable Trust, Michael *501*
Woodlands Trust *501*
Woolf Charitable Trust, The *502*
Worms Charitable Trust, The Freda and Della *504*
Worshipful Company of Engineers' Charitable Trust Fund, The *504*
Wyford Charitable Trust, The *507*
Wylde Memorial Charity, The Anthony and Gwendoline *507*

■ One parent families

Funding priority
Ballinger Charitable Trust, The *32*
Blackburn Trust, The *51*
Carnegie United Kingdom Trust, The *82*
Four Winds Trust *168*
Homeless International *225*
Lane Foundation, The Allen *263*
Melchett Children's Trust, The Violet *305*
Wakeham Trust, The *476*

Will consider
Abbey National Charitable Trust *4*
Abel Charitable Trust *5*
Ashley Foundation, The Laura *24*
Astor Foundation, The *26*
Barnabas Charitable Trust *34*
Beckwith Charitable Settlement, The Heather *39*
Carlton Television Trust *81*
Cobb Charity *103*
Curzon Charitable Trust, The Wallace *120*
Dacorum Community Trust *121*
Earley Charity, The *142*
Emmandjay Charitable Trust *150*
Handicapped Children's Aid Committee *207*

Harford Charitable Trust *209*
Hiley Trust, Joseph and Mary *219*
Jackson Trust for Charity, The Isaac and Harriet *240*
Kyte Charitable Trust, The *259*
London Taxi Drivers' Fund for Underprivileged Children, The *280*
Low & Bonar Charitable Fund, The *284*
Marmor Charitable Trust, The Julie *299*
Mental Health Foundation, The *305*
Milburn Charitable Trust, Frederick *310*
Muslim Hands *324*
Newby Trust Ltd *332*
Noel Buxton Trust, The *335*
Norman Family Charitable Trust, The *337*
Older's School Charity, William *345*
Payne Trust, The Harry *356*
Reeve's Foundation *382*
Rest-Harrow Trust, The *382*
Riddleston Charity of Leicester, The Harry James *385*
Robinson Brothers (Ryders Green) Ltd, Charitable Trust *388*
Sargeant's Charitable Trust, Mrs M E *407*
Shepherd Charitable Trust, The Sylvia and Colin *418*
South Square Trust *430*
Southover Manor General Education Trust Ltd *433*
Truemark Trust, The *461*
Van Leer Foundation UK Trust, Bernard *470*
Variety Club Children's Charity Limited, The *471*
Wiltshire Community Foundation *495*

■ Opera
see also **Arts & arts facilities**
Funding priority
Arts Council of England, The *23*
Arts Council of Wales, The *23*
Delius Trust, The *129*
Elmchurch Trust, The *148*
Fletcher Charitable Trust, The Joyce *164*
Harding Trust, The *209*
Hinrichsen Foundation, The *221*
Hughes Charitable Trust, The Geoffery C *230*
North West Arts Board *337*
Northern Arts *339*
Royal Victoria Hall Foundation, The *396*

South Square Trust *430*
Tutton Charitable Trust, Miss
S M *465*
Yorkshire and Humberside Arts
510

Will consider
Allnatt Charitable Foundation,
Angus *14*
Anstey Charitable Settlement,
J C W *18*
Astor Foundation, The *26*
Beckwith Charitable
Settlement, The Heather *39*
Broadley Charitable Trust, The
64
Bulmer Charitable Trust, Becket
68
Cadbury Trust (1928), The
Edward & Dorothy *76*
Carnegie Dunfermline Trust *82*
Carnegie United Kingdom
Trust, The *82*
Coates Charitable Trust, The
John *103*
Colyer-Fergusson Charitable
Trust, The *107*
Cripplegate Foundation *118*
D'Avigdor Goldsmid Charitable
Trust, The Sarah *125*
Debtors' Relief Fund Charity
128
Digby Charitable Trust, Simon
133
Dixon Charitable Trust, F E *134*
Edgar Foundation, The Gilbert
and Eileen *145*
Finzi Charitable Trust, Gerald
162
Follett Trust, The *166*
Garnett Charitable Trust, The
178
Granada Foundation, The *190*
Great Britain Sasakawa
Foundation, The *193*
Greenaway Foundation, The Sir
Derek *194*
Halkes Settlement, John Robert
204
Hamlyn Foundation, The Paul
205
Hudson Benevolent Trust, The
Thomas *230*
Hunter Charitable Trust, The
Claire *231*
Inverforth Charitable Trust, The
236
Ireland Funds, The *237*
Laing Charitable Trust, The
David *260*
Laing Foundation, The
Christopher *260*
Leche Trust, The *268*
Lee Foundation, The Edgar
269
Lewis Foundation, The John
Spedan *274*

Linford Charitable Trust, The
Fred *276*
Lowenthal Charitable Trust,
The L and C *285*
Lower Hall Charitable Trust
285
Lynn Foundation, The *288*
Mackintosh Foundation, The
292
Milton Keynes Community
Trust Ltd, The *312*
Mitchell Trust, Esme *315*
Music Sales Charitable Trust,
The *324*
Needham Cooper Charitable
Trust, The *331*
New Court Charitable Trust
332
Notgrove Trust, The *341*
Oldham Foundation *345*
Owen Family Trust, The *348*
PF Charitable Trust *350*
Paragon Concert Society *352*
Payne Trust, The Harry *356*
Provincial Trust for Kendal, The
370
Reader's Digest Trust, The *380*
St Katharine & Shadwell Trust
404
Sobell Welsh People's
Charitable Association,
Michael *429*
Somerfield Curtis Will Trust,
The Dorothy *430*
Strauss Charitable Trust *440*
Summerfield Charitable Trust,
The *442*
Taylor Charitable Trust, The B R
450
Thomson Foundation, The Sue
454
Turner Trust, The Douglas *464*
Walker Trust, The *477*
Wates Charitable Trust, John
481
Wates Foundation, The *481*
Whitaker Charitable Trust *489*
Williams Charitable Trust,
Alfred *493*

....

■ **Opera buildings**
see **Theatres & opera
houses**

....

■ **Opera companies,
opera groups**
see also **Community arts &
recreation**

Funding priority
Calypso Browning Trust *78*
Carnegie United Kingdom
Trust, The *82*
Delius Trust, The *129*

Fletcher Charitable Trust, The
Joyce *164*
North West Arts Board *337*
Northern Arts *339*
Tutton Charitable Trust, Miss
S M *465*
Yorkshire and Humberside Arts
510

Will consider
Anstey Charitable Settlement,
J C W *18*
Arts Council of England, The
23
Beckwith Charitable
Settlement, The Heather *39*
Belmont Trust, The *42*
Blay Trust, The Robert *54*
Broadley Charitable Trust, The
64
Brooke Benevolent Fund,
William *65*
Bulmer Charitable Trust, Becket
68
Cadbury Trust (1928), The
Edward & Dorothy *76*
Carlton Television Trust *81*
Carnegie Dunfermline Trust *82*
Clifford Charity Oxford, The
100
County Durham Foundation
115
Debtors' Relief Fund Charity
128
Digby Charitable Trust, Simon
133
Dixon Charitable Trust, F E *134*
Edgar Foundation, The Gilbert
and Eileen *145*
Finzi Charitable Trust, Gerald
162
Fogel Charitable Trust, The
Gerald *165*
Follett Trust, The *166*
Granada Foundation, The *190*
Great Britain Sasakawa
Foundation, The *193*
Greenaway Foundation, The Sir
Derek *194*
Grocers' Charity *197*
Hamlyn Foundation, The Paul
205
Harding Trust, The *209*
Hinrichsen Foundation, The
221
Hudson Benevolent Trust, The
Thomas *230*
Hunter Charitable Trust, The
Claire *231*
Ireland Funds, The *237*
Lawley Foundation, The Edgar
E *267*
Leche Trust, The *268*
Lee Foundation, The Edgar
269
Lewis Foundation, The John
Spedan *274*

Littler Foundation, The Emile *277*

Lynn Foundation, The *288*

Mackintosh Foundation, The *292*

Milton Keynes Community Trust Ltd, The *312*

Mitchell Trust, Esme *315*

Needham Cooper Charitable Trust, The *331*

New Court Charitable Trust *332*

Northern Ireland Voluntary Trust *339*

Oldham Foundation *345*

Owen Family Trust, The *348*

PF Charitable Trust *350*

Paragon Concert Society *352*

Payne Trust, The Harry *356*

Persula Foundation, The *360*

Reader's Digest Trust, The *380*

Royal Victoria Hall Foundation, The *396*

St Katharine & Shadwell Trust *404*

Sobell Welsh People's Charitable Association, Michael *429*

South Square Trust *430*

Summerfield Charitable Trust, The *442*

Turner Trust, The Douglas *464*

Wates Charitable Trust, John *481*

Wates Foundation, The *481*

Whitaker Charitable Trust *489*

Williams Charitable Trust, Alfred *493*

■ Ophthalmology

see also **Medical studies & research**

Funding priority

Devon Association for the Blind *131*

Frost Charitable Trust, T F C *174*

Garthgwynion Charities *179*

Owen Trust, Margaret *348*

Wiseman Memorial Fund Limited, The Max *497*

■ Orchestras

see also **Community arts & recreation**

Funding priority

Calypso Browning Trust *78*

Carnegie United Kingdom Trust, The *82*

Delius Trust, The *129*

Finzi Charitable Trust, Gerald *162*

Fletcher Charitable Trust, The Joyce *164*

Hudson Benevolent Trust, The Thomas *230*

North West Arts Board *337*

Northern Arts *339*

Yorkshire and Humberside Arts *510*

Will consider

Anstey Charitable Settlement, J C W *18*

Arts Council of England, The *23*

Astor Foundation, The *26*

Belmont Trust, The *42*

Blay Trust, The Robert *54*

Broadley Charitable Trust, The *64*

Brooke Benevolent Fund, William *65*

Bulmer Charitable Trust, Becket *68*

Cadbury Trust (1928), The Edward & Dorothy *76*

Carlton Television Trust *81*

Carnegie Dunfermline Trust *82*

Clifford Charity Oxford, The *100*

Colyer-Fergusson Charitable Trust, The *107*

County Durham Foundation *115*

Debtors' Relief Fund Charity *128*

Digby Charitable Trust, Simon *133*

Dixon Charitable Trust, F E *134*

Dumbreck Charity *139*

Edgar Foundation, The Gilbert and Eileen *145*

Fogel Charitable Trust, The Gerald *165*

Granada Foundation, The *190*

Great Britain Sasakawa Foundation, The *193*

Greenaway Foundation, The Sir Derek *194*

Grocers' Charity *197*

Halkes Settlement, John Robert *204*

Hamlyn Foundation, The Paul *205*

Harbinson Charitable Trust, Roderick *208*

Harding Trust, The *209*

Hinrichsen Foundation, The *221*

Howard Charitable Trust, John & Ruth *229*

Hunter Charitable Trust, The Claire *231*

Ireland Funds, The *237*

JMK Charitable Trust *239*

Lawley Foundation, The Edgar E *267*

Lawson Charitable Trust, Raymond and Blanche *267*

Leche Trust, The *268*

Lee Foundation, The Edgar *269*

Lewis Foundation, The John Spedan *274*

Linford Charitable Trust, The Fred *276*

Littler Foundation, The Emile *277*

Lower Hall Charitable Trust *285*

Lynn Foundation, The *288*

Mackintosh Foundation, The *292*

Milton Keynes Community Trust Ltd, The *312*

Mitchell Trust, Esme *315*

Needham Cooper Charitable Trust, The *331*

New Court Charitable Trust *332*

Northern Ireland Voluntary Trust *339*

Notgrove Trust, The *341*

Oldham Foundation *345*

Owen Family Trust, The *348*

PF Charitable Trust *350*

Paragon Concert Society *352*

Payne Trust, The Harry *356*

Persula Foundation, The *360*

Reader's Digest Trust, The *380*

Ripley's Charitable Trust, Pat *386*

Rookes Charitable Trust, C A *390*

St Katharine & Shadwell Trust *404*

South Square Trust *430*

Summerfield Charitable Trust, The *442*

Turner Trust, The Douglas *464*

Wakefield (Tower Hill, Trinity Square) Trust *476*

Wander Charitable Fund, The Dr Albert *479*

Wates Charitable Trust, John *481*

Wates Foundation, The *481*

Whitaker Charitable Trust *489*

Williams Charitable Trust, Alfred *493*

■ Organic food production

see also **Environment & animal sciences**

Funding priority

Eaton Charitable Trust, J C J *143*

Paget Trust, The *351*

■ Ornithology & zoology

see also Environment & animal sciences

Funding priority

Cobb Charity *103*
GW Trust, The *176*

Will consider

Ashley Foundation, The Laura *24*
Astor Foundation, The *26*
Butler Charitable Trust, The A S *71*
Chippindale Foundation, Sam *93*
Clark 1965 Charitable Trust, Stephen *98*
Clutterbuck Charitable Trust, Robert *102*
Coates Charitable Trust 1969, Lance *103*
David Trust, The Lesley *124*
D'Avigdor Goldsmid Charitable Trust, The Sarah *125*
Digby Charitable Trust, Simon *133*
Earwicker Trust *142*
Great Britain Sasakawa Foundation, The *193*
Greenaway Foundation, The Sir Derek *194*
Horn Trust, The Cuthbert *227*
Isle of Dogs Community Foundation *238*
Laing Charitable Trust, The David *260*
Lloyd Charity, The S and D *278*
MacKintosh Charitable Trust, Viscount *292*
MacRobert Trusts, The *294*
Marchig Animal Welfare Trust *297*
Mattock Charitable Trust, The W T *302*
Measures Charity, The James Frederick and Ethel Anne *303*
Mitchell Trust *315*
Nathan Charitable Trust, Peter *326*
Oldham Foundation *345*
Owen Family Trust, The *348*
Pilkington Charitable Trust, Cecil *363*
Shaw Foundation, The Linley *416*
Whitaker Charitable Trust *489*
Young Explorers' Trust *511*

■ Outings

see Holidays & outings

■ Paediatric diseases

Funding priority

Children's Research Fund, The *92*
Toy Trust, The *459*

■ Parents & children

Funding priority

Access 4 Trust *6*
Artemis Charitable Trust, The *22*
Ballinger Charitable Trust, The *32*
Betteshanger Charitable Trust *46*
Blackburn Trust, The *51*
Carnegie United Kingdom Trust, The *82*
Four Winds Trust *168*
Hiley Trust, Joseph and Mary *219*
Homeless International *225*
Melchett Children's Trust, The Violet *305*
Rocket Club Benevolent Fund, The *389*
Wakeham Trust, The *476*

Will consider

Abbey National Charitable Trust *4*
Ashley Foundation, The Laura *24*
Astor Foundation, The *26*
Barnabas Charitable Trust *34*
Beckwith Charitable Settlement, The Heather *39*
Carlton Television Trust *81*
Cobb Charity *103*
Curzon Charitable Trust, The Wallace *120*
Dacorum Community Trust *121*
David Trust, The Lesley *124*
Emmandjay Charitable Trust *150*
Ferguson Benevolent Fund Limited *161*
GW Trust, The *176*
Gluckstein Charitable Settlement, The Penelope *185*
Handicapped Children's Aid Committee *207*
Jackson Trust for Charity, The Isaac and Harriet *240*
Kyte Charitable Trust, The *259*
Lane Foundation, The Allen *263*
Lass Charities Limited, Rachel and Jack *265*
Lloyd Charity, The S and D *278*
London Taxi Drivers' Fund for Underprivileged Children, The *280*

Marmor Charitable Trust, The Julie *299*
Measures Charity, The James Frederick and Ethel Anne *303*
Mental Health Foundation, The *305*
Milburn Charitable Trust, Frederick *310*
Milward Charity, The Edgar *313*
Moore Foundation, The George A *316*
Muslim Hands *324*
Newby Trust Ltd *332*
Noel Buxton Trust, The *335*
Paget Trust, The *351*
Payne Trust, The Harry *356*
Reeve's Foundation *382*
Shepherd Charitable Trust, The Sylvia and Colin *418*
South Square Trust *430*
Southover Manor General Education Trust Ltd *433*
Stevens Foundation, The June *437*
Thomson Foundation, The Sue *454*
Truemark Trust, The *461*
Van Leer Foundation UK Trust, Bernard *470*
Variety Club Children's Charity Limited, The *471*

■ Parkinson's disease

Funding priority

Elkes Charity Fund, The Wilfred & Elsie *147*

■ Parks

see also Community facilities

Funding priority

David Trust, The Lesley *124*
Isle of Dogs Community Foundation *238*
Knott Trust, Sir James *258*
Lancaster's Trust, Bryan *263*

Will consider

Angler's Inn Trust *17*
Ashley Foundation, The Laura *24*
Astor Foundation, The *26*
Astor of Hever Trust, The *26*
Boots Charitable Trust *56*
Bowland Charitable Trust, The *57*
Brand Trust, The *59*
Bullough Tompson Settlement, The *68*
Butler's Trust, Lord *71*
Campden Charities, The *79*
Carnegie Dunfermline Trust *82*

Clutterbuck Charitable Trust, Robert *102*
Cobb Charity *103*
Community Trust for Greater Manchester, The *108*
Curriers Company Charitable Fund *119*
Curzon Charitable Trust, The Wallace *120*
de Freitas Charitable Trust, The Helen and Geoffrey *126*
Digby Charitable Trust, Simon *133*
Direct Response *134*
Dulverton Trust, The *139*
Dumbreck Charity *139*
Edgar Foundation, The Gilbert and Eileen *145*
Education Services *145*
Elkes Charity Fund, The Wilfred & Elsie *147*
Fairway Trust, The *158*
Fletcher Trust, Roy *165*
Ford of Britain Trust *166*
Four Winds Trust *168*
Frognal Trust *174*
Gannochy Trust, The *177*
Grange Farm Centre Trust *191*
Great Britain Sasakawa Foundation, The *193*
Greenaway Foundation, The Sir Derek *194*
Gwent County Council Welsh Church Fund *200*
Harford Charitable Trust *209*
Hillards Charitable Trust, Gay & Peter Hartley's *220*
JCSCJ Charitable Trust, The *238*
Jewish Childs' Day *245*
Johnson Foundation, The *246*
Laing Charitable Trust, The David *260*
Laing Foundation, The Christopher *260*
Lee Foundation, The Edgar *269*
Lewis Partnership, John *274*
Littler Foundation, The Emile *277*
Living and Waking Naturally *278*
Lyndhurst Settlement *287*
Marriage's Charitable Trust, Miss G M *299*
Moore Foundation, The George A *316*
Morel Charitable Trust, The *318*
Newby Trust Ltd *332*
Norfolk's Family Charitable Trust, Lavinia *336*
North West Arts Board *337*
Payne Trust, The Harry *356*
Porter Foundation *366*
Reekie Trust, R A & V B *381*
St Katharine & Shadwell Trust *404*

Scott Charitable Trust, The Francis C *412*
Sheepdrove Trust, The *417*
Shepherd Family Charitable Trust, The Sir Peter *418*
Skelton Bounty, The *423*
Spoore, Merry & Rixman Foundation, The *434*
Stevens Foundation, The June *437*
Summerfield Charitable Trust, The *442*
Swan Mountain Trust *444*
Symons Charitable Trust, The Stella *446*
TSB Foundation for Scotland *447*
Wall Trust, Thomas *478*
Wesleyan Charitable Trust, The *485*
Whitaker Charitable Trust *489*
Wills 1961 Charitable Trust, Mr Frederick *493*
Women Caring Trust, The *500*
Wylde Memorial Charity, The Anthony and Gwendoline *507*

■ **Pastoral care**
see Community services

■ **Peace**
see Campaigning (social issues)

■ **Peace studies**
see Academic subjects, sciences & research
see also Campaigning (social issues)

■ **Penal reform (campaigning)**
Funding priority
Fleurus Trust, The *165*
Lyndhurst Settlement *287*

■ **Performing arts**
see Arts

■ **Personal development**
see Training for personal development

■ **Personnel & human resource services**
see also Infrastructure & technical support
Will consider
Aston Charities Trust Ltd *25*
Berkshire Community Trust *45*
Clifford Charity Oxford, The *100*
Collier Charitable Trust, The *105*
County Durham Foundation *115*
Daily Telegraph Charitable Trust *122*
Digby Charitable Trust, Simon *133*
Egerton of Tatton Will Trust, Lord *146*
Homeless International *225*
Hyde Park Place Estate Charity, The *232*
IBM United Kingdom Trust *233*
Ireland Funds, The *237*
Iris Trust, The *237*
Isle of Dogs Community Foundation *238*
Lane Foundation, The Allen *263*
Licensed Trade Charities Trust, The *274*
Northern Arts *339*
Paristamen Foundation, The *352*
Scott Bader Commonwealth Ltd, The *411*
Skelton Bounty, The *423*
Tear Fund *450*
Wakefield (Tower Hill, Trinity Square) Trust *476*
Whitaker Charitable Trust *489*

■ **Physical impairment**
see Disabled people (physical, sensory, learning impairments)

■ **Physics**
see also Academic subjects, sciences & research
Funding priority
Royal Commission for the Exhibition of 1851 *395*

Will consider
Beit Trust, The *40*
Cassel Educational Trust (Mountbatten Memorial Grants to Commonwealth Students), The Sir Ernest *84*

Coutts Charitable Trust, The
116

Digby Charitable Trust, Simon
133

Holly Hill Charitable Trust 224

Humanitarian Trust, The 230

Worshipful Company of
Engineers' Charitable Trust
Fund, The 504

■ Playgrounds

see also Community
facilities

Funding priority

Angler's Inn Trust 17

Aston Charities Trust Ltd 25

Blakey Charitable Trust, The
Celia and Conrad 53

Bowland Charitable Trust, The
57

Butler's Trust, Lord 71

Fairway Trust, The 158

Gluckstein Charitable
Settlement, The Penelope
185

Grange Farm Centre Trust 191

Hudson Benevolent Trust, The
Thomas 230

Isle of Dogs Community
Foundation 238

Lancaster's Trust, Bryan 263

Peirce Memorial Trust, The Joe
358

Rayner Charitable Trust, The
John 380

Spoore, Merry & Rixman
Foundation, The 434

Toy Trust, The 459

Will consider

Ammco Trust, The 15

Amory Charitable Trust,
Viscount 16

Aquarius Charitable
Foundation, The 19

Archer Trust, The 20

Ashley Foundation, The Laura
24

Askew Trust, The Dorothy 25

Astor of Hever Trust, The 26

BBC Children in Need Appeal,
The 29

Barbour Trust, The 33

Barratt Charitable Trust, The
Elaine 36

Berkshire Community Trust 45

Blanchminster Trust, The 54

Boots Charitable Trust 56

Brand Trust, The 59

Bridge Trust, The 60

Brough Charitable Trust,
Joseph 65

Buckinghamshire Masonic
Centenary Fund 67

Bullough Tompson Settlement,
The 68

Burton 1960 Charitable
Settlement, Audrey &
Stanley 70

CLA Charitable Trust 74

Campden Charities, The 79

Carnegie Dunfermline Trust 82

Challice Trust, The 87

Chapman Foundation 88

Chrimes Family Charitable
Trust, The 93

Clifford Charity Oxford, The
100

Clinton's Charitable Trust, Lord
100

Clutterbuck Charitable Trust,
Robert 102

Community Trust for Greater
Manchester, The 108

County Durham Foundation
115

Coutts Charitable Trust, The
116

Curriers Company Charitable
Fund 119

Curzon Charitable Trust, The
Wallace 120

de Freitas Charitable Trust, The
Helen and Geoffrey 126

Derbyshire Trust, J N 130

Digby Charitable Trust, Simon
133

Direct Response 134

Dixon Charitable Trust, F E 134

Dulverton Trust, The 139

Dumbreck Charity 139

Ebb and Flow Charitable Trust
144

Edgar Foundation, The Gilbert
and Eileen 145

Education Services 145

Elkes Charity Fund, The Wilfred
& Elsie 147

Emmandjay Charitable Trust
150

Fletcher Charitable Trust, The
Joyce 164

Fletcher Trust, Roy 165

Ford of Britain Trust 166

Four Lanes Trust, The 168

Four Winds Trust 168

Frognal Trust 174

Gannochy Trust, The 177

Gardner Charitable Trust, R & J
178

Grant Foundation, The
Raymond 191

Grant-Lawson Charitable Trust,
Lady Virginia 192

Great Britain Sasakawa
Foundation, The 193

Grocers' Charity 197

Grundy Foundation, The
Stanley 198

Gwent County Council Welsh
Church Fund 200

Hamlyn Foundation, The Paul
205

Hannay Charitable Trust, The
Lennox 208

Hannay Memorial Charity,
Kathleen 208

Harford Charitable Trust 209

Hartley Memorial Trust, The N
& P 211

Hertfordshire Community
Trust, The 217

Hillards Charitable Trust, Gay &
Peter Hartley's 220

Homfray Trust, The 226

Ingles Charitable Trust, The
234

JCSCJ Charitable Trust, The
238

JDM Charitable Trust 239

Jewish Childs' Day 245

Johnson Foundation, The 246

Johnson Group Cleaners
Charity 247

Knott Trust, Sir James 258

Laing Charitable Trust, The
David 260

Laing Foundation, The
Christopher 260

Leach Fourteenth Trust, The
267

Lee Foundation, The Edgar
269

Leech Charity, The William 269

Lewis Partnership, John 274

Littler Foundation, The Emile
277

Living and Waking Naturally
278

(Lloyds) TSB Foundation for
England and Wales 279

Lord's Taverners, The 281

Mackintosh Foundation, The
292

Marchday Charitable Fund, The
296

Margaret Foundation, The 297

Marriage's Charitable Trust,
Miss G M 299

Middlesex County Rugby
Football Union Memorial
Fund 309

Moore Foundation, The
George A 316

Morel Charitable Trust, The
318

NR Charitable Trust, The 325

National Power Charitable
Trust, The 330

Needham Cooper Charitable
Trust, The 331

Newby Trust Ltd 332

Norfolk's Family Charitable
Trust, Lavinia 336

Norman Family Charitable
Trust, The 337

North West Arts Board 337

Northcott Devon Foundation
338

Norton Foundation, The 340

Norwich Church of England
Young Men's Society *340*
Oakdale Trust, The *343*
Owen Family Trust, The *348*
PF Charitable Trust *350*
Parivar Trust, The *353*
Paterson Charitable
Foundation, The Constance
354
Paterson Charitable Trust,
Arthur James *354*
Patients' Aid Association
Hospital and Medical
Charities Trust *354*
Payne Trust, The Harry *356*
Persula Foundation, The *360*
Pilkington Trust, The Austin
and Hope *363*
Porter Foundation *366*
Provincial Trust for Kendal, The
370
Pye Christian Trust, The *371*
Pyke Charity Trust *372*
Reekie Trust, R A & V B *381*
Richard Charitable Trust, The
Cliff *383*
Rookes Charitable Trust, C A
390
Rothley Trust, The *392*
Royle Memorial Trust, Kirstin
397
Rugby Football Union
Charitable Fund, The *398*
SMB Trust, The *400*
St Katharine & Shadwell Trust
404
Saint Sarkis Charity Trust *404*
Scott Charitable Trust, The
Francis C *412*
Shelroy Charitable Trust, The
417
Shepherd Family Charitable
Trust, The Sir Peter *418*
Skelton Bounty, The *423*
Sobell Welsh People's
Charitable Association,
Michael *429*
Stevens Foundation, The June
437
Stoate Charitable Trust, The
Leonard Laity *438*
Summerfield Charitable Trust,
The *442*
Swan Mountain Trust *444*
Symons Charitable Trust, The
Stella *446*
TSB Foundation for Northern
Ireland *447*
TSB Foundation for Scotland
447
Tisbury Telegraph Trust, The
457
Torquay Charities, The *458*
Towler Charity Trust, The Fred
459
Travis Charitable Trust,
Constance *460*
Truemark Trust, The *461*

Tyne & Wear Foundation *466*
Wakefield (Tower Hill, Trinity
Square) Trust *476*
Wall Trust, Thomas *478*
Wander Charitable Fund, The
Dr Albert *479*
Wates Foundation, The *481*
Wesleyan Charitable Trust, The
485
Whitaker Charitable Trust *489*
Whitehall Charitable
Foundation Limited *490*
Wills 1961 Charitable Trust, Mr
Frederick *493*
Wolfe Family's Charitable
Trust, The *498*
Women Caring Trust, The *500*
Wylde Memorial Charity, The
Anthony and Gwendoline
507
Yorkshire Bank Charitable
Trust, The *510*

....

■ Playschemes

see also Community
services

Funding priority

Army Benevolent Fund, The *22*
Aston Charities Trust Ltd *25*
Blackburn Trust, The *51*
Challice Trust, The *87*
Christmas Cracker Trust *95*
Community Trust for Greater
Manchester, The *108*
County Durham Foundation
115
Curriers Company Charitable
Fund *119*
Egerton of Tatton Will Trust,
Lord *146*
Fletcher Charitable Trust, The
Joyce *164*
Gluckstein Charitable
Settlement, The Penelope
185
Hartley Memorial Trust, The N
& P *211*
Hudson Benevolent Trust, The
Thomas *230*
Humphreys Charitable
Settlement, J A M *231*
Ingles Charitable Trust, The
234
Isle of Dogs Community
Foundation *238*
Lancaster's Trust, Bryan *263*
Minet Trust, The Peter *313*
Moores Foundation, John *318*
Nunburnholme Trust, The
Incorporated Trustees of the
342
Roedean School Mission Fund
390
SMB Trust, The *400*
St Katharine & Shadwell Trust
404

TSB Foundation for Scotland
447
Toy Trust, The *459*
Wade & Others, The Charity of
Thomas *475*
Wedge, The *483*

Will consider

AB Charitable Trust *3*
Access 4 Trust *6*
Ammco Trust, The *15*
Amory Charitable Trust,
Viscount *16*
Archer Trust, The *20*
Barbour Trust, The *33*
Barratt Charitable Trust, The
Elaine *36*
Berkshire Community Trust *45*
BibleLands *47*
Blakenham's Charity Trust,
Lady *53*
Blanchminster Trust, The *54*
Boots Charitable Trust *56*
Bowland Charitable Trust, The
57
Bridge Trust, The *60*
Brighton & Hove Charitable
Youth Trust *60*
Brotherton Trust, The Charles
65
Brough Charitable Trust,
Joseph *65*
Buckinghamshire Masonic
Centenary Fund *67*
Burton 1960 Charitable
Settlement, Audrey &
Stanley *70*
CLA Charitable Trust *74*
Camelot Foundation, The *78*
Campden Charities, The *79*
Carlton Television Trust *81*
Carnegie Dunfermline Trust *82*
Chapman Foundation *88*
Chrimes Family Charitable
Trust, The *93*
Clinton's Charitable Trust, Lord
100
Cloudesley's Charity/School
Parents & Friends
Association, Richard *102*
Coutts Charitable Trust, The
116
Curzon Charitable Trust, The
Wallace *120*
de Freitas Charitable Trust, The
Helen and Geoffrey *126*
Derbyshire Trust, J N *130*
Digby Charitable Trust, Simon
133
Direct Response *134*
Dorus Trust *136*
Dumbreck Charity *139*
Ebb and Flow Charitable Trust
144
Edgar Trust, The Gilbert *145*
Elkes Charity Fund, The Wilfred
& Elsie *147*

Emmandjay Charitable Trust 150
Fairway Trust, The 158
Ferguson Benevolent Fund Limited 161
Fletcher Trust, Roy 165
Four Lanes Trust, The 168
Four Winds Trust 168
Franklin Trust, Jill 170
Gibbins Trust, The 181
Grant Foundation, The Raymond 191
Grant-Lawson Charitable Trust, Lady Virginia 192
Grocers' Charity 197
Grosshill Charitable Trust 197
Halkes Settlement, John Robert 204
Hamlyn Foundation, The Paul 205
Harford Charitable Trust 209
Hertfordshire Community Trust, The 217
Homfray Trust, The 226
Ireland Funds, The 237
JMK Charitable Trust 239
Jarman Charitable Trust, The 243
Johnson Foundation, The 246
Knott Trust, Sir James 258
Kyte Charitable Trust, The 259
Laing Foundation, The Christopher 260
Lankelly Foundation, The 264
Lawson Charitable Trust, Raymond and Blanche 267
Leech Charity, The William 269
Lewis Partnership, John 274
(Lloyds) TSB Foundation for England and Wales 279
London Taxi Drivers' Fund for Underprivileged Children, The 280
Lowe Trust, Mrs D G 285
Mackintosh Foundation, The 292
Manning Trust, Leslie & Lilian 296
Marchday Charitable Fund, The 296
Margaret Foundation, The 297
Measures Charity, The James Frederick and Ethel Anne 303
Melchett Children's Trust, The Violet 305
Mental Health Foundation, The 305
Middlesex County Rugby Football Union Memorial Fund 309
Milburn Charitable Trust, Frederick 310
Milton Keynes Community Trust Ltd, The 312
NR Charitable Trust, The 325
National Power Charitable Trust, The 330

Needham Cooper Charitable Trust, The 331
New Court Charitable Trust 332
Newby Trust Ltd 332
Noel Buxton Trust, The 335
Norman Family Charitable Trust, The 337
North West Arts Board 337
Northcott Devon Foundation 338
Norton Foundation, The 340
Norwich Church of England Young Men's Society 340
Oakdale Trust, The 343
Oldham Foundation 345
PF Charitable Trust 350
Parivar Trust, The 353
Paterson Charitable Foundation, The Constance 354
Paterson Charitable Trust, Arthur James 354
Patients' Aid Association Hospital and Medical Charities Trust 354
Payne Trust, The Harry 356
Persula Foundation, The 360
Porter Foundation 366
Powell Foundation, The 367
Provincial Trust for Kendal, The 370
Pyke Charity Trust 372
Ravenscroft Foundation, The 379
Rayner Charitable Trust, The John 380
Richard Charitable Trust, The Cliff 383
Rothley Trust, The 392
Rowbotham Charitable Trust, The Christopher 393
Sainsbury Charitable Fund Ltd, The 402
Saint Edmund King and Martyr Trust 402
Seagram Distillers Charitable Trust 413
Shepherd Family Charitable Trust, The Sir Peter 418
Skelton Bounty, The 423
Sparkhill Trust, The 433
Stevens Foundation, The June 437
Stoate Charitable Trust, The Leonard Laity 438
Summerfield Charitable Trust, The 442
Sussman Charitable Trust, Adrienne & Leslie 443
Swan Mountain Trust 444
TSB Foundation for Northern Ireland 447
Tear Fund 450
Thomson Foundation, The Sue 454
Tisbury Telegraph Trust, The 457

Torquay Charities, The 458
Towler Charity Trust, The Fred 459
Tyne & Wear Foundation 466
Van Leer Foundation UK Trust, Bernard 470
Wakefield (Tower Hill, Trinity Square) Trust 476
Wakeham Trust, The 476
Wall Trust, Thomas 478
Wates Foundation, The 481
Wesleyan Charitable Trust, The 485
Westcroft Trust 486
Whitaker Charitable Trust 489
Whitecourt Charitable Trust, The 490
Wills 1961 Charitable Trust, Mr Frederick 493
Women Caring Trust, The 500
Wright Deceased Trust, John William 506
Wylde Memorial Charity, The Anthony and Gwendoline 507
Yorkshire Bank Charitable Trust, The 510

....

■ **Poets**
see Writers & poets

....

■ **Polio**
Funding priority
Hodge Foundation, The Jane 223

....

■ **Poor**
see Disadvantaged by poverty

....

■ **Postgraduate education**
see also Schools & colleges
Funding priority
Jeffreys Road Fund, Rees 243
Woolmen's Company Charitable Trust, The 503

....

■ **Poverty**
see Disadvantaged by poverty

■ Pre-school education

see also Schools & colleges

Funding priority

BBC Children in Need Appeal, The 29

Catholic Education Service for England and Wales 86

Christmas Cracker Trust 95

Clark Charitable Trust, J Anthony 98

Community Trust for Greater Manchester, The 108

County Durham Foundation 115

Cripplegate Foundation 118

Dulverton Trust, The 139

Ebb and Flow Charitable Trust 144

Hertfordshire Community Trust, The 217

Ingles Charitable Trust, The 234

Isle of Dogs Community Foundation 238

Roedean School Mission Fund 390

St Katharine & Shadwell Trust 404

Will consider

Amory Charitable Trust, Viscount 16

Archer Trust, The 20

Arts Council of Wales, The 23

Berkshire Community Trust 45

BibleLands 47

Boots Charitable Trust 56

Buckinghamshire Masonic Centenary Fund 67

Bulmer Charitable Trust, Becket 68

Camelot Foundation, The 78

Campbell Charitable Foundation, The Ellis 79

Carlton Television Trust 81

Carnegie Dunfermline Trust 82

Chrimes Family Charitable Trust, The 93

Commonwealth Relations Trust 108

Derbyshire Trust, J N 130

Dibden Allotments Charity 132

Digby Charitable Trust, Simon 133

Dixon Charitable Trust, F E 134

Elkes Charity Fund, The Wilfred & Elsie 147

Emmandjay Charitable Trust 150

Ferguson Benevolent Fund Limited 161

Four Lanes Trust, The 168

Four Winds Trust 168

Garnett Charitable Trust, The 178

Hamlyn Foundation, The Paul 205

Hillards Charitable Trust, Gay & Peter Hartley's 220

Hudson Benevolent Trust, The Thomas 230

Hussey for Africans, Charity of Rebecca 231

Ireland Funds, The 237

JMK Charitable Trust 239

Jewish Childs' Day 245

Lawson Charitable Trust, Raymond and Blanche 267

Leadbeater Trust, The Alfred 268

Leech Charity, The William 269

Littler Foundation, The Emile 277

(Lloyds) TSB Foundation for England and Wales 279

Low & Bonar Charitable Fund, The 284

Milton Keynes Community Trust Ltd, The 312

Milward Charity, The Edgar 313

Minet Trust, The Peter 313

Montefiore Trust, The David 316

NR Charitable Trust, The 325

National Lottery Charities Board 328

Newby Trust Ltd 332

Newcomen Collett Foundation 333

Notgrove Trust, The 341

Oldham Foundation 345

Owen Family Trust, The 348

Patients' Aid Association Hospital and Medical Charities Trust 354

Powell Foundation, The 367

Prendergast Charitable Trust, The Simone 368

Provincial Trust for Kendal, The 370

Pyke Charity Trust 372

Ravenscroft Foundation, The 379

Rayner Charitable Trust, The John 380

Reader's Digest Trust, The 380

Salters Charities 405

Sheepdrove Trust, The 417

Shepherd Charitable Trust, The Sylvia and Colin 418

Simon's Charity 422

Skelton Bounty, The 423

Stevens Foundation, The June 437

Stoate Charitable Trust, The Leonard Laity 438

Stonehouse Trust Ltd, Eric 438

Summerfield Charitable Trust, The 442

TSB Foundation for Northern Ireland 447

Tear Fund 450

Thomson Foundation, The Sue 454

Tisbury Telegraph Trust, The 457

Torquay Charities, The 458

Van Leer Foundation UK Trust, Bernard 470

Wakefield (Tower Hill, Trinity Square) Trust 476

Wall Trust, Thomas 478

Whitehead Charitable Trust, J E 490

Wills 1961 Charitable Trust, Mr Frederick 493

Wylde Memorial Charity, The Anthony and Gwendoline 507

■ Prevention of disease

see Health education

■ Primary health care

see also Health care

Funding priority

Allied Dunbar Charitable Trust Limited, The 13

Birmingham Amenities and Welfare Trust, The 49

Coxen Trust Fund, Sir William 116

Davis Charitable Trust, Wilfrid Bruce 126

Grant Charitable Trust, The 191

Heath Charitable Trust 214

Kroch Foundation, The Heinz & Anna 259

Lawson Charitable Trust, Raymond and Blanche 267

Lloyd's Charities Trust 278

Parivar Trust, The 353

SMB Trust, The 400

Strangward Trust, The 439

Will consider

Ammco Trust, The 15

Army Benevolent Fund, The 22

Astor Foundation, The 26

Beckwith Charitable Settlement, The Heather 39

BibleLands 47

Birtwistle Memorial Trust, The G E 50

Bottom Charitable Trust, Harry 56

Bourne-May Charitable Trust, The 57

British Dietetic Association General and Education Trust Fund, The 61

Commonwealth Relations Trust 108

Coutts Charitable Trust, The 116

Curzon Charitable Trust, The Wallace 120

Dean Refugee Trust Fund, The Miriam 128

Digby Charitable Trust, Simon 133

Direct Response 134

Dorus Trust 136

Earley Charity, The 142

Edgar Foundation, The Gilbert and Eileen 145

Edgar Trust, The Gilbert 145

Elkes Charity Fund, The Wilfred & Elsie 147

Emmandjay Charitable Trust 150

Epigoni Trust 152

Follett Trust, The 166

Foreman Foundation, The Carl & Eve 167

Gibbins Trust, The 181

Good Neighbours Trust, The 188

Grant Foundation, The Raymond 191

Gray Charitable Trust, R B 192

Great Britain Sasakawa Foundation, The 193

Greenaway Foundation, The Sir Derek 194

Grocers' Charity 197

Hawley Residuary Fund, Harry Fieldsend 212

Innes Memorial Fund 235

Isle of Dogs Community Foundation 238

Laing Foundation, The Kirby 261

Leech Charity, The William 269

Linmardon Trust 276

Lloyd Charity, The S and D 278

London Law Trust 280

Lowenthal Charitable Trust, The L and C 285

Lynall Foundation, The D G 287

Manning Trust, Leslie & Lilian 296

Mental Health Foundation, The 305

Middlesex County Rugby Football Union Memorial Fund 309

Needham Cooper Charitable Trust, The 331

New Court Charitable Trust 332

Penny in the Pound Fund Charitable Trust 359

Rowbotham Charitable Trust, The Christopher 393

Seagram Distillers Charitable Trust 413

South Square Trust 430

Stonehouse Trust Ltd, Eric 438

Tear Fund 450

Thompson Charitable Trust, The 453

Tisbury Telegraph Trust, The 457

Travis Charitable Trust, Constance 460

Tudor Trust, The 463

Van Leer Foundation UK Trust, Bernard 470

....

■ Primary schools

see also Schools & colleges

Funding priority

Catholic Education Service for England and Wales 86

Christmas Cracker Trust 95

Clark Charitable Trust, J Anthony 98

Dulverton Trust, The 139

Hillards Charitable Trust, Gay & Peter Hartley's 220

Humphreys Charitable Settlement, J A M 231

Hussey for Africans, Charity of Rebecca 231

Ingles Charitable Trust, The 234

Newman's Charity, John 334

St Katharine & Shadwell Trust 404

Will consider

Archer Trust, The 20

Arts Council of Wales, The 23

BBC Children in Need Appeal, The 29

BibleLands 47

Boots Charitable Trust 56

Buckinghamshire Masonic Centenary Fund 67

Bulmer Charitable Trust, Becket 68

Campbell Charitable Foundation, The Ellis 79

Carlton Television Trust 81

Carnegie Dunfermline Trust 82

Chrimes Family Charitable Trust, The 93

Commonwealth Relations Trust 108

Cripplegate Foundation 118

Derbyshire Trust, J N 130

Dibden Allotments Charity 132

Digby Charitable Trust, Simon 133

Direct Response 134

Dixon Charitable Trust, F E 134

Ebb and Flow Charitable Trust 144

Elkes Charity Fund, The Wilfred & Elsie 147

Emmandjay Charitable Trust 150

Ferguson Benevolent Fund Limited 161

Four Lanes Trust, The 168

Four Winds Trust 168

Garnett Charitable Trust, The 178

Goldsmiths' Company's Charities, The 188

Great Britain Sasakawa Foundation, The 193

Hamlyn Foundation, The Paul 205

Howard Charitable Trust, John & Ruth 229

Hudson Benevolent Trust, The Thomas 230

Ireland Funds, The 237

Isle of Dogs Community Foundation 238

JMK Charitable Trust 239

Jewish Childs' Day 245

Leonard Trust, The Mark 271

Lewis Foundation, The John Spedan 274

Linmardon Trust 276

Littler Foundation, The Emile 277

Mackintosh Foundation, The 292

Marriage's Charitable Trust, Miss G M 299

Milward Charity, The Edgar 313

Montefiore Trust, The David 316

Newby Trust Ltd 332

Newcomen Collett Foundation 333

Oldham Foundation 345

Owen Family Trust, The 348

Provincial Trust for Kendal, The 370

Pye Christian Trust, The 371

Pyke Charity Trust 372

Ravenscroft Foundation, The 379

Rhodes Trust – Public Purposes Fund, The 383

Salters Charities 405

Sheepdrove Trust, The 417

Simon's Charity 422

Skelton Bounty, The 423

Sport Aid 88 Trust 434

Summerfield Charitable Trust, The 442

Tear Fund 450

Tisbury Telegraph Trust, The 457

Torquay Charities, The 458

Travis Charitable Trust, Constance 460

Upjohn Charitable Trust, The 469

Van Leer Foundation UK Trust, Bernard 470

Wakefield (Tower Hill, Trinity Square) Trust 476

Wall Trust, Thomas 478

Wates Foundation, The 481

Whitehead Charitable Trust, J E 490

Wills 1961 Charitable Trust, Mr
Frederick *493*
Woodroffe Benton Foundation,
The *502*
Wylde Memorial Charity, The
Anthony and Gwendoline
507
Yorkshire Agricultural Society
509

....

■ Printing

see **Publishing & printing**

....

■ Prison reform

see **Penal reform
(campaigning)**

....

■ Professional bodies

see also **Health professional
bodies, Social care
professional bodies**

Funding priority

Aga Khan Foundation (UK) *7*
Berkshire Community Trust *45*
Franklin Trust, Jill *170*
International Bar Association
Educational Trust *236*
Lacy Charity Trust, The Late Sir
Pierce *260*

Will consider

AHJ Charitable Trust, The *3*
Achiezer Association Limited *6*
Airflow Community Ltd, The *9*
Ajahma Charitable Trust, The
9
Aleh Charitable Foundation,
The *10*
Allachy Trust, The *12*
Anderson Trust, Andrew *16*
Andrew Charitable Trust, The
Prince *16*
Angler's Inn Trust *17*
Appelbe Trust, Ambrose & Ann
19
Aquarius Charitable
Foundation, The *19*
Aquinas Trust *20*
Askew Charitable Trust, The
Ian *25*
Assembled Church of Christ
Trust, The *25*
Assheton-Smith Charitable
Trust *25*
Astor of Hever Trust, The *26*
Astor's 1969 Charity, The Hon
M L *26*
Barbour Trust, The *33*
Barnby's Foundation, Lord *35*
Barnsbury Charitable Trust *35*
Barton Trust, Eleanor *37*
Bateman Charitable Trust, Lady
Margaret *37*

Bealey Foundation, The *38*
Beckwith Charitable Trust, The
Peter *40*
Beckwith-Smith's Charitable
Settlement, Mrs *40*
Bergqvist Charitable Trust *44*
Black Foundation, The Bertie
51
Blagrave Charitable Trust, The
Herbert and Peter *52*
Blakenham's Charity Trust,
Lady *53*
Blakey Charitable Trust, The
Celia and Conrad *53*
Blank Donations Ltd, The David
54
Boltons Trust, The *55*
Borthwick Memorial Trust, The
Oliver *56*
Bottom Charitable Trust, Harry
56
Bowland Charitable Trust, The
57
British Sugar Foundation *63*
Brook Charitable Settlement,
R E *64*
Brookhouse's Will Trust, Mr
John Charles *65*
Brotherton Trust, The Charles
65
Burn Charity Trust, The J H *70*
Burns Charity, The Dorothy *70*
Burry Charitable Trust, The *70*
Butler's Trust, Lord *71*
Butler's Trust, Lucilla *72*
Cadbury Schweppes
Foundation, The *76*
Cardiff & Swansea Methodist
District Charitable Trust
Fund *80*
Carron Charitable Trust, The
83
Castang Charitable Trust, H
and M *85*
Charity Projects *90*
Chrimes Family Charitable
Trust, The *93*
Christian Aid *94*
Cinderford Charitable Trust,
The *96*
Clark Charitable Trust, J
Anthony *98*
Closehelm Ltd *101*
Clutterbuck Charitable Trust,
Robert *102*
Coates Charitable Settlement,
The *102*
Coates Charitable Trust 1969,
Lance *103*
Cohen Charitable Trust, The
Vivienne and Samuel *104*
Cohen Charity Trust, Lucy *104*
Collier Charitable Trust, The
105
Company of Tobacco Pipe
Makers and Tobacco
Blenders Benevolent Fund
109

Condon Family Trust *109*
Cope Charitable Trust, Alfred
112
Crescent Trust, The *117*
Cripplegate Foundation *118*
Curry Charitable Trust, Dennis
119
Cymerman Trust Limited,
Itzchok Meyer *120*
Daily Telegraph Charitable
Trust *122*
Dandeen Charitable Trust *123*
Davy Foundation, The J *126*
De Avenley Foundation, The
126
De La Rue Charitable Trust
127
De Rothschild 1981 Charitable
Trust, The Edmund *127*
De Yong Charitable Trust, The
Emma *128*
Delmar Charitable Trust *129*
Denne Charitable Trust *130*
Denton Charitable Trust, The
130
Desmond Charitable Trust, The
Richard *131*
Deutsch Charitable Trust, The
Andre *131*
Deutsch Charitable Trust, The
H & M *131*
Dicken Charitable Trust, The
Albert *133*
Dinam Charity *134*
Djanogly Foundation, The *135*
Doughty Charity Trust, The
136
D'Oyly Carte Charitable Trust,
The *137*
Drayton Trust, The *138*
Dulverton Trust, The *139*
Dunn Charitable Trust, The
Harry *140*
Earmark Trust, The *142*
Ebenezer Trust *144*
Edinburgh Trust, No 2 Account
145
Egerton of Tatton Will Trust,
Lord *146*
Eling Trust *147*
Ellis 1985 Charitable Trust,
Edith M *148*
Elshore Limited *149*
Family Trust, The *158*
Famos Foundation Trust *158*
Fletcher Trust, Roy *165*
Foreman Foundation, The Carl
& Eve *167*
Foyle Trust, Charles Henry *169*
Franklin Bequest, The Rosalind
169
Franklin Deceased's New
Second Charity, Sydney E
170
Fry Charitable Trust, Maurice
174
Garthgwynion Charities *179*

Gibson's Charity Trust, The Hon Mr & Mrs Clive *182*

Gillett Charitable Trust, J A *183*

Gill's Charitable Trust, Mrs M M *184*

Girdlers' Company Charitable Trust, The *184*

Gold Hill Church Trust *186*

Goldberg Charitable Trust, The Lewis *186*

Goodman Charitable Foundation, The Everard and Mina *188*

Goodman Trust, The *189*

Gradel Foundation, The *189*

Green Foundation, Constance *194*

Gross Charities Limited, M & R *197*

Grosshill Charitable Trust *197*

Grut Charitable Trust, The *198*

HB Charitable Trust *201*

Hacking & Sons Ltd Charitable Trust, C G *201*

Hamilton Educational Trust, Eleanor *205*

Harbour Foundation Ltd, The *208*

Harvey Charitable Trust, Gordon *211*

Hawthorne Charitable Trust, The *212*

Heinz Company Limited Charitable Trust, The H J *215*

Held Settlement, The Gisela *215*

Hertfordshire Community Trust, The *217*

Hillards Charitable Trust, Gay & Peter Hartley's *220*

Holford Trust Fund *224*

Hoover Foundation, The *226*

Horn Trust, The Cuthbert *227*

Hornby Charitable Trust, Miss D *227*

Hornton Trust, The *228*

Hughes Charitable Trust, The Geoffery C *230*

Humphreys Charitable Settlement, J A M *231*

Hussey for Africans, Charity of Rebecca *231*

Hyde Park Place Estate Charity, The *232*

IPE Charitable Trust, The *233*

Inman Charity, The *235*

Ireland Funds, The *237*

Isle of Dogs Community Foundation *238*

James Foundation, The Catherine and Lady Grace *241*

Jones Trust, Cemlyn *248*

Jubilee Outreach Yorkshire *248*

KC Charitable Trust, The *250*

Karten Charitable Trust, The Ian *250*

Keyes Trust, The Ursula *253*

Kingsgrove Charitable Trust, The *255*

Kinnison Charitable Trust, R O *256*

Kleinwort Charitable Trust, The Ernest *257*

Knott Trust, Sir James *258*

Kobler Trust, The *258*

Kreitman Foundation *258*

Kulika Charitable Trust, The *259*

Kweller Charitable Trust, The Harry *259*

Laing Foundation, The Christopher *260*

Landy Charitable Trust, Harry and Gertrude *263*

Lane Foundation, The Allen *263*

Lanvern Foundation *265*

Laski Memorial Charitable Trust, Nathan *265*

Laspen Trust *265*

Lauffer Charitable Foundation, The R & D *266*

Lavender Trust, The *267*

Lawley Foundation, The Edgar E *267*

Leach Fourteenth Trust, The *267*

Leigh-Bramwell Trust 'E', P *270*

Levy Charitable Foundation, Joseph *272*

Liffe Benefit *274*

Lingwood Charitable Trust, The *276*

Lloyd's Charities Trust *278*

Localtrent Ltd *279*

Low & Bonar Charitable Fund, The *284*

Lucas Charitable Trust Limited, The Joseph *286*

Lunzer Charitable Trust, The Ruth & Jack *287*

Lynwood Charitable Trust, The *288*

Lyons Charitable Trust, The *288*

MacAndrew Trust, The E M *289*

McKechnie Foundation, A N *292*

McKenzie Trust, The Robert *292*

McLaren Foundation *292*

McLaren Memorial Trust, The Martin *293*

MacRobert Trusts, The *294*

Margadale Charitable Trust, Lord *297*

Marks Charitable Trust, Michael *298*

Markus Charitable Foundation, The Erich *298*

Marr-Munning Trust *299*

Marshall Charitable Trust, The Charlotte *300*

Martin Trust, The Sir George *300*

Material World Charitable Foundation Limited, The *301*

Mattock Charitable Trust, The W T *302*

Mayfair Charities Limited *303*

Medlock Charitable Trust, The *304*

Mellows Charitable Settlement, The Anthony and Elizabeth *305*

Millett Charitable Trust, The Alan and Janet *312*

Millichope Foundation, The *312*

Modiano Charitable Trust *315*

Montefiore Trust, The David *316*

Moore Charitable Trust, The Horace *316*

Morel Charitable Trust, The *318*

Morgan Crucible Company plc Charitable Trust, The *319*

Morris Charitable Trust, The Willie & Mabel *320*

Moulton Charitable Trust, The *321*

Multithon Trust, The *323*

Music for World Development *323*

Music Sales Charitable Trust, The *324*

National Lottery Charities Board *328*

National Power Charitable Trust, The *330*

Newcastle's 1986 Charitable Trust, Duke of *333*

Newman Charitable Trust, Mr and Mrs F E F *334*

Newstead Charity, The *334*

Norfolk's Family Charitable Trust, Lavinia *336*

Northcott Charity Trust, The *338*

Northern Electric Employee Charity Association *339*

Northern Ireland Voluntary Trust *339*

Noswad Charity, The *341*

Old Possums Practical Trust, The *344*

Oppenheimer Charitable Trust *346*

Owen Trust, Margaret *348*

PDC Trust, The *349*

PJD Charitable Trust *350*

Palmer Trust, The Gerald *352*

Paristamen Foundation, The *352*

Parivar Trust, The *353*

Pascoe Charitable Trust, Alan *354*

Paul Charitable Trust, The Late Barbara May *355*
Paul Charitable Trust, Margaret Jeanne *355*
Paul Charitable Trust, Pamela Milton *355*
Paul Foundation, The *355*
Paul's Charitable Trust, R J *355*
Payne Charitable Trust, The *355*
Pelech Charitable Trust, The *358*
Perry Charitable Trust, Miss Frances Lucille *359*
Pershore Nashdom & Elmore Trust Ltd, The *360*
Persula Foundation, The *360*
Peskin Charitable Trust, The Hazel and Leslie *360*
Phillips Charitable Foundation, Reginald M *361*
Pitt Trust, Headley *364*
Powys Welsh Church Fund *367*
Puebla Charitable Trust Limited, The *371*
QAS Charitable Trust *373*
Quothquan Charitable Trust, The Second *373*
RT Trust, The *374*
Rackham Charitable Trust, The Mr & Mrs Philip *375*
Radley Charitable Trust *375*
Rae Charity, H J *375*
Rav Chesed Trust, The *379*
Reekie Trust, R A & V B *381*
Richard Charitable Trust, The Cliff *383*
Richards Charity, The Clive *384*
Riley-Smith Charitable Trust, The F A *386*
Ripley's Charitable Trust, Pat *386*
Rivendell Trust, The *387*
Robbins Trust, The Cheshire *387*
Rodewald's Charitable Settlement, Mr C A *389*
Rogers Charitable Settlement, The Richard *390*
Rolfe Charitable Trust, The *390*
Rosen Foundation, Cecil *392*
Rowan Charitable Trust, The *393*
S Group Charitable Trust *399*
St Jude's Trust *403*
Samuel Charitable Trust, M J *406*
Sargeant's Charitable Trust, Mrs M E *407*
Save & Prosper Foundation *409*
Scarr-Hall Memorial Trust, The *409*
Seva Trust, Rampaba Sadhu *415*
Sherman Charitable Trust, The Archie *419*

Shifrin Charitable Trust, The Maurice and Hilda *419*
Sidbury Trust, The Second *421*
Silvester Charitable Gift Trust *422*
Skelton Bounty, The *423*
Society of Friends of the Torah, The *429*
Solomons Charitable Trust, David *430*
Somerfield Curtis Will Trust, The Dorothy *430*
Stanley Foundation Limited *435*
Stewart Charitable Trust, Mary Stephanie *437*
Summer's and I May's Charitable Settlement, The Late Misses (A N) *442*
Symons Charitable Trust, The Stella *446*
TSB Foundation for Northern Ireland *447*
TSB Foundation for Scotland *447*
Taylor Charitable Trust, The B R *450*
Terry Charitable Trust, Noel Goddard *451*
Tesco Charity Trust *452*
Tesler Foundation, The *452*
Van Leer Foundation UK Trust, Bernard *470*
Van Norden's Charitable Foundation, Mrs Maud *471*
Vineyard Christian Fellowship of South West *473*
Vinson Charity Trust, The 1969 *473*
Vogel Charitable Trust, The Nathan *474*
Wakefield Trust, The *476*
War on Want *479*
Ward Blenkinsop Trust, The *480*
Weinstock Fund, The *484*
Weir Foundation, The James *484*
Westminster Amalgamated Charity *487*
Whetherly's Charitable Trust, The Hon Mrs R G A *489*
Whitehead Charitable Trust, J E *490*
Whittington Charitable Trust, The *491*
Wiggins Charity Trust, Cyril *491*
Wilde Charitable Trust, The Felicity *492*
Woburn 1986 Charitable Trust *498*
Wohl Charitable Trust, The Maurice *498*
Wolff Charity Trust *498*
Wolfson Family Charitable Trust, The *499*

Woodhouse Charitable Trust, Edwin *501*
Woods Charitable Foundation, Geoffrey *502*
Worms Charitable Trust, The Freda and Della *504*
Worshipful Company of Needlemakers' Charitable Fund *505*
Wychdale Limited *507*
Youell Foundation Ltd, The *510*
Zaiger Trust, The Elizabeth and Prince *512*

························

■ Professional, specialist training

see also **Education & training**

Funding priority

Allnatt Charitable Foundation, Angus *14*
British Heart Foundation *62*
Brotherton Trust, The Charles *65*
Christmas Cracker Trust *95*
Company of Chartered Surveyors Charitable Trust Fund, The *108*
Dove-Bowerman Trust *137*
Homeless International *225*
International Bar Association Educational Trust *236*
Judge Charitable Foundation *249*
Liebes Charitable Trust, The Martha Bud *274*
RVW Trust *374*
Sumner's Trust Section 'A', Sir John *443*
Vinten Trust, The William and Ellen *474*
Watson's Trust, John *482*
Worshipful Company of Engineers' Charitable Trust Fund, The *504*
Worshipful Company of Weavers Textile Education Fund, The *506*

Will consider

Alcohol Education and Research Council *9*
Arts Council of Wales, The *23*
Ashley Foundation, The Laura *24*
BibleLands *47*
British Dietetic Association General and Education Trust Fund, The *61*
Camelot Foundation, The *78*
Campden Charities, The *79*
Cancer Relief Macmillan Fund *79*
Carlton Television Trust *81*

Cassel Educational Trust
(Mountbatten Memorial
Grants to Commonwealth
Students), The Sir Ernest *84*
Chrimes Family Charitable
Trust, The *93*
Clinton's Charitable Trust, Lord
100
Cobb Charity *103*
Collier Charitable Trust, The
105
Commonwealth Relations Trust
108
Community Trust for Greater
Manchester, The *108*
County Durham Foundation
115
Curriers Company Charitable
Fund *119*
Dibden Allotments Charity *132*
Digby Charitable Trust, Simon
133
Direct Response *134*
Ebb and Flow Charitable Trust
144
Edgar Trust, The Gilbert *145*
Education Services *145*
Fogel Charitable Trust, The
Gerald *165*
Follett Trust, The *166*
Ford of Britain Trust *166*
GABO Trust for Sculpture
Conservation *175*
Gelston Charitable Trust, The
179
Goldsmiths' Company's
Charities, The *188*
Great Britain Sasakawa
Foundation, The *193*
Holly Hill Charitable Trust *224*
Humanitarian Trust, The *230*
Hussey for Africans, Charity of
Rebecca *231*
Idlewild Trust, The *234*
Isle of Dogs Community
Foundation *238*
KC Charitable Trust, The *250*
Linford Charitable Trust, The
Fred *276*
Lloyd Charity, The S and D *278*
London Law Trust *280*
Middlesex County Rugby
Football Union Memorial
Fund *309*
Milton Keynes Community
Trust Ltd, The *312*
NR Charitable Trust, The *325*
Paristamen Foundation, The
352
Persula Foundation, The *360*
Porcupine Trust, The *366*
Powell Foundation, The *367*
Radcliffe's Trust, Dr *375*
Rest-Harrow Trust, The *382*
Said Foundation, The Karim
Rida *401*
Sheepdrove Trust, The *417*

Shelroy Charitable Trust, The
417
Smallpeice Trust, The *425*
South Square Trust *430*
Summerfield Charitable Trust,
The *442*
Swann-Morton Foundation,
The *444*
TSB Foundation for Northern
Ireland *447*
Tear Fund *450*
Thomson Foundation, The Sue
454
Thorpe Charity Trust, The *455*
Thriplow Charitable Trust *456*
Tisbury Telegraph Trust, The
457
Upjohn Charitable Trust, The
469
Van Leer Foundation UK Trust,
Bernard *470*
Wates Charitable Trust, John
481
Wates Foundation, The *481*
Wincott Foundation, The *496*
Wolfson Foundation, The *499*
Yorkshire Agricultural Society
509

....

■ **Psoriasis**
Funding priority
Psoriasis Association Research
Fund (1968), The *371*

....

■ **Publishing &
printing**
see also Infrastructure &
technical support
Funding priority
Daily Telegraph Charitable
Trust *122*
Drummond Trust, The *138*
National Committee of The
Women's World Day of
Prayer for England, Wales
and Northern Ireland, The
327

Will consider
Berkshire Community Trust *45*
County Durham Foundation
115
Digby Charitable Trust, Simon
133
Duncan Literary Fund, Ronald
139
Egerton of Tatton Will Trust,
Lord *146*
Great Britain Sasakawa
Foundation, The *193*
Homeless International *225*
IBM United Kingdom Trust
233
Iris Trust, The *237*

Isle of Dogs Community
Foundation *238*
Jarrold Trust Ltd, John *243*
Moores Foundation, John *318*
Northern Arts *339*
Paristamen Foundation, The
352
Skelton Bounty, The *423*
Tear Fund *450*
Thomson Foundation, The Sue
454
Wakefield (Tower Hill, Trinity
Square) Trust *476*
Wincott Foundation, The *496*

....

■ **Quakers**
Funding priority
Cadbury Trust (1928), The
Edward & Dorothy *76*
Cadbury Trust, A Account, The
George *77*
Clark Charitable Trust, Hilda &
Alice *98*
Ellis 1985 Charitable Trust,
Edith M *148*
Gillett Charitable Trust, J A
183
Hickinbotham Charitable Trust
218
Lancaster's Trust, Bryan *263*
Oakdale Trust, The *343*
Pitt Trust, Headley *364*
Polden-Puckham Charitable
Foundation, The *365*
Reckitt Charity, Sir James *381*
Rowntree Charitable Trust, The
Joseph *394*
Sewell Charitable Trust, The
416
Southall Charitable Trust,
Kenneth & Phyllis *431*
Southall Trust, W F *432*
Westcroft Trust *486*

....

■ **Race relations**
see Racial equality

....

■ **Racial equality,
discrimination,
relations
(campaigning)**
see also Campaigning
(social issues)
Funding priority
Aston Charities Trust Ltd *25*
Cadbury Trust, The Barrow *76*
City Parochial Foundation *96*
Lyndhurst Settlement *287*
Moores Family Charity
Foundation, The *317*
Morel Charitable Trust, The
318

National Power Charitable Trust, The *330*

Noah Trust, The *335*

Pilkington Trust, The Austin and Hope *363*

Rowntree Charitable Trust, The Joseph *394*

Will consider

AB Charitable Trust *3*

Allachy Trust, The *12*

Body Shop Foundation, The *55*

Cadbury Charitable Trust (Incorporated), Edward *75*

Cadbury Trust (1928), The Edward & Dorothy *76*

Clark 1965 Charitable Trust, Stephen *98*

Coutts Charitable Trust, The *116*

Dibs Charitable Trust, The *133*

Digby Charitable Trust, Simon *133*

Emanuel Charitable Settlement, Ralph and Muriel *150*

Fogel Charitable Trust, The Gerald *165*

Follett Trust, The *166*

Franklin Trust, Jill *170*

Garthgwynion Charities *179*

Hamlyn Foundation, The Paul *205*

Harford Charitable Trust *209*

Hilden Charitable Fund, The *219*

Ireland Funds, The *237*

Iris Trust, The *237*

Isle of Dogs Community Foundation *238*

JCSCJ Charitable Trust, The *238*

Kroch Foundation, The Heinz & Anna *259*

Laing Foundation, The Christopher *260*

Lane Foundation, The Allen *263*

Leech Charity, The William *269*

Music for World Development *323*

New Court Charitable Trust *332*

North West Arts Board *337*

Northern Ireland Voluntary Trust *339*

Owen Family Trust, The *348*

Patients' Aid Association Hospital and Medical Charities Trust *354*

Payne Trust, The Harry *356*

Persula Foundation, The *360*

Puebla Charitable Trust Limited, The *371*

Rest-Harrow Trust, The *382*

Sheepdrove Trust, The *417*

Skelton Bounty, The *423*

Summerfield Charitable Trust, The *442*

Symons Charitable Trust, The Stella *446*

TSB Foundation for Northern Ireland *447*

Tisbury Telegraph Trust, The *457*

Tyne & Wear Foundation *466*

Wakefield (Tower Hill, Trinity Square) Trust *476*

Wiltshire Community Foundation *495*

Wingfield's Charitable Trust, Mrs *496*

Woodhouse Charitable Trust, Edwin *501*

....

■ Racial justice

see **Racial equality**

....

■ Recreation

see **Community arts & recreation**

....

■ Recreation grounds

see also **Community facilities**

Funding priority

Aston Charities Trust Ltd *25*

Blakey Charitable Trust, The Celia and Conrad *53*

Bowland Charitable Trust, The *57*

Butler's Trust, Lord *71*

Clutterbuck Charitable Trust, Robert *102*

Corbett's Charity, Thomas *112*

Dixon Charitable Trust, F E *134*

Fairway Trust, The *158*

Grange Farm Centre Trust *191*

Gwent County Council Welsh Church Fund *200*

Hudson Benevolent Trust, The Thomas *230*

Isle of Dogs Community Foundation *238*

Peirce Memorial Trust, The Joe *358*

Rayner Charitable Trust, The John *380*

Spoore, Merry & Rixman Foundation, The *434*

Will consider

Ammco Trust, The *15*

Amory Charitable Trust, Viscount *16*

Angler's Inn Trust *17*

Aquarius Charitable Foundation, The *19*

Astor Foundation, The *26*

Astor of Hever Trust, The *26*

Barbour Trust, The *33*

Berkshire Community Trust *45*

Blanchminster Trust, The *54*

Boots Charitable Trust *56*

Brand Trust, The *59*

Bridge Trust, The *60*

Brough Charitable Trust, Joseph *65*

Buckinghamshire Masonic Centenary Fund *67*

Bullough Tompson Settlement, The *68*

Campden Charities, The *79*

Carnegie Dunfermline Trust *82*

Challice Trust, The *87*

Chapman Foundation *88*

Chrimes Family Charitable Trust, The *93*

Clifford Charity Oxford, The *100*

Clinton's Charitable Trust, Lord *100*

Community Trust for Greater Manchester, The *108*

County Durham Foundation *115*

Coutts Charitable Trust, The *116*

Curriers Company Charitable Fund *119*

Curzon Charitable Trust, The Wallace *120*

de Freitas Charitable Trust, The Helen and Geoffrey *126*

Debtors' Relief Fund Charity *128*

Derbyshire Trust, J N *130*

Digby Charitable Trust, Simon *133*

Direct Response *134*

Dulverton Trust, The *139*

Dumbreck Charity *139*

Edgar Foundation, The Gilbert and Eileen *145*

Education Services *145*

Elkes Charity Fund, The Wilfred & Elsie *147*

Emmandjay Charitable Trust *150*

Fletcher Charitable Trust, The Joyce *164*

Fletcher Trust, Roy *165*

Four Lanes Trust, The *168*

Four Winds Trust *168*

Gannochy Trust, The *177*

Grant Foundation, The Raymond *191*

Grant-Lawson Charitable Trust, Lady Virginia *192*

Grocers' Charity *197*

Grundy Foundation, The Stanley *198*

Hannay Memorial Charity, Kathleen *208*

Harford Charitable Trust *209*

Hertfordshire Community Trust, The *217*

Hillards Charitable Trust, Gay & Peter Hartley's *220*
Hunter Charitable Trust, The Claire *231*
Ingles Charitable Trust, The *234*
Jewish Childs' Day *245*
Johnson Foundation, The *246*
Johnson Group Cleaners Charity *247*
Knott Trust, Sir James *258*
Laing Charitable Trust, The David *260*
Laing Foundation, The Christopher *260*
Lancaster's Trust, Bryan *263*
Lee Foundation, The Edgar *269*
Leech Charity, The William *269*
Lewis Partnership, John *274*
Littler Foundation, The Emile *277*
Living and Waking Naturally *278*
(Lloyds) TSB Foundation for England and Wales *279*
Lord's Taverners, The *281*
Mackintosh Foundation, The *292*
Marriage's Charitable Trust, Miss G M *299*
Middlesex County Rugby Football Union Memorial Fund *309*
Moore Foundation, The George A *316*
Morel Charitable Trust, The *318*
National Power Charitable Trust, The *330*
Needham Cooper Charitable Trust, The *331*
Newby Trust Ltd *332*
Norfolk's Family Charitable Trust, Lavinia *336*
Norman Family Charitable Trust, The *337*
North West Arts Board *337*
Norton Foundation, The *340*
Norwich Church of England Young Men's Society *340*
Owen Family Trust, The *348*
Persula Foundation, The *360*
Porter Foundation *366*
Provincial Trust for Kendal, The *370*
Pyke Charity Trust *372*
Reekie Trust, R A & V B *381*
Richard Charitable Trust, The Cliff *383*
Rookes Charitable Trust, C A *390*
Royle Memorial Trust, Kirstin *397*
Rugby Football Union Charitable Fund, The *398*
St Katharine & Shadwell Trust *404*

Scott Charitable Trust, The Francis C *412*
Shelroy Charitable Trust, The *417*
Shepherd Family Charitable Trust, The Sir Peter *418*
Skelton Bounty, The *423*
Sobell Welsh People's Charitable Association, Michael *429*
Stevens Foundation, The June *437*
Stoate Charitable Trust, The Leonard Laity *438*
Summerfield Charitable Trust, The *442*
Sykes Trust, The Charles *445*
Symons Charitable Trust, The Stella *446*
TSB Foundation for Scotland *447*
Tisbury Telegraph Trust, The *457*
Torquay Charities, The *458*
Towler Charity Trust, The Fred *459*
Travis Charitable Trust, Constance *460*
Tyne & Wear Foundation *466*
Wall Trust, Thomas *478*
Wander Charitable Fund, The Dr Albert *479*
Wates Foundation, The *481*
Whitehall Charitable Foundation Limited *490*
Williams Charitable Trust, Alfred *493*
Wills 1961 Charitable Trust, Mr Frederick *493*
Wills 1962 Charitable Trust, P J H *494*
Wolfe Family's Charitable Trust, The *498*
Women Caring Trust, The *500*
Wylde Memorial Charity, The Anthony and Gwendoline *507*
Yorkshire Bank Charitable Trust, The *510*

....

■ Recruitment services

see also **Infrastructure & technical support**

Will consider

Berkshire Community Trust *45*
Clifford Charity Oxford, The *100*
County Durham Foundation *115*
Daily Telegraph Charitable Trust *122*
Debtors' Relief Fund Charity *128*
Digby Charitable Trust, Simon *133*

Franklin Trust, Jill *170*
IBM United Kingdom Trust *233*
Ireland Funds, The *237*
Isle of Dogs Community Foundation *238*
Lloyd's Charities Trust *278*
Paristamen Foundation, The *352*

....

■ Refugees

Funding priority

Aid to the Church in Need (United Kingdom) *8*
Blond Charitable Trust, Neville & Elaine *54*
Buxton Trust, Denis *72*
Carlton Television Trust *81*
Clark 1965 Charitable Trust, Stephen *98*
Clifford Charity Oxford, The *100*
Cobb Charity *103*
Cole Charitable Trust, The *105*
De Yong Charitable Trust, The Emma *128*
De Yong's Charitable Trust 1984, Nicholas *128*
Ericson Trust *152*
Fogel Charitable Trust, The Gerald *165*
Fund for Human Need *175*
HACT (The Housing Association's Charitable Trust) *201*
Harbinson Charitable Trust, Roderick *208*
Harbour Foundation Ltd, The *208*
Hartley Memorial Trust, The N & P *211*
Held Settlement, The Gisela *215*
Hertfordshire Community Trust, The *217*
Hiley Trust, Joseph and Mary *219*
Humphreys Charitable Settlement, J A M *231*
King's Fund, The *255*
Lane Foundation, The Allen *263*
Lyndhurst Settlement *287*
Mackintosh Foundation, The *292*
Neave Trust, The Airey *330*
Oxfam (United Kingdom and Ireland) *348*
Paristamen Foundation, The *352*
Rowntree Charitable Trust, The Joseph *394*
Said Foundation, The Karim Rida *401*
Swindon Charitable Trust, The Walter *445*

Tear Fund 450
Tisbury Telegraph Trust, The 457
Trust for London 461
Wates Foundation, The 481
Westcroft Trust 486
World University Service (UK) – WUS (UK) 504

Will consider
AB Charitable Trust 3
Alexandra Trust 11
Ammco Trust, The 15
Archer Trust, The 20
Askew Trust, The Dorothy 25
Barbour Trust, The 33
Birtwistle Memorial Trust, The G E 50
Blake Charitable Trust, The Morgan 53
Butlin Charity Trust, Bill 72
Camelot Foundation, The 78
Campbell Charitable Foundation, The Ellis 79
Catto Charitable Settlement, The Thomas Sivewright 86
Challice Trust, The 87
Charity Projects 90
Church Urban Fund 95
Clinton's Charitable Trust, Lord 100
Collier Charitable Trust, The 105
Coutts Charitable Trust, The 116
Digbeth Trust Ltd, The 133
Direct Response 134
Early's Charitable Settlement, Richard 142
Ebb and Flow Charitable Trust 144
Edgar Foundation, The Gilbert and Eileen 145
Elkes Charity Fund, The Wilfred & Elsie 147
Emmaus Christian Foundation 150
Fletcher Charitable Trust, The Joyce 164
Fletcher Trust, Roy 165
Four Winds Trust 168
Garbacz Charitable Trust, The Bernard & Vera 178
Goldsmiths' Company's Charities, The 188
Grant-Lawson Charitable Trust, Lady Virginia 192
Griffiths Trust, The E E and D M 196
Groves Charitable Trust, The 197
Hampstead Wells and Campden Trust 206
Hanley Trust (1987), The 207
Hill Memorial Trust, L E 219
Hopkinson Educational Trust, Robert Addy 227

Humanitarian Trust, The 230
Iris Trust, The 237
JCSCJ Charitable Trust, The 238
Jarrold Trust Ltd, John 243
Keeling Charitable Trust, The Petronella 251
Laing Charitable Trust, The David 260
Laing Foundation, The Christopher 260
Laing Foundation, The Kirby 261
Laing Foundation, The Maurice 261
Laing Trust, Beatrice 261
Laspen Trust 265
Leach Fourteenth Trust, The 267
Linford Charitable Trust, The Fred 276
Lloyd's Charities Trust 278
(Lloyds) TSB Foundation for England and Wales 279
Lowenthal Charitable Trust, The L and C 285
Lunn-Rockliffe Charitable Trust, Paul 286
Lyons Charitable Trust, The 288
McCarthy Foundation, The John 290
Manning Trust, Leslie & Lilian 296
Marriage's Charitable Trust, Miss G M 299
Mental Health Foundation, The 305
Milton Keynes Community Trust Ltd, The 312
Minet Trust, The Peter 313
Moores Foundation, John 318
Music for World Development 323
NR Charitable Trust, The 325
Nathan Charitable Trust 326
New Court Charitable Trust 332
New Durlston Trust, The 332
Newby Trust Ltd 332
Noah Trust, The 335
Noel Buxton Trust, The 335
Norton Foundation, The 340
Owen Family Trust, The 348
Parivar Trust, The 353
Peppiatt Charitable Trust, The Brian 359
Persula Foundation, The 360
Polden-Puckham Charitable Foundation, The 365
Pratt Charitable Trust, The W L 367
Pye Christian Trust, The 371
Rest-Harrow Trust, The 382
Rope Third Charitable Settlement, The Mrs 391
St Christopher's Trust, The 402

Schuster Charitable Trust, The 410
Seagram Distillers Charitable Trust 413
South Square Trust 430
Stonehouse Trust Ltd, Eric 438
Summer's and I May's Charitable Settlement, The Late Misses (A N) 442
Swan Mountain Trust 444
Swann-Morton Foundation, The 444
TSB Foundation for Scotland 447
Trust for the Homeless 462
Tudor Trust, The 463
Van Berchem Charitable Trust, The Alec 470
Van Leer Foundation UK Trust, Bernard 470
Variety Club Children's Charity Limited, The 471
Wagstaff Charitable Trust, Bob 475
Wakefield (Tower Hill, Trinity Square) Trust 476
Wakeham Trust, The 476
Wallington Missionary Mart & Auctions 478
Whitecourt Charitable Trust, The 490
Wills 1962 Charitable Trust, P J H 494

■ Rehabilitation centres

see also **Health facilities & buildings**

Funding priority

Andrew Convalescent Trust, The Frederick 17
Army Benevolent Fund, The 22
Cooper Charitable Trust 111
Debtors' Relief Fund Charity 128
Frognal Trust 174
Hardy Trust, The Patsy 209
Heath Charitable Trust 214
Lacy Charity Trust, The Late Sir Pierce 260
Noswad Charity, The 341
Pryor Charitable Trust, The John 370
Royal Theatrical Fund, The 396
Stone Foundation, The 438
Strangward Trust, The 439

Will consider
Ammco Trust, The 15
Andrew Charitable Trust, The Prince 16
Anstey Charitable Settlement, J C W 18
Archer Trust, The 20
Astor Foundation, The 26

Balney Charitable Trust, The 32

Bancroft Trust, The 33

Barratt Charitable Trust, The Elaine 36

Beit Trust, The 40

BibleLands 47

Birtwistle Memorial Trust, The G E 50

Britton Charitable Trust, The J & M 63

Brooke Benevolent Fund, William 65

Brough Charitable Trust, Joseph 65

Bullough Tompson Settlement, The 68

Burdall Charity, H M 69

Camelot Foundation, The 78

Cancer Relief Macmillan Fund 79

Celebrities Guild of Great Britain, The 87

Chase Charity, The 91

Chiddick Charitable Trust 92

Clinton's Charitable Trust, Lord 100

Coates Charitable Trust, The John 103

Collier Charitable Trust, The 105

Community Trust for Greater Manchester, The 108

Corbett's Charity, Thomas 112

Denne Charitable Trust 130

Derbyshire Trust, J N 130

Digby Charitable Trust, Simon 133

Dorus Trust 136

Dumbreck Charity 139

Edgar Trust, The Gilbert 145

Egerton of Tatton Will Trust, Lord 146

Elkes Charity Fund, The Wilfred & Elsie 147

Epigoni Trust 152

Fishmongers' Company's Charitable Trust 163

Fleming Charitable Trust, The Ian 164

Ford of Britain Trust 166

Franklin Deceased's New Second Charity, Sydney E 170

Gladstone Charitable Trust, The E W 184

Good Neighbours Trust, The 188

Graves Charitable Trust, J G 192

Gray Charitable Trust, R B 192

Greater Bristol Foundation 193

Greenaway Foundation, The Alan 194

Greenaway Foundation, The Sir Derek 194

Grocers' Charity 197

Haines Charitable Trust, The Alfred 203

Hannay Charitable Trust, The Lennox 208

Harford Charitable Trust 209

Harvey Charitable Trust, Gordon 211

Haywood Charitable Trust 214

Hopkins Charitable Foundation, The Sir Anthony 226

Inman Charity, The 235

Isle of Dogs Community Foundation 238

JDM Charitable Trust 239

JHL Trust, The 239

Johnson Group Cleaners Charity 247

Laing Charitable Trust, The David 260

Laing Foundation, The Kirby 261

Laing Foundation, The Maurice 261

Laing Trust, Beatrice 261

Lankelly Foundation, The 264

Lawson Charitable Trust, Raymond and Blanche 267

Lee Foundation, The Edgar 269

Leech Charity, The William 269

Lloyd Charity, The S and D 278

(Lloyds) TSB Foundation for England and Wales 279

London Law Trust 280

Luke Trust, The 286

MacKintosh Charitable Trust, Viscount 292

Marchday Charitable Fund, The 296

Mellows Charitable Settlement, The Anthony and Elizabeth 305

Middlesex County Rugby Football Union Memorial Fund 309

Milburn Charitable Trust, Frederick 310

Minet Trust, The Peter 313

Morris Charitable Trust, The Douglas 320

Natwest Staff Samaritan Fund 330

Needham Cooper Charitable Trust, The 331

Norman Family Charitable Trust, The 337

Owen Family Trust, The 348

Paget Trust, The 351

Paul's Charitable Trust, R J 355

Penny in the Pound Fund Charitable Trust 359

Persula Foundation, The 360

Reader's Digest Trust, The 380

Royal's Memorial Fund, Princess 396

SMB Trust, The 400

Seagram Distillers Charitable Trust 413

Sheldon Trust, The 417

Shelroy Charitable Trust, The 417

Simon's Charity 422

Smith & Mount Trust, The Mrs 426

Smith (Estates Charities), Henry 426

Smith Foundation, The Leslie 427

Sportsman's Aid Charity Ltd, The 434

Stonehouse Trust Ltd, Eric 438

Sykes Trust, The Charles 445

TSB Foundation for Northern Ireland 447

TSB Foundation for Scotland 447

Tear Fund 450

Templeton Goodwill Trust 451

Thackray General Charitable Trust, The P & L 452

Thompson Charitable Trust, The 453

Travis Charitable Trust, Constance 460

Turner Trust, The Douglas 464

Van Berchem Charitable Trust, The Alec 470

Van Neste Foundation, The 471

Victoria & Johnson Memorial Trust, Queen 472

Wall Trust, Thomas 478

Weir Foundation, The James 484

Whesby Ltd 488

Will Charitable Trust, The 492

Woodlands Trust 501

Woodroffe Benton Foundation, The 502

Woolton Charitable Trust, The 503

Wylde Memorial Charity, The Anthony and Gwendoline 507

....

■ Religion

see **Advancement of religion**

....

■ Religious ancillary buildings

see also **Religious buildings**

Funding priority

Chesters Settlement for Methodist Church Purposes, Mr H G 91

Will consider

Almond Trust, The 14

Beckwith-Smith's Charitable Settlement, Mrs 40

Britland Charitable Trust, The
63

Derbyshire Trust, J N *130*

Digby Charitable Trust, Simon
133

Fulham Cross Christian Mission
175

Grant-Lawson Charitable Trust,
Lady Virginia *192*

Greenaway Foundation, The Sir
Derek *194*

Hillards Charitable Trust, Gay &
Peter Hartley's *220*

Hudson Benevolent Trust, The
Thomas *230*

James Trust, The *242*

Laspen Trust *265*

Marriage's Charitable Trust,
Miss G M *299*

Moore Charitable Trust, The
Horace *316*

Peppiatt Charitable Trust, The
Brian *359*

Rainbow Charitable Trust *376*

Saunderson Foundation, The
408

Tisbury Telegraph Trust, The
457

Vineyard Christian Fellowship
of South West *473*

Warren Foundation, The John
480

■ Religious buildings

see also Cemeteries & burial
grounds, Churches,
Mosques, Religious ancillary
buildings, Synagogues,
Temples, gurdwaras

Funding priority

AB Charitable Trust, The *3*

Aid to the Church in Need
(United Kingdom) *8*

Aldwyns Trust, The *10*

Astor of Hever Trust, The *26*

Barleycorn Trust, The *34*

Bateman Charitable Trust, Lady
Margaret *37*

Bear Mordechai Ltd *39*

Bell Trust and Additional Fund,
The Barron *41*

Black Foundation, The Bertie
51

Blank Donations Ltd, The David
54

Bottom Charitable Trust, Harry
56

Brough Charitable Trust,
Joseph *65*

Buckingham Trust *67*

Carmichael-Montgomery
Charitable Trust, The *81*

Clark Charitable Trust *98*

Cockenzie Charitable Trust, The
103

Cope Charitable Trust, Alfred
112

Cripps Foundation *118*

Dandeen Charitable Trust *123*

Elshore Limited *149*

Fairway Trust, The *158*

Famos Foundation Trust *158*

Ferguson Benevolent Fund
Limited *161*

Friends of Essex Churches, The
172

Friends of Friendless Churches,
The *173*

Goodman Trust, The *189*

Grahame Charitable
Foundation, The *190*

Gwent County Council Welsh
Church Fund *200*

IPE Charitable Trust, The *233*

James Foundation, The
Catherine and Lady Grace
241

Jones Trust, Cemlyn *248*

Lancaster's Trust, Bryan *263*

Leche Trust, The *268*

Leigh-Bramwell Trust 'E', P *270*

Lester Trust Fund, The *271*

Lucas Charitable Trust Limited,
The Joseph *286*

Lynwood Charitable Trust, The
288

McLaren Memorial Trust, The
Martin *293*

Marks Foundation, The Hilda
and Samuel *298*

Marshall's Charity *300*

Morgan Foundation, The Mr &
Mrs J T *319*

Newman Charitable Trust, Mr
and Mrs F E F *334*

Pilkington Trust, The Austin
and Hope *363*

Richards Charity, The Clive *384*

Rutland Historic Churches
Preservation Trust *399*

St Jude's Trust *403*

Seva Trust, Rampaba Sadhu
415

Sewell Charitable Trust, The
416

Somerfield Curtis Will Trust,
The Dorothy *430*

Stoate Charitable Trust, The
Leonard Laity *438*

Strict And Particular Baptist
Trust Corporation, The *440*

Trenance Charitable Trust *460*

Woods Charitable Foundation,
Geoffrey *502*

Woolf Charitable Trust, The
502

Worshipful Company of
Needlemakers' Charitable
Fund *505*

Zaiger Trust, The Elizabeth and
Prince *512*

Will consider

AHJ Charitable Trust, The *3*

Achiezer Association Limited *6*

Airflow Community Ltd, The *9*

Aleh Charitable Foundation,
The *10*

Alliance Family Foundation
Limited *13*

Anderson Trust, Andrew *16*

Angler's Inn Trust *17*

Appelbe Trust, Ambrose & Ann
19

Aquinas Trust *20*

Askew Charitable Trust, The
Ian *25*

Astor Foundation, The *26*

Astor's 1969 Charity, The Hon
M L *26*

Barbour Trust, The *33*

Barnby's Foundation, Lord *35*

Barnsbury Charitable Trust *35*

Barton Trust, Eleanor *37*

Bealey Foundation, The *38*

Beattie Charitable Trust, The
James *39*

Beckwith Charitable Trust, The
Peter *40*

Bergqvist Charitable Trust *44*

Black Charitable Trust, The
Cyril W *51*

Black Charitable Trust, Sydney
51

Blagrave Charitable Trust, The
Herbert and Peter *52*

Blakey Charitable Trust, The
Celia and Conrad *53*

Boltons Trust, The *55*

Borthwick Memorial Trust, The
Oliver *56*

Bowland Charitable Trust, The
57

British Sugar Foundation *63*

Brook Charitable Settlement,
R E *64*

Brookhouse's Will Trust, Mr
John Charles *65*

Burn Charity Trust, The J H *70*

Burns Charity, The Dorothy *70*

Burry Charitable Trust, The *70*

Burton Charitable Trust, The
Geoffrey *71*

Butler's Trust, Lord *71*

Butler's Trust, Lucilla *72*

Cadbury Schweppes
Foundation, The *76*

Cadbury Trust (1928), The
Edward & Dorothy *76*

Carron Charitable Trust, The
83

Castang Charitable Trust, H
and M *85*

Catto Charitable Settlement,
The Thomas Sivewright *86*

Charity Projects *90*

Cinderford Charitable Trust,
The *96*

Clark Charitable Trust, J
Anthony *98*

Clutterbuck Charitable Trust, Robert *102*

Coates Charitable Settlement, The *102*

Coates Charitable Trust 1969, Lance *103*

Cohen Charitable Trust, The Vivienne and Samuel *104*

Cohen Charity Trust, Lucy *104*

Company of Tobacco Pipe Makers and Tobacco Blenders Benevolent Fund *109*

Condon Family Trust *109*

Crescent Trust, The *117*

Curry Charitable Trust, Dennis *119*

Cymerman Trust Limited, Itzchok Meyer *120*

Daily Telegraph Charitable Trust *122*

Davy Foundation, The J *126*

De Avenley Foundation, The *126*

De La Rue Charitable Trust *127*

De Rothschild 1981 Charitable Trust, The Edmund *127*

De Yong Charitable Trust, The Emma *128*

Delmar Charitable Trust *129*

Denton Charitable Trust, The *130*

Desmond Charitable Trust, The Richard *131*

Deutsch Charitable Trust, The Andre *131*

Deutsch Charitable Trust, The H & M *131*

Dicken Charitable Trust, The Albert *133*

Dinam Charity *134*

Djanogly Foundation, The *135*

D'Oyly Carte Charitable Trust, The *137*

Drayton Trust, The *138*

Dunn Charitable Trust, The Harry *140*

Earmark Trust, The *142*

Edinburgh Trust, No 2 Account *145*

Family Trust, The *158*

Foreman Foundation, The Carl & Eve *167*

Foyle Trust, Charles Henry *169*

Franklin Bequest, The Rosalind *169*

Fry Charitable Trust, Maurice *174*

Garthgwynion Charities *179*

Gibbs Charitable Trusts, The *181*

Gibson's Charity Trust, The Hon Mr & Mrs Clive *182*

Gillett Charitable Trust, J A *183*

Gill's Charitable Trust, Mrs M M *184*

Girdlers' Company Charitable Trust, The *184*

Gold Hill Church Trust *186*

Goldberg Charitable Trust, The Lewis *186*

Goodman Charitable Foundation, The Everard and Mina *188*

Gradel Foundation, The *189*

Green Foundation, Constance *194*

Grut Charitable Trust, The *198*

HB Charitable Trust *201*

Hacking & Sons Ltd Charitable Trust, C G *201*

Hamilton Educational Trust, Eleanor *205*

Harbour Foundation Ltd, The *208*

Harvey Charitable Trust, Gordon *211*

Hawthorne Charitable Trust, The *212*

Held Settlement, The Gisela *215*

Hodge Foundation, The Jane *223*

Holford Trust Fund *224*

Hoover Foundation, The *226*

Horn Trust, The Cuthbert *227*

Hornton Trust, The *228*

Hughes Charitable Trust, The Geoffery C *230*

Hurst Will Trust, Arthur *231*

Inman Charity, The *235*

Jubilee Outreach Yorkshire *248*

KC Charitable Trust, The *250*

Kalms Foundation, The Stanley *250*

Karten Charitable Trust, The Ian *250*

Keyes Trust, The Ursula *253*

Kingsgrove Charitable Trust, The *255*

Kinnison Charitable Trust, R O *256*

Kleinwort Charitable Trust, The Ernest *257*

Kobler Trust, The *258*

Kreitman Foundation *258*

Kulika Charitable Trust, The *259*

Kweller Charitable Trust, Harry *259*

Laing's Charitable Trust *262*

Landy Charitable Trust, Harry and Gertrude *263*

Langley Charitable Trust, The *264*

Lanvern Foundation *265*

Laski Memorial Charitable Trust, Nathan *265*

Lauffer Charitable Foundation, The R & D *266*

Lavender Trust, The *267*

Lawley Foundation, The Edgar E *267*

Levy Charitable Foundation, Joseph *272*

Liffe Benefit *274*

Lunzer Charitable Trust, The Ruth & Jack *287*

Lyons Charitable Trust, The *288*

MDM Memorial Trust *289*

MacAndrew Trust, The E M *289*

Maccabi Foundation, The *290*

McKechnie Foundation, A N *292*

McKenzie Trust, The Robert *292*

MacKintosh Charitable Trust, Viscount *292*

McLaren Foundation *292*

Margadale Charitable Trust, Lord *297*

Marks Charitable Trust, Michael *298*

Markus Charitable Foundation, The Erich *298*

Marr-Munning Trust *299*

Martin Trust, The Sir George *300*

Material World Charitable Foundation Limited, The *301*

Mattock Charitable Trust, The W T *302*

Medlock Charitable Trust, The *304*

Mellows Charitable Settlement, The Anthony and Elizabeth *305*

Milburn Charitable Trust, Frederick *310*

Millett Charitable Trust, The Alan and Janet *312*

Millichope Foundation, The *312*

Modiano Charitable Trust *315*

Montefiore Trust, The David *316*

Morel Charitable Trust, The *318*

Morris Charitable Trust, The Willie & Mabel *320*

Moulton Charitable Trust, The *321*

Music Sales Charitable Trust, The *324*

Newcastle's 1986 Charitable Trust, Duke of *333*

Newstead Charity, The *334*

Northcott Charity Trust, The *338*

Northern Arts *339*

Northern Electric Employee Charity Association *339*

Old Possums Practical Trust, The *344*

Oppenheimer Charitable Trust *346*

Owen Trust, Margaret *348*

PDC Trust, The *349*

PJD Charitable Trust *350*
Palmer Trust, The Gerald *352*
Pascoe Charitable Trust, Alan *354*
Paul Charitable Trust, The Late Barbara May *355*
Paul Charitable Trust, Margaret Jeanne *355*
Paul Charitable Trust, Pamela Milton *355*
Paul Foundation, The *355*
Paul's Charitable Trust, R J *355*
Payne Charitable Trust, The *355*
Pelech Charitable Trust, The *358*
Perry Charitable Trust, Miss Frances Lucille *359*
Pershore Nashdom & Elmore Trust Ltd, The *360*
Peskin Charitable Trust, The Hazel and Leslie *360*
Phillips Charitable Foundation, Reginald M *361*
Pilgrim Trust, The *362*
Podde Trust *365*
QAS Charitable Trust *373*
RT Trust, The *374*
Rackham Charitable Trust, The Mr & Mrs Philip *375*
Radley Charitable Trust *375*
Rae Charity, H J *375*
Rav Chesed Trust, The *379*
Reekie Trust, R A & V B *381*
Richmond Parish Lands Charity *384*
Riggs Charity, The *386*
Rivendell Trust, The *387*
Rodewald's Charitable Settlement, Mr C A *389*
Rogers Charitable Settlement, The Richard *390*
Rolfe Charitable Trust, The *390*
Rosen Foundation, Cecil *392*
Samuel Charitable Trust, M J *406*
Save & Prosper Foundation *409*
Scarr-Hall Memorial Trust, The *409*
Sherman Charitable Trust, The Archie *419*
Shifrin Charitable Trust, The Maurice and Hilda *419*
Sidbury Trust, The Second *421*
Silvester Charitable Gift Trust *422*
Society of Friends of the Torah, The *429*
Solomons Charitable Trust, David *430*
Stanley Foundation Limited *435*
Stewart Charitable Trust, Mary Stephanie *437*
Taylor Charitable Trust, The B R *450*

Terry Charitable Trust, Noel Goddard *451*
Tesco Charity Trust *452*
Tesler Foundation, The *452*
3i Charitable Trust, The *455*
van Geest Foundation, The John and Lucille *470*
Van Norden's Charitable Foundation, Mrs Maud *471*
Vincent Trust Fund, Eric W *473*
Vinson Charity Trust, The 1969 *473*
Wakefield Trust, The *476*
Ward Blenkinsop Trust, The *480*
Weinstock Fund, The *484*
Welby Trust, The Barbara *484*
Whetherly's Charitable Trust, The Hon Mrs R G A *489*
Whitehead Charitable Trust, J E *490*
Whittington Charitable Trust, The *491*
Wiggins Charity Trust, Cyril *491*
Wilde Charitable Trust, The Felicity *492*
Wills 1961 Charitable Trust, Major Michael Thomas *494*
Woburn 1986 Charitable Trust *498*
Wohl Charitable Foundation, The Maurice *498*
Wohl Charitable Trust, The Maurice *498*
Wolfson Family Charitable Trust, The *499*
Worms Charitable Trust, The Freda and Della *504*
Youell Foundation Ltd, The *510*

....

■ Religious teaching

see Cultural & religious teaching

....

■ Religious umbrella bodies

see also Catholic bodies, Diocesan boards

Funding priority

AB Charitable Trust, The *3*
Aid to the Church in Need (United Kingdom) *8*
Alglen Ltd *11*
Almond Trust, The *14*
Astor Foundation, The *26*
Astor of Hever Trust, The *26*
Avon Trust, The *28*
Bateman Charitable Trust, Lady Margaret *37*
Bear Mordechai Ltd *39*
Beauland Ltd *39*
Belljoe Tzedoko Ltd *42*

Black Foundation, The Bertie *51*
Blank Donations Ltd, The David *54*
Bottom Charitable Trust, Harry *56*
Brushmill Ltd *66*
Buckingham Trust *67*
Carmichael-Montgomery Charitable Trust, The *81*
Cen Foundation, The Hyman *87*
Chesters Settlement for Methodist Church Purposes, Mr H G *91*
Clark Charitable Trust *98*
Cockenzie Charitable Trust, The *103*
Cope Charitable Trust, Alfred *112*
Dandeen Charitable Trust *123*
David Trust, The Lesley *124*
Dulverton Trust, The *139*
Elshore Limited *149*
Famos Foundation Trust *158*
Feed the Minds *160*
Fencewood Trust, The *161*
Goodman Trust, The *189*
Grahame Charitable Foundation, The *190*
Gross Charities Limited, M & R *197*
Haddon Charitable Trust, William *202*
IPE Charitable Trust, The *233*
JMK Charitable Trust *239*
James Foundation, The Catherine and Lady Grace *241*
Jarrold Trust Ltd, John *243*
Jones Trust, Cemlyn *248*
Kahn Charitable Trust, Bernard *250*
Kalms Foundation, The Stanley *250*
Kingston Religious Trust Fund, The *256*
Leech Charity, The William *269*
Leigh-Bramwell Trust 'E', P *270*
Lester Trust Fund, The *271*
Localtrent Ltd *279*
Lucas Charitable Trust Limited, The Joseph *286*
Lynwood Charitable Trust, The *288*
McLaren Memorial Trust, The Martin *293*
Marks Foundation, The Hilda and Samuel *298*
Medlock Charitable Trust, The *304*
Morgan Foundation, The Mr & Mrs J T *319*
NR Charitable Trust, The *325*
Newman Charitable Trust, Mr and Mrs F E F *334*
Noah Trust, The *335*
Norwood Settlement *340*

Paristamen Foundation, The 352

Pye Christian Trust, The 371

Richards Charity, The Clive 384

St Jude's Trust 403

St Luke's College Foundation 404

Saunderson Foundation, The 408

Seedfield Trust, The 414

Seva Trust, Rampaba Sadhu 415

Sewell Charitable Trust, The 416

Skinner Charitable Trust, Edward 424

Somerfield Curtis Will Trust, The Dorothy 430

Spalding Trust 433

Stow Allen Trust, The 439

Trenance Charitable Trust 460

Truemark Trust, The 461

Woods Charitable Foundation, Geoffrey 502

Woolf Charitable Trust, The 502

Worshipful Company of Needlemakers' Charitable Fund 505

Wright Deceased Trust, John William 506

Zaiger Trust, The Elizabeth and Prince 512

Will consider

AHJ Charitable Trust, The 3

Airflow Community Ltd, The 9

Aleh Charitable Foundation, The 10

Alliance Family Foundation Limited 13

Anderson Trust, Andrew 16

Angler's Inn Trust 17

Appelbe Trust, Ambrose & Ann 19

Aquinas Trust 20

Askew Charitable Trust, The Ian 25

Astor's 1969 Charity, The Hon M L 26

Barnby's Foundation, Lord 35

Barnsbury Charitable Trust 35

Barton Trust, Eleanor 37

Bealey Foundation, The 38

Beckwith Charitable Trust, The Peter 40

Beckwith-Smith's Charitable Settlement, Mrs 40

Bergqvist Charitable Trust 44

BibleLands 47

Black Charitable Trust, The Cyril W 51

Black Charitable Trust, Sydney 51

Blagrave Charitable Trust, The Herbert and Peter 52

Blakey Charitable Trust, The Celia and Conrad 53

Boltons Trust, The 55

Borthwick Memorial Trust, The Oliver 56

Bowland Charitable Trust, The 57

British Sugar Foundation 63

Brook Charitable Settlement, R E 64

Brookhouse's Will Trust, Mr John Charles 65

Burn Charity Trust, The J H 70

Burns Charity, The Dorothy 70

Burry Charitable Trust, The 70

Burton Charitable Trust, The Geoffrey 71

Butler's Trust, Lord 71

Butler's Trust, Lucilla 72

Cadbury Schweppes Foundation, The 76

Carron Charitable Trust, The 83

Castang Charitable Trust, H and M 85

Charity Projects 90

Cinderford Charitable Trust, The 96

Clark Charitable Trust, J Anthony 98

Clutterbuck Charitable Trust, Robert 102

Coates Charitable Settlement, The 102

Coates Charitable Trust 1969, Lance 103

Cohen Charitable Trust, The Vivienne and Samuel 104

Cohen Charity Trust, Lucy 104

Company of Tobacco Pipe Makers and Tobacco Blenders Benevolent Fund 109

Condon Family Trust 109

Crescent Trust, The 117

Curry Charitable Trust, Dennis 119

Cymerman Trust Limited, Itzchok Meyer 120

Daily Telegraph Charitable Trust 122

Davy Foundation, The J 126

De Avenley Foundation, The 126

De La Rue Charitable Trust 127

De Rothschild 1981 Charitable Trust, The Edmund 127

De Yong Charitable Trust, The Emma 128

Delmar Charitable Trust 129

Denton Charitable Trust, The 130

Desmond Charitable Trust, The Richard 131

Deutsch Charitable Trust, The Andre 131

Deutsch Charitable Trust, The H & M 131

Dicken Charitable Trust, The Albert 133

Dinam Charity 134

Djanogly Foundation, The 135

D'Oyly Carte Charitable Trust, The 137

Drayton Trust, The 138

Dunn Charitable Trust, The Harry 140

Earmark Trust, The 142

Edinburgh Trust, No 2 Account 145

Eling Trust 147

Ellis 1985 Charitable Trust, Edith M 148

Fairway Trust, The 158

Family Trust, The 158

Forbesville Limited 166

Foreman Foundation, The Carl & Eve 167

Foyle Trust, Charles Henry 169

Franklin Bequest, The Rosalind 169

Franklin Deceased's New Second Charity, Sydney E 170

Fry Charitable Trust, Maurice 174

Garthgwynion Charities 179

Gibbs Charitable Trusts, The 181

Gibson's Charity Trust, The Hon Mr & Mrs Clive 182

Gillett Charitable Trust, J A 183

Gill's Charitable Trust, Mrs M M 184

Girdlers' Company Charitable Trust, The 184

Gold Hill Church Trust 186

Goldberg Charitable Trust, The Lewis 186

Goodman Charitable Foundation, The Everard and Mina 188

Gradel Foundation, The 189

Green Foundation, Constance 194

Grut Charitable Trust, The 198

HB Charitable Trust 201

Hacking & Sons Ltd Charitable Trust, C G 201

Hamilton Educational Trust, Eleanor 205

Harbour Foundation Ltd, The 208

Harvey Charitable Trust, Gordon 211

Hawthorne Charitable Trust, The 212

Held Settlement, The Gisela 215

Hillards Charitable Trust, Gay & Peter Hartley's 220

Hodge Foundation, The Jane 223

Holford Trust Fund *224*
Hoover Foundation, The *226*
Horn Trust, The Cuthbert *227*
Hornton Trust, The *228*
Hughes Charitable Trust, The Geoffery C *230*
Hussey for Africans, Charity of Rebecca *231*
Inman Charity, The *235*
Jubilee Outreach Yorkshire *248*
KC Charitable Trust, The *250*
Karten Charitable Trust, The Ian *250*
Keyes Trust, The Ursula *253*
Kingsgrove Charitable Trust, The *255*
Kinnison Charitable Trust, R O *256*
Kleinwort Charitable Trust, The Ernest *257*
Kobler Trust, The *258*
Kreitman Foundation *258*
Kulika Charitable Trust, The *259*
Kweller Charitable Trust, The Harry *259*
Laing Foundation, The Maurice *261*
Landy Charitable Trust, Harry and Gertrude *263*
Langley Charitable Trust, The *264*
Lanvern Foundation *265*
Laski Memorial Charitable Trust, Nathan *265*
Laspen Trust *265*
Lauffer Charitable Foundation, The R & D *266*
Lavender Trust, The *267*
Lawley Foundation, The Edgar E *267*
Levy Charitable Foundation, Joseph *272*
Liffe Benefit *274*
Lunzer Charitable Trust, The Ruth & Jack *287*
Lyons Charitable Trust, The *288*
MDM Memorial Trust *289*
MacAndrew Trust, The E M *289*
Maccabi Foundation, The *290*
McKechnie Foundation, A N *292*
McKenzie Trust, The Robert *292*
McLaren Foundation *292*
Margadale Charitable Trust, Lord *297*
Marks Charitable Trust, Michael *298*
Markus Charitable Foundation, The Erich *298*
Marr-Munning Trust *299*
Martin Trust, The Sir George *300*

Material World Charitable Foundation Limited, The *301*
Mattock Charitable Trust, The W T *302*
Mellows Charitable Settlement, The Anthony and Elizabeth *305*
Millett Charitable Trust, The Alan and Janet *312*
Millichope Foundation, The *312*
Modiano Charitable Trust *315*
Montefiore Trust, The David *316*
Moore Charitable Trust, The Horace *316*
Morel Charitable Trust, The *318*
Morgan Crucible Company plc Charitable Trust, The *319*
Morris Charitable Trust, The Willie & Mabel *320*
Moulton Charitable Trust, The *321*
Music Sales Charitable Trust, The *324*
Newcastle's 1986 Charitable Trust, Duke of *333*
Newstead Charity, The *334*
Norfolk's Family Charitable Trust, Lavinia *336*
Northcott Charity Trust, The *338*
Northern Arts *339*
Northern Electric Employee Charity Association *339*
Old Possums Practical Trust, The *344*
Oppenheimer Charitable Trust *346*
Owen Trust, Margaret *348*
PDC Trust, The *349*
PJD Charitable Trust *350*
Palmer Trust, The Gerald *352*
Pascoe Charitable Trust, Alan *354*
Paul Charitable Trust, The Late Barbara May *355*
Paul Charitable Trust, Margaret Jeanne *355*
Paul Charitable Trust, Pamela Milton *355*
Paul Foundation, The *355*
Paul's Charitable Trust, R J *355*
Payne Charitable Trust, The *355*
Pelech Charitable Trust, The *358*
Perry Charitable Trust, Miss Frances Lucille *359*
Pershore Nashdom & Elmore Trust Ltd, The *360*
Peskin Charitable Trust, The Hazel and Leslie *360*
Phillips Charitable Foundation, Reginald M *361*
Pitt Trust, Headley *364*

Podde Trust *365*
Powys Welsh Church Fund *367*
QAS Charitable Trust *373*
Quothquan Charitable Trust, The Second *373*
RT Trust, The *374*
Rackham Charitable Trust, The Mr & Mrs Philip *375*
Radley Charitable Trust *375*
Rae Charity, H J *375*
Rav Chesed Trust, The *379*
Reekie Trust, R A & V B *381*
Richard Charitable Trust, The Cliff *383*
Riggs Charity, The *386*
Rivendell Trust, The *387*
Robinson Brothers (Ryders Green) Ltd, Charitable Trust *388*
Rodewald's Charitable Settlement, Mr C A *389*
Rogers Charitable Settlement, The Richard *390*
Rolfe Charitable Trust, The *390*
Rosen Foundation, Cecil *392*
Samuel Charitable Trust, M J *406*
Save & Prosper Foundation *409*
Scarr-Hall Memorial Trust, The *409*
Sherman Charitable Trust, The Archie *419*
Shifrin Charitable Trust, The Maurice and Hilda *419*
Sidbury Trust, The Second *421*
Silvester Charitable Gift Trust *422*
Society of Friends of the Torah, The *429*
Solomons Charitable Trust, David *430*
Sparkhill Trust, The *433*
Stanley Foundation Limited *435*
Stewart Charitable Trust, Mary Stephanie *437*
Taylor Charitable Trust, The B R *450*
Terry Charitable Trust, Noel Goddard *451*
Tesco Charity Trust *452*
Tesler Foundation, The *452*
Thorpe Charity Trust, The *455*
van Geest Foundation, The John and Lucille *470*
Van Norden's Charitable Foundation, Mrs Maud *471*
Vineyard Christian Fellowship of South West *473*
Vinson Charity Trust, The 1969 *473*
Wakefield Trust, The *476*
Ward Blenkinsop Trust, The *480*
Weinstock Fund, The *484*
Whetherly's Charitable Trust, The Hon Mrs R G A *489*

Whitecourt Charitable Trust, The *490*

Whitehead Charitable Trust, J E *490*

Whittington Charitable Trust, The *491*

Wiggins Charity Trust, Cyril *491*

Wilde Charitable Trust, The Felicity *492*

Wills 1961 Charitable Trust, Major Michael Thomas *494*

Woburn 1986 Charitable Trust *498*

Wohl Charitable Foundation, The Maurice *498*

Wohl Charitable Trust, The Maurice *498*

Wolfson Family Charitable Trust, The *499*

Worms Charitable Trust, The Freda and Della *504*

Wychdale Limited *507*

Youell Foundation Ltd, The *510*

....
■ Renewable energy, renewable power

see also **Conservation & campaigning**

Funding priority

Ashden Charitable Trust, The *24*

Bell's Charitable Trust, Lady Mary *42*

Cobb Charity *103*

Harbinson Charitable Trust, Roderick *208*

Homeless International *225*

Leonard Trust, The Mark *271*

Living and Waking Naturally *278*

Staples Trust *435*

Tisbury Telegraph Trust, The *457*

Whitaker Charitable Trust *489*

Will consider

Allied Domecq Trust *13*

Barnby's Foundation, Lord *35*

Beckwith-Smith's Charitable Settlement, Mrs *40*

Carron Charitable Trust, The *83*

Coates Charitable Trust 1969, Lance *103*

de Freitas Charitable Trust, The Helen and Geoffrey *126*

Digby Charitable Trust, Simon *133*

Early's Charitable Settlement, Richard *142*

Earwicker Trust *142*

Edgar Foundation, The Gilbert and Eileen *145*

Education Services *145*

Four Winds Trust *168*

Great Britain Sasakawa Foundation, The *193*

Greenaway Foundation, The Sir Derek *194*

Hill Memorial Trust, L E *219*

Isle of Dogs Community Foundation *238*

JJ Charitable Trust, The *239*

Laing Foundation, The Christopher *260*

Lane Foundation, The Allen *263*

Lee Foundation, The Edgar *269*

Lyndhurst Settlement *287*

Marchday Charitable Fund, The *296*

Marchig Animal Welfare Trust *297*

Mellows Charitable Settlement, The Anthony and Elizabeth *305*

Mitchell Trust *315*

Morphy Memorial Fund, Arthur *319*

Noah Trust, The *335*

North West Arts Board *337*

Paget Trust, The *351*

Polden-Puckham Charitable Foundation, The *365*

S Group Charitable Trust *399*

Summerfield Charitable Trust, The *442*

Tyne & Wear Foundation *466*

Worshipful Company of Engineers' Charitable Trust Fund, The *504*

....
■ Research

see **Academic subjects, Sciences & research, Medical studies & research, Specialist research**

....
■ Research institutes

see also **Academic subjects, sciences & research**

Funding priority

Alcohol Education and Research Council *9*

Ciba Fellowship Trust, The *95*

Eranda Foundation, The *152*

Melville Trust for Care and Cure of Cancer *305*

Mental Health Foundation, The *305*

Oldacre Foundation, The John *345*

Stonehouse Trust Ltd, Eric *438*

Thriplow Charitable Trust *456*

Wellcome Trust, The *485*

Will consider

Abbeydale Trust *5*

Beit Trust, The *40*

British Dietetic Association General and Education Trust Fund, The *61*

Burden Trust, The *69*

Chrimes Family Charitable Trust, The *93*

Commonwealth Relations Trust *108*

Cooper Charitable Trust *111*

Coutts Charitable Trust, The *116*

Digby Charitable Trust, Simon *133*

Edgar Foundation, The Gilbert and Eileen *145*

Edgar Trust, The Gilbert *145*

Education Services *145*

Emanuel Charitable Settlement, Ralph and Muriel *150*

Frazer Charities Trust, The *171*

Galinski Charitable Trust *177*

Gardner Charitable Trust, R & J *178*

Gibbins Trust, The *181*

Graham Charitable Trust, Reginald *190*

Great Britain Sasakawa Foundation, The *193*

Holly Hill Charitable Trust *224*

Ireland Funds, The *237*

Kiln Charitable Trust, Robert *254*

Lee Foundation, The Edgar *269*

London Law Trust *280*

Lynall Foundation, The D G *287*

McDougall Trust, The *291*

NR Charitable Trust, The *325*

Needham Cooper Charitable Trust, The *331*

Owen Family Trust, The *348*

PF Charitable Trust *350*

Pilkington Charitable Trust, Cecil *363*

Rayner Charitable Trust, The John *380*

Rest-Harrow Trust, The *382*

Rhodes Trust – Public Purposes Fund, The *383*

SMB Trust, The *400*

Shepherd Charitable Trust, The Sylvia and Colin *418*

South Square Trust *430*

Upjohn Charitable Trust, The *469*

Webber Trust Fund, Ethel *483*

Weir Foundation, The James *484*

Wincott Foundation, The *496*

Wolfe Family's Charitable Trust, The *498*

Yorkshire Agricultural Society *509*

■ **Residences**

see also Arts & arts facilities

Funding priority

Granada Foundation, The *190*

■ **Residential facilities**

see also Residential facilities & services

Funding priority

Baker Charitable Trust, The *30*

Bilton Charity, The Percy *48*

Cope Charitable Trust, Alfred *112*

Curriers Company Charitable Fund *119*

Dahl Foundation, The Roald *122*

Davenport's Charity Trust, Baron *124*

Grundy Foundation, The Stanley *198*

HACT (The Housing Association's Charitable Trust) *201*

Hyde Charitable Trust *232*

Lacy Charity Trust, The Late Sir Pierce *260*

Merchant Taylors' Consolidated Charities for the Infirm *306*

Metropolitan Hospital-Sunday Fund, The *308*

Needham Cooper Charitable Trust, The *331*

Nidditch Foundation, The Laurie *335*

Paul Charitable Trust, The Late Barbara May *355*

Paul Charitable Trust, Margaret Jeanne *355*

Paul Charitable Trust, Pamela Milton *355*

Pitt Trust, Headley *364*

Rae Charity, H J *375*

Richards Charity, The Violet M *384*

Williams Trust, The Neville *493*

Woburn 1986 Charitable Trust *498*

Youell Foundation Ltd, The *510*

Will consider

AB Charitable Trust *3*

Alexis Trust, The *11*

Ammco Trust, The *15*

Anstey Charitable Settlement, J C W *18*

Army Benevolent Fund, The *22*

Ashden Charitable Trust, The *24*

Astor Foundation, The *26*

Avenal *27*

Balint Charitable Trust, Paul *31*

Barbour Trust, The *33*

Benham Charitable Trust, Hervey *43*

Blake Charitable Trust, The Hubert *53*

Boots Charitable Trust *56*

Borthwick Memorial Trust, The Oliver *56*

Brotherton Trust, The Charles *65*

Brough Charitable Trust, Joseph *65*

Buckingham Trust *67*

Bullough Tompson Settlement, The *68*

Burden Trust, The *69*

CLA Charitable Trust *74*

Cadbury Trust (1928), The Edward & Dorothy *76*

Calypso Browning Trust *78*

Camelot Foundation, The *78*

Campden Charities, The *79*

Charities Fund *89*

Charity Projects *90*

Chase Charity, The *91*

Cooper Charitable Trust *111*

County Durham Foundation *115*

Coutts Charitable Trust, The *116*

de Freitas Charitable Trust, The Helen and Geoffrey *126*

Dean Refugee Trust Fund, The Miriam *128*

Derbyshire Trust, J N *130*

Digby Charitable Trust, Simon *133*

Egerton of Tatton Will Trust, Lord *146*

Elkes Charity Fund, The Wilfred & Elsie *147*

Emmaus Christian Foundation *150*

Eventhall Family Charitable Trust, The *155*

Ferguson Benevolent Fund Limited *161*

Follett Trust, The *166*

Ford of Britain Trust *166*

Frognal Trust *174*

Greenaway Foundation, The Sir Derek *194*

Hannay Charitable Trust, The Lennox *208*

Harford Charitable Trust *209*

Harvey Charitable Trust, Gordon *211*

Held Settlement, The Gisela *215*

Hudson Benevolent Trust, The Thomas *230*

Isle of Dogs Community Foundation *238*

JDM Charitable Trust *239*

Jewish Childs' Day *245*

Johnson Foundation, The *246*

King Charitable Trust, The Lorna *254*

Kroch Foundation, The Heinz & Anna *259*

Laing Charitable Trust, The David *260*

Laing Foundation, The Christopher *260*

Lankelly Foundation, The *264*

Leech Charity, The William *269*

Lewis Partnership, John *274*

Licensed Trade Charities Trust, The *274*

Linmardon Trust *276*

Lynall Foundation, The D G *287*

Lyons Charitable Trust, The *288*

McCarthy Foundation, The John *290*

Mackintosh Foundation, The *292*

Manning Trust, Leslie & Lilian *296*

Marchday Charitable Fund, The *296*

Marriage's Charitable Trust, Miss G M *299*

Mental Health Foundation, The *305*

Morphy Memorial Fund, Arthur *319*

Morrison Bequest Fund, Thomas Wharrie *320*

NR Charitable Trust, The *325*

New Court Charitable Trust *332*

Newby Trust Ltd *332*

Norman Family Charitable Trust, The *337*

Northern Ireland Voluntary Trust *339*

Norton Foundation, The *340*

PF Charitable Trust *350*

Paterson Charitable Foundation, The Constance *354*

Paterson Charitable Trust, Arthur James *354*

Payne Trust, The Harry *356*

Pratt Charitable Trust, The W L *367*

Pryor Charitable Trust, The John *370*

Reader's Digest Trust, The *380*

Rest-Harrow Trust, The *382*

Rowbotham Charitable Trust, The Christopher *393*

Rowntree Foundation, Joseph *394*

Scott Bader Commonwealth Ltd, The *411*

Seagram Distillers Charitable Trust *413*

Sheepdrove Trust, The *417*

Sheldon Trust, The *417*

Smith & Mount Trust, The Mrs *426*

South Square Trust *430*

Sparkhill Trust, The *433*

Summerfield Charitable Trust, The *442*

Swan Mountain Trust *444*

Sykes Trust, The Charles *445*

Tisbury Telegraph Trust, The *457*

Trust for the Homeless *462*

Tudor Trust, The *463*

Unitek Foundation *469*

Van Neste Foundation, The *471*

Victoria & Johnson Memorial Trust, Queen *472*

Wall Trust, Thomas *478*

Wander Charitable Fund, The Dr Albert *479*

Wesleyan Charitable Trust, The *485*

Whitaker Charitable Trust *489*

Will Charitable Trust, The *492*

Woodlands Trust *501*

Woodroffe Benton Foundation, The *502*

Wyford Charitable Trust, The *507*

....

■ Residential facilities & services

see also **Advice & information (housing), Almshouses, Emergency & short-term housing, Holiday accommodation, Hostels, Housing associations, Residential facilities, Respite, Sheltered accommodation**

Funding priority

Alexandra Trust *11*

Allied Dunbar Staff Charity Fund *13*

Army Benevolent Fund, The *22*

CLA Charitable Trust *74*

D'Avigdor Goldsmid Charitable Trust, The Sarah *125*

Devon Association for the Blind *131*

Fishmongers' Company's Charitable Trust *163*

George's Fund for Sailors, King *180*

Good Neighbours Trust, The *188*

HACT (The Housing Association's Charitable Trust) *201*

Hartley Memorial Trust, The N & P *211*

Help the Homeless *215*

Hertfordshire Community Trust, The *217*

Hussey for Africans, Charity of Rebecca *231*

Lewis Partnership, John *274*

Lloyd's Charities Trust *278*

Man of the People Fund *295*

Nidditch Foundation, The Laurie *335*

Northcott Devon Foundation *338*

Paul's Charitable Trust, R J *355*

Persula Foundation, The *360*

Pitman Charitable Trust, The John *364*

Rogers Charitable Settlement, The Richard *390*

SMB Trust, The *400*

Seva Trust, Rampaba Sadhu *415*

Skerritt Trust *423*

Stevens Foundation, The June *437*

Swan Mountain Trust *444*

TSB Foundation for Scotland *447*

Trust for the Homeless *462*

Wates Foundation, The *481*

Westminster Amalgamated Charity *487*

Wiltshire Community Foundation *495*

Woodcote Trust, The *501*

Yapp Welfare Trust, The *508*

Will consider

AHJ Charitable Trust, The *3*

Achiezer Association Limited *6*

Airflow Community Ltd, The *9*

Aleh Charitable Foundation, The *10*

Ancaster Trust, The *16*

Anderson Trust, Andrew *16*

Andrew Charitable Trust, The Prince *16*

Angler's Inn Trust *17*

Appelbe Trust, Ambrose & Ann *19*

Aquarian Healing Trust *19*

Aquarius Charitable Foundation, The *19*

Aquinas Trust *20*

Askew Charitable Trust, The Ian *25*

Askew Trust, The Dorothy *25*

Assembled Church of Christ Trust, The *25*

Assheton-Smith Charitable Trust *25*

Astor Foundation, The *26*

Astor of Hever Trust, The *26*

Astor's 1969 Charity, The Hon M L *26*

Austin of Longbridge Will Trust, The Rt Hon Herbert, Baron *27*

BBC Children in Need Appeal, The *29*

Baker Charitable Trust, The *30*

Barbour Trust, The *33*

Baring Foundation, The *34*

Barnby's Foundation Appointed Fund, Lord *35*

Barnby's Foundation, Lord *35*

Barnes Workhouse Fund *35*

Barnsbury Charitable Trust *35*

Barton Trust, Eleanor *37*

Bateman Charitable Trust, Lady Margaret *37*

Bealey Foundation, The *38*

Beattie Charitable Trust, The James *39*

Beckwith Charitable Settlement, The Heather *39*

Beckwith Charitable Trust, The Peter *40*

Beckwith-Smith's Charitable Settlement, Mrs *40*

Bengough Trust, The *43*

Benham Charitable Trust, Hervey *43*

Bentall Charity Trust, Rowan *44*

Bergqvist Charitable Trust *44*

Berris Charitable Trust *45*

Bilton Charity, The Percy *48*

Black Charitable Trust, Edna *51*

Black Charitable Trust, Sydney *51*

Black Foundation, The Bertie *51*

Blackman Foundation, Isabel *52*

Blagrave Charitable Trust, The Herbert and Peter *52*

Blake Charitable Trust, The Hubert *53*

Blakenham's Charity Trust, Lady *53*

Blakey Charitable Trust, The Celia and Conrad *53*

Blank Donations Ltd, The David *54*

Boltons Trust, The *55*

Borthwick Memorial Trust, The Oliver *56*

Bottom Charitable Trust, Harry *56*

Bowland Charitable Trust, The *57*

Brand Trust, The *59*

British Sugar Foundation *63*

Brook Charitable Settlement, R E *64*

Brookhouse's Will Trust, Mr John Charles *65*

Brough Charitable Trust, Joseph *65*

Burden Trust, The *69*

Burn Charity Trust, The J H *70*

Burns Charity, The Dorothy *70*

Burry Charitable Trust, The *70*

Burton Charitable Trust, The Geoffrey *71*

Butler's Trust, Lord *71*

Butler's Trust, Lucilla *72*

Buxton Trust, Denis *72*

Cadbury Schweppes Foundation, The *76*

Camelot Foundation, The *78*

Campden Charities, The *79*

Candap Trust, The *80*

Cardiff & Swansea Methodist District Charitable Trust Fund *80*

Carron Charitable Trust, The *83*

Castang Charitable Trust, H and M *85*

Cathedral Nursing Society Charitable Trust *85*

Charity Projects *90*

Chippindale Foundation, Sam *93*

Christian Renewal Trust, The *94*

Christmas Cracker Trust *95*

Cinderford Charitable Trust, The *96*

Clark Charitable Trust, J Anthony *98*

Closehelm Ltd *101*

Clutterbuck Charitable Trust, Robert *102*

Coates Charitable Settlement, The *102*

Coates Charitable Trust 1969, Lance *103*

Cohen Charitable Trust, The Vivienne and Samuel *104*

Cohen Charity Trust, Lucy *104*

Cole Charitable Trust, The *105*

Collinson Charitable Trust, The Norman *106*

Company of Tobacco Pipe Makers and Tobacco Blenders Benevolent Fund *109*

Condon Family Trust *109*

Cope Charitable Trust, Alfred *112*

Cotton Trust, The *114*

Crescent Trust, The *117*

Curry Charitable Trust, Dennis *119*

Curzon Charitable Trust, The Wallace *120*

Cymerman Trust Limited, Itzchok Meyer *120*

Daily Telegraph Charitable Trust *122*

Dandeen Charitable Trust *123*

Davy Foundation, The J *126*

De Avenley Foundation, The *126*

De La Rue Charitable Trust *127*

De Rothschild 1981 Charitable Trust, The Edmund *127*

De Yong Charitable Trust, The Emma *128*

Denby Charitable Foundation, The *130*

Denton Charitable Trust, The *130*

Derbyshire Trust, J N *130*

Desmond Charitable Trust, The Richard *131*

Deutsch Charitable Trust, The Andre *131*

Deutsch Charitable Trust, The H & M *131*

Dibden Allotments Charity *132*

Dibs Charitable Trust, The *133*

Dicken Charitable Trust, The Albert *133*

Dinam Charity *134*

Djanogly Foundation, The *135*

Doughty Charity Trust, The *136*

D'Oyly Carte Charitable Trust, The *137*

Drayton Trust, The *138*

Dulverton Trust, The *139*

Dunhill Medical Trust, The *140*

Dunn Charitable Trust, The Harry *140*

Earley Charity, The *142*

Earmark Trust, The *142*

Edinburgh Trust, No 2 Account *145*

Egerton of Tatton Will Trust, Lord *146*

Eling Trust *147*

Elkes Charity Fund, The Wilfred & Elsie *147*

Elshore Limited *149*

Elvetham Charitable Trust, The *149*

Eventhall Family Charitable Trust, The *155*

Fairbairn Charitable Trust, The Esmee *157*

Family Trust, The *158*

Famos Foundation Trust *158*

Federation of Jewish Relief Organisations *160*

Ferguson Benevolent Fund Limited *161*

Fletcher Trust, Roy *165*

Foreman Foundation, The Carl & Eve *167*

Foyle Trust, Charles Henry *169*

Franklin Bequest, The Rosalind *169*

Franklin Deceased's New Second Charity, Sydney E *170*

Friarsgate Trust *172*

Frome Christian Fellowship *174*

Fry Charitable Trust, Maurice *174*

Garnett Charitable Trust, The *178*

Garthgwynion Charities *179*

Gelston Charitable Trust, The *179*

Gibbins Trust, The *181*

Gibbs Charitable Trusts, The *181*

Gibson's Charity Trust, The Hon Mr & Mrs Clive *182*

Gillett Charitable Trust, J A *183*

Gill's Charitable Trust, Mrs M M *184*

Girdlers' Company Charitable Trust, The *184*

Gold Hill Church Trust *186*

Goldberg Charitable Trust, The Lewis *186*

Golders Green Foundation *187*

Goldsmiths' Company's Charities, The *188*

Goodman Charitable Foundation, The Everard and Mina *188*

Goodman Trust, The *189*

Goodman Trust, The S & F *189*

Gradel Foundation, The *189*

Graves Charitable Trust, J G *192*

Green Foundation, Constance *194*

Greenaway Foundation, The Sir Derek *194*

Griffiths Trust, The E E and D M *196*

Grocers' Charity *197*

Gross Charities Limited, M & R *197*

Grosshill Charitable Trust *197*

Grut Charitable Trust, The *198*

HB Charitable Trust *201*

Hacking & Sons Ltd Charitable Trust, C G *201*

Haines Charitable Trust, The Alfred *203*

Hamilton Educational Trust, Eleanor *205*

Hamlyn Foundation, The Helen *205*

Hampstead Wells and Campden Trust *206*

Harbour Foundation Ltd, The *208*

Harford Charitable Trust *209*

Harvey Charitable Trust, Gordon *211*

Hawthorne Charitable Trust, The *212*

Heinz Company Limited Charitable Trust, The H J *215*

Held Settlement, The Gisela *215*

Hillards Charitable Trust, Gay & Peter Hartley's *220*

Holford Trust Fund *224*

Hoover Foundation, The *226*

Horn Trust, The Cuthbert *227*

Hornby Charitable Trust, Miss D *227*

Hornton Trust, The *228*

Hospital of God at Greatham , The *229*

Hughes Charitable Trust, The Geoffery C *230*

Hyde Park Place Estate Charity, The *232*

IPE Charitable Trust, The *233*

Inman Charity, The *235*

International Arab Women's Council Charities Fund 236

Irving Charitable Trust, The Charles 237

JCSCJ Charitable Trust, The 238

James Foundation, The Catherine and Lady Grace 241

Jarrold Trust Ltd, John 243

Johnson Foundation, The Beth 247

Jones Trust, Cemlyn 248

KC Charitable Trust, The 250

Karten Charitable Trust, The Ian 250

Keyes Trust, The Ursula 253

Kingsgrove Charitable Trust, The 255

Kinnison Charitable Trust, R O 256

Kleinwort Charitable Trust, The Ernest 257

Knott Trust, Sir James 258

Kobler Trust, The 258

Kreitman Foundation 258

Kulika Charitable Trust, The 259

Kweller Charitable Trust, The Harry 259

Laing Charitable Trust, The David 260

Laing Trust, Beatrice 261

Landy Charitable Trust, Harry and Gertrude 263

Langley Charitable Trust, The 264

Lankelly Foundation, The 264

Lanvern Foundation 265

Laski Memorial Charitable Trust, Nathan 265

Laspen Trust 265

Lauffer Charitable Foundation, The R & D 266

Lavender Trust, The 267

Lawley Foundation, The Edgar E 267

Leach Fourteenth Trust, The 267

Leigh-Bramwell Trust 'E', P 270

Levy Charitable Foundation, Joseph 272

Liffe Benefit 274

Lingwood Charitable Trust, The 276

Lloyd's Charities Trust 278

(Lloyds) TSB Foundation for England and Wales 279

Localtrent Ltd 279

Low & Bonar Charitable Fund, The 284

Lucas Charitable Trust Limited, The Joseph 286

Lunzer Charitable Trust, The Ruth & Jack 287

Lynn Foundation, The 288

Lynwood Charitable Trust, The 288

Lyons Charitable Trust, The 288

Lyons Charitable Trust, Sir Jack 288

MDM Memorial Trust 289

MacAndrew Trust, The E M 289

McKechnie Foundation, A N 292

McKenzie Trust, The Robert 292

Mackintosh Foundation, The 292

McLaren Foundation 292

McLaren Memorial Trust, The Martin 293

MacRobert Trusts, The 294

Marchday Charitable Fund, The 296

Margadale Charitable Trust, Lord 297

Marks Charitable Trust, Michael 298

Marks Foundation, The Hilda and Samuel 298

Markus Charitable Foundation, The Erich 298

Marmor Charitable Trust, The Julie 299

Marriage's Charitable Trust, Miss G M 299

Marr-Munning Trust 299

Marshall Charitable Trust, The Charlotte 300

Martin Trust, The Sir George 300

Matchan Fund Limited, The Leonard 301

Material World Charitable Foundation Limited, The 301

Mattock Charitable Trust, The W T 302

Mayfair Charities Limited 303

Measures Charity, The James Frederick and Ethel Anne 303

Meath, Charity of Mary Jane, Countess of 304

Medlock Charitable Trust, The 304

Mellows Charitable Settlement, The Anthony and Elizabeth 305

Mid Moss Charitable Trust, The 309

Milburn Charitable Trust, Frederick 310

Millett Charitable Trust, The Alan and Janet 312

Millfield House Foundation 312

Millichope Foundation, The 312

Modiano Charitable Trust 315

Montefiore Trust, The David 316

Moore Charitable Trust, The Horace 316

Morel Charitable Trust, The 318

Morgan Crucible Company plc Charitable Trust, The 319

Morphy Memorial Fund, Arthur 319

Morris Charitable Trust, The Willie & Mabel 320

Moulton Charitable Trust, The 321

Music Sales Charitable Trust, The 324

National Lottery Charities Board 328

National Power Charitable Trust, The 330

Needham Cooper Charitable Trust, The 331

Newcastle's 1986 Charitable Trust, Duke of 333

Newman Charitable Trust, Mr and Mrs F E F 334

Newstead Charity, The 334

Norfolk's Family Charitable Trust, Lavinia 336

North West Arts Board 337

Northcott Charity Trust, The 338

Northern Arts 339

Northern Dairies Educational Trust 339

Northern Electric Employee Charity Association 339

Northern Ireland Voluntary Trust 339

Old Possums Practical Trust, The 344

Oliver Trust, Kate Wilson 345

Oppenheimer Charitable Trust 346

Owen Trust, Margaret 348

PDC Trust, The 349

PJD Charitable Trust 350

Palmer Trust, The Gerald 352

Parivar Trust, The 353

Pascoe Charitable Trust, Alan 354

Paul Charitable Trust, The Late Barbara May 355

Paul Charitable Trust, Margaret Jeanne 355

Paul Charitable Trust, Pamela Milton 355

Paul Foundation, The 355

Payne Charitable Trust, The 355

Pelech Charitable Trust, The 358

Perry Charitable Trust, Miss Frances Lucille 359

Pershore Nashdom & Elmore Trust Ltd, The 360

Peskin Charitable Trust, The Hazel and Leslie 360

Phillips Charitable Foundation, Reginald M 361

Pick Charitable Trust, The George and Jessie *362*
Pilkington Charitable Trust, Cecil *363*
Pitt Trust, Headley *364*
Powys Welsh Church Fund *367*
Prendergast Charitable Trust, The Simone *368*
Proctor Charitable Trust, The Albert Edward *370*
Puebla Charitable Trust Limited, The *371*
QAS Charitable Trust *373*
Quothquan Charitable Trust, The Second *373*
RT Trust, The *374*
Rackham Charitable Trust, The Mr & Mrs Philip *375*
Radley Charitable Trust *375*
Rae Charity, H J *375*
Rainford Trust, The *376*
Rav Chesed Trust, The *379*
Reekie Trust, R A & V B *381*
Rest-Harrow Trust, The *382*
Richards Charity, The Clive *384*
Richards Charity, The Violet M *384*
Richmond Parish Lands Charity *384*
Rivendell Trust, The *387*
Robbins Trust, The Cheshire *387*
Rodewald's Charitable Settlement, Mr C A *389*
Rolfe Charitable Trust, The *390*
Rope Third Charitable Settlement, The Mrs *391*
Rosen Foundation, Cecil *392*
Rozel Trust, The *397*
S Group Charitable Trust *399*
St Jude's Trust *403*
Salters Charities *405*
Samuel Charitable Trust, M J *406*
Sargeant's Charitable Trust, Mrs M E *407*
Save & Prosper Foundation *409*
Scarr-Hall Memorial Trust, The *409*
Scott Charitable Trust, The Francis C *412*
Seva Trust, Rampaba Sadhu *415*
Sheepdrove Trust, The *417*
Sherman Charitable Trust, The Archie *419*
Shifrin Charitable Trust, The Maurice and Hilda *419*
Shine No 2 Charitable Trust, The Barnett and Sylvia *420*
Sidbury Trust, The Second *421*
Silvester Charitable Gift Trust *422*
Simon's Charity *422*
Skelton Bounty, The *423*
Skinners' Company Lady Neville Charity *424*

Salter Trust Ltd *424*
Society of Friends of the Torah, The *429*
Solomons Charitable Trust, David *430*
Somerfield Curtis Will Trust, The Dorothy *430*
Southall Charitable Trust, Kenneth & Phyllis *431*
Southall Trust, W F *432*
Sparkhill Trust, The *433*
Stanley Foundation Limited *435*
Stewart Charitable Trust, Mary Stephanie *437*
Sumner's Trust Section 'A', Sir John *443*
Symons Charitable Trust, The Stella *446*
TSB Foundation for Scotland *447*
TSB Foundation for the Channel Islands *447*
Tait Charity, The Richard *448*
Taylor Charitable Trust, The B R *450*
Terry Charitable Trust, Noel Goddard *451*
Tesco Charity Trust *452*
Tesler Foundation, The *452*
Thornton-Smith Trust, The *455*
3i Charitable Trust, The *455*
Timson Family Charitable Trust *457*
Towler Charity Trust, The Fred *459*
Turkish Women's Philanthropic Association of England *463*
Turner Charitable Settlement, The Sir Mark and Lady *464*
Tyne & Wear Foundation *466*
Unitek Foundation *469*
van Geest Foundation, The John and Lucille *470*
Van Norden's Charitable Foundation, Mrs Maud *471*
Vincent Trust Fund, Eric W *473*
Vineyard Christian Fellowship of South West *473*
Vinson Charity Trust, The 1969 *473*
Vogel Charitable Trust, The Nathan *474*
Wagstaff Charitable Trust, Bob *475*
Wakefield Trust, The *476*
Ward Blenkinsop Trust, The *480*
Weinstock Fund, The *484*
Welby Trust, The Barbara *484*
Whetherly's Charitable Trust, The Hon Mrs R G A *489*
Whitaker Charitable Trust *489*
Whitehead Charitable Trust, J E *490*
Whitley Trust, Sheila *491*
Whittington Charitable Trust, The *491*

Wiggins Charity Trust, Cyril *491*
Wilde Charitable Trust, The Felicity *492*
Wills 1961 Charitable Trust, Major Michael Thomas *494*
Wiltshire Community Foundation *495*
Winstone Foundation, Hyman *497*
Woburn 1986 Charitable Trust *498*
Wohl Charitable Foundation, The Maurice *498*
Wohl Charitable Trust, The Maurice *498*
Wolff Charity Trust *498*
Wolfson Family Charitable Trust, The *499*
Woodhouse Charitable Trust, Edwin *501*
Woods Charitable Foundation, Geoffrey *502*
Worms Charitable Trust, The Freda and Della *504*
Worshipful Company of Founders Charities, The *505*
Worshipful Company of Needlemakers' Charitable Fund *505*
Wychdale Limited *507*
Youell Foundation Ltd, The *510*
Zaiger Trust, The Elizabeth and Prince *512*

....

■ Respite

see also **Residential facilities & services**

Funding priority
AB Charitable Trust *3*
Allied Dunbar Charitable Trust Limited, The *13*
Army Benevolent Fund, The *22*
Bilton Charity, The Percy *48*
Boots Charitable Trust *56*
Coutts Charitable Trust, The *116*
Hyde Charitable Trust *232*
Leech Charity, The William *269*
Marchday Charitable Fund, The *296*
Needham Cooper Charitable Trust, The *331*
Whitaker Charitable Trust *489*

Will consider
Abbey National Charitable Trust *4*
Alexis Trust, The *11*
Ammco Trust, The *15*
Anstey Charitable Settlement, J C W *18*
Aquarius Charitable Foundation, The *19*
Archer Trust, The *20*

Astor Foundation, The *26*
Avon Trust, The *28*
Balney Charitable Trust, The *32*
Barbour Trust, The *33*
Barrie Charitable Trust, The Misses *36*
Beit Trust, The *40*
Bell's Charitable Trust, Lady Mary *42*
Benham Charitable Trust, Hervey *43*
Berkshire Community Trust *45*
Birtwistle Memorial Trust, The G E *50*
Borthwick Memorial Trust, The Oliver *56*
Brough Charitable Trust, Joseph *65*
Bullough Tompson Settlement, The *68*
Burdall Charity, H M *69*
Burden Trust, The *69*
Butlin Charity Trust, Bill *72*
Cadbury Trust (1928), The Edward & Dorothy *76*
Camelot Foundation, The *78*
Campden Charities, The *79*
Charities Fund *89*
Charity Projects *90*
Chase Charity, The *91*
Christmas Cracker Trust *95*
Clipsham Charitable Settlement, R E *101*
Cooper Charitable Trust *111*
County Durham Foundation *115*
Curriers Company Charitable Fund *119*
D'Avigdor Goldsmid Charitable Trust, The Sarah *125*
de Freitas Charitable Trust, The Helen and Geoffrey *126*
Denne Charitable Trust *130*
Derbyshire Trust, J N *130*
Dibs Charitable Trust, The *133*
Digby Charitable Trust, Simon *133*
Direct Response *134*
Dumbreck Charity *139*
Early's Charitable Settlement, Richard *142*
Edgar Trust, The Gilbert *145*
Egerton of Tatton Will Trust, Lord *146*
Elkes Charity Fund, The Wilfred & Elsie *147*
Emmandjay Charitable Trust *150*
Emmaus Christian Foundation *150*
Eventhall Family Charitable Trust, The *155*
Ferguson Benevolent Fund Limited *161*
Firdale Christian Trust, The *162*
Fogel Charitable Trust, The Gerald *165*

Follett Trust, The *166*
Ford of Britain Trust *166*
Four Winds Trust *168*
Franklin Trust, Jill *170*
Frognal Trust *174*
Garnett Charitable Trust, The *178*
Gelston Charitable Trust, The *179*
Grant Charitable Trust, The *191*
Grant-Lawson Charitable Trust, Lady Virginia *192*
Greenaway Foundation, The Sir Derek *194*
HACT (The Housing Association's Charitable Trust) *201*
Hannay Charitable Trust, The Lennox *208*
Harford Charitable Trust *209*
Hartley Memorial Trust, The N & P *211*
Harvey Charitable Trust, Gordon *211*
Held Settlement, The Gisela *215*
Hudson Benevolent Trust, The Thomas *230*
Inverforth Charitable Trust, The *236*
Isle of Dogs Community Foundation *238*
JDM Charitable Trust *239*
Johnson Group Cleaners Charity *247*
King Charitable Settlement, Philip *254*
Kroch Foundation, The Heinz & Anna *259*
Lacy Charity Trust, The Late Sir Pierce *260*
Laing Charitable Trust, The David *260*
Laing Foundation, The Christopher *260*
Lancaster's Trust, Bryan *263*
Lankelly Foundation, The *264*
Lawson Charitable Trust, Raymond and Blanche *267*
Lee Foundation, The Edgar *269*
Lewis Partnership, John *274*
London Taxi Drivers' Fund for Underprivileged Children, The *280*
Lynall Foundation, The D G *287*
Lyons Charitable Trust, The *288*
McCarthy Foundation, The John *290*
Mackintosh Foundation, The *292*
Manning Trust, Leslie & Lilian *296*
Margaret Foundation, The *297*

Marriage's Charitable Trust, Miss G M *299*
Merchant Taylors' Consolidated Charities for the Infirm *306*
Metropolitan Hospital-Sunday Fund, The *308*
Milburn Charitable Trust, Frederick *310*
Moores Foundation, John *318*
Morphy Memorial Fund, Arthur *319*
Morris Charitable Trust, The Douglas *320*
NR Charitable Trust, The *325*
Natwest Staff Samaritan Fund *330*
New Court Charitable Trust *332*
Newby Trust Ltd *332*
Northern Ireland Voluntary Trust *339*
Norton Foundation, The *340*
Oldham Foundation *345*
Owen Family Trust, The *348*
Paget Trust, The *351*
Paristamen Foundation, The *352*
Paterson Charitable Foundation, The Constance *354*
Paterson Charitable Trust, Arthur James *354*
Payne Trust, The Harry *356*
Pryor Charitable Trust, The John *370*
Pye Christian Trust, The *371*
Reader's Digest Trust, The *380*
Rest-Harrow Trust, The *382*
Robinson Brothers (Ryders Green) Ltd, Charitable Trust *388*
Rope Third Charitable Settlement, The Mrs *391*
Rothley Trust, The *392*
Rowbotham Charitable Trust, The Christopher *393*
Rowntree Foundation, Joseph *394*
Royal's Memorial Fund, Princess *396*
St Christopher's Trust, The *402*
Saint Edmund King and Martyr Trust *402*
Seagram Distillers Charitable Trust *413*
Sheepdrove Trust, The *417*
Sheldon Trust, The *417*
Smith & Mount Trust, The Mrs *426*
South Square Trust *430*
Sparkhill Trust, The *433*
Sportsman's Aid Charity Ltd, The *434*
Stonehouse Trust Ltd, Eric *438*
Summerfield Charitable Trust, The *442*

Summer's and I May's
Charitable Settlement, The
Late Misses (A N) *442*
Sussman Charitable Trust,
Adrienne & Leslie *443*
Swan Mountain Trust *444*
Sykes Trust, The Charles *445*
TSB Foundation for Northern
Ireland *447*
Thackray General Charitable
Trust, The P & L *452*
Tisbury Telegraph Trust, The
457
Travis Charitable Trust,
Constance *460*
Truemark Trust, The *461*
Trust for the Homeless *462*
Tudor Trust, The *463*
Unitek Foundation *469*
Van Neste Foundation, The
471
Victoria & Johnson Memorial
Trust, Queen *472*
Wall Trust, Thomas *478*
Wander Charitable Fund, The
Dr Albert *479*
Webber Trust Fund, Ethel *483*
Weir Foundation, The James
484
Wesleyan Charitable Trust, The
485
Whesby Ltd *488*
Whitecourt Charitable Trust,
The *490*
Williams Trust, The Neville *493*
Wiltshire Community
Foundation *495*
Woburn 1986 Charitable Trust
498
Wolfe Family's Charitable
Trust, The *498*
Woodlands Trust *501*
Woodroffe Benton Foundation,
The *502*
Wyford Charitable Trust, The
507
Wylde Memorial Charity, The
Anthony and Gwendoline
507

∎ **Respite care, care
for carers**

see also Health care

Funding priority
Allied Dunbar Charitable Trust
Limited, The *13*
Ammco Trust, The *15*
Berkshire Community Trust *45*
Community Trust for Greater
Manchester, The *108*
Davis Charitable Trust, Wilfrid
Bruce *126*
Gardner Charitable Trust, R & J
178
Gladstone Charitable Trust, The
E W *184*

Grant Charitable Trust, The
191
Hussey Trust, The *232*
Johnson Group Cleaners
Charity *247*
Lacy Charity Trust, The Late Sir
Pierce *260*
Lawson Charitable Trust,
Raymond and Blanche *267*
League of the Helping Hand,
The *268*
Leech Charity, The William *269*
Lloyd's Charities Trust *278*
(Lloyds) TSB Foundation for
England and Wales *279*
Loseley & Guildway Charitable
Trust, The *281*
Moore Foundation, The
George A *316*
Moores Foundation, John *318*
Needham Cooper Charitable
Trust, The *331*
Robinson Trust 4, The J C *388*
Rocket Club Benevolent Fund,
The *389*
Royal Theatrical Fund, The *396*
SMB Trust, The *400*
Wakeham Trust, The *476*
Wiltshire Community
Foundation *495*

Will consider
AB Charitable Trust *3*
Abbey National Charitable
Trust *4*
Andrew Charitable Trust, The
Prince *16*
Anstey Charitable Settlement,
J C W *18*
Archer Trust, The *20*
Army Benevolent Fund, The *22*
Astor Foundation, The *26*
Balint Charitable Trust, Paul *31*
Barbour Trust, The *33*
Barrie Charitable Trust, The
Misses *36*
Beckwith Charitable
Settlement, The Heather *39*
Berris Charitable Trust *45*
Birmingham Amenities and
Welfare Trust, The *49*
Birtwistle Memorial Trust, The
G E *50*
Bottom Charitable Trust, Harry
56
Bourne-May Charitable Trust,
The *57*
Britton Charitable Trust, The J
& M *63*
Brough Charitable Trust,
Joseph *65*
Buckinghamshire Masonic
Centenary Fund *67*
Burdall Charity, H M *69*
Butlin Charity Trust, Bill *72*
Cadbury Trust (1928), The
Edward & Dorothy *76*

Camelot Foundation, The *78*
Campden Charities, The *79*
Cancer Relief Macmillan Fund
79
Cathedral Nursing Society
Charitable Trust *85*
Chase Charity, The *91*
Cleopatra Trust *99*
Collier Charitable Trust, The
105
Cooper Charitable Trust *111*
Cottingham Charitable Trust,
Mrs Diana Mary *114*
County Durham Foundation
115
Coutts Charitable Trust, The
116
Cripplegate Foundation *118*
Dahl Foundation, The Roald
122
Denne Charitable Trust *130*
Dibden Allotments Charity *132*
Digby Charitable Trust, Simon
133
Dorus Trust *136*
Dumbreck Charity *139*
Earley Charity, The *142*
Early's Charitable Settlement,
Richard *142*
Edgar Foundation, The Gilbert
and Eileen *145*
Edgar Trust, The Gilbert *145*
Elkes Charity Fund, The Wilfred
& Elsie *147*
Emmandjay Charitable Trust
150
Emmaus Christian Foundation
150
Epigoni Trust *152*
Eventhall Family Charitable
Trust, The *155*
Ferguson Benevolent Fund
Limited *161*
Firdale Christian Trust, The *162*
Fishmongers' Company's
Charitable Trust *163*
Fleming Charitable Trust, The
Ian *164*
Follett Trust, The *166*
Foreman Foundation, The Carl
& Eve *167*
Fortune Trust, The *167*
Franklin Trust, Jill *170*
GW Trust, The *176*
Gibbins Trust, The *181*
Goldsmiths' Company's
Charities, The *188*
Good Neighbours Trust, The
188
Grant Foundation, The
Raymond *191*
Grant-Lawson Charitable Trust,
Lady Virginia *192*
Greenaway Foundation, The
Alan *194*
Greenaway Foundation, The Sir
Derek *194*
Grocers' Charity *197*

Haines Charitable Trust, The Alfred 203

Harford Charitable Trust 209

Hawley Residuary Fund, Harry Fieldsend 212

Humanitarian Trust, The 230

Isle of Dogs Community Foundation 238

JDM Charitable Trust 239

Laing Charitable Trust, The David 260

Laing Foundation, The Kirby 261

Laing Foundation, The Maurice 261

Laing Trust, Beatrice 261

Lankelly Foundation, The 264

Leach Fourteenth Trust, The 267

Lee Foundation, The Edgar 269

Lloyd Charity, The S and D 278

London Law Trust 280

Lynall Foundation, The D G 287

MacKintosh Charitable Trust, Viscount 292

Marchday Charitable Fund, The 296

Measures Charity, The James Frederick and Ethel Anne 303

Mental Health Foundation, The 305

Merchants House of Glasgow 307

Mercury Phoenix Trust 307

Metropolitan Hospital-Sunday Fund, The 308

Milburn Charitable Trust, Frederick 310

Milton Keynes Community Trust Ltd, The 312

Milward Charity, The Edgar 313

Minet Trust, The Peter 313

Morris Charitable Trust, The Douglas 320

Multithon Trust, The 323

Natwest Staff Samaritan Fund 330

New Court Charitable Trust 332

Newby Trust Ltd 332

North British Hotel Trust 337

Noswad Charity, The 341

Owen Family Trust, The 348

Paget Trust, The 351

Payne Trust, The Harry 356

Persula Foundation, The 360

Pye Christian Trust, The 371

Pyke Charity Trust 372

Reader's Digest Trust, The 380

Rest-Harrow Trust, The 382

Robinson Brothers (Ryders Green) Ltd, Charitable Trust 388

Rothley Trust, The 392

Rowbotham Charitable Trust, The Christopher 393

Royal's Memorial Fund, Princess 396

St Christopher's Trust, The 402

Salamander Charitable Trust, The 405

Seagram Distillers Charitable Trust 413

Sheepdrove Trust, The 417

Sheldon Trust, The 417

Shepherd Charitable Trust, The Sylvia and Colin 418

Simon's Charity 422

Skelton Bounty, The 423

Smith & Mount Trust, The Mrs 426

South Square Trust 430

Stoate Charitable Trust, The Leonard Laity 438

Stonehouse Trust Ltd, Eric 438

Summerfield Charitable Trust, The 442

Sussman Charitable Trust, Adrienne & Leslie 443

Sykes Trust, The Charles 445

TSB Foundation for Northern Ireland 447

Tear Fund 450

Thackray General Charitable Trust, The P & L 452

Thompson Charitable Trust, The 453

Thomson Foundation, The Sue 454

Tisbury Telegraph Trust, The 457

Travis Charitable Trust, Constance 460

Truemark Trust, The 461

Tudor Trust, The 463

Turner Trust, The Douglas 464

Tyne & Wear Foundation 466

Van Leer Foundation UK Trust, Bernard 470

Victoria & Johnson Memorial Trust, Queen 472

Wakefield (Tower Hill, Trinity Square) Trust 476

Wall Trust, Thomas 478

Westcroft Trust 486

Whitaker Charitable Trust 489

Woodlands Trust 501

Woodroffe Benton Foundation, The 502

Worshipful Company of Engineers' Charitable Trust Fund, The 504

■ Retired

Funding priority

AB Charitable Trust 3

Alexis Trust, The 11

Barbour Trust, The 33

Beresford Trust, The 44

Betard Bequest 46

Blott Charitable Settlement, Robert Orpwood 55

Buccleuch Place Trust 67

Buckingham Trust 67

Cam, Charity of Ann 78

Chownes Foundation, The 93

Clover Trust 102

Collier Charitable Trust, The 105

Collins Charity, The George Henry 106

Corbett's Charity, Thomas 112

Davenport's Charity Trust, Baron 124

Elkes Charity Fund, The Wilfred & Elsie 147

Grange Farm Centre Trust 191

HACT (The Housing Association's Charitable Trust) 201

Hamlyn Foundation, The Helen 205

Hertfordshire Community Trust, The 217

Hopkins, The Charity of Joseph 227

Hudson Benevolent Trust, The Thomas 230

Jackson Trust for Charity, The Isaac and Harriet 240

Jewish Aged Needy Pension Society, The 245

Keller Charitable Trust, Samuel 251

Luke Trust, The 286

McCarthy Foundation, The John 290

Merchant Taylors' Consolidated Charities for the Infirm 306

Mid Moss Charitable Trust, The 309

Morrison Bequest Fund, Thomas Wharrie 320

Ogilvie Charities (Deed No 2) 344

Park Hill Trust, The 353

Pearson Foundation, The Frank 357

Powell Foundation, The 367

Sparkes Charitable Trust, The Eric F 433

Thornton-Smith Trust, The 455

Winham Foundation, The Francis 497

Woburn 1986 Charitable Trust 498

Wyford Charitable Trust, The 507

■ Rheumatism

see **Arthritis & rheumatism**

■ Roman Catholics

Funding priority

Aid to the Church in Need (United Kingdom) 8
Ballinger Charitable Trust, The 32
Bisgood Trust, The 50
Bisgood's Charitable Trust, Miss Jeanne 50
Brinton Foundation, Lady Mary 61
Catholic Education Service for England and Wales 86
Catholic Foreign Missions 86
Coote Charitable Trust, Nicholas 111
Delacour, Charity of Theresa Harriet Mary 129
Digby Charitable Trust, The Marcella and Claude 133
Fattorini Charitable Trust, James J 160
Lacy Charity Trust, The Late Sir Pierce 260
Lloyd Foundation, The Charles 278
Marshall Charitable Trust, The Charlotte 300
National Catholic Fund 327
Perth's Charitable Trust, The Earl of 360
Simpson Foundation, The 422
Sylvanus Charitable Trust, The 446
Thorpe Charity Trust, The 455

■ Rural areas – living in

Funding priority

Brotherton Trust, The Charles 65
Cobb Charity 103
Construction Industry Trust for Youth, The 110
Fletcher Trust, Roy 165
HACT (The Housing Association's Charitable Trust) 201
Hiley Trust, Joseph and Mary 219
Hudson Benevolent Trust, The Thomas 230
Lane Foundation, The Allen 263
(Lloyds) TSB Foundation for England and Wales 279
Oxfam (United Kingdom and Ireland) 348
Paget Trust, The 351
Sainsbury Charitable Fund Ltd, The 402
Skerritt Trust 423

TSB Foundation for Scotland 447
Wiltshire Community Foundation 495

Will consider

Adnams Charity, The 7
Ammco Trust, The 15
Archer Trust, The 20
Arkleton Trust, The 21
Askew Trust, The Dorothy 25
Astor Foundation, The 26
Atwell's Charity (Skinner's Company), Lawrence 27
Barbour Trust, The 33
Beckwith Charitable Settlement, The Heather 39
Benham Charitable Trust, Hervey 43
Birtwistle Memorial Trust, The G E 50
Blake Charitable Trust, The Morgan 53
Boots Charitable Trust 56
Bridge Trust, The 60
Buckinghamshire Masonic Centenary Fund 67
Buxton Trust, Denis 72
Camelot Foundation, The 78
Campbell Charitable Foundation, The Ellis 79
Carlton Television Trust 81
Carnegie United Kingdom Trust, The 82
Catto Charitable Settlement, The Thomas Sivewright 86
Challice Trust, The 87
Charity Projects 90
Clark 1965 Charitable Trust, Stephen 98
Clinton's Charitable Trust, Lord 100
Company of Chartered Surveyors Charitable Trust Fund, The 108
Cottingham Charitable Trust, Mrs Diana Mary 114
Coutts Charitable Trust, The 116
De Yong Charitable Trust, The Emma 128
Direct Response 134
Dorus Trust 136
Ebb and Flow Charitable Trust 144
Edgar Foundation, The Gilbert and Eileen 145
Edgar Trust, The Gilbert 145
Elkes Charity Fund, The Wilfred & Elsie 147
Epigoni Trust 152
Ericson Trust 152
Fletcher Charitable Trust, The Joyce 164
Four Winds Trust 168
GNC Trust 175

Gibson Charitable Trust, The Simon 182
Goldsmiths' Company's Charities, The 188
Grant-Lawson Charitable Trust, Lady Virginia 192
Groves Charitable Trust, The 197
Hanley Trust (1987), The 207
Harbinson Charitable Trust, Roderick 208
Harbour Foundation Ltd, The 208
Hayward Trust, The Charles 213
Held Settlement, The Gisela 215
Hertfordshire Community Trust, The 217
Hopkinson Educational Trust, Robert Addy 227
Hudson Charitable Trust, The 230
Hunter Charitable Trust, The Claire 231
Innes Memorial Fund 235
Iris Trust, The 237
JCSCJ Charitable Trust, The 238
Johnson Foundation, The 246
Keeling Charitable Trust, The Petronella 251
King Charitable Trust, The Lorna 254
Laing Charitable Trust, The David 260
Laing Foundation, The Christopher 260
Laing Foundation, The Kirby 261
Laing Foundation, The Maurice 261
Laing Trust, Beatrice 261
Laspen Trust 265
Leach Fourteenth Trust, The 267
Lewis Foundation, The John Spedan 274
Lloyd Charity, The S and D 278
Lloyd's Charities Trust 278
Lloyd's Patriotic Fund 279
Lynall Foundation, The D G 287
Lyons Charitable Trust, The 288
McCarthy Foundation, The John 290
MacKintosh Charitable Trust, Viscount 292
Mackintosh Foundation, The 292
Manning Trust, Leslie & Lilian 296
Marriage's Charitable Trust, Miss G M 299
Mental Health Foundation, The 305

Milburn Charitable Trust, Frederick *310*

Milton Keynes Community Trust Ltd, The *312*

Minge's Gift *314*

Moore Foundation, The George A *316*

Moores Foundation, John *318*

Music for World Development *323*

NR Charitable Trust, The *325*

Nathan Charitable Trust *326*

Natwest Staff Samaritan Fund *330*

Needham Cooper Charitable Trust, The *331*

New Court Charitable Trust *332*

New Durlston Trust, The *332*

Newby Trust Ltd *332*

Noel Buxton Trust, The *335*

Norman Family Charitable Trust, The *337*

Norton Foundation, The *340*

Oakdale Trust, The *343*

Oldham Foundation *345*

Owen Family Trust, The *348*

Paristamen Foundation, The *352*

Parivar Trust, The *353*

Payne Trust, The Harry *356*

Persula Foundation, The *360*

Pike Woodlands Trust, Claude & Margaret *362*

Pilgrim Trust, The *362*

Pratt Charitable Trust, The W L *367*

Prince's Trust - BRO, The *369*

Pye Christian Trust, The *371*

Pyke Charity Trust *372*

Ravenscroft Foundation, The *379*

Rope Third Charitable Settlement, The Mrs *391*

Rowbotham Charitable Trust, The Christopher *393*

Rowntree Foundation, Joseph *394*

Said Foundation, The Karim Rida *401*

St Christopher's Trust, The *402*

Schuster Charitable Trust, The *410*

Seagram Distillers Charitable Trust *413*

Sheldon Trust, The *417*

Shelroy Charitable Trust, The *417*

Shepherd Charitable Trust, The Sylvia and Colin *418*

South Square Trust *430*

Staples Trust *435*

Stevens Foundation, The June *437*

Stoate Charitable Trust, The Leonard Laity *438*

Stonehouse Trust Ltd, Eric *438*

Summerfield Charitable Trust, The *442*

Summer's and I May's Charitable Settlement, The Late Misses (A N) *442*

TSB Foundation for Northern Ireland *447*

Tear Fund *450*

Thornton-Smith Trust, The *455*

Tisbury Telegraph Trust, The *457*

Trust for the Homeless *462*

Tudor Trust, The *463*

Van Berchem Charitable Trust, The Alec *470*

Van Leer Foundation UK Trust, Bernard *470*

Variety Club Children's Charity Limited, The *471*

Vec Acorn Trust, The *472*

Wakeham Trust, The *476*

Waley-Cohen Charitable Trust, Robert & Felicity *477*

Wallace Charity Trust, The A F *478*

Wesleyan Charitable Trust, The *485*

Westcroft Trust *486*

Whitecourt Charitable Trust, The *490*

Woodlands Trust *501*

Worshipful Company of Glass Sellers' Charity Trust, The *505*

·····················

■ Rural arts

see **Community arts & recreation**

·····················

■ Rural Community Council (RCC)

see also **Charity or voluntary umbrella bodies**

Funding priority

Berkshire Community Trust *45*

Community Trust for Greater Manchester, The *108*

County Durham Foundation *115*

Pilkington Charitable Trust, Cecil *363*

Will consider

Amory Charitable Trust, Viscount *16*

Astor Foundation, The *26*

Barbour Trust, The *33*

Boots Charitable Trust *56*

Brotherton Trust, The Charles *65*

Camelot Foundation, The *78*

Carnegie United Kingdom Trust, The *82*

Digby Charitable Trust, Simon *133*

Edgar Foundation, The Gilbert and Eileen *145*

Gardner Charitable Trust, R & J *178*

Harford Charitable Trust *209*

Leech Charity, The William *269*

Milton Keynes Community Trust Ltd, The *312*

Noel Buxton Trust, The *335*

Northern Arts *339*

Persula Foundation, The *360*

Richmond Parish Lands Charity *384*

Rope Third Charitable Settlement, The Mrs *391*

Rowntree Foundation, Joseph *394*

Shepherd Charitable Trust, The Sylvia and Colin *418*

Summerfield Charitable Trust, The *442*

Wiltshire Community Foundation *495*

Woodlands Trust *501*

Woolton Charitable Trust, The *503*

·····················

■ Sail training

see **Education & training**

·····················

■ Scholarships

see also **Costs of study**

Funding priority

Alcohol Education and Research Council *9*

Baker Trust, The C Alma *31*

Carnegie Trust for the Universities of Scotland *82*

Company of Chartered Surveyors Charitable Trust Fund, The *108*

Garnett Charitable Trust, The *178*

Hopkinson Educational Trust, Robert Addy *227*

International Bar Association Educational Trust *236*

Jeffreys Road Fund, Rees *243*

McCallum Bequest Fund *290*

Maxwell Law Scholarship Trust, The Alexander *303*

Oldacre Foundation, The John *345*

Peacock Charitable Foundation, The Michael *356*

RVW Trust *374*

Shipwrights' Company Educational Trust, The *420*

Simon Population Trust, The *422*

South Square Trust *430*

Thriplow Charitable Trust 456
Wingate Foundation, The
  Harold Hyam 496

Will consider
Ambika Paul Foundation 15
Arts Council of Wales, The 23
Ashby Charitable Trust, The 23
Ashley Foundation, The Laura
  24
Beit Trust, The 40
Bulmer Charitable Trust, Becket
  68
Carlton Television Trust 81
Cooper Charitable Trust 111
Digby Charitable Trust, Simon
  133
Dixon Charitable Trust, F E 134
Earley Charity, The 142
Education Services 145
GABO Trust for Sculpture
  Conservation 175
Holly Hill Charitable Trust 224
Hudson Benevolent Trust, The
  Thomas 230
Humanitarian Trust, The 230
Ireland Funds, The 237
Linford Charitable Trust, The
  Fred 276
NR Charitable Trust, The 325
Needham Cooper Charitable
  Trust, The 331
Newby Trust Ltd 332
Oldham Foundation 345
Owen Family Trust, The 348
Parivar Trust, The 353
Patients' Aid Association
  Hospital and Medical
  Charities Trust 354
Pilkington Charitable Trust,
  Cecil 363
Radcliffe's Trust, Dr 375
Rayner Charitable Trust, The
  John 380
Rhodes Trust – Public Purposes
  Fund, The 383
Royal Commission for the
  Exhibition of 1851 395
Spooner Charitable Trust, W W
  434
Summerfield Charitable Trust,
  The 442
Tear Fund 450
Yorkshire Agricultural Society
  509

■ **School nature
reserves & schemes**
see Conservation

■ **Schools & colleges**
see also Business schools,
Church schools,
Independent schools, Junior
schools, Language schools,
Postgraduate education,
Pre-school education,
Primary schools, Secondary
schools, Special schools,
Tertiary & higher education

Funding priority
AB Charitable Trust, The 3
Achiezer Association Limited 6
Aga Khan Foundation (UK) 7
Airflow Community Ltd, The 9
Aldwyns Trust, The 10
Aleh Charitable Foundation,
  The 10
Alexander Charitable Trust,
  The 10
Alexander Charitable Trust,
  Mrs K L 11
Alliance Family Foundation
  Limited 13
Allsop Charitable Trust, Pat 14
Angler's Inn Trust 17
Appelbe Trust, Ambrose & Ann
  19
Ashton Foundation, The
  Norman C 24
Astor of Hever Trust, The 26
Barnes Workhouse Fund 35
Beacon Trust 38
Bear Mordechai Ltd 39
Bestway Foundation, The 46
Betton's Charity (Educational),
  Mr Thomas 46
Black Foundation, The Bertie
  51
Blank Donations Ltd, The David
  54
Bottom Charitable Trust, Harry
  56
Bowland Charitable Trust, The
  57
Bridgeman TRA Foundation,
  The Dick 60
British Friends of Chinuch
  Atzmai Trust, The 62
British Sugar Foundation 63
Broadley Charitable Trust, The
  64
Burden Trust, The 69
CfBT Education Services 74
Cadbury Schweppes
  Foundation, The 76
Careers Services Trust 81
Carron Charitable Trust, The
  83
Carter Trust, The Frederick
  William 84
Cen Foundation, The Hyman
  87
Chippindale Foundation, Sam
  93
Christmas Cracker Trust 95
Clark Charitable Trust 98

Coates Charitable Settlement,
  The 102
Coates Charitable Trust, The
  John 103
Cohen Charitable Trust, The
  Vivienne and Samuel 104
Company of Tobacco Pipe
  Makers and Tobacco
  Blenders Benevolent Fund
  109
Crescent Trust, The 117
Cripps Foundation 118
Curry Charitable Trust, Dennis
  119
Daily Telegraph Charitable
  Trust 122
Daiwa Anglo-Japanese
  Foundation, The 122
Dandeen Charitable Trust 123
Davy Foundation, The J 126
De La Rue Charitable Trust
  127
Deutsch Charitable Trust, The
  Andre 131
Deutsch Charitable Trust, The
  H & M 131
Diamond Industry Educational
  Charity, The 132
Djanogly Foundation, The 135
Doughty Charity Trust, The
  136
Edinburgh Trust, No 2 Account
  145
Elephant Jobs Charity 146
Ellis 1985 Charitable Trust,
  Edith M 148
Fairway Trust, The 158
Famos Foundation Trust 158
Fishmongers' Company's
  Charitable Trust 163
Foyle Trust, Charles Henry 169
Franklin Bequest, The Rosalind
  169
Franklin Deceased's New
  Second Charity, Sydney E
  170
Gardner Memorial Trust, The
  Samuel 178
Gibbs Charitable Trusts, The
  181
Gill's Charitable Trust, Mrs M M
  184
Girdlers' Company Charitable
  Trust, The 184
Glebe Charitable Trust 185
Good Neighbours Trust, The
  188
Goodman Charitable
  Foundation, The Everard
  and Mina 188
Goodman Trust, The 189
Grahame Charitable
  Foundation, The 190
Greenwood Charitable Trust,
  The G B 195
Griffiths Trust, The E E and
  D M 196

Gross Charities Limited, M & R 197

Grosshill Charitable Trust 197

Gwent County Council Welsh Church Fund 200

Hamilton Educational Trust, Eleanor 205

Harbour Foundation Ltd, The 208

Hargreaves Trust, The Kenneth 210

Heinz Company Limited Charitable Trust, The H J 215

Held Settlement, The Gisela 215

Highcroft Charitable Trust 218

Hitachi Charitable Trust, The 222

Hopkinson Educational Trust, Robert Addy 227

Horne Foundation, The 228

IBM United Kingdom Trust 233

IPE Charitable Trust, The 233

JCA Charitable Foundation 238

James Foundation, The Catherine and Lady Grace 241

Jewish Philanthropic Association for Israel and the Middle East, The 245

Jones Trust, Cemlyn 248

Kahn Charitable Trust, Bernard 250

Karten Charitable Trust, The Ian 250

Kobler Trust, The 258

Kreitman Foundation 258

Kulika Charitable Trust, The 259

Kweller Charitable Trust, The Harry 259

Lacy Charity Trust, The Late Sir Pierce 260

Landy Charitable Trust, Harry and Gertrude 263

Lanvern Foundation 265

Laski Memorial Charitable Trust, Nathan 265

Lauffer Charitable Foundation, The R & D 266

Leigh-Bramwell Trust 'E', P 270

Lester Trust Fund, The 271

Lewis Partnership, John 274

Lucas Charitable Trust Limited, The Joseph 286

Lunzer Charitable Trust, The Ruth & Jack 287

Lyons Charitable Trust, Sir Jack 288

Lyon's Charity, John 288

Maccabi Foundation, The 290

McKenzie Trust, The Robert 292

MacRobert Trusts, The 294

Marks Foundation, The Hilda and Samuel 298

Marmor Charitable Trust, The Julie 299

Marr-Munning Trust 299

Marshall Charitable Trust, The Charlotte 300

Martin Trust, The Sir George 300

Mayfair Charities Limited 303

Medlock Charitable Trust, The 304

Mellows Charitable Settlement, The Anthony and Elizabeth 305

Merchants House of Glasgow 307

Millett Charitable Trust, The Alan and Janet 312

Modiano Charitable Trust 315

Moore Charitable Trust, The Horace 316

Moores Foundation, The Peter 318

Morgan Foundation, The Mr & Mrs J T 319

Muslim Hands 324

Naaman Trust, The 325

Newman Charitable Trust, Mr and Mrs F E F 334

Nidditch Foundation, The Laurie 335

Northern Dairies Educational Trust 339

Old Possums Practical Trust, The 344

Oldacre Foundation, The John 345

Oxford Trust, The 349

Paddington Charitable Estates Educational Fund 351

Pelech Charitable Trust, The 358

QAS Charitable Trust 373

RVW Trust 374

Rayne Foundation, The 379

Robbins Trust, The Cheshire 387

Robyn Charitable Trust 389

Rozel Trust, The 397

St Jude's Trust 403

St Luke's College Foundation 404

Sarum St Michael Educational Charity, The 408

Save & Prosper Educational Trust 408

Save & Prosper Foundation 409

Scarr-Hall Memorial Trust, The 409

Scopus Jewish Educational Trust 411

Seva Trust, Rampaba Sadhu 415

Shah Trust, The Dr N K 416

Sherman Charitable Trust, The Archie 419

Shine No 2 Charitable Trust, The Barnett and Sylvia 420

Sidbury Trust, The Second 421

Simon Population Trust, The 422

Salter Trust Ltd 424

Society of Friends of the Torah, The 429

South Square Trust 430

Southall Charitable Trust, Kenneth & Phyllis 431

Southall Trust, W F 432

Spoore, Merry & Rixman Foundation, The 434

Stanley Foundation Limited 435

Stathern Chapel Close Trust, The 436

Stewart Charitable Trust, Mary Stephanie 437

Street Charitable Foundation, W O 440

Swan Mountain Trust 444

TSB Foundation for the Channel Islands 447

Tesco Charity Trust 452

Tesler Foundation, The 452

Thompson Memorial Fund, The Edwin John 453

Timson Family Charitable Trust 457

Tyndale Trust 466

United Kingdom Friends for Further Education in Israel 468

Wates Foundation, The 481

Weinstock Fund, The 484

Westminster Amalgamated Charity 487

White Rose Children's Aid International Charity 489

Wohl Charitable Foundation, The Maurice 498

Wohl Charitable Trust, The Maurice 498

Wolff Charity Trust 498

Wolfson Family Charitable Trust, The 499

Wolverhampton Rotary Club Charitable Trust 500

Woodhouse Charitable Trust, Edwin 501

Woods Charitable Foundation, Geoffrey 502

Worms Charitable Trust, The Freda and Della 504

Worshipful Company of Needlemakers' Charitable Fund 505

Zaiger Trust, The Elizabeth and Prince 512

Will consider

AHJ Charitable Trust, The 3

Acacia Charitable Trust 6

Allied Domecq Trust 13

Anderson Trust, Andrew 16

Anglo Hong Kong Trust, The 17

Aquarian Healing Trust *19*

Aquarius Charitable Foundation, The *19*

Aquinas Trust *20*

Ashby Charitable Trust, The *23*

Askew Charitable Trust, The Ian *25*

Assembled Church of Christ Trust, The *25*

Assheton-Smith Charitable Trust *25*

Asthma Allergy and Inflammation Research Trust *25*

Astor's 1969 Charity, The Hon M L *26*

BUPA Foundation, The *29*

Bachad Fellowship – Friends of Bnei Akiva *30*

Barnby's Foundation, Lord *35*

Barnsbury Charitable Trust *35*

Barton Trust, Eleanor *37*

Bateman Charitable Trust, Lady Margaret *37*

Bealey Foundation, The *38*

Beattie Charitable Trust, The James *39*

Beckwith Charitable Trust, The Peter *40*

Beckwith-Smith's Charitable Settlement, Mrs *40*

Bergqvist Charitable Trust *44*

Bilton Charity, The Percy *48*

Blagrave Charitable Trust, The Herbert and Peter *52*

Blakey Charitable Trust, The Celia and Conrad *53*

Blanchminster Trust, The *54*

Boltons Trust, The *55*

Borthwick Memorial Trust, The Oliver *56*

Brook Charitable Settlement, R E *64*

Brookhouse's Will Trust, Mr John Charles *65*

Brotherton Trust, The Charles *65*

Burn Charity Trust, The J H *70*

Burns Charity, The Dorothy *70*

Burry Charitable Trust, The *70*

Burton Charitable Trust, The Geoffrey *71*

Butler's Trust, Lord *71*

Butler's Trust, Lucilla *72*

Campden Charities, The *79*

Cardiff & Swansea Methodist District Charitable Trust Fund *80*

Cass's Foundation, Sir John *85*

Castang Charitable Trust, H and M *85*

Charity Projects *90*

Childtime Trust, The *92*

Christian Aid *94*

Cinderford Charitable Trust, The *96*

Closehelm Ltd *101*

Clutterbuck Charitable Trust, Robert *102*

Coates Charitable Trust 1969, Lance *103*

Cobb Charity *103*

Cohen Charity Trust, Lucy *104*

Cohen Foundation, The John S *104*

Condon Family Trust *109*

Cope Charitable Trust, Alfred *112*

Curzon Charitable Trust, The Wallace *120*

Cymerman Trust Limited, Itzchok Meyer *120*

De Avenley Foundation, The *126*

De Rothschild 1981 Charitable Trust, The Edmund *127*

De Yong Charitable Trust, The Emma *128*

Denton Charitable Trust, The *130*

Desmond Charitable Trust, The Richard *131*

Dicken Charitable Trust, The Albert *133*

Dinam Charity *134*

D'Oyly Carte Charitable Trust, The *137*

Drapers' Charitable Fund *137*

Drayton Trust, The *138*

Dunn Charitable Trust, The Harry *140*

Earmark Trust, The *142*

Egerton of Tatton Will Trust, Lord *146*

Eling Trust *147*

Elmgrant Trust *149*

Elshore Limited *149*

Family Trust, The *158*

Farmers' Company Charitable Fund, The *159*

Federation of Jewish Relief Organisations *160*

Fletcher Trust, Roy *165*

Ford of Britain Trust *166*

Foreman Foundation, The Carl & Eve *167*

Fry Charitable Trust, Maurice *174*

Gardner Charitable Trust, R & J *178*

Garthgwynion Charities *179*

Gibson's Charity Trust, The Hon Mr & Mrs Clive *182*

Gillett Charitable Trust, J A *183*

Gladstone Charitable Trust, The E W *184*

Gold Hill Church Trust *186*

Goldberg Charitable Trust, The Lewis *186*

Goodman Trust, The S & F *189*

Gradel Foundation, The *189*

Green Foundation, Constance *194*

Grut Charitable Trust, The *198*

Gulbenkian Foundation (Lisbon) United Kingdom Branch, Calouste *199*

HB Charitable Trust *201*

Hacking & Sons Ltd Charitable Trust, C G *201*

Hale Trust, The *203*

Halkes Settlement, John Robert *204*

Hampton Fuel Allotment Charity *207*

Handicapped Children's Aid Committee *207*

Harford Charitable Trust *209*

Harvey Charitable Trust, Gordon *211*

Hawthorne Charitable Trust, The *212*

Hewett/Driver Education Trust, The *217*

Hicks Foundation, The Sir John *218*

Hodge Foundation, The Jane *223*

Holford Trust Fund *224*

Hoover Foundation, The *226*

Horn Trust, The Cuthbert *227*

Hornby Charitable Trust, Miss D *227*

Hornton Trust, The *228*

Hughes Charitable Trust, The Geoffery C *230*

Hyde Park Place Estate Charity, The *232*

Inman Charity, The *235*

JCSCJ Charitable Trust, The *238*

Jarrold Trust Ltd, John *243*

Johnson Foundation, The *246*

KC Charitable Trust, The *250*

Kalms Foundation, The Stanley *250*

Keyes Trust, The Ursula *253*

Kingsgrove Charitable Trust, The *255*

Kinnison Charitable Trust, R O *256*

Kleinwort Charitable Trust, The Ernest *257*

Knott Trust, Sir James *258*

Laing Foundation, The Christopher *260*

Laing's Charitable Trust *262*

Laspen Trust *265*

Lavender Trust, The *267*

Lawley Foundation, The Edgar E *267*

Leonard Trust, The Mark *271*

Levy Charitable Foundation, Joseph *272*

Liffe Benefit *274*

Lingwood Charitable Trust, The *276*

Littler Foundation, The Emile *277*

Lloyd Charity, The S and D *278*

Localtrent Ltd *279*

Locker Foundation, The *280*

Lynwood Charitable Trust, The 288
Lyons Charitable Trust, The 288
MDM Memorial Trust 289
MacAndrew Trust, The E M 289
McKechnie Foundation, A N 292
McLaren Foundation 292
McLaren Memorial Trust, The Martin 293
Margadale Charitable Trust, Lord 297
Marks Charitable Trust, Michael 298
Markus Charitable Foundation, The Erich 298
Matchan Fund Limited, The Leonard 301
Material World Charitable Foundation Limited, The 301
Mattock Charitable Trust, The W T 302
Mercers' Company Educational Trust Fund, The 306
Millfield House Foundation 312
Millichope Foundation, The 312
Moores Foundation, John 318
Morel Charitable Trust, The 318
Morgan Crucible Company plc Charitable Trust, The 319
Morphy Memorial Fund, Arthur 319
Morris Charitable Trust, The Willie & Mabel 320
Moulton Charitable Trust, The 321
Music Sales Charitable Trust, The 324
New Court Charitable Trust 332
Newcastle's 1986 Charitable Trust, Duke of 333
Newstead Charity, The 334
Norfolk's Family Charitable Trust, Lavinia 336
North West Arts Board 337
Northcott Charity Trust, The 338
Northern Arts 339
Northern Electric Employee Charity Association 339
Norton Foundation, The 340
Nuffield Foundation 342
Oldham Foundation 345
Owen Trust, Margaret 348
PDC Trust, The 349
PJD Charitable Trust 350
Palmer Trust, The Gerald 352
Pascoe Charitable Trust, Alan 354
Paul Charitable Trust, The Late Barbara May 355

Paul Charitable Trust, Margaret Jeanne 355
Paul Charitable Trust, Pamela Milton 355
Paul Foundation, The 355
Paul's Charitable Trust, R J 355
Payne Charitable Trust, The 355
Perry Charitable Trust, Miss Frances Lucille 359
Pershore Nashdom & Elmore Trust Ltd, The 360
Peskin Charitable Trust, The Hazel and Leslie 360
Phillips Charitable Foundation, Reginald M 361
Pitt Trust, Headley 364
Porter Foundation 366
Powys Welsh Church Fund 367
Prendergast Charitable Trust, The Simone 368
Puebla Charitable Trust Limited, The 371
Queen Anne Street Educational Trust Limited 373
RT Trust, The 374
Rackham Charitable Trust, The Mr & Mrs Philip 375
Radley Charitable Trust 375
Rae Charity, H J 375
Rainford Trust, The 376
Rav Chesed Trust, The 379
Reekie Trust, R A & V B 381
Reuter Foundation, The 382
Richards Charity, The Clive 384
Richmond Parish Lands Charity 384
Rivendell Trust, The 387
Rodewald's Charitable Settlement, Mr C A 389
Rogers Charitable Settlement, The Richard 390
Rokeby Charitable Trust 390
Rolfe Charitable Trust, The 390
Rosen Foundation, Cecil 392
S Group Charitable Trust 399
Salamander Charitable Trust, The 405
Samuel Charitable Trust, M J 406
Shepherd Conservation Foundation, The David 418
Shifrin Charitable Trust, The Maurice and Hilda 419
Silvester Charitable Gift Trust 422
Slater Foundation Ltd, The 424
Smith Foundation, The Leslie 427
Solomons Charitable Trust, David 430
Somerfield Curtis Will Trust, The Dorothy 430
South East Arts Board 430
Southern Arts 432
Southover Manor General Education Trust Ltd 433

Sumner's Trust Section 'A', Sir John 443
Symons Charitable Trust, The Stella 446
Taylor Charitable Trust, The B R 450
Terry Charitable Trust, Noel Goddard 451
Thompson Charitable Trust, The 453
3i Charitable Trust, The 455
van Geest Foundation, The John and Lucille 470
Van Norden's Charitable Foundation, Mrs Maud 471
Vincent Trust Fund, Eric W 473
Vineyard Christian Fellowship of South West 473
Vinson Charity Trust, The 1969 473
Vogel Charitable Trust, The Nathan 474
Wakefield Trust, The 476
Ward Blenkinsop Trust, The 480
Watson's Trust, John 482
Welby Trust, The Barbara 484
Whetherly's Charitable Trust, The Hon Mrs R G A 489
Whittington Charitable Trust, The 491
Wiggins Charity Trust, Cyril 491
Wilde Charitable Trust, The Felicity 492
Wills 1961 Charitable Trust, Major Michael Thomas 494
Winstone Foundation, Hyman 497
Woburn 1986 Charitable Trust 498
Worshipful Company of Founders Charities, The 505
Wychdale Limited 507
Yapp Education and Research Trust, The 508
Youell Foundation Ltd, The 510

■ Science & technology

see also **Academic subjects, sciences & research**

Funding priority

Eastwood Memorial Trust, Sybil 143
MacRobert Trusts, The 294
Nuffield Foundation 342
Phillips Charitable Foundation, Reginald M 361
Wolfson Foundation, The 499

■ **Sciences**

see **Academic subjects, sciences & research**

■ **Scientists**

Funding priority

Royal Commission for the Exhibition of 1851 *395*

Wellcome Trust, The *485*

■ **Seafarers & fishermen**

Funding priority

Black's Charity, Sir Alec *52*

Blott Charitable Settlement, Robert Orpwood *55*

Burn Charity Trust, The J H *70*

Corbett's Charity, Thomas *112*

George's Fund for Sailors, King *180*

Worshipful Company of Shipwrights Charitable Fund, The *506*

■ **Secondary schools**

see also **Schools & colleges**

Funding priority

Beit Trust, The *40*

Catholic Education Service for England and Wales *86*

Clark Charitable Trust, J Anthony *98*

Dulverton Trust, The *139*

Garnett Charitable Trust, The *178*

Hillards Charitable Trust, Gay & Peter Hartley's *220*

Hussey for Africans, Charity of Rebecca *231*

Newman's Charity, John *334*

St Katharine & Shadwell Trust *404*

Woodroffe Benton Foundation, The *502*

Will consider

Archer Trust, The *20*

Arts Council of Wales, The *23*

BBC Children in Need Appeal, The *29*

BibleLands *47*

Boots Charitable Trust *56*

Bulmer Charitable Trust, Becket *68*

Carlton Television Trust *81*

Carnegie Dunfermline Trust *82*

Clifford Charity Oxford, The *100*

Commonwealth Relations Trust *108*

Cripplegate Foundation *118*

Curriers Company Charitable Fund *119*

Derbyshire Trust, J N *130*

Dibden Allotments Charity *132*

Digby Charitable Trust, Simon *133*

Ebb and Flow Charitable Trust *144*

Elkes Charity Fund, The Wilfred & Elsie *147*

Four Lanes Trust, The *168*

Four Winds Trust *168*

Goldsmiths' Company's Charities, The *188*

Great Britain Sasakawa Foundation, The *193*

Hamlyn Foundation, The Paul *205*

Holly Hill Charitable Trust *224*

Homeless International *225*

Howard Charitable Trust, John & Ruth *229*

Ingles Charitable Trust, The *234*

Ireland Funds, The *237*

Isle of Dogs Community Foundation *238*

Jewish Childs' Day *245*

Leonard Trust, The Mark *271*

Lewis Foundation, The John Spedan *274*

Licensed Trade Charities Trust, The *274*

Linmardon Trust *276*

Littler Foundation, The Emile *277*

McDougall Trust, The *291*

Milward Charity, The Edgar *313*

Montefiore Trust, The David *316*

Newcomen Collett Foundation *333*

Norman, The Educational Foundation of Alderman John *337*

Oldham Foundation *345*

Owen Family Trust, The *348*

Provincial Trust for Kendal, The *370*

Pyke Charity Trust *372*

Rhodes Trust – Public Purposes Fund, The *383*

Royal Commission for the Exhibition of 1851 *395*

Said Foundation, The Karim Rida *401*

Salters Charities *405*

Simon's Charity *422*

Sport Aid 88 Trust *434*

Summerfield Charitable Trust, The *442*

Torquay Charities, The *458*

Travis Charitable Trust, Constance *460*

Upjohn Charitable Trust, The *469*

Wakefield (Tower Hill, Trinity Square) Trust *476*

Wates Foundation, The *481*

Whitehead Charitable Trust, J E *490*

Worshipful Company of Engineers' Charitable Trust Fund, The *504*

Wylde Memorial Charity, The Anthony and Gwendoline *507*

Yorkshire Agricultural Society *509*

■ **Self help groups**

see **Support, self help groups**

■ **Sensory impairment**

see **Disabled people (physical, sensory, learning impairments), hearing loss, sight loss**

■ **Service people**

see **Ex-service & service people**

■ **Sheltered accommodation**

see also **Residential facilities & services**

Funding priority

AB Charitable Trust *3*

Ammco Trust, The *15*

Army Benevolent Fund, The *22*

Bilton Charity, The Percy *48*

Coutts Charitable Trust, The *116*

Curriers Company Charitable Fund *119*

HACT (The Housing Association's Charitable Trust) *201*

Hudson Benevolent Trust, The Thomas *230*

Humphreys Charitable Settlement, J A M *231*

Hyde Charitable Trust *232*

King Charitable Trust, The Lorna *254*

Merchant Taylors' Consolidated Charities for the Infirm *306*

Metropolitan Hospital-Sunday Fund, The *308*

Needham Cooper Charitable Trust, The *331*

Pye Christian Trust, The *371*

Rae Charity, H J *375*

Woburn 1986 Charitable Trust 498

Wohl Charitable Foundation, The Maurice 498

Wohl Charitable Trust, The Maurice 498

Will consider

Abel Charitable Trust 5

Amory Charitable Trust, Viscount 16

Anstey Charitable Settlement, J C W 18

Aquarius Charitable Foundation, The 19

Archer Trust, The 20

Astor Foundation, The 26

Avon Trust, The 28

Baker Charitable Trust, The 30

Balney Charitable Trust, The 32

Barbour Trust, The 33

Barnabas Charitable Trust 34

Barratt Charitable Trust, The Elaine 36

Beit Trust, The 40

Berkshire Community Trust 45

Birtwistle Memorial Trust, The G E 50

Blake Charitable Trust, The Hubert 53

Boots Charitable Trust 56

Borthwick Memorial Trust, The Oliver 56

Brotherton Trust, The Charles 65

Brough Charitable Trust, Joseph 65

Buckingham Trust 67

Bullough Tompson Settlement, The 68

Burden Trust, The 69

Butlin Charity Trust, Bill 72

Cadbury Trust (1928), The Edward & Dorothy 76

Camelot Foundation, The 78

Campden Charities, The 79

Cazalet Charitable Trust, The Raymond 87

Challice Trust, The 87

Charities Fund 89

Charity Projects 90

Chase Charity, The 91

Coates Charitable Trust, The John 103

County Durham Foundation 115

David Trust, The Lesley 124

de Freitas Charitable Trust, The Helen and Geoffrey 126

Derbyshire Trust, J N 130

Dibs Charitable Trust, The 133

Digby Charitable Trust, Simon 133

Direct Response 134

Edgar Foundation, The Gilbert and Eileen 145

Edgar Trust, The Gilbert 145

Egerton of Tatton Will Trust, Lord 146

Elkes Charity Fund, The Wilfred & Elsie 147

Emanuel Charitable Settlement, Ralph and Muriel 150

Emmandjay Charitable Trust 150

Emmaus Christian Foundation 150

Eventhall Family Charitable Trust, The 155

Ferguson Benevolent Fund Limited 161

Follett Trust, The 166

Ford of Britain Trust 166

Frognal Trust 174

Grant-Lawson Charitable Trust, Lady Virginia 192

Greenaway Foundation, The Sir Derek 194

Harford Charitable Trust 209

Hartley Memorial Trust, The N & P 211

Harvey Charitable Trust, Gordon 211

Heath Charitable Trust 214

Held Settlement, The Gisela 215

Isle of Dogs Community Foundation 238

Johnson Foundation, The 246

Keeling Charitable Trust, The Petronella 251

King Charitable Settlement, Philip 254

Laing Charitable Trust, The David 260

Laing Foundation, The Christopher 260

Lankelly Foundation, The 264

Lawson Charitable Trust, Raymond and Blanche 267

Leach Fourteenth Trust, The 267

Leech Charity, The William 269

Lewis Partnership, John 274

Licensed Trade Charities Trust, The 274

Lyons Charitable Trust, The 288

McCarthy Foundation, The John 290

Mackintosh Foundation, The 292

Marchday Charitable Fund, The 296

Marriage's Charitable Trust, Miss G M 299

Mental Health Foundation, The 305

Morphy Memorial Fund, Arthur 319

Morrison Bequest Fund, Thomas Wharrie 320

NR Charitable Trust, The 325

Natwest Staff Samaritan Fund 330

New Court Charitable Trust 332

Newby Trust Ltd 332

Nidditch Foundation, The Laurie 335

Norman Family Charitable Trust, The 337

North British Hotel Trust 337

Northern Ireland Voluntary Trust 339

Norton Foundation, The 340

Noswad Charity, The 341

Oldham Foundation 345

Owen Family Trust, The 348

PF Charitable Trust 350

Payne Trust, The Harry 356

Pryor Charitable Trust, The John 370

Rest-Harrow Trust, The 382

Ripley's Charitable Trust, Pat 386

Robinson Brothers (Ryders Green) Ltd, Charitable Trust 388

Rowbotham Charitable Trust, The Christopher 393

Rowntree Foundation, Joseph 394

Royal's Memorial Fund, Princess 396

Sargeant's Charitable Trust, Mrs M E 407

Seagram Distillers Charitable Trust 413

Sheldon Trust, The 417

Smith & Mount Trust, The Mrs 426

Sparkhill Trust, The 433

Stevens Foundation, The June 437

Stoate Charitable Trust, The Leonard Laity 438

Stonehouse Trust Ltd, Eric 438

Summerfield Charitable Trust, The 442

Sussman Charitable Trust, Adrienne & Leslie 443

Swan Mountain Trust 444

Sykes Trust, The Charles 445

TSB Foundation for Northern Ireland 447

Tear Fund 450

Thackray General Charitable Trust, The P & L 452

Tisbury Telegraph Trust, The 457

Torquay Charities, The 458

Travis Charitable Trust, Constance 460

Tudor Trust, The 463

Unitek Foundation 469

Van Neste Foundation, The 471

Wander Charitable Fund, The Dr Albert 479

Wesleyan Charitable Trust, The 485

Whitaker Charitable Trust 489

Whitecourt Charitable Trust, The 490

Whitehall Charitable Foundation Limited 490

Williams Trust, The Neville 493

Wills 1961 Charitable Trust, Mr Frederick 493

Wills 1962 Charitable Trust, P J H 494

Wolfe Family's Charitable Trust, The 498

Woodlands Trust 501

Woodroffe Benton Foundation, The 502

Wyford Charitable Trust, The 507

■ Short-term housing

see Emergency & short-term housing

■ Sight loss

Funding priority

Baker Charitable Trust, The 30

Blakenham's Charity Trust, Lady 53

British Council for Prevention of Blindness 61

Cassel Educational Trust (Mountbatten Memorial Grants to Commonwealth Students), The Sir Ernest 84

Corbett's Charity, Thomas 112

Devon Association for the Blind 131

Ferguson Benevolent Fund Limited 161

Fraser Trust, The 170

Frognal Trust 174

Frost Charitable Trust, T F C 174

Gardner's Trust for the Blind 178

Garnett's 1973 Charitable Trust, Mrs A M 178

Gray Trust, The 192

HB Charitable Trust 201

Harbinson Charitable Trust, Roderick 208

Hertfordshire Society for the Blind, The 217

Kennel Club Charitable Trust, The 252

Lamb's Bequest 262

MacKintosh Charitable Trust, Viscount 292

Man of the People Fund 295

Mattock Charitable Trust, The W T 302

Meridian Broadcasting Charitable Trust 307

Natwest Staff Samaritan Fund 330

Nidditch Foundation, The Laurie 335

Owen Trust, Margaret 348

Packlington, The Gift of Thomas 350

Paget Trust, The 351

RED Trust, The 374

Rest-Harrow Trust, The 382

Rosen Foundation, Cecil 392

Street Charitable Foundation, W O 440

Summer's and I May's Charitable Settlement, The Late Misses (A N) 442

Ulverscroft Foundation, The 468

Vision Charity 474

West & Others, Charity of John 486

Wiseman Memorial Fund Limited, The Max 497

Woolton Charitable Trust, The 503

■ Single Mothers

see One parent families

■ Small enterprises

see also Infrastructure development

Funding priority

British Sugar Foundation 63

Ferguson Benevolent Fund Limited 161

Grant Charitable Trust, The 191

Homeless International 225

Hood's Charitable Trust, Sir Harold 226

Whitaker Charitable Trust 489

Will consider

Ashby Charitable Trust, The 23

BibleLands 47

Brotherton Trust, The Charles 65

CLA Charitable Trust 74

Camelot Foundation, The 78

Campden Charities, The 79

Chrimes Family Charitable Trust, The 93

Christmas Cracker Trust 95

Collier Charitable Trust, The 105

de Freitas Charitable Trust, The Helen and Geoffrey 126

Debtors' Relief Fund Charity 128

Digby Charitable Trust, Simon 133

Direct Response 134

Ford of Britain Trust 166

Greenaway Foundation, The Sir Derek 194

Humanitarian Trust, The 230

Hussey for Africans, Charity of Rebecca 231

Knott Trust, Sir James 258

Lane Foundation, The Allen 263

Lewis Foundation, The John Spedan 274

London Law Trust 280

Marr-Munning Trust 299

Milton Keynes Community Trust Ltd, The 312

Minet Trust, The Peter 313

National Power Charitable Trust, The 330

New Chasers Charitable Trust, The 332

Notgrove Trust, The 341

Parivar Trust, The 353

Puebla Charitable Trust Limited, The 371

Rope Third Charitable Settlement, The Mrs 391

Rowbotham Charitable Trust, The Christopher 393

Skelton Bounty, The 423

Summerfield Charitable Trust, The 442

Sykes Trust, The Charles 445

Tear Fund 450

Wakefield (Tower Hill, Trinity Square) Trust 476

Wall Trust, Thomas 478

Wills 1962 Charitable Trust, P J H 494

■ Social care professional bodies

see also Professional bodies

Funding priority

Ajahma Charitable Trust, The 9

Christian Vision 94

Fogel Charitable Trust, The Gerald 165

Humphreys Charitable Settlement, J A M 231

Millfield House Foundation 312

Robinson Brothers (Ryders Green) Ltd, Charitable Trust 388

Whitaker Charitable Trust 489

Will consider

Aston Charities Trust Ltd 25

Barbour Trust, The 33

Boots Charitable Trust 56

Buxton Trust, Denis 72

Camelot Foundation, The 78

Cottingham Charitable Trust, Mrs Diana Mary 114

County Durham Foundation *115*

Debtors' Relief Fund Charity *128*

Denne Charitable Trust *130*

Digby Charitable Trust, Simon *133*

Edgar Foundation, The Gilbert and Eileen *145*

Franklin Trust, Jill *170*

Great Britain Sasakawa Foundation, The *193*

Hobbs Trust Limited, The Betty *222*

Humanitarian Trust, The *230*

Lawson Charitable Trust, Raymond and Blanche *267*

Leech Charity, The William *269*

Lynall Foundation, The D G *287*

Newby Trust Ltd *332*

Persula Foundation, The *360*

Rowntree Foundation, Joseph *394*

Sargeant's Charitable Trust, Mrs M E *407*

Sheldon Trust, The *417*

Summer's and I May's Charitable Settlement, The Late Misses (A N) *442*

Wakefield (Tower Hill, Trinity Square) Trust *476*

Webber Trust Fund, Ethel *483*

Whesby Ltd *488*

....

■ Socially isolated

Funding priority

Access 4 Trust *6*

Alexandra Trust *11*

Archer Trust, The *20*

Barnes Workhouse Fund *35*

Betard Bequest *46*

Carlton Television Trust *81*

Church Urban Fund *95*

Clark 1965 Charitable Trust, Stephen *98*

Clifford Charity Oxford, The *100*

Cobb Charity *103*

Collins Charity, The George Henry *106*

Curriers Company Charitable Fund *119*

Ericson Trust *152*

Fletcher Trust, Roy *165*

HACT (The Housing Association's Charitable Trust) *201*

Hamlyn Foundation, The Helen *205*

Hanley Trust (1987), The *207*

Hertfordshire Community Trust, The *217*

Hiley Trust, Joseph and Mary *219*

Isle of Dogs Community Foundation *238*

McCarthy Foundation, The John *290*

Morrison Bequest Fund, Thomas Wharrie *320*

Paristamen Foundation, The *352*

Rowbotham Charitable Trust, The Christopher *393*

Swan Mountain Trust *444*

TSB Foundation for Scotland *447*

Thornton-Smith Trust, The *455*

Wakeham Trust, The *476*

Wates Foundation, The *481*

Williams Trust, The Neville *493*

Wiltshire Community Foundation *495*

Will consider

AB Charitable Trust *3*

Abbey National Charitable Trust *4*

Adnams Charity, The *7*

Allen Trust, Mrs M H *13*

Ammco Trust, The *15*

Andrew Charitable Trust, The Prince *16*

Arbib Trust, The Annie *20*

Astor Foundation, The *26*

Barbour Trust, The *33*

Barnabas Charitable Trust *34*

Barratt Charitable Trust, The Elaine *36*

Bartholomew Christian Trust *36*

Bell Charitable Trust, John *41*

Benham Charitable Trust, Hervey *43*

Berris Charitable Trust *45*

Bewley Charitable Trust, The *46*

Birmingham Amenities and Welfare Trust, The *49*

Birtwistle Memorial Trust, The G E *50*

Blake Charitable Trust, The Morgan *53*

Boots Charitable Trust *56*

Bridge Trust, The *60*

Butlin Charity Trust, Bill *72*

Buxton Trust, Denis *72*

Camelot Foundation, The *78*

Campbell Charitable Foundation, The Ellis *79*

Carnegie United Kingdom Trust, The *82*

Catto Charitable Settlement, The Thomas Sivewright *86*

Challice Trust, The *87*

Clinton's Charitable Trust, Lord *100*

Cole Charitable Trust, The *105*

Coutts Charitable Trust, The *116*

David Trust, The Lesley *124*

De Yong Charitable Trust, The Emma *128*

Digbeth Trust Ltd, The *133*

Dorus Trust *136*

Earley Charity, The *142*

Ebb and Flow Charitable Trust *144*

Edgar Foundation, The Gilbert and Eileen *145*

Elkes Charity Fund, The Wilfred & Elsie *147*

Epigoni Trust *152*

Essex Radio Helping Hands Trust, The *154*

Eveson Charitable Trust, The *155*

Fane Research Trust, The Edmund *159*

Fletcher Charitable Trust, The Joyce *164*

Four Winds Trust *168*

GNC Trust *175*

Getty Jr General Charitable Trust, J Paul *181*

Gibson Charitable Trust, The Simon *182*

Goldsmiths' Company's Charities, The *188*

Grant-Lawson Charitable Trust, Lady Virginia *192*

Greater Bristol Foundation *193*

Groves Charitable Trust, The *197*

Hampstead Wells and Campden Trust *206*

Harbour Foundation Ltd, The *208*

Held Settlement, The Gisela *215*

Hilden Charitable Fund, The *219*

Hobbs Trust Limited, The Betty *222*

Hopkinson Educational Trust, Robert Addy *227*

Hudson Benevolent Trust, The Thomas *230*

Iris Trust, The *237*

Irving Charitable Trust, The Charles *237*

JCSCJ Charitable Trust, The *238*

Johnson Group Cleaners Charity *247*

Keeling Charitable Trust, The Petronella *251*

King Charitable Trust, The Lorna *254*

King's Fund, The *255*

Laing Charitable Trust, The David *260*

Laing Foundation, The Christopher *260*

Laing Foundation, The Kirby *261*

Laing Foundation, The Maurice *261*

Lane Foundation, The Allen 263

Laspen Trust 265

Leach Fourteenth Trust, The 267

Lewis Foundation, The John Spedan 274

Linford Charitable Trust, The Fred 276

Lloyd's Charities Trust 278

Lloyd's Patriotic Fund 279

(Lloyds) TSB Foundation for England and Wales 279

Luke Trust, The 286

Lyons Charitable Trust, The 288

MacKintosh Charitable Trust, Viscount 292

Mackintosh Foundation, The 292

Manning Trust, Leslie & Lilian 296

Marriage's Charitable Trust, Miss G M 299

Mental Health Foundation, The 305

Milburn Charitable Trust, Frederick 310

Milton Keynes Community Trust Ltd, The 312

Minet Trust, The Peter 313

Minge's Gift 314

Moore Foundation, The George A 316

Moores Foundation, John 318

Music for World Development 323

NR Charitable Trust, The 325

Nathan Charitable Trust 326

Needham Cooper Charitable Trust, The 331

New Court Charitable Trust 332

New Durlston Trust, The 332

Newby Trust Ltd 332

Norton Foundation, The 340

Oakdale Trust, The 343

Open Door Women's Trust 346

Owen Family Trust, The 348

Parivar Trust, The 353

Payne Trust, The Harry 356

Persula Foundation, The 360

Pilgrim Trust, The 362

Pratt Charitable Trust, The W L 367

Pye Christian Trust, The 371

Pyke Charity Trust 372

Rest-Harrow Trust, The 382

Rope Third Charitable Settlement, The Mrs 391

Rowntree Foundation, Joseph 394

Royal's Memorial Fund, Princess 396

Sainsbury Charitable Fund Ltd, The 402

St Christopher's Trust, The 402

Saint Sarkis Charity Trust 404

Schuster Charitable Trust, The 410

Scott Bader Commonwealth Ltd, The 411

Seagram Distillers Charitable Trust 413

Sheldon Trust, The 417

Smith & Mount Trust, The Mrs 426

South Square Trust 430

Stoate Charitable Trust, The Leonard Laity 438

Stonehouse Trust Ltd, Eric 438

Summerfield Charitable Trust, The 442

Summer's and I May's Charitable Settlement, The Late Misses (A N) 442

Swann-Morton Foundation, The 444

TSB Foundation for Northern Ireland 447

Tear Fund 450

Thorpe Charity Trust, The 455

Tisbury Telegraph Trust, The 457

Trust for the Homeless 462

Tudor Trust, The 463

Van Berchem Charitable Trust, The Alec 470

Van Leer Foundation UK Trust, Bernard 470

Van Neste Foundation, The 471

Variety Club Children's Charity Limited, The 471

Vec Acorn Trust, The 472

Wagstaff Charitable Trust, Bob 475

Wakefield (Tower Hill, Trinity Square) Trust 476

Wesleyan Charitable Trust, The 485

Westcroft Trust 486

Whitecourt Charitable Trust, The 490

Wix Charitable Trust, Michael and Anna 497

Woodlands Trust 501

Woodroffe Benton Foundation, The 502

....

■ Special needs education

see also Education & training

Funding priority

CLA Charitable Trust 74

Campbell Charitable Foundation, The Ellis 79

Fishmongers' Company's Charitable Trust 163

Franklin Trust, Jill 170

Lankelly Foundation, The 264

Mental Health Foundation, The 305

Rowntree Foundation, Joseph 394

Save & Prosper Foundation 409

Strangward Trust, The 439

....

■ Special schools

see also Schools & colleges

Funding priority

Allied Dunbar Charitable Trust Limited, The 13

Ammco Trust, The 15

BibleLands 47

Campbell Charitable Foundation, The Ellis 79

Catholic Education Service for England and Wales 86

Christmas Cracker Trust 95

Clark Charitable Trust, J Anthony 98

Community Trust for Greater Manchester, The 108

County Durham Foundation 115

Dulverton Trust, The 139

Edgar Trust, The Gilbert 145

Ellerman Foundation, The John 148

Grant Charitable Trust, The 191

Hertfordshire Community Trust, The 217

Hudson Benevolent Trust, The Thomas 230

Hussey for Africans, Charity of Rebecca 231

Ingles Charitable Trust, The 234

LSA Charitable Trust 260

Moore Foundation, The George A 316

National Power Charitable Trust, The 330

Newcomen Collett Foundation 333

Persula Foundation, The 360

Trust Fund for the Training of Handicapped Children in Arts and Crafts 462

Will consider

AB Charitable Trust 3

Archer Trust, The 20

Army Benevolent Fund, The 22

Arts Council of Wales, The 23

Ashley Foundation, The Laura 24

Aston Charities Trust Ltd 25

Aylesfield Foundation, The 28

BBC Children in Need Appeal, The 29

Barbour Trust, The 33

Beit Trust, The 40

Boots Charitable Trust 56

Bridge Trust, The 60

Brotherton Trust, The Charles 65
Bulmer Charitable Trust, Becket 68
Butlin Charity Trust, Bill 72
Carlton Television Trust 81
Carnegie Dunfermline Trust 82
Cazalet Charitable Trust, The Raymond 87
Chrimes Family Charitable Trust, The 93
Commonwealth Relations Trust 108
Coutts Charitable Trust, The 116
Cripplegate Foundation 118
Curriers Company Charitable Fund 119
Curzon Charitable Trust, The Wallace 120
Denne Charitable Trust 130
Derbyshire Trust, J N 130
Dibden Allotments Charity 132
Digby Charitable Trust, Simon 133
Ebb and Flow Charitable Trust 144
Egerton of Tatton Will Trust, Lord 146
Elkes Charity Fund, The Wilfred & Elsie 147
Emmandjay Charitable Trust 150
Emmaus Christian Foundation 150
Fogel Charitable Trust, The Gerald 165
Follett Trust, The 166
Four Lanes Trust, The 168
Four Winds Trust 168
Gardner Charitable Trust, R & J 178
Gibbins Trust, The 181
Glebe Charitable Trust 185
Goldsmiths' Company's Charities, The 188
Good Neighbours Trust, The 188
Grant Foundation, The Raymond 191
Great Britain Sasakawa Foundation, The 193
Greenaway Foundation, The Sir Derek 194
Hamlyn Foundation, The Paul 205
Henderson's Settlement, J R 216
Hillards Charitable Trust, Gay & Peter Hartley's 220
Holly Hill Charitable Trust 224
Idlewild Trust, The 234
Inverforth Charitable Trust, The 236
Isle of Dogs Community Foundation 238
JDM Charitable Trust 239
JHL Trust, The 239

Jewish Childs' Day 245
Leech Charity, The William 269
Leonard Trust, The Mark 271
Linmardon Trust 276
Littler Foundation, The Emile 277
Lloyd's Charities Trust 278
(Lloyds) TSB Foundation for England and Wales 279
London Law Trust 280
London Taxi Drivers' Fund for Underprivileged Children, The 280
Low & Bonar Charitable Fund, The 284
Mackintosh Foundation, The 292
Measures Charity, The James Frederick and Ethel Anne 303
Milburn Charitable Trust, Frederick 310
Milton Keynes Community Trust Ltd, The 312
Milward Charity, The Edgar 313
Minet Trust, The Peter 313
Montefiore Trust, The David 316
Morphy Memorial Fund, Arthur 319
Morris Charitable Trust, The Douglas 320
NR Charitable Trust, The 325
Natwest Staff Samaritan Fund 330
New Chasers Charitable Trust, The 332
Newby Trust Ltd 332
Norman, The Educational Foundation of Alderman John 337
Norwich Church of England Young Men's Society 340
Oldham Foundation 345
Owen Family Trust, The 348
PF Charitable Trust 350
Paget Trust, The 351
Parivar Trust, The 353
Patients' Aid Association Hospital and Medical Charities Trust 354
Pilkington Charitable Trust, Cecil 363
Powell Foundation, The 367
Provincial Trust for Kendal, The 370
Pye Christian Trust, The 371
Pyke Charity Trust 372
Ravenscroft Foundation, The 379
Rayner Charitable Trust, The John 380
Reader's Digest Trust, The 380
Ripley's Charitable Trust, Pat 386

Robinson Brothers (Ryders Green) Ltd, Charitable Trust 388
Rothley Trust, The 392
Royal Victoria Hall Foundation, The 396
Said Foundation, The Karim Rida 401
St Katharine & Shadwell Trust 404
Salters Charities 405
Sheepdrove Trust, The 417
Shepherd Charitable Trust, The Sylvia and Colin 418
Simon's Charity 422
Skelton Bounty, The 423
Stoate Charitable Trust, The Leonard Laity 438
Stonehouse Trust Ltd, Eric 438
Summerfield Charitable Trust, The 442
Summer's and I May's Charitable Settlement, The Late Misses (A N) 442
Swann-Morton Foundation, The 444
TSB Foundation for Northern Ireland 447
Tear Fund 450
Tisbury Telegraph Trust, The 457
Travis Charitable Trust, Constance 460
Van Leer Foundation UK Trust, Bernard 470
Wade & Others, The Charity of Thomas 475
Wakefield (Tower Hill, Trinity Square) Trust 476
Wall Trust, Thomas 478
Wates Foundation, The 481
Webber Trust Fund, Ethel 483
Whesby Ltd 488
Whitehead Charitable Trust, J E 490
Wills 1961 Charitable Trust, Mr Frederick 493
Wingfield's Charitable Trust, Mrs 496
Woodlands Trust 501
Wylde Memorial Charity, The Anthony and Gwendoline 507

....
■ Specialist research
see also **Academic subjects, sciences & research**

Funding priority
Alcohol Education and Research Council 9
Arkleton Trust, The 21
Cassel Educational Trust (Overseas Research Grants), Sir Ernest 84
Ciba Fellowship Trust, The 95
Colt Foundation, The 107

Eranda Foundation, The *152*
Jeffreys Road Fund, Rees *243*
Leech Charity, The William *269*
McDougall Trust, The *291*
Melville Trust for Care and
   Cure of Cancer *305*
Mental Health Foundation, The
   305
Oldacre Foundation, The John
   345
Peacock Charitable Foundation,
   The Michael *356*
Richard III and Yorkist History
   Trust *384*
Rowntree Foundation, Joseph
   394
Shipwrights' Company
   Educational Trust, The *420*
Simon Population Trust, The
   422
Thriplow Charitable Trust *456*
Wellcome Trust, The *485*

Will consider
Baring Foundation, The *34*
Beit Trust, The *40*
British Dietetic Association
   General and Education Trust
   Fund, The *61*
Burden Trust, The *69*
Carlton Television Trust *81*
Chrimes Family Charitable
   Trust, The *93*
Clifford Charity Oxford, The
   100
Commonwealth Relations Trust
   108
Cooper Charitable Trust *111*
Coutts Charitable Trust, The
   116
Digby Charitable Trust, Simon
   133
Edgar Foundation, The Gilbert
   and Eileen *145*
Edgar Trust, The Gilbert *145*
Education Services *145*
Emmandjay Charitable Trust
   150
European Cultural Foundation
   (UK Committee) *154*
Galinski Charitable Trust *177*
Gardner Charitable Trust, R & J
   178
Gibbins Trust, The *181*
Great Britain Sasakawa
   Foundation, The *193*
Holly Hill Charitable Trust *224*
Homeless International *225*
Ireland Funds, The *237*
Kiln Charitable Trust, Robert
   254
Lee Foundation, The Edgar
   269
Leukaemia Research Fund *271*
Lindeth Charitable Trust, The
   276
London Law Trust *280*

Marriage's Charitable Trust,
   Miss G M *299*
Milward Charity, The Edgar
   313
Mitchell Trust, Esme *315*
NR Charitable Trust, The *325*
Needham Cooper Charitable
   Trust, The *331*
Newby Trust Ltd *332*
Owen Family Trust, The *348*
PF Charitable Trust *350*
Patients' Aid Association
   Hospital and Medical
   Charities Trust *354*
Payne Trust, The Harry *356*
Pilkington Charitable Trust,
   Cecil *363*
Rayner Charitable Trust, The
   John *380*
Rest-Harrow Trust, The *382*
Robinson Brothers (Ryders
   Green) Ltd, Charitable Trust
   388
SMB Trust, The *400*
St Katharine & Shadwell Trust
   404
Shepherd Charitable Trust, The
   Sylvia and Colin *418*
South Square Trust *430*
Stonehouse Trust Ltd, Eric *438*
Upjohn Charitable Trust, The
   469
Weir Foundation, The James
   484
Wincott Foundation, The *496*
Wolfe Family's Charitable
   Trust, The *498*
Woolmen's Company
   Charitable Trust, The *503*
Yorkshire Agricultural Society
   509

....
■ **Specialist training**
see **Professional, specialist
training**
....

■ **Sports centres**
see also **Community
facilities**

Funding priority
Angler's Inn Trust *17*
Aston Charities Trust Ltd *25*
Astor of Hever Trust, The *26*
Blakey Charitable Trust, The
   Celia and Conrad *53*
Clarke Trust, The Thomas
   Edward *99*
Clutterbuck Charitable Trust,
   Robert *102*
Dixon Charitable Trust, F E *134*
Hudson Benevolent Trust, The
   Thomas *230*
Isle of Dogs Community
   Foundation *238*

Peirce Memorial Trust, The Joe
   358
Spoore, Merry & Rixman
   Foundation, The *434*
Swale Charity Trust *443*

Will consider
Ammco Trust, The *15*
Aquarius Charitable
   Foundation, The *19*
Barrie Charitable Trust, The
   Misses *36*
Blanchminster Trust, The *54*
Bowland Charitable Trust, The
   57
Brand Trust, The *59*
Bullough Tompson Settlement,
   The *68*
Butler's Trust, Lord *71*
CLA Charitable Trust *74*
Campden Charities, The *79*
Carnegie Dunfermline Trust *82*
Chapman Foundation *88*
Chrimes Family Charitable
   Trust, The *93*
Clark 1965 Charitable Trust,
   Stephen *98*
Clifford Charity Oxford, The
   100
Clinton's Charitable Trust, Lord
   100
Community Trust for Greater
   Manchester, The *108*
Curzon Charitable Trust, The
   Wallace *120*
de Freitas Charitable Trust, The
   Helen and Geoffrey *126*
Debtors' Relief Fund Charity
   128
Derbyshire Trust, J N *130*
Digby Charitable Trust, Simon
   133
Dulverton Trust, The *139*
Dumbreck Charity *139*
Early's Charitable Settlement,
   Richard *142*
Edgar Foundation, The Gilbert
   and Eileen *145*
Elkes Charity Fund, The Wilfred
   & Elsie *147*
Fairway Trust, The *158*
Ford of Britain Trust *166*
Four Lanes Trust, The *168*
Gannochy Trust, The *177*
Grange Farm Centre Trust *191*
Grant Foundation, The
   Raymond *191*
Grant-Lawson Charitable Trust,
   Lady Virginia *192*
Grocers' Charity *197*
Gwent County Council Welsh
   Church Fund *200*
Halkes Settlement, John Robert
   204
Hillards Charitable Trust, Gay &
   Peter Hartley's *220*

Hunter Charitable Trust, The
  Claire *231*
Ingles Charitable Trust, The
  234
Ireland Funds, The *237*
Johnson Group Cleaners
  Charity *247*
Knott Trust, Sir James *258*
Laing Charitable Trust, The
  David *260*
Laing Foundation, The
  Christopher *260*
Lancaster's Trust, Bryan *263*
Lee Foundation, The Edgar
  269
Leech Charity, The William *269*
Lewis Partnership, John *274*
(Lloyds) TSB Foundation for
  England and Wales *279*
Lord's Taverners, The *281*
Middlesex County Rugby
  Football Union Memorial
  Fund *309*
Moore Foundation, The
  George A *316*
Morel Charitable Trust, The
  318
National Power Charitable
  Trust, The *330*
Needham Cooper Charitable
  Trust, The *331*
Newby Trust Ltd *332*
Norfolk's Family Charitable
  Trust, Lavinia *336*
Norman Family Charitable
  Trust, The *337*
Norton Foundation, The *340*
Payne Trust, The Harry *356*
Provincial Trust for Kendal, The
  370
Pyke Charity Trust *372*
Rayner Charitable Trust, The
  John *380*
Reekie Trust, R A & V B *381*
Richard Charitable Trust, The
  Cliff *383*
Ripley's Charitable Trust, Pat
  386
Royle Memorial Trust, Kirstin
  397
Rugby Football Union
  Charitable Fund, The *398*
Scott Charitable Trust, The
  Francis C *412*
Shepherd Family Charitable
  Trust, The Sir Peter *418*
Skelton Bounty, The *423*
Sobell Welsh People's
  Charitable Association,
  Michael *429*
Stevens Foundation, The June
  437
Stoate Charitable Trust, The
  Leonard Laity *438*
Summerfield Charitable Trust,
  The *442*
Symons Charitable Trust, The
  Stella *446*

TSB Foundation for Scotland
  447
Tisbury Telegraph Trust, The
  457
Torquay Charities, The *458*
Wall Trust, Thomas *478*
Wander Charitable Fund, The
  Dr Albert *479*
Wates Foundation, The *481*
Williams Charitable Trust,
  Alfred *493*
Wills 1961 Charitable Trust, Mr
  Frederick *493*
Women Caring Trust, The *500*
Woodlands Trust *501*
Wylde Memorial Charity, The
  Anthony and Gwendoline
  507

■ Sportsmen & women
Funding priority
Blagrave Charitable Trust, The
  Herbert and Peter *52*
Clarke Trust, The Thomas
  Edward *99*
Lord's Taverners, The *281*
Lottery Sports Funds for
  England, Northern Ireland,
  Scotland and Wales *283*
Marriage's Charitable Trust,
  Miss G M *299*
Royle Memorial Trust, Kirstin
  397
Rugby Football Union
  Charitable Fund, The *398*
Swale Charity Trust *443*

■ Street children
  see Homeless

■ Street events
  see Community arts &
  recreation

■ Stroke
Funding priority
Owen Family Trust, The *348*
Stroke Association, The *441*

■ Students
Funding priority
AIIT (The Ancient India and
  Iran Trust) *3*
Armourers' & Brasiers' Gauntlet
  Trust, The *21*
BP Conservation Programme
  29

Balint Charitable Trust, Andrew
  31
Barnabas Charitable Trust *34*
Benlian Trust, The *44*
Biological Trust, The *49*
Brand Charitable Trust *58*
British Friends of Chinuch
  Atzmai Trust, The *62*
British Institute of Archaeology
  at Ankara *62*
British Schools and Universities
  Foundation (Inc) *62*
Careers Services Trust *81*
Carnegie Trust for the
  Universities of Scotland *82*
Cass's Foundation, Sir John *85*
Clifford Charity Oxford, The
  100
Collier Charitable Trust, The
  105
Colt Foundation, The *107*
Emmott Foundation Limited,
  The *151*
Eranda Foundation, The *152*
Gardner Memorial Trust, The
  Samuel *178*
Gilchrist Educational Trust *183*
Historical Research Trust, The
  222
Hopkinson Educational Trust,
  Robert Addy *227*
Hornsey Parochial Charities
  (Educational and Vocational
  Foundation), The *228*
Jackson Trust for Charity, The
  Isaac and Harriet *240*
Karten Charitable Trust, The
  Ian *250*
Keswick Foundation Ltd *253*
Kings Medical Research Trust,
  The *255*
LSA Charitable Trust *260*
Leche Trust, The *268*
Lewis Foundation, The John
  Spedan *274*
Lower Hall Charitable Trust
  285
McCallum Bequest Fund *290*
Mercers' Company Educational
  Trust Fund, The *306*
Montefiore Trust, The David
  316
N D Educational Trust *325*
New Durlston Trust, The *332*
Newitt Fund, Richard *333*
Noah Trust, The *335*
Older's School Charity, William
  345
Oxford Trust, The *349*
Rainbow Charitable Trust *376*
Reeve's Foundation *382*
Rhodes Trust – Public Purposes
  Fund, The *383*
Richard III and Yorkist History
  Trust *384*
Said Foundation, The Karim
  Rida *401*
St Christopher's Trust, The *402*

Scarr-Hall Memorial Trust, The *409*

Shipwrights' Company Educational Trust, The *420*

Simon Population Trust, The *422*

Smith Trust, The Sydney *428*

South Square Trust *430*

Southern Arts *432*

Stewards' Charitable Trust, The *437*

Thompson Memorial Fund, The Edwin John *453*

Thornton Fund, The *455*

Watson's Trust, John *482*

Wiseman Memorial Fund Limited, The Max *497*

Worshipful Company of Cutlers, The *504*

Worshipful Company of Shipwrights Charitable Fund, The *506*

Yorkshire Field Studies Trust *510*

■ Substance misuse

Funding priority

Alcohol Education and Research Council *9*

Charity Projects *90*

Fleurus Trust, The *165*

Hanley Trust (1987), The *207*

Moores Foundation, John *318*

Rosen Foundation, Cecil *392*

Smith Foundation, The Leslie *427*

Southall Trust, W F *432*

Stone Foundation, The *438*

Tudor Trust, The *463*

■ Support, self help groups

see also Health care

Funding priority

Allied Dunbar Charitable Trust Limited, The *13*

Berkshire Community Trust *45*

British Diabetic Association, The *61*

Cobb Charity *103*

Community Trust for Greater Manchester, The *108*

Davis Charitable Trust, Wilfrid Bruce *126*

Grant Charitable Trust, The *191*

Heath Charitable Trust *214*

Humphreys Charitable Settlement, J A M *231*

Hussey Trust, The *232*

Lacy Charity Trust, The Late Sir Pierce *260*

Leech Charity, The William *269*

Loseley & Guildway Charitable Trust, The *281*

Manning Trust, Leslie & Lilian *296*

Mental Health Foundation, The *305*

Moores Family Charity Foundation, The *317*

Royal Theatrical Fund, The *396*

SMB Trust, The *400*

Seagram Distillers Charitable Trust *413*

Strangward Trust, The *439*

Trust for London *461*

Wakeham Trust, The *476*

Will consider

AB Charitable Trust *3*

Allen Trust, Mrs M H *13*

Ammco Trust, The *15*

Andrew Charitable Trust, The Prince *16*

Archer Trust, The *20*

Army Benevolent Fund, The *22*

Astor Foundation, The *26*

Barbour Trust, The *33*

Berris Charitable Trust *45*

Bewley Charitable Trust, The *46*

Birtwistle Memorial Trust, The G E *50*

Bottom Charitable Trust, Harry *56*

Britton Charitable Trust, The J & M *63*

Brooke Benevolent Fund, William *65*

Brotherton Trust, The Charles *65*

Brough Charitable Trust, Joseph *65*

Buckinghamshire Masonic Centenary Fund *67*

Burdall Charity, H M *69*

Camelot Foundation, The *78*

Campden Charities, The *79*

Clinton's Charitable Trust, Lord *100*

Cole Charitable Trust, The *105*

Collier Charitable Trust, The *105*

Cottingham Charitable Trust, Mrs Diana Mary *114*

County Durham Foundation *115*

Coutts Charitable Trust, The *116*

Coxen Trust Fund, Sir William *116*

Cripplegate Foundation *118*

Curzon Charitable Trust, The Wallace *120*

Dean Refugee Trust Fund, The Miriam *128*

Digby Charitable Trust, Simon *133*

Dorus Trust *136*

Dumbreck Charity *139*

Edgar Foundation, The Gilbert and Eileen *145*

Elkes Charity Fund, The Wilfred & Elsie *147*

Emmandjay Charitable Trust *150*

Epigoni Trust *152*

Fishmongers' Company's Charitable Trust *163*

Follett Trust, The *166*

Foreman Foundation, The Carl & Eve *167*

Franklin Trust, Jill *170*

Gardner Charitable Trust, R & J *178*

Getty Jr General Charitable Trust, J Paul *181*

Gibbins Trust, The *181*

Goldsmiths' Company's Charities, The *188*

Good Neighbours Trust, The *188*

Greater Bristol Foundation *193*

Greenaway Foundation, The Alan *194*

Greenaway Foundation, The Sir Derek *194*

Grocers' Charity *197*

Haines Charitable Trust, The Alfred *203*

Hardy Trust, The Patsy *209*

Hawley Residuary Fund, Harry Fieldsend *212*

Hertfordshire Community Trust, The *217*

Innes Memorial Fund *235*

Isle of Dogs Community Foundation *238*

Jarman Charitable Trust, The *243*

Johnson Group Cleaners Charity *247*

Laing Foundation, The Kirby *261*

Laing Foundation, The Maurice *261*

Lawson Charitable Trust, Raymond and Blanche *267*

Leach Fourteenth Trust, The *267*

Lee Foundation, The Edgar *269*

Linmardon Trust *276*

Lloyd's Charities Trust *278*

(Lloyds) TSB Foundation for England and Wales *279*

London Law Trust *280*

Lynall Foundation, The D G *287*

Marchday Charitable Fund, The *296*

Measures Charity, The James Frederick and Ethel Anne *303*

Mercury Phoenix Trust *307*

Milton Keynes Community Trust Ltd, The *312*

Milward Charity, The Edgar 313
Minet Trust, The Peter 313
Natwest Staff Samaritan Fund 330
Needham Cooper Charitable Trust, The 331
New Court Charitable Trust 332
Newby Trust Ltd 332
Noswad Charity, The 341
Oakdale Trust, The 343
Owen Family Trust, The 348
Payne Trust, The Harry 356
Persula Foundation, The 360
Pyke Charity Trust 372
Reader's Digest Trust, The 380
Rest-Harrow Trust, The 382
Robinson Brothers (Ryders Green) Ltd, Charitable Trust 388
Rowbotham Charitable Trust, The Christopher 393
Royal's Memorial Fund, Princess 396
Saint Sarkis Charity Trust 404
Sheepdrove Trust, The 417
Sheldon Trust, The 417
Simon's Charity 422
Skelton Bounty, The 423
Smith & Mount Trust, The Mrs 426
South Square Trust 430
Staples Trust 435
Summerfield Charitable Trust, The 442
Sussman Charitable Trust, Adrienne & Leslie 443
TSB Foundation for Northern Ireland 447
Tear Fund 450
Thackray General Charitable Trust, The P & L 452
Thompson Charitable Trust, The 453
Thomson Foundation, The Sue 454
Truemark Trust, The 461
Tudor Trust, The 463
Tyne & Wear Foundation 466
Van Berchem Charitable Trust, The Alec 470
Van Leer Foundation UK Trust, Bernard 470
Victoria & Johnson Memorial Trust, Queen 472
Wakefield (Tower Hill, Trinity Square) Trust 476
Weir Foundation, The James 484
Westcroft Trust 486
Whesby Ltd 488
Whitaker Charitable Trust 489
Wiltshire Community Foundation 495
Woodlands Trust 501

■ Support to voluntary & community organisations

see also Infrastructure development

Funding priority

Aston Charities Trust Ltd 25
Baring Foundation, The 34
Berkshire Community Trust 45
Charity Know How Fund 89
Community Trust for Greater Manchester, The 108
County Durham Foundation 115
Ferguson Benevolent Fund Limited 161
Grant Charitable Trust, The 191
HACT (The Housing Association's Charitable Trust) 201
Hertfordshire Community Trust, The 217
Homeless International 225
Humphreys Charitable Settlement, J A M 231
IBM United Kingdom Trust 233
Isle of Dogs Community Foundation 238
Lacy Charity Trust, The Late Sir Pierce 260
Leech Charity, The William 269
Marr-Munning Trust 299
Milton Keynes Community Trust Ltd, The 312
Moores Foundation, John 318
Northern Ireland Voluntary Trust 339
Paristamen Foundation, The 352
Powell Foundation, The 367
Prince's Trust (now includes King George's Jubilee Trust (1935) and the Queen's Silver Jubilee Trust (1977)), The 369
Puebla Charitable Trust Limited, The 371
Rope Third Charitable Settlement, The Mrs 391
Rothley Trust, The 392
SMB Trust, The 400
St Katharine & Shadwell Trust 404
Singer Foundation 423
Skerritt Trust 423
Tyne & Wear Foundation 466
Wakeham Trust, The 476
War on Want 479
Wiltshire Community Foundation 495

Will consider

Abel Charitable Trust 5
Barbour Trust, The 33
BibleLands 47
Blake Charitable Trust, The Hubert 53
Body Shop Foundation, The 55
British Sugar Foundation 63
Brotherton Trust, The Charles 65
Brough Charitable Trust, Joseph 65
CLA Charitable Trust 74
Cadbury Trust (1928), The Edward & Dorothy 76
Camelot Foundation, The 78
Campden Charities, The 79
Carnegie Dunfermline Trust 82
Carnegie United Kingdom Trust, The 82
Chrimes Family Charitable Trust, The 93
Clifford Charity Oxford, The 100
Collier Charitable Trust, The 105
Cottingham Charitable Trust, Mrs Diana Mary 114
Coutts Charitable Trust, The 116
Cripplegate Foundation 118
de Freitas Charitable Trust, The Helen and Geoffrey 126
Debtors' Relief Fund Charity 128
Digby Charitable Trust, Simon 133
Direct Response 134
Ford of Britain Trust 166
Four Winds Trust 168
Franklin Trust, Jill 170
Goldsmiths' Company's Charities, The 188
Great Britain Sasakawa Foundation, The 193
Greenaway Foundation, The Sir Derek 194
Growth Building Trust, The 198
Harford Charitable Trust 209
Hobbs Trust Limited, The Betty 222
Humanitarian Trust, The 230
Hussey for Africans, Charity of Rebecca 231
Hyde Park Place Estate Charity, The 232
Ireland Funds, The 237
Johnson Foundation, The 246
Knott Trust, Sir James 258
Lane Foundation, The Allen 263
Lawson Charitable Trust, Raymond and Blanche 267
Linford Charitable Trust, The Fred 276
Lloyd's Charities Trust 278
London Law Trust 280

Low & Bonar Charitable Fund, The *284*

Lunn-Rockliffe Charitable Trust, Paul *286*

Manning Trust, Leslie & Lilian *296*

Measures Charity, The James Frederick and Ethel Anne *303*

Minet Trust, The Peter *313*

National Power Charitable Trust, The *330*

Noah Trust, The *335*

Noel Buxton Trust, The *335*

Norwich Church of England Young Men's Society *340*

Owen Family Trust, The *348*

PF Charitable Trust *350*

Parivar Trust, The *353*

Persula Foundation, The *360*

Pilkington Charitable Trust, Cecil *363*

Pratt Charitable Trust, The W L *367*

Ravenscroft Foundation, The *379*

Robinson Brothers (Ryders Green) Ltd, Charitable Trust *388*

Rowbotham Charitable Trust, The Christopher *393*

Rowntree Charitable Trust, The Joseph *394*

Rowntree Foundation, Joseph *394*

Sainsbury Charitable Fund Ltd, The *402*

Scott Bader Commonwealth Ltd, The *411*

Sheepdrove Trust, The *417*

Skelton Bounty, The *423*

Smith & Mount Trust, The Mrs *426*

South Yorkshire Community Foundation *431*

Stonehouse Trust Ltd, Eric *438*

Summerfield Charitable Trust, The *442*

Swan Mountain Trust *444*

Sykes Trust, The Charles *445*

TSB Foundation for Northern Ireland *447*

Tear Fund *450*

Thomson Foundation, The Sue *454*

Van Leer Foundation UK Trust, Bernard *470*

Victoria & Johnson Memorial Trust, Queen *472*

Wade & Others, The Charity of Thomas *475*

Wakefield (Tower Hill, Trinity Square) Trust *476*

Wall Trust, Thomas *478*

Whesby Ltd *488*

Whitaker Charitable Trust *489*

Williams Charitable Trust, Alfred *493*

Wingfield's Charitable Trust, Mrs *496*

Woodlands Trust *501*

Wylde Memorial Charity, The Anthony and Gwendoline *507*

....
■ Support to volunteers

see also Infrastructure development

Funding priority

Baring Foundation, The *34*

Berkshire Community Trust *45*

Community Trust for Greater Manchester, The *108*

Hertfordshire Community Trust, The *217*

Lacy Charity Trust, The Late Sir Pierce *260*

Leech Charity, The William *269*

(Lloyds) TSB Foundation for England and Wales *279*

Milton Keynes Community Trust Ltd, The *312*

Moores Foundation, John *318*

Northern Ireland Voluntary Trust *339*

Powell Foundation, The *367*

Prince's Trust (now includes King George's Jubilee Trust (1935) and the Queen's Silver Jubilee Trust (1977)), The *369*

Rope Third Charitable Settlement, The Mrs *391*

SMB Trust, The *400*

St Katharine & Shadwell Trust *404*

Singer Foundation *423*

Tyne & Wear Foundation *466*

Wakeham Trust, The *476*

War on Want *479*

Wiltshire Community Foundation *495*

Will consider

Ashden Charitable Trust, The *24*

Barbour Trust, The *33*

BibleLands *47*

British Sugar Foundation *63*

Brotherton Trust, The Charles *65*

CLA Charitable Trust *74*

Cadbury Trust (1928), The Edward & Dorothy *76*

Camelot Foundation, The *78*

Campden Charities, The *79*

Carnegie Dunfermline Trust *82*

Carnegie United Kingdom Trust, The *82*

Chrimes Family Charitable Trust, The *93*

Christmas Cracker Trust *95*

Clifford Charity Oxford, The *100*

Collier Charitable Trust, The *105*

Cottingham Charitable Trust, Mrs Diana Mary *114*

County Durham Foundation *115*

Coutts Charitable Trust, The *116*

Cripplegate Foundation *118*

de Freitas Charitable Trust, The Helen and Geoffrey *126*

Debtors' Relief Fund Charity *128*

Derbyshire Trust, J N *130*

Digby Charitable Trust, Simon *133*

Direct Response *134*

Ford of Britain Trust *166*

Four Winds Trust *168*

Franklin Trust, Jill *170*

Goldsmiths' Company's Charities, The *188*

Graves Charitable Trust, J G *192*

Great Britain Sasakawa Foundation, The *193*

Greenaway Foundation, The Sir Derek *194*

Growth Building Trust, The *198*

Harford Charitable Trust *209*

Hobbs Trust Limited, The Betty *222*

Hussey for Africans, Charity of Rebecca *231*

Hyde Park Place Estate Charity, The *232*

IBM United Kingdom Trust *233*

Ireland Funds, The *237*

Isle of Dogs Community Foundation *238*

James Charitable Trust, John *241*

Knott Trust, Sir James *258*

Lane Foundation, The Allen *263*

Lawson Charitable Trust, Raymond and Blanche *267*

Linford Charitable Trust, The Fred *276*

London Law Trust *280*

Manning Trust, Leslie & Lilian *296*

Marr-Munning Trust *299*

Measures Charity, The James Frederick and Ethel Anne *303*

National Power Charitable Trust, The *330*

New Chasers Charitable Trust, The *332*

Newby Trust Ltd *332*

Noel Buxton Trust, The *335*

Owen Family Trust, The *348*

PF Charitable Trust *350*

Parivar Trust, The *353*
Persula Foundation, The *360*
Puebla Charitable Trust
Limited, The *371*
Ravenscroft Foundation, The
379
Robinson Brothers (Ryders
Green) Ltd, Charitable Trust
388
Rowbotham Charitable Trust,
The Christopher *393*
Rowntree Foundation, Joseph
394
Scott Bader Commonwealth
Ltd, The *411*
Sheldon Trust, The *417*
Skelton Bounty, The *423*
Smith & Mount Trust, The Mrs
426
Summerfield Charitable Trust,
The *442*
Swan Mountain Trust *444*
Sykes Trust, The Charles *445*
TSB Foundation for Northern
Ireland *447*
Tudor Trust, The *463*
Van Leer Foundation UK Trust,
Bernard *470*
Victoria & Johnson Memorial
Trust, Queen *472*
Wade & Others, The Charity of
Thomas *475*
Wakefield (Tower Hill, Trinity
Square) Trust *476*
Wall Trust, Thomas *478*
Whesby Ltd *488*
Whitaker Charitable Trust *489*
Williams Charitable Trust,
Alfred *493*
Woodlands Trust *501*
Wylde Memorial Charity, The
Anthony and Gwendoline
507

■ Synagogues
see also **Religious buildings**
Funding priority
Achiezer Association Limited *6*
Beauland Ltd *39*
Cen Foundation, The Hyman
87
Cohen and William Leech
Foundation, Sebag *103*
Forbesville Limited *166*
Franklin Deceased's New
Second Charity, Sydney E
170
Joseph Charitable Trust, J E
248
Kermaville Ltd *253*
Locker Foundation, The *280*
Maypride Ltd *303*
Noswal Charitable Trust, The
341
Rav Chesed Trust, The *379*

Sassoon Charitable Trust, The
Late Aaron D *408*
Tesler Foundation, The *452*
Wingate Foundation, The
Harold Hyam *496*

Will consider
Alglen Ltd *11*
Beckwith-Smith's Charitable
Settlement, Mrs *40*
Belljoe Tzedoko Ltd *42*
Bloom Foundation, Abraham
Algy *54*
Brushmill Ltd *66*
Chesters Settlement for
Methodist Church Purposes,
Mr H G *91*
Closehelm Ltd *101*
David Trust, The Lesley *124*
Digby Charitable Trust, Simon
133
Doughty Charity Trust, The
136
Federation of Jewish Relief
Organisations *160*
Fogel Charitable Trust, The
Gerald *165*
Garbacz Charitable Trust, The
Bernard & Vera *178*
Gladstone Charitable Trust, The
E W *184*
Greenaway Foundation, The Sir
Derek *194*
Gross Charities Limited, M & R
197
Grosshill Charitable Trust *197*
Highcroft Charitable Trust *218*
Hillards Charitable Trust, Gay &
Peter Hartley's *220*
Kahn Charitable Trust, Bernard
250
Localtrent Ltd *279*
Mayfair Charities Limited *303*
Moore Charitable Trust, The
Horace *316*
Porter Foundation *366*
Tudor Rose Ltd *463*
Vogel Charitable Trust, The
Nathan *474*
Wolff Charity Trust *498*
Wychdale Limited *507*

■ Teacher training colleges
see **Tertiary & higher
education**

■ Teachers & governesses
Funding priority
CfBT Education Services *74*
Hussey for Africans, Charity of
Rebecca *231*
Ogilvie Charities (Deed No 2)
344

■ Technical services
see **Infrastructure &
technical support**

■ Temples, gurdwaras
see also **Religious buildings**
Will consider
Beckwith-Smith's Charitable
Settlement, Mrs *40*
Chesters Settlement for
Methodist Church Purposes,
Mr H G *91*
Digby Charitable Trust, Simon
133
Greenaway Foundation, The Sir
Derek *194*
Hillards Charitable Trust, Gay &
Peter Hartley's *220*
Moore Charitable Trust, The
Horace *316*

■ Terminally ill
Funding priority
Clark Charitable Trust,
Elizabeth *98*
Foreman Foundation, The Carl
& Eve *167*
Hill Memorial Trust, L E *219*
Lynall Foundation, The D G
287
Morris Charitable Trust, The
Douglas *320*

■ Tertiary & higher education
see also **Schools & colleges**
Funding priority
All Saints Educational Trust *12*
Anstruther Memorial Trust, The
Fagus *19*
Beit Trust, The *40*
Biological Trust, The *49*
British Schools and Universities
Foundation (Inc) *62*
Cassel Educational Trust
(Grants for Educational
Purposes), Sir Ernest *84*
Cassel Educational Trust
(Mountbatten Memorial

Grants to Commonwealth Students), The Sir Ernest *84*

Chartered Institute of Management Accountants' General Charitable Trust, The *90*

Clark Charitable Trust, J Anthony *98*

Dulverton Trust, The *139*

Ellinson Foundation Limited *148*

Gatsby Charitable Foundation, The *179*

Graham Charitable Trust, Reginald *190*

Harvey Charitable Trust, Gordon *211*

Hoover Foundation, The *226*

Hopkinson Educational Trust, Robert Addy *227*

Hussey for Africans, Charity of Rebecca *231*

Jeffreys Road Fund, Rees *243*

Mediterranean Archaeological Trust *304*

Montefiore Trust, The David *316*

Needham Cooper Charitable Trust, The *331*

Oldacre Foundation, The John *345*

Older's School Charity, William *345*

Richard III and Yorkist History Trust *384*

Royal Commission for the Exhibition of 1851 *395*

St Katharine & Shadwell Trust *404*

Shipwrights' Company Educational Trust, The *420*

Thriplow Charitable Trust *456*

Trades Union Congress Educational Trust *460*

Worshipful Company of Engineers' Charitable Trust Fund, The *504*

Will consider

Ambika Paul Foundation *15*

Archer Trust, The *20*

Arts Council of Wales, The *23*

Ashley Foundation, The Laura *24*

Barbour Trust, The *33*

Boots Charitable Trust *56*

British Dietetic Association General and Education Trust Fund, The *61*

Bullough Tompson Settlement, The *68*

Bulmer Charitable Trust, Becket *68*

Cancer Relief Macmillan Fund *79*

Carnegie Dunfermline Trust *82*

Carnegie Trust for the Universities of Scotland *82*

Clifford Charity Oxford, The *100*

Commonwealth Relations Trust *108*

Company of Chartered Surveyors Charitable Trust Fund, The *108*

Cooper Charitable Trust *111*

Cripplegate Foundation *118*

Curriers Company Charitable Fund *119*

Davies Charity, The Gwendoline and Margaret *125*

Derbyshire Trust, J N *130*

Dibden Allotments Charity *132*

Digby Charitable Trust, Simon *133*

Ebb and Flow Charitable Trust *144*

Edgar Trust, The Gilbert *145*

Education Services *145*

Elkes Charity Fund, The Wilfred & Elsie *147*

Follett Trust, The *166*

Four Lanes Trust, The *168*

Four Winds Trust *168*

Goldsmiths' Company's Charities, The *188*

Great Britain Sasakawa Foundation, The *193*

Hamlyn Foundation, The Paul *205*

Hillards Charitable Trust, Gay & Peter Hartley's *220*

Hockerill Educational Foundation *223*

Holly Hill Charitable Trust *224*

Homeless International *225*

Howard Charitable Trust, John & Ruth *229*

Humanitarian Trust, The *230*

Idlewild Trust, The *234*

Ireland Funds, The *237*

Isle of Dogs Community Foundation *238*

Lewis Foundation, The John Spedan *274*

Littler Foundation, The Emile *277*

Lloyd's Charities Trust *278*

McDougall Trust, The *291*

Milward Charity, The Edgar *313*

Morphy Memorial Fund, Arthur *319*

Newby Trust Ltd *332*

Newcomen Collett Foundation *333*

Norman, The Educational Foundation of Alderman John *337*

Oldham Foundation *345*

Owen Family Trust, The *348*

PF Charitable Trust *350*

Paristamen Foundation, The *352*

Pilkington Charitable Trust, Cecil *363*

Porcupine Trust, The *366*

Provincial Trust for Kendal, The *370*

Radcliffe's Trust, Dr *375*

Rainbow Charitable Trust *376*

Rhodes Trust – Public Purposes Fund, The *383*

Richards Charity, The Violet M *384*

Said Foundation, The Karim Rida *401*

Salters Charities *405*

Simon's Charity *422*

Spooner Charitable Trust, W W *434*

Summerfield Charitable Trust, The *442*

Swann-Morton Foundation, The *444*

Tear Fund *450*

Tisbury Telegraph Trust, The *457*

Upjohn Charitable Trust, The *469*

Whitehead Charitable Trust, J E *490*

Wingate Foundation, The Harold Hyam *496*

Woolmen's Company Charitable Trust, The *503*

Wylde Memorial Charity, The Anthony and Gwendoline *507*

Yorkshire Agricultural Society *509*

■ **Textile workers & designers**

Funding priority

Barnby's Foundation Appointed Fund, Lord *35*

Worshipful Company of Weavers Textile Education Fund, The *506*

■ **Textiles & upholstery**

see also **Education & training**

Funding priority

Woolmen's Company Charitable Trust, The *503*

Worshipful Company of Weavers Textile Education Fund, The *506*

....
■ Theatre

see also Arts & arts facilities

Funding priority

Arts Council of England, The *23*

Arts Council of Wales, The *23*

Blay Trust, The Robert *54*

Fletcher Charitable Trust, The Joyce *164*

Lower Hall Charitable Trust *285*

Mackintosh Foundation, The *292*

Merchants House of Glasgow *307*

North West Arts Board *337*

Northern Arts *339*

Royal Victoria Hall Foundation, The *396*

Strauss Charitable Trust *440*

Wates Charitable Trust, John *481*

Yorkshire and Humberside Arts *510*

Will consider

Anstey Charitable Settlement, J C W *18*

Astor Foundation, The *26*

Beckwith Charitable Settlement, The Heather *39*

Broadley Charitable Trust, The *64*

Brooke Benevolent Fund, William *65*

Bulmer Charitable Trust, Becket *68*

Cadbury Trust (1928), The Edward & Dorothy *76*

Campden Charities, The *79*

Carnegie Dunfermline Trust *82*

Carnegie United Kingdom Trust, The *82*

Cazalet Charitable Trust, The Raymond *87*

Coates Charitable Trust, The John *103*

Colyer-Fergusson Charitable Trust, The *107*

Cripplegate Foundation *118*

D'Avigdor Goldsmid Charitable Trust, The Sarah *125*

Debtors' Relief Fund Charity *128*

Digby Charitable Trust, Simon *133*

Dixon Charitable Trust, F E *134*

Dumbreck Charity *139*

Early's Charitable Settlement, Richard *142*

Edgar Foundation, The Gilbert and Eileen *145*

Finzi Charitable Trust, Gerald *162*

Follett Trust, The *166*

Granada Foundation, The *190*

Great Britain Sasakawa Foundation, The *193*

Greenaway Foundation, The Sir Derek *194*

Grundy Foundation, The Stanley *198*

Halkes Settlement, John Robert *204*

Hamlyn Foundation, The Paul *205*

Harding Trust, The *209*

Henderson's Settlement, J R *216*

Hopkins Charitable Foundation, The Sir Anthony *226*

Howard Charitable Trust, John & Ruth *229*

Hudson Benevolent Trust, The Thomas *230*

Hughes Charitable Trust, The Geoffery C *230*

Hunter Charitable Trust, The Claire *231*

Inverforth Charitable Trust, The *236*

Ireland Funds, The *237*

JMK Charitable Trust *239*

Laing Charitable Trust, The David *260*

Laing Foundation, The Christopher *260*

Leche Trust, The *268*

Lee Foundation, The Edgar *269*

Lewis Foundation, The John Spedan *274*

Linford Charitable Trust, The Fred *276*

Littler Foundation, The Emile *277*

Lowenthal Charitable Trust, The L and C *285*

Milton Keynes Community Trust Ltd, The *312*

Mitchell Trust, Esme *315*

Music Sales Charitable Trust, The *324*

Needham Cooper Charitable Trust, The *331*

New Court Charitable Trust *332*

Notgrove Trust, The *341*

Oldham Foundation *345*

Owen Family Trust, The *348*

PF Charitable Trust *350*

Paragon Concert Society *352*

Provincial Trust for Kendal, The *370*

St Katharine & Shadwell Trust *404*

Snipe Charitable Trust *428*

Sobell Welsh People's Charitable Association, Michael *429*

Somerfield Curtis Will Trust, The Dorothy *430*

South Square Trust *430*

Summerfield Charitable Trust, The *442*

Taylor Charitable Trust, The B R *450*

Thomson Foundation, The Sue *454*

Walker Trust, The *477*

Wates Foundation, The *481*

Whitaker Charitable Trust *489*

Williams Charitable Trust, Alfred *493*

....
■ Theatres & opera houses

see also Community facilities

Funding priority

Beckwith Charitable Settlement, The Heather *39*

Daiwa Anglo-Japanese Foundation, The *122*

Fletcher Charitable Trust, The Joyce *164*

Follett Trust, The *166*

Grundy Foundation, The Stanley *198*

Mackintosh Foundation, The *292*

Morel Charitable Trust, The *318*

Northern Arts *339*

Pilkington Trust, The Austin and Hope *363*

Southern Arts *432*

Will consider

Abbey National Charitable Trust *4*

Ammco Trust, The *15*

Angler's Inn Trust *17*

Anstey Charitable Settlement, J C W *18*

Aquarius Charitable Foundation, The *19*

Astor Foundation, The *26*

Astor of Hever Trust, The *26*

Beit Trust, The *40*

Bowland Charitable Trust, The *57*

Brand Trust, The *59*

Brooke Benevolent Fund, William *65*

Bullough Tompson Settlement, The *68*

Burton 1960 Charitable Settlement, Audrey & Stanley *70*

Butler's Trust, Lord *71*

Campden Charities, The *79*

Chase Charity, The *91*

Chiddick Charitable Trust *92*

Clark 1965 Charitable Trust, Stephen *98*

Clutterbuck Charitable Trust, Robert *102*

Coates Charitable Trust, The John *103*

Cobb Charity *103*

Colyer-Fergusson Charitable Trust, The *107*

Community Trust for Greater Manchester, The *108*

Debtors' Relief Fund Charity *128*

Digby Charitable Trust, Simon *133*

Direct Response *134*

Dixon Charitable Trust, F E *134*

Dulverton Trust, The *139*

Dumbreck Charity *139*

Early's Charitable Settlement, Richard *142*

Edgar Foundation, The Gilbert and Eileen *145*

Feeney Charitable Bequest, The John *161*

Four Lanes Trust, The *168*

Gardner Charitable Trust, R & J *178*

Garnett Charitable Trust, The *178*

Great Britain Sasakawa Foundation, The *193*

Greenaway Foundation, The Sir Derek *194*

Grocers' Charity *197*

Gwent County Council Welsh Church Fund *200*

Halkes Settlement, John Robert *204*

Hamlyn Foundation, The Paul *205*

Harbinson Charitable Trust, Roderick *208*

Hillards Charitable Trust, Gay & Peter Hartley's *220*

Hopkins Charitable Foundation, The Sir Anthony *226*

Hudson Benevolent Trust, The Thomas *230*

Hunter Charitable Trust, The Claire *231*

Ingles Charitable Trust, The *234*

Inverforth Charitable Trust, The *236*

Ireland Funds, The *237*

Isle of Dogs Community Foundation *238*

JMK Charitable Trust *239*

Knott Trust, Sir James *258*

Laing Charitable Trust, The David *260*

Laing Foundation, The Christopher *260*

Lawson Charitable Trust, Raymond and Blanche *267*

Leche Trust, The *268*

Lee Foundation, The Edgar *269*

Littler Foundation, The Emile *277*

(Lloyds) TSB Foundation for England and Wales *279*

Low & Bonar Charitable Fund, The *284*

Marriage's Charitable Trust, Miss G M *299*

Moore Foundation, The George A *316*

Needham Cooper Charitable Trust, The *331*

Norfolk's Family Charitable Trust, Lavinia *336*

North West Arts Board *337*

Notgrove Trust, The *341*

Oakdale Trust, The *343*

Owen Family Trust, The *348*

PF Charitable Trust *350*

Payne Trust, The Harry *356*

Persula Foundation, The *360*

Porter Foundation *366*

Rayner Charitable Trust, The John *380*

Reekie Trust, R A & V B *381*

Richard Charitable Trust, The Cliff *383*

Ripley's Charitable Trust, Pat *386*

Rookes Charitable Trust, C A *390*

Royal Victoria Hall Foundation, The *396*

Scholes Charitable Trust, The R H *410*

Scott Charitable Trust, The Francis C *412*

Shepherd Family Charitable Trust, The Sir Peter *418*

South Square Trust *430*

Strauss Charitable Trust *440*

Summerfield Charitable Trust, The *442*

Symons Charitable Trust, The Stella *446*

TSB Foundation for Scotland *447*

Wagstaff Charitable Trust, Bob *475*

Walker Trust, The *477*

Wander Charitable Fund, The Dr Albert *479*

Whitaker Charitable Trust *489*

Whitecourt Charitable Trust, The *490*

Williams Charitable Trust, Alfred *493*

Wingate Foundation, The Harold Hyam *496*

Wingfield's Charitable Trust, Mrs *496*

Wylde Memorial Charity, The Anthony and Gwendoline *507*

■ Theatrical companies, theatre groups

see also Community arts & recreation

Funding priority

Carnegie United Kingdom Trust, The *82*

Ireland Funds, The *237*

Mackintosh Foundation, The *292*

Noah Trust, The *335*

North West Arts Board *337*

Northern Arts *339*

Royal Victoria Hall Foundation, The *396*

Yorkshire and Humberside Arts *510*

Will consider

Anstey Charitable Settlement, J C W *18*

Arts Council of England, The *23*

Ashden Charitable Trust, The *24*

Astor Foundation, The *26*

Blay Trust, The Robert *54*

Brooke Benevolent Fund, William *65*

Bulmer Charitable Trust, Becket *68*

Cadbury Trust (1928), The Edward & Dorothy *76*

Calypso Browning Trust *78*

Carlton Television Trust *81*

Carnegie Dunfermline Trust *82*

Clifford Charity Oxford, The *100*

County Durham Foundation *115*

de Freitas Charitable Trust, The Helen and Geoffrey *126*

Digby Charitable Trust, Simon *133*

Dixon Charitable Trust, F E *134*

Early's Charitable Settlement, Richard *142*

Edgar Foundation, The Gilbert and Eileen *145*

Fletcher Charitable Trust, The Joyce *164*

Follett Trust, The *166*

Granada Foundation, The *190*

Great Britain Sasakawa Foundation, The *193*

Greenaway Foundation, The Sir Derek *194*

Grocers' Charity *197*

Grundy Foundation, The Stanley *198*

Hamlyn Foundation, The Paul *205*

Hinrichsen Foundation, The *221*

Hopkins Charitable Foundation,
The Sir Anthony *226*
Howard Charitable Trust, John
& Ruth *229*
Hudson Benevolent Trust, The
Thomas *230*
Hunter Charitable Trust, The
Claire *231*
Lawley Foundation, The Edgar
E *267*
Leche Trust, The *268*
Lee Foundation, The Edgar
269
Lewis Foundation, The John
Spedan *274*
Littler Foundation, The Emile
277
Lower Hall Charitable Trust
285
Marriage's Charitable Trust,
Miss G M *299*
Milton Keynes Community
Trust Ltd, The *312*
Needham Cooper Charitable
Trust, The *331*
New Court Charitable Trust
332
Northern Ireland Voluntary
Trust *339*
Oldham Foundation *345*
Owen Family Trust, The *348*
PF Charitable Trust *350*
Persula Foundation, The *360*
Richard Charitable Trust, The
Cliff *383*
Ripley's Charitable Trust, Pat
386
St Katharine & Shadwell Trust
404
Snipe Charitable Trust *428*
South Square Trust *430*
Summerfield Charitable Trust,
The *442*
Turner Trust, The Douglas *464*
Wakefield (Tower Hill, Trinity
Square) Trust *476*
Wates Foundation, The *481*
Williams Charitable Trust,
Alfred *493*

■ **Tourism**

see also Infrastructure
development

Funding priority

Northern Arts *339*

Will consider

BibleLands *47*
British Sugar Foundation *63*
Camelot Foundation, The *78*
Carnegie Dunfermline Trust *82*
Digby Charitable Trust, Simon
133
Marr-Munning Trust *299*

Measures Charity, The James
Frederick and Ethel Anne
303
PF Charitable Trust *350*
Puebla Charitable Trust
Limited, The *371*
Wylde Memorial Charity, The
Anthony and Gwendoline
507

■ **Training**

see Education & training

■ **Training for
community
development**

see also Education &
training

Funding priority

Bilton Charity, The Percy *48*
Carlton Television Trust *81*
Community Trust for Greater
Manchester, The *108*
County Durham Foundation
115
Curriers Company Charitable
Fund *119*
Hopkinson Educational Trust,
Robert Addy *227*
Hudson Benevolent Trust, The
Thomas *230*
Moore Foundation, The
George A *316*
Moores Family Charity
Foundation, The *317*
Moores Foundation, John *318*
St Katharine & Shadwell Trust
404
Simon Population Trust, The
422

Will consider

Abel Charitable Trust *5*
Arts Council of Wales, The *23*
Ashley Foundation, The Laura
24
Barbour Trust, The *33*
Beit Trust, The *40*
BibleLands *47*
Boots Charitable Trust *56*
Brotherton Trust, The Charles
65
Brough Charitable Trust,
Joseph *65*
CLA Charitable Trust *74*
Cadbury Trust (1928), The
Edward & Dorothy *76*
Camelot Foundation, The *78*
Campden Charities, The *79*
Carnegie United Kingdom
Trust, The *82*
Chrimes Family Charitable
Trust, The *93*

Clinton's Charitable Trust, Lord
100
Collier Charitable Trust, The
105
Company of Chartered
Surveyors Charitable Trust
Fund, The *108*
Coutts Charitable Trust, The
116
Cripplegate Foundation *118*
Curzon Charitable Trust, The
Wallace *120*
de Freitas Charitable Trust, The
Helen and Geoffrey *126*
Dibden Allotments Charity *132*
Digby Charitable Trust, Simon
133
Direct Response *134*
Ebb and Flow Charitable Trust
144
Edgar Trust, The Gilbert *145*
Education Services *145*
Elmgrant Trust *149*
Emanuel Charitable Settlement,
Ralph and Muriel *150*
Ferguson Benevolent Fund
Limited *161*
Follett Trust, The *166*
Ford of Britain Trust *166*
Four Winds Trust *168*
Gelston Charitable Trust, The
179
Gluckstein Charitable
Settlement, The Penelope
185
Glynde Place Charitable Trust
(1974), The *186*
Great Britain Sasakawa
Foundation, The *193*
Hamlyn Foundation, The Paul
205
Hertfordshire Community
Trust, The *217*
Holly Hill Charitable Trust *224*
Hussey for Africans, Charity of
Rebecca *231*
Ingles Charitable Trust, The
234
Ireland Funds, The *237*
Isle of Dogs Community
Foundation *238*
KC Charitable Trust, The *250*
Laing's Charitable Trust *262*
Lankelly Foundation, The *264*
Leech Charity, The William *269*
Lewis Partnership, John *274*
Lloyd Charity, The S and D *278*
(Lloyds) TSB Foundation for
England and Wales *279*
London Law Trust *280*
Milton Keynes Community
Trust Ltd, The *312*
NR Charitable Trust, The *325*
National Power Charitable
Trust, The *330*
Needham Cooper Charitable
Trust, The *331*

New Chasers Charitable Trust, The *332*
Oldham Foundation *345*
Owen Family Trust, The *348*
Paristamen Foundation, The *352*
Persula Foundation, The *360*
Powell Foundation, The *367*
Rayner Charitable Trust, The John *380*
Reader's Digest Trust, The *380*
Rest-Harrow Trust, The *382*
Rowntree Foundation, Joseph *394*
SMB Trust, The *400*
Said Foundation, The Karim Rida *401*
Sheldon Trust, The *417*
Simon's Charity *422*
Skelton Bounty, The *423*
South Square Trust *430*
South Yorkshire Community Foundation *431*
Summerfield Charitable Trust, The *442*
Swann-Morton Foundation, The *444*
TSB Foundation for Northern Ireland *447*
Tear Fund *450*
Thorpe Charity Trust, The *455*
Thriplow Charitable Trust *456*
Tisbury Telegraph Trust, The *457*
Tyne & Wear Foundation *466*
Van Berchem Charitable Trust, The Alec *470*
Van Leer Foundation UK Trust, Bernard *470*
Wade & Others, The Charity of Thomas *475*
Wakefield (Tower Hill, Trinity Square) Trust *476*
Wall Trust, Thomas *478*
Wates Foundation, The *481*
Wiltshire Community Foundation *495*
Woodlands Trust *501*
Worshipful Company of Engineers' Charitable Trust Fund, The *504*
Yorkshire Bank Charitable Trust, The *510*

■ Training for personal development

see also Education & training

Funding priority
Carlton Television Trust *81*
Clifford Charity Oxford, The *100*
County Durham Foundation *115*

Coutts Charitable Trust, The *116*
Duveen Trust, The *141*
Hopkinson Educational Trust, Robert Addy *227*
Hussey for Africans, Charity of Rebecca *231*
London Law Trust *280*
Oldham Foundation *345*
St Katharine & Shadwell Trust *404*
Trades Union Congress Educational Trust *460*
Van Berchem Charitable Trust, The Alec *470*

Will consider
Amory Charitable Trust, Viscount *16*
Army Benevolent Fund, The *22*
Arts Council of Wales, The *23*
Ashley Foundation, The Laura *24*
Barbour Trust, The *33*
Beit Trust, The *40*
BibleLands *47*
Bilton Charity, The Percy *48*
Boots Charitable Trust *56*
Brotherton Trust, The Charles *65*
Brough Charitable Trust, Joseph *65*
CLA Charitable Trust *74*
Camelot Foundation, The *78*
Campden Charities, The *79*
Clinton's Charitable Trust, Lord *100*
Company of Chartered Surveyors Charitable Trust Fund, The *108*
Cripplegate Foundation *118*
Curriers Company Charitable Fund *119*
Curzon Charitable Trust, The Wallace *120*
de Freitas Charitable Trust, The Helen and Geoffrey *126*
Dibden Allotments Charity *132*
Digby Charitable Trust, Simon *133*
Direct Response *134*
Ebb and Flow Charitable Trust *144*
Edgar Trust, The Gilbert *145*
Education Services *145*
Elmgrant Trust *149*
Ferguson Benevolent Fund Limited *161*
Ford of Britain Trust *166*
Gelston Charitable Trust, The *179*
Gluckstein Charitable Settlement, The Penelope *185*
Great Britain Sasakawa Foundation, The *193*

Hamlyn Foundation, The Paul *205*
Hertfordshire Community Trust, The *217*
Holly Hill Charitable Trust *224*
Hudson Benevolent Trust, The Thomas *230*
Ingles Charitable Trust, The *234*
Ireland Funds, The *237*
Isle of Dogs Community Foundation *238*
KC Charitable Trust, The *250*
Laing Foundation, The Maurice *261*
Lewis Foundation, The John Spedan *274*
Lewis Partnership, John *274*
Linford Charitable Trust, The Fred *276*
(Lloyds) TSB Foundation for England and Wales *279*
Middlesex County Rugby Football Union Memorial Fund *309*
Milward Charity, The Edgar *313*
Moore Foundation, The George A *316*
Moores Foundation, John *318*
Morris Charitable Trust, The Douglas *320*
NR Charitable Trust, The *325*
National Power Charitable Trust, The *330*
Needham Cooper Charitable Trust, The *331*
New Chasers Charitable Trust, The *332*
Newby Trust Ltd *332*
Patients' Aid Association Hospital and Medical Charities Trust *354*
Rest-Harrow Trust, The *382*
Ripley's Charitable Trust, Pat *386*
Sheepdrove Trust, The *417*
Simon's Charity *422*
Smith (Estates Charities), Henry *426*
Summerfield Charitable Trust, The *442*
Swann-Morton Foundation, The *444*
TSB Foundation for Northern Ireland *447*
Tear Fund *450*
Thomson Foundation, The Sue *454*
Thorpe Charity Trust, The *455*
Tyne & Wear Foundation *466*
Van Leer Foundation UK Trust, Bernard *470*
Vincent Trust Fund, Eric W *473*
Wakefield (Tower Hill, Trinity Square) Trust *476*
Wall Trust, Thomas *478*
Wates Foundation, The *481*

Wiltshire Community Foundation 495
Worshipful Company of Engineers' Charitable Trust Fund, The 504
Yorkshire Bank Charitable Trust, The 510
Yorkshire Field Studies Trust 510

■ Training for work

see also Education & training

Funding priority

Boots Charitable Trust 56
Brotherton Trust, The Charles 65
Carlton Television Trust 81
Cassel Educational Trust (Mountbatten Memorial Grants to Commonwealth Students), The Sir Ernest 84
Company of Chartered Surveyors Charitable Trust Fund, The 108
Coutts Charitable Trust, The 116
Curriers Company Charitable Fund 119
Dove-Bowerman Trust 137
Hussey for Africans, Charity of Rebecca 231
Hyde Charitable Trust 232
Ireland Funds, The 237
Isle of Dogs Community Foundation 238
Liebes Charitable Trust, The Martha Bud 274
Moore Foundation, The George A 316
Plaisterers' Company Charitable Trust, The 364
St Katharine & Shadwell Trust 404
Shipwrights' Company Educational Trust, The 420

Will consider

Amory Charitable Trust, Viscount 16
Army Benevolent Fund, The 22
Ashden Charitable Trust, The 24
Ashley Foundation, The Laura 24
Barbour Trust, The 33
Beit Trust, The 40
BibleLands 47
Bilton Charity, The Percy 48
CLA Charitable Trust 74
Camelot Foundation, The 78
Campden Charities, The 79
Chrimes Family Charitable Trust, The 93
Clifford Charity Oxford, The 100

Clinton's Charitable Trust, Lord 100
County Durham Foundation 115
Cripplegate Foundation 118
Curzon Charitable Trust, The Wallace 120
de Freitas Charitable Trust, The Helen and Geoffrey 126
Dibden Allotments Charity 132
Digby Charitable Trust, Simon 133
Direct Response 134
Earley Charity, The 142
Ebb and Flow Charitable Trust 144
Edgar Trust, The Gilbert 145
Education Services 145
Elmgrant Trust 149
Emmandjay Charitable Trust 150
Ferguson Benevolent Fund Limited 161
Ford of Britain Trust 166
Galinski Charitable Trust 177
Gelston Charitable Trust, The 179
Goldsmiths' Company's Charities, The 188
Great Britain Sasakawa Foundation, The 193
Hamlyn Foundation, The Paul 205
Hertfordshire Community Trust, The 217
Holly Hill Charitable Trust 224
Howard Charitable Trust, John & Ruth 229
Hudson Benevolent Trust, The Thomas 230
KC Charitable Trust, The 250
Lee Foundation, The Edgar 269
Leech Charity, The William 269
Lewis Foundation, The John Spedan 274
Lewis Partnership, John 274
(Lloyds) TSB Foundation for England and Wales 279
London Law Trust 280
Lunn-Rockliffe Charitable Trust, Paul 286
Mackintosh Foundation, The 292
Minet Trust, The Peter 313
Morphy Memorial Fund, Arthur 319
Morris Charitable Trust, The Douglas 320
NR Charitable Trust, The 325
National Power Charitable Trust, The 330
Needham Cooper Charitable Trust, The 331
Newby Trust Ltd 332
Oldham Foundation 345
Owen Family Trust, The 348
Paget Trust, The 351

Payne Trust, The Harry 356
Persula Foundation, The 360
Pyke Charity Trust 372
Radcliffe's Trust, Dr 375
Rayner Charitable Trust, The John 380
Reader's Digest Trust, The 380
Rest-Harrow Trust, The 382
Royal Victoria Hall Foundation, The 396
SMB Trust, The 400
Said Foundation, The Karim Rida 401
Sheepdrove Trust, The 417
Sheldon Trust, The 417
Simon's Charity 422
Skelton Bounty, The 423
Skinners' Company Lady Neville Charity 424
South Square Trust 430
Summerfield Charitable Trust, The 442
Swann-Morton Foundation, The 444
TSB Foundation for Northern Ireland 447
Tear Fund 450
Thomson Foundation, The Sue 454
Tisbury Telegraph Trust, The 457
Upjohn Charitable Trust, The 469
Vincent Trust Fund, Eric W 473
Wakefield (Tower Hill, Trinity Square) Trust 476
Wall Trust, Thomas 478
Wates Foundation, The 481
Woodlands Trust 501
Woolmen's Company Charitable Trust, The 503
Yorkshire Bank Charitable Trust, The 510

■ Transport & alternative transport

see also Conservation & campaigning

Funding priority

Campbell Charitable Foundation, The Ellis 79
Paget Trust, The 351

see also Campaigning (social issues)

■ Transport proposals (campaigning)

Funding priority

Staples Trust 435

Will consider

Allachy Trust, The *12*
Bell's Charitable Trust, Lady
  Mary *42*
Body Shop Foundation, The *55*
Bridge Trust, The *60*
Campden Charities, The *79*
Clark 1965 Charitable Trust,
  Stephen *98*
Coutts Charitable Trust, The
  116
David Trust, The Lesley *124*
Dibs Charitable Trust, The *133*
Digby Charitable Trust, Simon
  133
Direct Response *134*
Early's Charitable Settlement,
  Richard *142*
Four Winds Trust *168*
Franklin Trust, Jill *170*
Garthgwynion Charities *179*
Great Britain Sasakawa
  Foundation, The *193*
Isle of Dogs Community
  Foundation *238*
JCSCJ Charitable Trust, The
  238
Knott Trust, Sir James *258*
Lane Foundation, The Allen
  263
Leech Charity, The William *269*
Lyndhurst Settlement *287*
Morel Charitable Trust, The
  318
Noah Trust, The *335*
North West Arts Board *337*
Northern Ireland Voluntary
  Trust *339*
Paget Trust, The *351*
Patients' Aid Association
  Hospital and Medical
  Charities Trust *354*
Puebla Charitable Trust
  Limited, The *371*
Skelton Bounty, The *423*
Summerfield Charitable Trust,
  The *442*
Symons Charitable Trust, The
  Stella *446*
TSB Foundation for Northern
  Ireland *447*
Tisbury Telegraph Trust, The
  457
Travis Charitable Trust,
  Constance *460*
Wiltshire Community
  Foundation *495*
Woodhouse Charitable Trust,
  Edwin *501*

■ Travellers
Funding priority
Lyndhurst Settlement *287*
Moores Foundation, John *318*
Noel Buxton Trust, The *335*

■ Tropical diseases
Funding priority
St Francis Leprosy Guild *402*
Stewart Trust, Sir Halley *437*

■ Tuberculosis
Funding priority
Hodge Foundation, The Jane
  223

■ Unborn children's rights (campaigning)
see also Campaigning
(social issues)
Will consider
Allachy Trust, The *12*
Bridge Trust, The *60*
Chrimes Family Charitable
  Trust, The *93*
Coutts Charitable Trust, The
  116
Dibs Charitable Trust, The *133*
Digby Charitable Trust, Simon
  133
Emmaus Christian Foundation
  150
Fletcher Trust, Roy *165*
Follett Trust, The *166*
Garthgwynion Charities *179*
Gelston Charitable Trust, The
  179
Griffiths Trust, The E E and
  D M *196*
JCSCJ Charitable Trust, The
  238
Laing Foundation, The
  Christopher *260*
Leech Charity, The William *269*
Morel Charitable Trust, The
  318
National Power Charitable
  Trust, The *330*
New Court Charitable Trust
  332
North West Arts Board *337*
Northern Ireland Voluntary
  Trust *339*
Patients' Aid Association
  Hospital and Medical
  Charities Trust *354*
Payne Trust, The Harry *356*
Puebla Charitable Trust
  Limited, The *371*
Rope Third Charitable
  Settlement, The Mrs *391*
TSB Foundation for Northern
  Ireland *447*
Tisbury Telegraph Trust, The
  457
Travis Charitable Trust,
  Constance *460*

■ Unemployed
Funding priority
Access 4 Trust *6*
Alexis Trust, The *11*
Barbour Trust, The *33*
Barnabas Charitable Trust *34*
Christmas Cracker Trust *95*
Cleveland Community
  Foundation *100*
Clifford Charity Oxford, The
  100
Emily Appeal Fund, The *150*
Englefield Charitable Trust, The
  151
Fleurus Trust, The *165*
Hertfordshire Community
  Trust, The *217*
Holmleigh Trust, The *225*
Jackson Trust for Charity, The
  Isaac and Harriet *240*
Mid Moss Charitable Trust, The
  309
N D Educational Trust *325*
Nunburnholme Trust, The
  Incorporated Trustees of the
  342
Rope Third Charitable
  Settlement, The Mrs *391*
St Christopher's Trust, The *402*
Smith Trust, The Sydney *428*
Thompson Memorial Fund, The
  Edwin John *453*
Woodlands Trust *501*

■ Unitarians
Funding priority
Thornton Fund, The *455*

■ Universities
see Tertiary & higher
education

■ Upholstery
see Textiles & upholstery

■ Urban areas – living in
Funding priority
Alexandra Trust *11*
Birmingham Amenities and
  Welfare Trust, The *49*
Church Urban Fund *95*
Cobb Charity *103*
Construction Industry Trust for
  Youth, The *110*
Curriers Company Charitable
  Fund *119*
Ericson Trust *152*
Four Winds Trust *168*

HACT (The Housing
Association's Charitable
Trust) *201*
Hiley Trust, Joseph and Mary
219
Isle of Dogs Community
Foundation *238*
King's Fund, The *255*
Morel Charitable Trust, The
318
Morrison Bequest Fund,
Thomas Wharrie *320*
Oxfam (United Kingdom and
Ireland) *348*
Paddington Welfare Charities
351
Said Foundation, The Karim
Rida *401*
Sainsbury Charitable Fund Ltd,
The *402*
Skerritt Trust *423*
TSB Foundation for Scotland
447
Tear Fund *450*
Wates Foundation, The *481*

Will consider

Adnams Charity, The *7*
Ammco Trust, The *15*
Archer Trust, The *20*
Astor Foundation, The *26*
Atwell's Charity (Skinner's
Company), Lawrence *27*
Barbour Trust, The *33*
Barnabas Charitable Trust *34*
Beckwith Charitable
Settlement, The Heather *39*
Bell Charitable Trust, John *41*
Benham Charitable Trust,
Hervey *43*
Birtwistle Memorial Trust, The
G E *50*
Blake Charitable Trust, The
Morgan *53*
Boots Charitable Trust *56*
Bridge Trust, The *60*
Brotherton Trust, The Charles
65
Buckinghamshire Masonic
Centenary Fund *67*
Burdall Charity, H M *69*
Buxton Trust, Denis *72*
Camelot Foundation, The *78*
Campbell Charitable
Foundation, The Ellis *79*
Carlton Television Trust *81*
Carnegie Dunfermline Trust *82*
Carnegie United Kingdom
Trust, The *82*
Catto Charitable Settlement,
The Thomas Sivewright *86*
Challice Trust, The *87*
Charity Projects *90*
Clark 1965 Charitable Trust,
Stephen *98*
Clinton's Charitable Trust, Lord
100

Cole Charitable Trust, The *105*
Company of Chartered
Surveyors Charitable Trust
Fund, The *108*
Coutts Charitable Trust, The
116
De Yong Charitable Trust, The
Emma *128*
Digbeth Trust Ltd, The *133*
Direct Response *134*
Dorus Trust *136*
Ebb and Flow Charitable Trust
144
Edgar Foundation, The Gilbert
and Eileen *145*
Edgar Trust, The Gilbert *145*
Elkes Charity Fund, The Wilfred
& Elsie *147*
Epigoni Trust *152*
Ferguson Benevolent Fund
Limited *161*
Fletcher Charitable Trust, The
Joyce *164*
Fletcher Trust, Roy *165*
GNC Trust *175*
Gibson Charitable Trust, The
Simon *182*
Goldsmiths' Company's
Charities, The *188*
Grant-Lawson Charitable Trust,
Lady Virginia *192*
Groves Charitable Trust, The
197
Hampstead Wells and
Campden Trust *206*
Hanley Trust (1987), The *207*
Harbour Foundation Ltd, The
208
Hayward Trust, The Charles
213
Held Settlement, The Gisela
215
Hertfordshire Community
Trust, The *217*
Hopkinson Educational Trust,
Robert Addy *227*
Hudson Charitable Trust, The
230
Innes Memorial Fund *235*
Iris Trust, The *237*
JCSCJ Charitable Trust, The
238
Johnson Foundation, The *246*
Johnson Group Cleaners
Charity *247*
Keeling Charitable Trust, The
Petronella *251*
King Charitable Trust, The
Lorna *254*
Laing Charitable Trust, The
David *260*
Laing Foundation, The
Christopher *260*
Laing Foundation, The Kirby
261
Laing Foundation, The Maurice
261
Laing Trust, Beatrice *261*

Lane Foundation, The Allen
263
Laspen Trust *265*
Leach Fourteenth Trust, The
267
Lewis Foundation, The John
Spedan *274*
Lloyd Charity, The S and D *278*
Lloyd's Charities Trust *278*
Lloyd's Patriotic Fund *279*
(Lloyds) TSB Foundation for
England and Wales *279*
Lunn-Rockliffe Charitable Trust,
Paul *286*
Lynall Foundation, The D G
287
Lyons Charitable Trust, The
288
McCarthy Foundation, The
John *290*
MacKintosh Charitable Trust,
Viscount *292*
Mackintosh Foundation, The
292
Manning Trust, Leslie & Lilian
296
Marriage's Charitable Trust,
Miss G M *299*
Mental Health Foundation, The
305
Metropolitan Hospital-Sunday
Fund, The *308*
Milburn Charitable Trust,
Frederick *310*
Milton Keynes Community
Trust Ltd, The *312*
Minet Trust, The Peter *313*
Minge's Gift *314*
Moore Foundation, The
George A *316*
Moores Foundation, John *318*
Music for World Development
323
NR Charitable Trust, The *325*
Nathan Charitable Trust *326*
Natwest Staff Samaritan Fund
330
Needham Cooper Charitable
Trust, The *331*
New Court Charitable Trust
332
New Durlston Trust, The *332*
Newby Trust Ltd *332*
Noel Buxton Trust, The *335*
Norman Family Charitable
Trust, The *337*
Norton Foundation, The *340*
Oakdale Trust, The *343*
Oldham Foundation *345*
Owen Family Trust, The *348*
Paristamen Foundation, The
352
Parivar Trust, The *353*
Payne Trust, The Harry *356*
Persula Foundation, The *360*
Pilgrim Trust, The *362*
Pratt Charitable Trust, The W L
367

Prince's Trust - BRO, The *369*
Pye Christian Trust, The *371*
Pyke Charity Trust *372*
Ravenscroft Foundation, The *379*
Rest-Harrow Trust, The *382*
Robinson Brothers (Ryders Green) Ltd, Charitable Trust *388*
Rope Third Charitable Settlement, The Mrs *391*
Rowbotham Charitable Trust, The Christopher *393*
Rowntree Foundation, Joseph *394*
St Christopher's Trust, The *402*
Schuster Charitable Trust, The *410*
Seagram Distillers Charitable Trust *413*
Sheldon Trust, The *417*
Shelroy Charitable Trust, The *417*
Shepherd Charitable Trust, The Sylvia and Colin *418*
South Square Trust *430*
Staples Trust *435*
Stevens Foundation, The June *437*
Stoate Charitable Trust, The Leonard Laity *438*
Stonehouse Trust Ltd, Eric *438*
Summerfield Charitable Trust, The *442*
Summer's and I May's Charitable Settlement, The Late Misses (A N) *442*
TSB Foundation for Northern Ireland *447*
Thornton-Smith Trust, The *455*
Tisbury Telegraph Trust, The *457*
Trust for the Homeless *462*
Tudor Trust, The *463*
Van Berchem Charitable Trust, The Alec *470*
Van Leer Foundation UK Trust, Bernard *470*
Variety Club Children's Charity Limited, The *471*
Vec Acorn Trust, The *472*
Wakefield (Tower Hill, Trinity Square) Trust *476*
Wakeham Trust, The *476*
Wesleyan Charitable Trust, The *485*
Westcroft Trust *486*
Whitecourt Charitable Trust, The *490*
Wiltshire Community Foundation *495*
Woodlands Trust *501*
Worshipful Company of Glass Sellers' Charity Trust, The *505*

■ Victims of abuse
Funding priority
Clifford Charity Oxford, The *100*
Emily Appeal Fund, The *150*

■ Victims of crime
Funding priority
Alexandra Trust *11*
Coutts Charitable Trust, The *116*
Franklin Trust, Jill *170*
Hiley Trust, Joseph and Mary *219*
Irving Charitable Trust, The Charles *237*
McCarthy Foundation, The John *290*
Moore Foundation, The George A *316*
Persula Foundation, The *360*
South Square Trust *430*
Wakeham Trust, The *476*
Wates Foundation, The *481*

Will consider
AB Charitable Trust *3*
Access 4 Trust *6*
Ammco Trust, The *15*
Askew Trust, The Dorothy *25*
Astor Foundation, The *26*
Barbour Trust, The *33*
Bartholomew Christian Trust *36*
Bell Charitable Trust, John *41*
Birtwistle Memorial Trust, The G E *50*
Blake Charitable Trust, The Morgan *53*
Boots Charitable Trust *56*
Bridge Trust, The *60*
Buckinghamshire Masonic Centenary Fund *67*
Burdall Charity, H M *69*
Butlin Charity Trust, Bill *72*
Buxton Trust, Denis *72*
Cadbury Charitable Trust (Incorporated), Edward *75*
Camelot Foundation, The *78*
Campbell Charitable Foundation, The Ellis *79*
Carlton Television Trust *81*
Carnegie United Kingdom Trust, The *82*
Catto Charitable Settlement, The Thomas Sivewright *86*
Challice Trust, The *87*
Charity Projects *90*
Clark 1965 Charitable Trust, Stephen *98*
Clinton's Charitable Trust, Lord *100*
Curriers Company Charitable Fund *119*
David Trust, The Lesley *124*

De Yong Charitable Trust, The Emma *128*
Digbeth Trust Ltd, The *133*
Dorus Trust *136*
Ebb and Flow Charitable Trust *144*
Edgar Foundation, The Gilbert and Eileen *145*
Edgar Trust, The Gilbert *145*
Elkes Charity Fund, The Wilfred & Elsie *147*
Epigoni Trust *152*
Ericson Trust *152*
Fishmongers' Company's Charitable Trust *163*
Fletcher Charitable Trust, The Joyce *164*
Fletcher Trust, Roy *165*
Four Winds Trust *168*
GNC Trust *175*
GW Trust, The *176*
Gibson Charitable Trust, The Simon *182*
Goldsmiths' Company's Charities, The *188*
Grant-Lawson Charitable Trust, Lady Virginia *192*
Greater Bristol Foundation *193*
Groves Charitable Trust, The *197*
Hampstead Wells and Campden Trust *206*
Hanley Trust (1987), The *207*
Harbour Foundation Ltd, The *208*
Held Settlement, The Gisela *215*
Hertfordshire Community Trust, The *217*
Hopkinson Educational Trust, Robert Addy *227*
Hudson Benevolent Trust, The Thomas *230*
Hudson Charitable Trust, The *230*
Ibbett Trust, The *233*
Inverforth Charitable Trust, The *236*
Iris Trust, The *237*
Isle of Dogs Community Foundation *238*
JCSCJ Charitable Trust, The *238*
Jarrold Trust Ltd, John *243*
Johnson Group Cleaners Charity *247*
Keeling Charitable Trust, The Petronella *251*
King's Fund, The *255*
Laing Charitable Trust, The David *260*
Laing Foundation, The Christopher *260*
Laing Foundation, The Kirby *261*
Laing Foundation, The Maurice *261*

Lane Foundation, The Allen 263
Laspen Trust 265
Lawson Charitable Trust, Raymond and Blanche 267
Linford Charitable Trust, The Fred 276
Lloyd's Charities Trust 278
(Lloyds) TSB Foundation for England and Wales 279
Low & Bonar Charitable Fund, The 284
Lyons Charitable Trust, The 288
MacKintosh Charitable Trust, Viscount 292
Mackintosh Foundation, The 292
Manning Trust, Leslie & Lilian 296
Marriage's Charitable Trust, Miss G M 299
Measures Charity, The James Frederick and Ethel Anne 303
Mental Health Foundation, The 305
Milburn Charitable Trust, Frederick 310
Milton Keynes Community Trust Ltd, The 312
Minge's Gift 314
Moores Foundation, John 318
NR Charitable Trust, The 325
Nathan Charitable Trust 326
Needham Cooper Charitable Trust, The 331
New Court Charitable Trust 332
New Durlston Trust, The 332
Newby Trust Ltd 332
Norman Family Charitable Trust, The 337
Norton Foundation, The 340
Owen Family Trust, The 348
Paristamen Foundation, The 352
Parivar Trust, The 353
Payne Trust, The Harry 356
Peppiatt Charitable Trust, The Brian 359
Pratt Charitable Trust, The W L 367
Pye Christian Trust, The 371
Pyke Charity Trust 372
Ravenscroft Foundation, The 379
Rope Third Charitable Settlement, The Mrs 391
Rowbotham Charitable Trust, The Christopher 393
Rowntree Foundation, Joseph 394
Sainsbury Charitable Fund Ltd, The 402
St Christopher's Trust, The 402
Schuster Charitable Trust, The 410

Seagram Distillers Charitable Trust 413
Shepherd Charitable Trust, The Sylvia and Colin 418
Stevens Foundation, The June 437
Summerfield Charitable Trust, The 442
Swan Mountain Trust 444
TSB Foundation for Northern Ireland 447
TSB Foundation for Scotland 447
Tudor Trust, The 463
Van Berchem Charitable Trust, The Alec 470
Vec Acorn Trust, The 472
Wagstaff Charitable Trust, Bob 475
Wakefield (Tower Hill, Trinity Square) Trust 476
Weir Foundation, The James 484
Wesleyan Charitable Trust, The 485
Westcroft Trust 486
Wills 1962 Charitable Trust, P J H 494
Wiltshire Community Foundation 495
Wolfe Family's Charitable Trust, The 498
Woodlands Trust 501
Woodroffe Benton Foundation, The 502

■ Victims of domestic violence
Funding priority
Alcohol Education and Research Council 9
Alexandra Trust 11
Ammco Trust, The 15
Buxton Trust, Denis 72
Carlton Television Trust 81
Clifford Charity Oxford, The 100
Curriers Company Charitable Fund 119
Fletcher Trust, Roy 165
Hiley Trust, Joseph and Mary 219
Irving Charitable Trust, The Charles 237
Johnson Group Cleaners Charity 247
Lane Foundation, The Allen 263
McCarthy Foundation, The John 290
Moores Foundation, John 318
Parivar Trust, The 353
Persula Foundation, The 360
Staples Trust 435
Toy Trust, The 459
Wates Foundation, The 481

Will consider
AB Charitable Trust 3
Abbey National Charitable Trust 4
Adnams Charity, The 7
Andrew Charitable Trust, The Prince 16
Archer Trust, The 20
Astor Foundation, The 26
Ballinger Charitable Trust, The 32
Barbour Trust, The 33
Bartholomew Christian Trust 36
Blake Charitable Trust, The Morgan 53
Boots Charitable Trust 56
Bridge Trust, The 60
Buckinghamshire Masonic Centenary Fund 67
Butlin Charity Trust, Bill 72
Cadbury Charitable Trust (Incorporated), Edward 75
Camelot Foundation, The 78
Campbell Charitable Foundation, The Ellis 79
Carnegie United Kingdom Trust, The 82
Challice Trust, The 87
Charity Projects 90
Clinton's Charitable Trust, Lord 100
Cole Charitable Trust, The 105
Coutts Charitable Trust, The 116
De Yong Charitable Trust, The Emma 128
Digbeth Trust Ltd, The 133
Dorus Trust 136
Ebb and Flow Charitable Trust 144
Edgar Foundation, The Gilbert and Eileen 145
Edgar Trust, The Gilbert 145
Elkes Charity Fund, The Wilfred & Elsie 147
Epigoni Trust 152
Ericson Trust 152
Ferguson Benevolent Fund Limited 161
Fletcher Charitable Trust, The Joyce 164
Four Winds Trust 168
Franklin Trust, Jill 170
GNC Trust 175
Gibson Charitable Trust, The Simon 182
Gluckstein Charitable Settlement, The Penelope 185
Goldsmiths' Company's Charities, The 188
Grant-Lawson Charitable Trust, Lady Virginia 192
Groves Charitable Trust, The 197
Hampstead Wells and Campden Trust 206

Victims of famine

Handicapped Children's Aid Committee *207*
Hanley Trust (1987), The *207*
Harbour Foundation Ltd, The *208*
Held Settlement, The Gisela *215*
Hertfordshire Community Trust, The *217*
Hopkinson Educational Trust, Robert Addy *227*
Hudson Charitable Trust, The *230*
Ibbett Trust, The *233*
Inverforth Charitable Trust, The *236*
Iris Trust, The *237*
Isle of Dogs Community Foundation *238*
JCSCJ Charitable Trust, The *238*
Keeling Charitable Trust, The Petronella *251*
King's Fund, The *255*
Laing Charitable Trust, The David *260*
Laing Foundation, The Christopher *260*
Laspen Trust *265*
Lawson Charitable Trust, Raymond and Blanche *267*
Leach Fourteenth Trust, The *267*
Linford Charitable Trust, The Fred *276*
Lloyd's Charities Trust *278*
(Lloyds) TSB Foundation for England and Wales *279*
Low & Bonar Charitable Fund, The *284*
Lyons Charitable Trust, The *288*
MacKintosh Charitable Trust, Viscount *292*
Manning Trust, Leslie & Lilian *296*
Marriage's Charitable Trust, Miss G M *299*
Mental Health Foundation, The *305*
Milburn Charitable Trust, Frederick *310*
Milton Keynes Community Trust Ltd, The *312*
Minge's Gift *314*
Moore Foundation, The George A *316*
Music for World Development *323*
NR Charitable Trust, The *325*
Nathan Charitable Trust *326*
New Court Charitable Trust *332*
New Durlston Trust, The *332*
Newby Trust Ltd *332*
Norman Family Charitable Trust, The *337*
Norton Foundation, The *340*

Owen Family Trust, The *348*
Paristamen Foundation, The *352*
Payne Trust, The Harry *356*
Peppiatt Charitable Trust, The Brian *359*
Pratt Charitable Trust, The W L *367*
Pye Christian Trust, The *371*
Pyke Charity Trust *372*
Ravenscroft Foundation, The *379*
Rope Third Charitable Settlement, The Mrs *391*
Rowntree Foundation, Joseph *394*
St Christopher's Trust, The *402*
Saint Sarkis Charity Trust *404*
Schuster Charitable Trust, The *410*
Scott Bader Commonwealth Ltd, The *411*
Seagram Distillers Charitable Trust *413*
Shepherd Charitable Trust, The Sylvia and Colin *418*
South Square Trust *430*
Summerfield Charitable Trust, The *442*
TSB Foundation for Northern Ireland *447*
TSB Foundation for Scotland *447*
Tisbury Telegraph Trust, The *457*
Van Berchem Charitable Trust, The Alec *470*
Van Leer Foundation UK Trust, Bernard *470*
Variety Club Children's Charity Limited, The *471*
Vec Acorn Trust, The *472*
Wagstaff Charitable Trust, Bob *475*
Wakefield (Tower Hill, Trinity Square) Trust *476*
Wakeham Trust, The *476*
Wesleyan Charitable Trust, The *485*
Westcroft Trust *486*
Whitecourt Charitable Trust, The *490*
Wills 1962 Charitable Trust, P J H *494*
Wiltshire Community Foundation *495*
Woodlands Trust *501*
Woodroffe Benton Foundation, The *502*
Yapp Welfare Trust, The *508*

■ Victims of famine

Funding priority

Buxton Trust, Denis *72*
Catto Charitable Settlement, The Thomas Sivewright *86*
De Yong Charitable Trust, The Emma *128*
De Yong's Charitable Trust 1984, Nicholas *128*
Dinam Charity *134*
Fund for Human Need *175*
Grant Charitable Trust, The *191*
Harbinson Charitable Trust, Roderick *208*
Harbour Foundation Ltd, The *208*
Hiley Trust, Joseph and Mary *219*
Humphreys Charitable Settlement, J A M *231*
Music for World Development *323*
Oxfam (United Kingdom and Ireland) *348*
Paristamen Foundation, The *352*
Parivar Trust, The *353*
Pratt Charitable Trust, The W L *367*
Summer's and I May's Charitable Settlement, The Late Misses (A N) *442*
Tisbury Telegraph Trust, The *457*
Toy Trust, The *459*
Trust for London *461*
Westcroft Trust *486*

Will consider

AB Charitable Trust *3*
Alexandra Trust *11*
Ammco Trust, The *15*
Archer Trust, The *20*
Askew Trust, The Dorothy *25*
Astor Foundation, The *26*
Ballinger Charitable Trust, The *32*
Barbour Trust, The *33*
Bartholomew Christian Trust *36*
Bell's Charitable Trust, Lady Mary *42*
Benesco Charity Limited *43*
Birmingham Amenities and Welfare Trust, The *49*
Birtwistle Memorial Trust, The G E *50*
Blake Charitable Trust, The Morgan *53*
Brooke Benevolent Fund, William *65*
Butlin Charity Trust, Bill *72*
Campbell Charitable Foundation, The Ellis *79*
Carlton Television Trust *81*
Charity Projects *90*

Clark 1965 Charitable Trust, Stephen *98*

Clinton's Charitable Trust, Lord *100*

Cottingham Charitable Trust, Mrs Diana Mary *114*

Coutts Charitable Trust, The *116*

DCW Trust *121*

Direct Response *134*

Dorus Trust *136*

Dumbreck Charity *139*

Early's Charitable Settlement, Richard *142*

Ebb and Flow Charitable Trust *144*

Edgar Foundation, The Gilbert and Eileen *145*

Edgar Trust, The Gilbert *145*

Elkes Charity Fund, The Wilfred & Elsie *147*

Emmaus Christian Foundation *150*

Epigoni Trust *152*

Ericson Trust *152*

Ferguson Benevolent Fund Limited *161*

Fletcher Charitable Trust, The Joyce *164*

Fletcher Trust, Roy *165*

Franklin Trust, Jill *170*

Gibson Charitable Trust, The Simon *182*

Grant-Lawson Charitable Trust, Lady Virginia *192*

Griffiths Trust, The E E and D M *196*

Groves Charitable Trust, The *197*

Hampstead Wells and Campden Trust *206*

Hanley Trust (1987), The *207*

Held Settlement, The Gisela *215*

Hudson Benevolent Trust, The Thomas *230*

Hudson Charitable Trust, The *230*

Humanitarian Trust, The *230*

JCSCJ Charitable Trust, The *238*

JMK Charitable Trust *239*

Jarrold Trust Ltd, John *243*

Keeling Charitable Trust, The Petronella *251*

Laing Charitable Trust, The David *260*

Laing Foundation, The Christopher *260*

Laing Foundation, The Kirby *261*

Laing Foundation, The Maurice *261*

Laing Trust, Beatrice *261*

Lane Foundation, The Allen *263*

Laspen Trust *265*

Leach Fourteenth Trust, The *267*

Linford Charitable Trust, The Fred *276*

Lloyd Charity, The S and D *278*

Lloyd's Charities Trust *278*

Lowenthal Charitable Trust, The L and C *285*

Lunn-Rockliffe Charitable Trust, Paul *286*

Lyons Charitable Trust, The *288*

McCarthy Foundation, The John *290*

MacKintosh Charitable Trust, Viscount *292*

Mackintosh Foundation, The *292*

Marriage's Charitable Trust, Miss G M *299*

Measures Charity, The James Frederick and Ethel Anne *303*

Mental Health Foundation, The *305*

Minge's Gift *314*

Multithon Trust, The *323*

NR Charitable Trust, The *325*

Nathan Charitable Trust *326*

New Court Charitable Trust *332*

New Durlston Trust, The *332*

Newby Trust Ltd *332*

Norman Family Charitable Trust, The *337*

Norton Foundation, The *340*

Oldham Foundation *345*

Owen Family Trust, The *348*

Paget Trust, The *351*

Payne Trust, The Harry *356*

Peppiatt Charitable Trust, The Brian *359*

Pye Christian Trust, The *371*

Rope Third Charitable Settlement, The Mrs *391*

Sainsbury Charitable Fund Ltd, The *402*

St Christopher's Trust, The *402*

Sargeant's Charitable Trust, Mrs M E *407*

Schuster Charitable Trust, The *410*

Scott Bader Commonwealth Ltd, The *411*

Seagram Distillers Charitable Trust *413*

South Square Trust *430*

Staples Trust *435*

Stonehouse Trust Ltd, Eric *438*

Swann-Morton Foundation, The *444*

TSB Foundation for Northern Ireland *447*

TSB Foundation for Scotland *447*

Tear Fund *450*

Thorpe Charity Trust, The *455*

Trust for the Homeless *462*

Van Berchem Charitable Trust, The Alec *470*

Van Leer Foundation UK Trust, Bernard *470*

Variety Club Children's Charity Limited, The *471*

Wagstaff Charitable Trust, Bob *475*

Wakeham Trust, The *476*

Wallington Missionary Mart & Auctions *478*

Webber Trust Fund, Ethel *483*

Whitecourt Charitable Trust, The *490*

Wills 1961 Charitable Trust, Mr Frederick *493*

Wills 1962 Charitable Trust, P J H *494*

Wolfson Charitable Trust, The Charles *499*

Woolton Charitable Trust, The *503*

■ Victims of man-made or natural disasters

Funding priority

Burgess Trust, The Michael *69*

Keymer Trust, The Ronald and Mary *253*

■ Victims of war

Funding priority

Catto Charitable Settlement, The Thomas Sivewright *86*

De Yong Charitable Trust, The Emma *128*

De Yong's Charitable Trust 1984, Nicholas *128*

Direct Response *134*

Ericson Trust *152*

Fund for Human Need *175*

Grant Charitable Trust, The *191*

Grundy Foundation, The Stanley *198*

Harbour Foundation Ltd, The *208*

Hiley Trust, Joseph and Mary *219*

Hudson Benevolent Trust, The Thomas *230*

Ireland Fund of Great Britain, The *237*

Mackintosh Foundation, The *292*

McLaren Foundation *292*

Music for World Development *323*

Nash Charity, The *326*

Oxfam (United Kingdom and Ireland) *348*

Paristamen Foundation, The *352*

Pratt Charitable Trust, The W L 367

Rowntree Charitable Trust, The Joseph 394

Said Foundation, The Karim Rida 401

Swindon Charitable Trust, The Walter 445

Tear Fund 450

Tisbury Telegraph Trust, The 457

Toy Trust, The 459

Trust for London 461

Westcroft Trust 486

Will consider

AB Charitable Trust 3

Alexandra Trust 11

Allen Trust, Mrs M H 13

Ammco Trust, The 15

Archer Trust, The 20

Astor Foundation, The 26

Ballinger Charitable Trust, The 32

Balney Charitable Trust, The 32

Barbour Trust, The 33

Barratt Charitable Trust, The Elaine 36

Bartholomew Christian Trust 36

Bell's Charitable Trust, Lady Mary 42

Benesco Charity Limited 43

Birmingham Amenities and Welfare Trust, The 49

Birtwistle Memorial Trust, The G E 50

Blake Charitable Trust, The Morgan 53

Bullough Tompson Settlement, The 68

Butlin Charity Trust, Bill 72

Campbell Charitable Foundation, The Ellis 79

Carlton Television Trust 81

Charity Projects 90

Clark 1965 Charitable Trust, Stephen 98

Clinton's Charitable Trust, Lord 100

Cottingham Charitable Trust, Mrs Diana Mary 114

Coutts Charitable Trust, The 116

DCW Trust 121

Digbeth Trust Ltd, The 133

Dorus Trust 136

Dumbreck Charity 139

Early's Charitable Settlement, Richard 142

Ebb and Flow Charitable Trust 144

Edgar Foundation, The Gilbert and Eileen 145

Elkes Charity Fund, The Wilfred & Elsie 147

Emmaus Christian Foundation 150

Epigoni Trust 152

Ferguson Benevolent Fund Limited 161

Fleming Charitable Trust, The Ian 164

Fletcher Charitable Trust, The Joyce 164

Fletcher Trust, Roy 165

Franklin Trust, Jill 170

Gibson Charitable Trust, The Simon 182

Goldsmiths' Company's Charities, The 188

Grant-Lawson Charitable Trust, Lady Virginia 192

Groves Charitable Trust, The 197

Hampstead Wells and Campden Trust 206

Hanley Trust (1987), The 207

Harbinson Charitable Trust, Roderick 208

Held Settlement, The Gisela 215

Hudson Charitable Trust, The 230

Humanitarian Trust, The 230

Inverforth Charitable Trust, The 236

JCSCJ Charitable Trust, The 238

JMK Charitable Trust 239

Jarrold Trust Ltd, John 243

Keeling Charitable Trust, The Petronella 251

King's Fund, The 255

Laing Charitable Trust, The David 260

Laing Foundation, The Christopher 260

Laing Foundation, The Kirby 261

Laing Foundation, The Maurice 261

Laing Trust, Beatrice 261

Lane Foundation, The Allen 263

Laspen Trust 265

Leach Fourteenth Trust, The 267

Linford Charitable Trust, The Fred 276

Lloyd Charity, The S and D 278

Lloyd's Charities Trust 278

Lloyd's Patriotic Fund 279

Lowenthal Charitable Trust, The L and C 285

Lunn-Rockliffe Charitable Trust, Paul 286

Lyons Charitable Trust, The 288

McCarthy Foundation, The John 290

Marriage's Charitable Trust, Miss G M 299

Measures Charity, The James Frederick and Ethel Anne 303

Mental Health Foundation, The 305

Minge's Gift 314

Moore Foundation, The George A 316

Multithon Trust, The 323

NR Charitable Trust, The 325

Nathan Charitable Trust 326

Needham Cooper Charitable Trust, The 331

New Court Charitable Trust 332

New Durlston Trust, The 332

Newby Trust Ltd 332

Norman Family Charitable Trust, The 337

Norton Foundation, The 340

Oakdale Trust, The 343

Oldham Foundation 345

Owen Family Trust, The 348

Paget Trust, The 351

Parivar Trust, The 353

Payne Trust, The Harry 356

Peppiatt Charitable Trust, The Brian 359

Pye Christian Trust, The 371

Pyke Charity Trust 372

Rope Third Charitable Settlement, The Mrs 391

Sainsbury Charitable Fund Ltd, The 402

St Christopher's Trust, The 402

Sargeant's Charitable Trust, Mrs M E 407

Schuster Charitable Trust, The 410

Scott Bader Commonwealth Ltd, The 411

Seagram Distillers Charitable Trust 413

South Square Trust 430

Staples Trust 435

Stonehouse Trust Ltd, Eric 438

Swann-Morton Foundation, The 444

TSB Foundation for Northern Ireland 447

TSB Foundation for Scotland 447

Trust for the Homeless 462

Van Berchem Charitable Trust, The Alec 470

Van Leer Foundation UK Trust, Bernard 470

Variety Club Children's Charity Limited, The 471

Wagstaff Charitable Trust, Bob 475

Wakeham Trust, The 476

Wates Foundation, The 481

Whitecourt Charitable Trust, The 490

Wills 1961 Charitable Trust, Mr Frederick 493

Wills 1962 Charitable Trust,
  P J H *494*
Wolfe Family's Charitable
  Trust, The *498*
Wolfson Charitable Trust, The
  Charles *499*

....

■ Video

see **Film, video, multimedia,
broadcasting**

....

■ Village halls

see **Community centres &
village halls**

....

■ Visual arts

see also **Arts & arts facilities**

Funding priority
Merchants House of Glasgow
  307

....

■ Visual impairment

see **Sight loss**

....

■ Vocational training

see also **Education &
training**

Funding priority
Atwell's Charity (Skinner's
  Company), Lawrence *27*
Bachad Fellowship – Friends of
  Bnei Akiva *30*
BibleLands *47*
Carlton Television Trust *81*
Christmas Cracker Trust *95*
Company of Chartered
  Surveyors Charitable Trust
  Fund, The *108*
Dove-Bowerman Trust *137*
Homeless International *225*
Humphreys Charitable
  Settlement, J A M *231*
KC Charitable Trust, The *250*
Leche Trust, The *268*
Said Foundation, The Karim
  Rida *401*
St Katharine & Shadwell Trust
  404
Shipwrights' Company
  Educational Trust, The *420*
Trades Union Congress
  Educational Trust *460*
Watson's Trust, John *482*
Worshipful Company of
  Engineers' Charitable Trust
  Fund, The *504*

Will consider
Alcohol Education and
  Research Council *9*
Army Benevolent Fund, The *22*
Arts Council of Wales, The *23*
Ashden Charitable Trust, The
  24
Ashley Foundation, The Laura
  24
Barbour Trust, The *33*
Beit Trust, The *40*
Bilton Charity, The Percy *48*
Boots Charitable Trust *56*
Brotherton Trust, The Charles
  65
Camelot Foundation, The *78*
Campden Charities, The *79*
Challice Trust, The *87*
Chrimes Family Charitable
  Trust, The *93*
Clifford Charity Oxford, The
  100
Clinton's Charitable Trust, Lord
  100
Cobb Charity *103*
Collier Charitable Trust, The
  105
Community Trust for Greater
  Manchester, The *108*
County Durham Foundation
  115
Cripplegate Foundation *118*
Curriers Company Charitable
  Fund *119*
de Freitas Charitable Trust, The
  Helen and Geoffrey *126*
Digby Charitable Trust, Simon
  133
Direct Response *134*
Earley Charity, The *142*
Ebb and Flow Charitable Trust
  144
Edgar Foundation, The Gilbert
  and Eileen *145*
Edgar Trust, The Gilbert *145*
Education Services *145*
Emmandjay Charitable Trust
  150
Follett Trust, The *166*
Ford of Britain Trust *166*
Galinski Charitable Trust *177*
Gelston Charitable Trust, The
  179
Goldsmiths' Company's
  Charities, The *188*
Great Britain Sasakawa
  Foundation, The *193*
Hertfordshire Community
  Trust, The *217*
Holly Hill Charitable Trust *224*
Hudson Benevolent Trust, The
  Thomas *230*
Hussey for Africans, Charity of
  Rebecca *231*
Isle of Dogs Community
  Foundation *238*
Lankelly Foundation, The *264*

Lewis Foundation, The John
  Spedan *274*
Linford Charitable Trust, The
  Fred *276*
Lloyd Charity, The S and D *278*
(Lloyds) TSB Foundation for
  England and Wales *279*
London Law Trust *280*
Measures Charity, The James
  Frederick and Ethel Anne
  303
Middlesex County Rugby
  Football Union Memorial
  Fund *309*
Minet Trust, The Peter *313*
NR Charitable Trust, The *325*
Newby Trust Ltd *332*
Paristamen Foundation, The
  352
Payne Trust, The Harry *356*
Persula Foundation, The *360*
Porcupine Trust, The *366*
Powell Foundation, The *367*
Radcliffe's Trust, Dr *375*
Rest-Harrow Trust, The *382*
SMB Trust, The *400*
Sheepdrove Trust, The *417*
Skelton Bounty, The *423*
Skinners' Company Lady Neville
  Charity *424*
Smallpeice Trust, The *425*
Summerfield Charitable Trust,
  The *442*
Swann-Morton Foundation,
  The *444*
Tear Fund *450*
Thomson Foundation, The Sue
  454
Tisbury Telegraph Trust, The
  457
Upjohn Charitable Trust, The
  469
Vincent Trust Fund, Eric W *473*
Wakefield (Tower Hill, Trinity
  Square) Trust *476*
Wall Trust, Thomas *478*
Wates Charitable Trust, John
  481
Wates Foundation, The *481*
Wiltshire Community
  Foundation *495*
Wincott Foundation, The *496*

....

■ Voluntary umbrella
bodies

see **Charity or voluntary
umbrella bodies**

■ Volunteer bureaux

see also **Charity or voluntary umbrella bodies**

Funding priority

Berkshire Community Trust 45
Community Trust for Greater Manchester, The 108
County Durham Foundation 115
Sainsbury Charitable Fund Ltd, The 402

Will consider

Amory Charitable Trust, Viscount 16
Aston Charities Trust Ltd 25
Barbour Trust, The 33
Boots Charitable Trust 56
Brotherton Trust, The Charles 65
Camelot Foundation, The 78
Campden Charities, The 79
Carnegie Dunfermline Trust 82
Carnegie United Kingdom Trust, The 82
Coutts Charitable Trust, The 116
Debtors' Relief Fund Charity 128
Digby Charitable Trust, Simon 133
Edgar Foundation, The Gilbert and Eileen 145
Ford of Britain Trust 166
Great Britain Sasakawa Foundation, The 193
Hampstead Wells and Campden Trust 206
Harford Charitable Trust 209
Isle of Dogs Community Foundation 238
Leech Charity, The William 269
MacKintosh Charitable Trust, Viscount 292
Milton Keynes Community Trust Ltd, The 312
Minet Trust, The Peter 313
Newby Trust Ltd 332
Norman Family Charitable Trust, The 337
Persula Foundation, The 360
Pilkington Charitable Trust, Cecil 363
Richmond Parish Lands Charity 384
Rope Third Charitable Settlement, The Mrs 391
Sargeant's Charitable Trust, Mrs M E 407
Scott Bader Commonwealth Ltd, The 411
Sheldon Trust, The 417
Summerfield Charitable Trust, The 442
Wade & Others, The Charity of Thomas 475
Whitaker Charitable Trust 489

Wiltshire Community Foundation 495
Woodlands Trust 501

■ Volunteers

Funding priority

Barbour Trust, The 33
Rope Third Charitable Settlement, The Mrs 391

■ War

see **Victims of war**

■ Waterways

see also **Conservation**

Funding priority

Clark Charitable Trust, J Anthony 98
Cobb Charity 103
Countryside Trust, The 115
Dulverton Trust, The 139
Nathan Charitable Trust, Peter 326

Will consider

Ammco Trust, The 15
Amory Charitable Trust, Viscount 16
Askew Charitable Trust, The Ian 25
Astor Foundation, The 26
Barnby's Foundation, Lord 35
Brook Charitable Settlement, R E 64
Butler Charitable Trust, The A S 71
CLA Charitable Trust 74
Cadbury Trust (1928), The Edward & Dorothy 76
Coates Charitable Trust, The John 103
Cole Charitable Trust, The 105
Community Trust for Greater Manchester, The 108
Cripplegate Foundation 118
David Trust, The Lesley 124
de Freitas Charitable Trust, The Helen and Geoffrey 126
Digby Charitable Trust, Simon 133
Direct Response 134
Early's Charitable Settlement, Richard 142
Earwicker Trust 142
Fishmongers' Company's Charitable Trust 163
Four Winds Trust 168
Franklin Trust, Jill 170
Goldsmiths' Company's Charities, The 188
Greenaway Foundation, The Sir Derek 194

Grocers' Charity 197
Haddon Charitable Trust, William 202
Halkes Settlement, John Robert 204
Harbinson Charitable Trust, Roderick 208
Hawthorne Charitable Trust, The 212
Inverforth Charitable Trust, The 236
Isle of Dogs Community Foundation 238
Kilverstone Wildlife Charitable Trust, The 254
Lawson Charitable Trust, Raymond and Blanche 267
Leach Fourteenth Trust, The 267
Lee Foundation, The Edgar 269
Lewis Foundation, The John Spedan 274
Living and Waking Naturally 278
Lower Hall Charitable Trust 285
Lyndhurst Settlement 287
MacKintosh Charitable Trust, Viscount 292
Mellows Charitable Settlement, The Anthony and Elizabeth 305
Mitchell Trust 315
Needham Cooper Charitable Trust, The 331
New Court Charitable Trust 332
Oakdale Trust, The 343
Paget Trust, The 351
Peppiatt Charitable Trust, The Brian 359
Persula Foundation, The 360
Powys Welsh Church Fund 367
Prince's Trust - BRO, The 369
Ravenscroft Foundation, The 379
Richard Charitable Trust, The Cliff 383
Rowbotham Charitable Trust, The Christopher 393
Schuster Charitable Trust, The 410
South Square Trust 430
Stevens Foundation, The June 437
Stoate Charitable Trust, The Leonard Laity 438
Summerfield Charitable Trust, The 442
Symons Charitable Trust, The Stella 446
Terry Charitable Trust, Noel Goddard 451
Tisbury Telegraph Trust, The 457
Unitek Foundation 469
Vincent Trust Fund, Eric W 473

Wade & Others, The Charity of Thomas *475*
Whitaker Charitable Trust *489*
Woodroffe Benton Foundation, The *502*
Worshipful Company of Engineers' Charitable Trust Fund, The *504*
Wylde Memorial Charity, The Anthony and Gwendoline *507*

■ Welfare services

see **Community facilities, Community services**

■ Well woman clinics

see also **Health care**

Funding priority

Allied Dunbar Charitable Trust Limited, The *13*
Blackburn Trust, The *51*
Edgar Trust, The Gilbert *145*
Kroch Foundation, The Heinz & Anna *259*

Will consider

Astor Foundation, The *26*
Barbour Trust, The *33*
Barrie Charitable Trust, The Misses *36*
Berkshire Community Trust *45*
Birmingham Amenities and Welfare Trust, The *49*
Birtwistle Memorial Trust, The G E *50*
Bottom Charitable Trust, Harry *56*
British Dietetic Association General and Education Trust Fund, The *61*
Community Trust for Greater Manchester, The *108*
Debtors' Relief Fund Charity *128*
Digby Charitable Trust, Simon *133*
Dorus Trust *136*
Edgar Foundation, The Gilbert and Eileen *145*
Elkes Charity Fund, The Wilfred & Elsie *147*
Epigoni Trust *152*
Follett Trust, The *166*
Foreman Foundation, The Carl & Eve *167*
Gibbins Trust, The *181*
Grant Foundation, The Raymond *191*
Grocers' Charity *197*
Isle of Dogs Community Foundation *238*
Lawson Charitable Trust, Raymond and Blanche *267*

Leech Charity, The William *269*
Moore Foundation, The George A *316*
Needham Cooper Charitable Trust, The *331*
New Court Charitable Trust *332*
Owen Family Trust, The *348*
Payne Trust, The Harry *356*
Ravenscroft Foundation, The *379*
Reader's Digest Trust, The *380*
Rest-Harrow Trust, The *382*
Sargeant's Charitable Trust, Mrs M E *407*
South Square Trust *430*
Staples Trust *435*
Stonehouse Trust Ltd, Eric *438*
Summerfield Charitable Trust, The *442*
Tear Fund *450*
Thompson Charitable Trust, The *453*
Tyne & Wear Foundation *466*
Van Berchem Charitable Trust, The Alec *470*
Wakeham Trust, The *476*
Westcroft Trust *486*
Wiltshire Community Foundation *495*
Wingfield's Charitable Trust, Mrs *496*

■ Widows & widowers

Funding priority

Lloyd's Patriotic Fund *279*
McLaren Foundation *292*
Wakeham Trust, The *476*

Will consider

Astor Foundation, The *26*
Ballinger Charitable Trust, The *32*
Beckwith Charitable Settlement, The Heather *39*
Clarke Charitable Settlement, The *99*
Cobb Charity *103*
Dacorum Community Trust *121*
David Trust, The Lesley *124*
Earley Charity, The *142*
Four Winds Trust *168*
Hurst Will Trust, Arthur *231*
Jackson Trust for Charity, The Isaac and Harriet *240*
Lloyd Charity, The S and D *278*
Marmor Charitable Trust, The Julie *299*
Measures Charity, The James Frederick and Ethel Anne *303*
Milward Charity, The Edgar *313*
Muslim Hands *324*
Newby Trust Ltd *332*

Payne Trust, The Harry *356*
Rest-Harrow Trust, The *382*
Robinson Brothers (Ryders Green) Ltd, Charitable Trust *388*
Royal's Memorial Fund, Princess *396*
South Square Trust *430*
Southover Manor General Education Trust Ltd *433*
Wyford Charitable Trust, The *507*

■ Wildflowers

see **Flora**

■ Wildlife areas

see **Wildlife parks**

■ Wildlife parks

see also **Animal facilities & services**

Funding priority

Brotherton Trust, The Charles *65*
Carron Charitable Trust, The *83*
Cinderford Charitable Trust, The *96*
Coote Animal Charity Fund, The Marjorie *111*
David Trust, The Lesley *124*
Four Winds Trust *168*
GW Trust, The *176*
Harbinson Charitable Trust, Roderick *208*
Nathan Charitable Trust, Peter *326*
Wicksteed Village Trust, The *491*

Will consider

Animal Defence Trust, The *18*
Astor Foundation, The *26*
Barnby's Foundation, Lord *35*
Beit Trust, The *40*
Bullough Tompson Settlement, The *68*
Buxton Trust, Denis *72*
CLA Charitable Trust *74*
Carnegie Dunfermline Trust *82*
Corden Trust, Cyril *113*
Digby Charitable Trust, Simon *133*
Dinam Charity *134*
Direct Response *134*
Dumbreck Charity *139*
Elkes Charity Fund, The Wilfred & Elsie *147*
Friends of the Animals *173*
Green Memorial Fund, The Barry *194*

Greenaway Foundation, The Sir Derek *194*

Holly Hill Charitable Trust *224*

Isle of Dogs Community Foundation *238*

Kiln Charitable Trust, Robert *254*

Kilverstone Wildlife Charitable Trust, The *254*

Laing Charitable Trust, The David *260*

Lankelly Foundation, The *264*

Leach Fourteenth Trust, The *267*

Lee Foundation, The Edgar *269*

Lewis Foundation, The John Spedan *274*

Lloyd Charity, The S and D *278*

Lowe Trust, Mrs D G *285*

Lyndhurst Settlement *287*

Marchday Charitable Fund, The *296*

Marchig Animal Welfare Trust *297*

Marriage's Charitable Trust, Miss G M *299*

Mitchell Trust *315*

NR Charitable Trust, The *325*

Norman Family Charitable Trust, The *337*

Oakdale Trust, The *343*

Owen Family Trust, The *348*

Paget Trust, The *351*

Perry Charitable Trust, Miss Frances Lucille *359*

Pilkington Charitable Trust, Cecil *363*

Ravenscroft Foundation, The *379*

South Square Trust *430*

Tisbury Telegraph Trust, The *457*

Vincent Wildlife Trust, The *473*

Walker 597 Trust, The *477*

Whitaker Charitable Trust *489*

Woodroffe Benton Foundation, The *502*

Wylde Memorial Charity, The Anthony and Gwendoline *507*

Wyre Animal Welfare *507*

Zaiger Trust, The Elizabeth and Prince *512*

■ Wildlife sanctuaries

see also **Animal facilities & services**

Funding priority

Brotherton Trust, The Charles *65*

Carron Charitable Trust, The *83*

Cinderford Charitable Trust, The *96*

Coote Animal Charity Fund, The Marjorie *111*

David Trust, The Lesley *124*

Harbinson Charitable Trust, Roderick *208*

Heath Charitable Trust *214*

Marchig Animal Welfare Trust *297*

Nathan Charitable Trust, Peter *326*

Sainsbury Animal Welfare Trust, Jean *401*

Vincent Wildlife Trust, The *473*

Zaiger Trust, The Elizabeth and Prince *512*

Will consider

Ammco Trust, The *15*

Animal Defence Trust, The *18*

Arbib Foundation *20*

Astor Foundation, The *26*

BP Conservation Programme *29*

Barnby's Foundation, Lord *35*

Beit Trust, The *40*

Body Charitable Trust, Bernard Richard *55*

Bullough Tompson Settlement, The *68*

Buxton Trust, Denis *72*

CLA Charitable Trust *74*

Carnegie Dunfermline Trust *82*

Community Trust for Greater Manchester, The *108*

Corden Trust, Cyril *113*

Digby Charitable Trust, Simon *133*

Dinam Charity *134*

Direct Response *134*

Dumbreck Charity *139*

Edgar Foundation, The Gilbert and Eileen *145*

Elkes Charity Fund, The Wilfred & Elsie *147*

Evetts & Robert Luff Animal Welfare Trust, Beryl *156*

Ford of Britain Trust *166*

Four Winds Trust *168*

Friends of the Animals *173*

Green Memorial Fund, The Barry *194*

Greenaway Foundation, The Sir Derek *194*

Holly Hill Charitable Trust *224*

Isle of Dogs Community Foundation *238*

Kiln Charitable Trust, Robert *254*

Kilverstone Wildlife Charitable Trust, The *254*

Laing Charitable Trust, The David *260*

Lankelly Foundation, The *264*

Leach Fourteenth Trust, The *267*

Lee Foundation, The Edgar *269*

Lewis Foundation, The John Spedan *274*

Lewis Partnership, John *274*

Lloyd Charity, The S and D *278*

Lowe Trust, Mrs D G *285*

Lyndhurst Settlement *287*

Minet Trust, The Peter *313*

Mitchell Trust *315*

NR Charitable Trust, The *325*

Norman Family Charitable Trust, The *337*

Oakdale Trust, The *343*

Owen Family Trust, The *348*

Paget Trust, The *351*

Perry Charitable Trust, Miss Frances Lucille *359*

Pilkington Charitable Trust, Cecil *363*

Ravenscroft Foundation, The *379*

Richard Charitable Trust, The Cliff *383*

Sargeant's Charitable Trust, Mrs M E *407*

Schuster Charitable Trust, The *410*

South Square Trust *430*

Tisbury Telegraph Trust, The *457*

Walker 597 Trust, The *477*

Whitaker Charitable Trust *489*

Woodroffe Benton Foundation, The *502*

Wylde Memorial Charity, The Anthony and Gwendoline *507*

Wyre Animal Welfare *507*

Young Explorers' Trust *511*

■ Work

see **Training for work**

■ Writers & poets

Funding priority

National Poetry Foundation, The *329*

■ Young adults

Funding priority

AB Charitable Trust *3*

AHJ Charitable Trust, The *3*

Abrahams 2nd Charitable Foundation, The Henry and Grete *5*

Ainsworth and Family Benevolent Fund, Green and Lilian F M *8*

Alexandra Rose Day *11*

Allnatt Charitable Foundation, Angus *14*

Almond Trust, The *14*

Ammco Trust, The *15*

Angler's Inn Trust *17*

Aquinas Trust 20
Arnopa Trust, The 22
Arts Council of Wales, The 23
Astor of Hever Trust, The 26
Austin of Longbridge Will Trust, The Rt Hon Herbert, Baron 27
BBC Children in Need Appeal, The 29
Bachad Fellowship – Friends of Bnei Akiva 30
Baker Charitable Trust, The 30
Balint Charitable Trust, Paul 31
Ballard Charitable Trust, The Stanton 32
Ballinger Charitable Trust, The 32
Baronets Trust, The 35
Bartholomew Christian Trust 36
Beattie Charitable Trust, The James 39
Bergqvist Charitable Trust 44
Betteshanger Charitable Trust 46
Betton's Charity (Educational), Mr Thomas 46
Bilton Charity, The Percy 48
Black Charitable Trust, The Cyril W 51
Black Charitable Trust, Edna 51
Black Charitable Trust, Sydney 51
Blagrave Charitable Trust, The Herbert and Peter 52
Blakey Charitable Trust, The Celia and Conrad 53
Bowland Charitable Trust, The 57
Bramall Charitable Trust, The Tony 58
Bridge Trust, The 60
Brighton & Hove Charitable Youth Trust 60
British Friends of Chinuch Atzmai Trust, The 62
Brook Charitable Trust 64
Brotherton Trust, The Charles 65
Burn Charity Trust, The J H 70
Burton Breweries Charitable Trust, The 70
Burton Charitable Trust, The Harriet 71
Butler's Trust, Lord 71
Butler's Trust, Lucilla 72
Butlin Charity Trust, Bill 72
Cadbury Charitable Trust, Richard 75
Campbell Charitable Foundation, The Ellis 79
Careers Services Trust 81
Carlton Television Trust 81
Cass's Foundation, Sir John 85
Catholic Education Service for England and Wales 86
Challice Trust, The 87

Charity Projects 90
Chase Charity, The 91
Child Growth Foundation 92
Children's Research Fund, The 92
Christmas Cracker Trust 95
Chronicle Cinderella Home Fund No 1, The 95
Clarke Trust, The Thomas Edward 99
Clifford Charity Oxford, The 100
Clipsham Charitable Settlement, R E 101
Clover Trust 102
Cobb Charity 103
Cohen and William Leech Foundation, Sebag 103
Collinson Charitable Trust, The Norman 106
Condon Family Trust 109
Construction Industry Trust for Youth, The 110
Corbett's Charity, Thomas 112
Coxen Trust Fund, Sir William 116
Crawford Children's Charity, Michael 117
Curtis Charitable Trust, The Thomas 120
Curzon Charitable Trust, The Wallace 120
Dahl Foundation, The Roald 122
Darell Charitable Trust 124
Davenport's Charity Trust, Baron 124
Dawson Educational Foundation, Thomas 126
De Yong Charitable Trust, The Emma 128
De Yong's Charitable Trust 1984, Nicholas 128
Delmar Charitable Trust 129
Denton Charitable Trust, The 130
Desmond Charitable Trust, The Richard 131
Diamond Industry Educational Charity, The 132
Dibden Allotments Charity 132
Dinam Charity 134
Djanogly Foundation, The 135
Dulverton Trust, The 139
Duveen Trust, The 141
Earmark Trust, The 142
Education Services 145
Egerton of Tatton Will Trust, Lord 146
Emerton-Christie Charity 150
Emmott Foundation Limited, The 151
Eveson Charitable Trust, The 155
Feeney Charitable Bequest, The John 161
Fleurus Trust, The 165

Foreman 1980 Charitable Trust, The Russell and Mary 167
Franklin Deceased's New Second Charity, Sydney E 170
French Charitable Trust, Charles S 171
Friarsgate Trust 172
Gallagher Memorial Fund, Angela 177
Gannochy Trust, The 177
Garnett Charitable Trust, The 178
Gatsby Charitable Foundation, The 179
Getty Jr General Charitable Trust, J Paul 181
Gibson's Charity Trust, The Hon Mr & Mrs Clive 182
Gill's Charitable Trust, Mrs M M 184
Glebe Charitable Trust 185
Gluckstein Charitable Settlement, The Penelope 185
Golders Green Foundation 187
Goodman Charitable Foundation, The Everard and Mina 188
Gough Charitable Trust, The 189
Grange Farm Centre Trust 191
Grant Charitable Trust, The 191
Grant-Lawson Charitable Trust, Lady Virginia 192
Greater Bristol Foundation 193
Green Foundation, The 193
Grocers' Charity 197
Gunnell Charitable Trust, The 199
HB Charitable Trust 201
Haines Charitable Trust, The Alfred 203
Hale Trust, The 203
Hall Charitable Trust, E F & M G 204
Hanley Trust (1987), The 207
Harding's Charity, William 209
Hardy Trust, The Patsy 209
Harford Charitable Trust 209
Harris Charity, The 211
Hartley Memorial Trust, The N & P 211
Hattori Foundation, The 212
Hawley Residuary Fund, Harry Fieldsend 212
Hawthorne Charitable Trust, The 212
Hertfordshire Community Trust, The 217
Historic Churches Preservation Trust, The 221
Hopkins, The Charity of Joseph 227
Hornby Charitable Trust, Miss D 227
Horne Foundation, The 228

Humphreys Charitable Settlement, J A M *231*

Isle of Dogs Community Foundation *238*

Jacobson Charitable Trust, The Yvette and Hermione *241*

Jewish Childs' Day *245*

Karimjee Trust, The Momamedali *250*

Keller Charitable Trust, Samuel *251*

Laing Charitable Trust, The David *260*

Lalonde Trust *262*

Lambourne Memorial Trust, The Emma *262*

Langdale Trust *264*

Lankelly Foundation, The *264*

Levy Charitable Foundation, Joseph *272*

Lewis Foundation, The John Spedan *274*

Lister Charitable Trust, The *277*

Liverpool Child Welfare Association Incorporated *277*

Living and Waking Naturally *278*

(Lloyds) TSB Foundation for England and Wales *279*

London Law Trust *280*

Lord's Taverners, The *281*

Lower Hall Charitable Trust *285*

Lowndes Charitable Trust, The Vanessa *285*

Ludgate Trust, The *286*

Lyons Charitable Trust, The *288*

Lyon's Charity, John *288*

MacAndrew Trust, The E M *289*

Maccabi Foundation, The *290*

Man of the People Fund *295*

Marmor Charitable Trust, The Julie *299*

Material World Charitable Foundation Limited, The *301*

Mellows Charitable Settlement, The Anthony and Elizabeth *305*

Mental Health Foundation, The *305*

Mercers' Company Educational Trust Fund, The *306*

Merchants House of Glasgow *307*

Mijoda Charitable Trust, The *310*

Milton Mount Foundation *313*

Milward Charity, The Edgar *313*

Minet Trust, The Peter *313*

Minge's Gift *314*

Montefiore Trust, The David *316*

Moore Charitable Trust, The Horace *316*

Moore Foundation, The George A *316*

Moores Family Charity Foundation, The *317*

Morgan Crucible Company plc Charitable Trust, The *319*

Murphy-Neumann Charity Company Limited *323*

Music Sales Charitable Trust, The *324*

New Chasers Charitable Trust, The *332*

New Durlston Trust, The *332*

Newcastle Children's Mission & Institute *333*

Newcastle's 1986 Charitable Trust, Duke of *333*

Newcomen Collett Foundation *333*

Newman's Charity, John *334*

Norman Trust, The *337*

North West Arts Board *337*

Norton Foundation, The *340*

Older's School Charity, William *345*

Oppenheimer Charitable Trust *346*

Ormsby Charitable Trust, The *347*

Owen Family Trust, The *348*

Paddington Charitable Estates Educational Fund *351*

Parivar Trust, The *353*

Pascoe Charitable Trust, Alan *354*

Paul's Charitable Trust, R J *355*

Pearson Foundation, The Frank *357*

Peirce Memorial Trust, The Joe *358*

Persula Foundation, The *360*

Pettit Charitable Trust *360*

Pickford Charitable Foundation, The David *362*

Priestman Trust, S H and E C *368*

Prince's Trust (now includes King George's Jubilee Trust (1935) and the Queen's Silver Jubilee Trust (1977)), The *369*

Proctor Charitable Trust, The Albert Edward *370*

RVW Trust *374*

Rangoonwala Foundation, ZVM *376*

Rank Xerox Trust, The *378*

Rayne Foundation, The *379*

Rayner Charitable Trust, The John *380*

Reeve's Foundation *382*

Ridgmount Foundation, The *386*

Robyn Charitable Trust *389*

Rolfe Charitable Trust, The *390*

Rope Third Charitable Settlement, The Mrs *391*

Rosca Trust *391*

Rothschild Group Charitable Trust, The J *393*

Royal Gardeners' Orphan Fund, The *395*

Royle Memorial Trust, Kirstin *397*

Rugby Football Union Charitable Fund, The *398*

Said Foundation, The Karim Rida *401*

St Hilda's Trust *403*

Sarum St Michael Educational Charity, The *408*

Save & Prosper Educational Trust *408*

Save & Prosper Foundation *409*

Scopus Jewish Educational Trust *411*

Scott Charitable Trust, The Francis C *412*

Seagram Distillers Charitable Trust *413*

Sedbury Trust, The *414*

Sell Charitable Trust, Leslie *415*

Sharon Trust, The *416*

Shelroy Charitable Trust, The *417*

Shipwrights' Company Educational Trust, The *420*

Shuttleworth Memorial Trust, Barbara A *421*

Silvester Charitable Gift Trust *422*

Singer Foundation *423*

Salter Trust Ltd *424*

Smith Foundation, The Leslie *427*

Snipe Charitable Trust *428*

Southdown Trust *432*

Southover Manor General Education Trust Ltd *433*

Spoore, Merry & Rixman Foundation, The *434*

Sportsman's Aid Charity Ltd, The *434*

Stevens Foundation, The June *437*

Stow Allen Trust, The *439*

Sulgrave Charitable Trust *442*

Sykes Trust, The Charles *445*

Thompson Charitable Trust, The *453*

Thompson Memorial Fund, The Edwin John *453*

Tillett Trust, The *456*

Towry Law Charitable Trust, The *459*

Trust Fund for the Training of Handicapped Children in Arts and Crafts *462*

Turner Charitable Settlement, The Sir Mark and Lady *464*

United Kingdom Friends for Further Education in Israel 468

Van Berchem Charitable Trust, The Alec 470

van Geest Foundation, The John and Lucille 470

Variety Club Children's Charity Limited, The 471

Wates Foundation, The 481

Watson Foundation, The Bertie 482

Watson's Trust, John 482

Weavers' Company Benevolent Fund, The 482

Wedge, The 483

Weinberg Foundation, The 483

White Rose Children's Aid International Charity 489

Whitehead's Charitable Trust, Sydney Dean 490

Wiltshire Community Foundation 495

Wohl Charitable Foundation, The Maurice 498

Wohl Charitable Trust, The Maurice 498

Woodhouse Charitable Trust, Edwin 501

Woodroffe Benton Foundation, The 502

Woolf Charitable Trust, The 502

Worms Charitable Trust, The Freda and Della 504

Worshipful Company of Shipwrights Charitable Fund, The 506

Yapp Welfare Trust, The 508

Yorkshire Field Studies Trust 510

Young Explorers' Trust 511

Youth Appeal for Eastern Europe 511

Will consider

Access 4 Trust 6

Adnams Charity, The 7

Alexis Trust, The 11

Ambika Paul Foundation 15

Anstey Charitable Settlement, J C W 18

Assembled Church of Christ Trust, The 25

Assheton-Smith Charitable Trust 25

Astor Foundation, The 26

Avenal 27

Aylesfield Foundation, The 28

Barnabas Charitable Trust 34

Barratt Charitable Trust, The Elaine 36

Bateman Charitable Trust, Lady Margaret 37

Beckwith Charitable Settlement, The Heather 39

Behrens Charitable Trust, E M 40

Beit Trust, The 40

Bell Charitable Trust, John 41

Benlian Trust, The 44

Bentall Charity Trust, Rowan 44

Birtwistle Memorial Trust, The G E 50

Blakenham's Charity Trust, Lady 53

Blott Charitable Settlement, Robert Orpwood 55

Bonhomie United Charity Society 56

Borthwick Memorial Trust, The Oliver 56

Bottom Charitable Trust, Harry 56

British Schools and Universities Foundation (Inc) 62

Buccleuch Place Trust 67

Buckingham Trust 67

Bulmer Charitable Trust, Becket 68

Carnegie United Kingdom Trust, The 82

Cazalet Charitable Trust, The Raymond 87

Chandris Foundation, The 88

Chownes Foundation, The 93

Christian Renewal Trust, The 94

Clinton's Charitable Trust, Lord 100

Commonweal Fund of the Trades House of Glasgow, The 108

Company of Chartered Surveyors Charitable Trust Fund, The 108

Cope Charitable Trust, Alfred 112

Dacorum Community Trust 121

Dashe Trust, The 124

David Trust, The Lesley 124

Dean Refugee Trust Fund, The Miriam 128

Delius Trust, The 129

Denne Charitable Trust 130

Derbyshire Trust, J N 130

Digby Charitable Trust, Simon 133

Direct Response 134

Doughty Charity Trust, The 136

Dumbreck Charity 139

Dunhill Medical Trust, The 140

Earley Charity, The 142

Early's Charitable Settlement, Richard 142

Edgar Trust, The Gilbert 145

Englass Charitable Trust, The 151

Family Trust, The 158

Fletcher Charitable Trust, The Joyce 164

Fogel Charitable Trust, The Gerald 165

GW Trust, The 176

Gale Charitable Trust, A W 176

Garbacz Charitable Trust, The Bernard & Vera 178

Gardner Memorial Trust, The Samuel 178

Gilchrist Educational Trust 183

Gold Hill Church Trust 186

Granada Foundation, The 190

Grand Metropolitan Charitable Trust, The 191

Gray Trust, The 192

Handicapped Children's Aid Committee 207

Harding Trust, The 209

Haymills Charitable Trust 213

Hinrichsen Foundation, The 221

Hobbs Trust Limited, The Betty 222

Horn Trust, The Cuthbert 227

Hornsey Parochial Charities (Educational and Vocational Foundation), The 228

Hudson Charitable Trust, The 230

Hurst Will Trust, Arthur 231

Hutchinson Charitable Trust, E B 232

Ibbett Trust, The 233

Ingles Charitable Trust, The 234

Inman Charity, The 235

Iris Trust, The 237

Jackson Trust for Charity, The Isaac and Harriet 240

Jacobsen Foundation Limited 240

James Charitable Trust, John 241

Joseph Charitable Trust, J E 248

Kleinwort Charitable Trust, The Ernest 257

LSA Charitable Trust 260

Lane Foundation, The Allen 263

Latham Trust, The 266

Lawley Foundation, The Edgar E 267

Leadbeater Trust, The Alfred 268

Lee Foundation, The Edgar 269

Leverhulme Trust, The 272

Licensed Trade Charities Trust, The 274

Littler Foundation, The Emile 277

London Taxi Drivers' Fund for Underprivileged Children, The 280

Lunn-Rockliffe Charitable Trust, Paul 286

Lynn Foundation, The 288

McDougall Trust, The 291

Margadale Charitable Trust, Lord *297*

Mount Everest Foundation, The *321*

Needham Cooper Charitable Trust, The *331*

Newby Trust Ltd *332*

Newitt Fund, Richard *333*

Nidditch Foundation, The Laurie *335*

Noel Buxton Trust, The *335*

Norman, The Educational Foundation of Alderman John *337*

Norman Family Charitable Trust, The *337*

Northcott Devon Foundation *338*

Oakdale Trust, The *343*

Oldham Foundation *345*

Oxford Trust, The *349*

PJD Charitable Trust *350*

Paragon Concert Society *352*

Paul Charitable Trust, The Late Barbara May *355*

Paul Charitable Trust, Margaret Jeanne *355*

Paul Charitable Trust, Pamela Milton *355*

Peppiatt Charitable Trust, The Brian *359*

Pitt Trust, Headley *364*

REMEDI (Rehabilitation and Medical Research Trust) *374*

Radcliffe's Trust, Dr *375*

Rae Charity, H J *375*

Rest-Harrow Trust, The *382*

Richards Charity, The Violet M *384*

Rickard Animals' Charity, Miss Maria Susan *385*

Rickard Cats' Charity, Miss Maria Susan *385*

Roberts Charitable Trust, F G *388*

Rocket Club Benevolent Fund, The *389*

Rokeby Charitable Trust *390*

Rothley Trust, The *392*

Rowntree Foundation, Joseph *394*

Royal Commission for the Exhibition of 1851 *395*

Sargeant's Charitable Trust, Mrs M E *407*

Shepherd Family Charitable Trust, The Sir Peter *418*

Shone Memorial Trust, J A *420*

Slater Foundation Ltd, The *424*

Slaughter Charitable Trust, The Ernest William *425*

Smallpeice Trust, The *425*

Smith (Estates Charities), Henry *426*

Smith Trust, The Sydney *428*

South Square Trust *430*

Sport Aid 88 Trust *434*

Stewards' Charitable Trust, The *437*

Street Charitable Foundation, W O *440*

Sugden-Wilson's Charitable Trust, Mrs Gabrielle Mary *441*

Summerfield Charitable Trust, The *442*

Swindon Charitable Trust, The Walter *445*

Timson Family Charitable Trust *457*

Trades Union Congress Educational Trust *460*

Travis Charitable Trust, Constance *460*

Turkish Women's Philanthropic Association of England *463*

29th May 1961 Charity, The *465*

Van Neste Foundation, The *471*

Van Norden's Charitable Foundation, Mrs Maud *471*

Vec Acorn Trust, The *472*

Vincent Trust Fund, Eric W *473*

Vodafone Group Charitable Trust, The *474*

Wakeham Trust, The *476*

Waley-Cohen Charitable Trust, Robert & Felicity *477*

Walker Trust, The *477*

Wallington Missionary Mart & Auctions *478*

Weinstock Fund, The *484*

Whitehall Charitable Foundation Limited *490*

Whitley Trust, Sheila *491*

Wills 1961 Charitable Trust, Mr Frederick *493*

Wimpey Charitable Trust, The George *495*

Wix Charitable Trust, Michael and Anna *497*

Woburn 1986 Charitable Trust *498*

Wolfson (Scotland) Trust, The Edith & Isaac *500*

Women Caring Trust, The *500*

Woodhead Charitable Trust, Michael *501*

Woolmen's Company Charitable Trust, The *503*

Worshipful Company of Engineers' Charitable Trust Fund, The *504*

Wylde Memorial Charity, The Anthony and Gwendoline *507*

Yorkshire Agricultural Society *509*

■ Zoology

see **Ornithology & zoology**

■ Zoos

see also **Animal facilities & services**

Funding priority

GW Trust, The *176*

Harbinson Charitable Trust, Roderick *208*

Tisbury Telegraph Trust, The *457*

Will consider

Animal Defence Trust, The *18*

Astor Foundation, The *26*

Barnby's Foundation, Lord *35*

Broadley Charitable Trust, The *64*

Brotherton Trust, The Charles *65*

Carron Charitable Trust, The *83*

Digby Charitable Trust, Simon *133*

Dinam Charity *134*

Dumbreck Charity *139*

Elkes Charity Fund, The Wilfred & Elsie *147*

Isle of Dogs Community Foundation *238*

Lee Foundation, The Edgar *269*

Lewis Foundation, The John Spedan *274*

Marriage's Charitable Trust, Miss G M *299*

Nathan Charitable Trust, Peter *326*

Owen Family Trust, The *348*

Paget Trust, The *351*

Perry Charitable Trust, Miss Frances Lucille *359*

South Square Trust *430*

Walker 597 Trust, The *477*

Zaiger Trust, The Elizabeth and Prince *512*

The directory of products and services

Craigmyle

FUND RAISING, MARKETING & CONSULTANCY

Craigmyle is the UK's longest established fund raising consultancy firm. With over 35 years' history of fund raising in the UK and overseas we have unmatched experience in the provision of consultancy services.

We specialise in all aspects of fund raising and strategic development. Services include:

♦ Fund raising audits
♦ Strategic planning and development
♦ Fund raising consultancy
♦ Major Gift campaigns
♦ Recruitment & Training
♦ Donor development & Legacy campaigns
♦ Charitable giving & taxation advisory service
♦ Advice on organisation and Governance

The breadth of our experience is exemplified by the more than 1,300 clients with whom we have worked (for some of them on two, three and even four separate services).

Initial meetings are free and without commitment, so if you would like to find out more about our experience, what we can do and how we might help with your plans please call Godfrey Jackson, Mark Jefferies or Trevor Barton.

Craigmyle & Co Ltd
The Grove, Harpenden, Herts AL5 1AH
Telephone: 01582 762441
Fax: 01582 461489

We solve problems and develop opportunities. If you have either... ...talk to us.

Fundraising

Management Consultancy

Communications

The Charity Specialists

Action Planning

Mid-Day Court, 30 Brighton Road, Sutton, Surrey, SM2 5BN
Tel: 0181 642 4122 Fax: 0181 770 2090

PERSONAL TELEPHONE FUNDRAISING

NEED A COMMITTED BASE OF FINANCIAL SUPPORT?

Personal Telephone Fundraising is the country's leading agency using the phone to speak to charities' individual supporters, working with 75 organisations, including seven of the top twenty charities. This method of recruiting covenants and committed giving, when in the right hands, is unsurpassed both in cost-effectiveness and in the building of bonds with your supporters.

Ring 01273 698 697 and speak to Chris Cunningham, Jane Cunningham or Anne Bolitho for a no-obligation discussion of how this powerful tool
can help your organisation.

WE'RE OPEN

to charities large and small.

At Kleinwort Benson, we like to give charities personal attention whatever their size. Our dedicated charities team provides a level of individual service not usually available to smaller charities. We also offer a larger range of Common Investment Funds than anyone else, giving smaller charities greater opportunity to diversify their investments. Call us now for further information, or a copy of our brochure.

0800 716 853

Kleinwort Benson
CHARITIES

Kleinwort Benson Charities
PO Box 191 10 Fenchurch Street London EC3M 3LB

Kleinwort Benson Charities
is a Division of Kleinwort Benson Investment Management Limited
Regulated by IMRO and a member firm of the London Stock Exchange

Member of the Dresdner Bank Group

This advertisement is issued by
Kleinwort Benson Investment Management Limited

THE PRICE OF UNITS AND THE INCOME FROM THEM MAY GO DOWN AS WELL AS UP, AND ON SELLING, AN INVESTOR MAY NOT GET BACK THE ORIGINAL AMOUNT INVESTED. THE PRICE OF UNITS MAY RISE OR FALL DUE TO FLUCTUATIONS IN RATES OF EXCHANGE WHICH MAY CAUSE INVESTMENTS DENOMINATED IN FOREIGN CURRENCIES TO DECREASE OR INCREASE IN VALUE.

COLLYER FINN LIMITED
FUNDRAISING SERVICES

We provide fundraising services to charities throughout England.
We act for national and regional charities
in the following disciplines

THE ARTS

CHURCHES

CONSERVATION & THE ENVIRONMENT

EDUCATION

MEDICINE

PATIENT CARE

PROFESSIONAL INSTITUTIONS

RESEARCH & SCIENTIFIC STUDIES

WELFARE AND HEALTH

LOTTERY & EUROPEAN APPLICATIONS

Collyer Finn Limited
38 Churchgate Street, Bury St Edmunds, Suffolk IP33 1RB
Tel: 01284 762256 Fax: 01284 704190

funderfinder
- software for grant-seekers

Need a quick way of identifying the right trusts?
Advise others about sources of funding?
Looking for money for individual clients?

funderfinder produces two applications that might be of interest:

 Groups in Need (GIN) references over 3,400 trusts and foundations that fund voluntary organisations

 People in Need (PIN) identifies funders that make grants to individuals - for 'relief-in-need' or for educational purposes

FunderFinder is regularly updated - GIN every six months, PIN annually - to incorporate changes in trusts' policies or contact details.

There are Windows, DOS and Apple Mac versions of GIN. PIN is only available as a Windows program.

FunderFinder's software is not available to for-profit companies

for more information contact

FunderFinder
65 Raglan Road
Leeds LS2 9DZ
phone 0113 243 3008
fax 0113 243 2966
email info@funderfinder.org.uk

or visit our website at
www.funderfinder.org.uk

Registered company No 2662629   Registered charity No 1010573

The Mercury Charity Investment Advice Helpline

Our free Charity Investment Advice Helpline, run by John Dockerill and Chris Georgiou, has assisted thousands of charitable organisations to fulfil their investment responsibilities.

You'll find their response friendly and informed. As did one charity trustee, who recently wrote:

"We would never have achieved our objective had it not been for your patience and advice. I have expressed my deep appreciation to you before and, without reservation, I do so again."

Mercury has already attracted over 9,400 charity portfolios to the specialist charity Funds Charinco and Charishare; and, as Britain's leading independent investment house, we offer a safe, secure choice for trustees.

If you'd like some help, ring John Dockerill or Chris Georgiou. The call, and the advice, are free. ☎ **0800 282 490**

CHARINCO and CHARISHARE

MERCURY
ASSET MANAGEMENT

BRITAIN'S LEADING INVESTMENT HOUSE

 # THE ASSOCIATION OF FUNDRAISING CONSULTANTS

■ Action Planning

We solve problems and develop opportunities. Our service is characterised by imagination, innovation and integrity, built on solid experience. Capital appeals, revenue fundraising, strategies – our in-house team and specialist associates will provide a tailored service to meet your needs.

Contact
DAVID SAINT
Mid-Day Court,
30 Brighton Road, Sutton,
Surrey SM2 5BN
Telephone: 0181-642 4122
Telefax: 0181-770 2090

■ AM&M Direct

A full service DM agency, with over 25 years experience. Our Low Cost Donor Acquisition Programme guarantees new donors at LOW prices. Our Computer Services division offers the whole range of computer bureau and database management services tailored to meet YOUR needs.

Contact
RONALD DICK
3/2–3/3 Harbour Yard,
Chelsea Harbour,
London SW10 0XD
Telephone: 0171-376 5727
Telefax: 0171-351 1138
Internet http://www.demon.
co.uk/ammdirect

■ Andrew de Mille Fundraising Consultants

A successful, committed professional support team built on Andrew de Mille's 25 years' experience. Clients: arts, conservation, education, elderly, medical, churches,welfare,international, sport, youth, community Services: strategic planning, feasibility studies, training, prospect research, campaign planning/management big gift fundraising. Fees: moderate, time-based. Free initial consultations. Members AFC/ICFM

Contact
ANDREW DE MILLE
Fundraising Consultants
Hedsordene, Cookham,
Berks SL6 9HW
Telephone: 01628 527753
Telefax: 01628 529938

■ Christa M Paxton Associates

The consultancy offers advisers with a proven track record in Strategic Planning and all aspects of income generation to large and small charities. We have extensive experience in management and fundraising and provide professional advice, assessment and realistic solutions for all your organisational needs.

Contact
CHRISTA M PAXTON
631 Kings Road,
London SW6 2DU
Telephone: 0171-736 1482
Telefax: 0171-386 8194

■ Craigmyle and Co Ltd

Craigmyle's range of clients includes national and local charities, schools, universities, hospitals, churches and cathedrals. Services include fundraising audits, strategic planning and development, fundraising consultancy, major gift campaigns, recruitment & training, donor development & legacy campaigns, charitable giving & taxation advice. Initial meetings are free and without commitment.

Contact
GODFREY JACKSON
The Grove, Harpenden,
Herts. AL5 1AH
Telephone: 01582 762441
Telefax: 01582 461489

■ Direct Results Fundraising

Total fundraising strategy. Capital and revenue funraising from individuals, companies, trusts and other sources.

Contact
C STODDARD
122 Winchcombe Street
Cheltenham, Glos GL52 2NW
Telephone: 01242 222362
Telefax: 01242 224138

■ Elizabeth Anderson & Associates

Practical, achievable solutions to funding problems and challenges. Established in 1983, we have a track-record of successful experience with arts education, environment, health, museums and social care charities large and small. Specialisms include Major Gift campaigns, marketing and PR, corporate sponsorship and capital appeals. Free initial consultation and proposal.

Contact

ELIZABETH ANDERSON
Mount Hooley,
Whittingham, Alnwick,
Northumberland NE66 4RN
Telephone: 01665 574631
Telefax: 01665 574354

■ Friedland Group

International management and fundraising consulting group. Services include strategic development planning, business and financial planning, fundraising strategy and National Lottery applications. Specialist expertise in major gift fundraising, membership schemes, bequests, corporate sponsorship and commercial development. We offer assistance with feasibility and planning studies, and implementation.

Contact

FREDA WOOLDRIDGE
15 Queens Gate, Place,
London SW7 5NX,
Telephone: 0171-581 5567
Telefax: 0171-823 7757

■ Jane Kaufman Associates

We offer tailored solutions to your organisation's specific needs. Specialists in: Fundraising Audits and Feasibility Studies for both Revenue and Capital Campaigns; Strategic Planning and the development and implementation of Fundraising and Communication Strategies to maximise your Income; Management Development – Organisational Reviews, Restructuring, Recruitment and Training. A network of Associates in London, Surrey and Hampshire.

Contact

JANE KAUFMAN or KATE BROOKS
Kennel Moor,
Lower Moushill Lane,
Milford, Surrey GU8 5JX
Telephone: 01483 416887
Telefax: 01483 418510

■ The Professional Fundraising Consultancy

We specialise in fundraising for education and the arts providing a range of service for capital appeals, development programmes and corporate sponsorship campaigns. The Principal, Susan Marsden, has 20 years experience and an excellent reputation.

Contact

SUSAN MARSDEN
Pendennis Lodge, Dryfield Lane,
Rivington, Bolton BL6 7RT
Telephone: 01204 669265
Telefax: 01204 699655

■ The Projects Company

The Projects Company offers Training and Consultancy in a range of trusteeship, management, planning, fundraising and related skills, for organisations of all sizes. Training is undertaken either in-house or for mixed groups by trainers who have 'hands–on' experience of the topic in which they are training.

Contact

GINA NEGUS or MAGGIE TAYLOR
Coopersale Hall Farm, Flux's Lane,
Epping, Essex CM16 7PE
Telephone: 0181-502 2327
Telefax: 01992 561991

■ Sparks Consultancy Services

Sparks Consultancy Services, established in 1958, offers flexible professional services for the varying needs of different organisations large or small, new and old. These services include free preliminary advice; development study; financial planning; appeal direction; training; consultancy; advisory and specialist services. A leaflet with further information is available.

Contact

J SPARKS
Lyncot, Queen Street, Stedham,
Midhurst, W Sussex GU29 0NW
Tel/Fax 01730 816886
Mobile: 0860 361060

■ UCS Consultants

UCS Consultants offers hands on fundraising, fundraising consultancy and training. It is particularly skilled in developing appropriate and sustainable fundraising for major capital and revenue needs and for 'challenging' appeals. UCS provides services throughout the UK and to the Irish Republic, Southern and Eastern Europe and Africa.

Contact

PETER PANTELI
Arden Croft, Queens Drive,
Ilkley, West Yorkshire LS29 9QW

Auditors, Accountants and Taxation

■ Chiene & Tait CA

3 Albyn Place,
Edinburgh EH2 4NQ

Tel: 0131 225 7515
Fax: 0131 220 1083
Email: chiene@chiene.demon.
co.uk

Jeremy Chittleburgh *Partner*

Chartered Accountants

■ Helmore, Helmore & Co

35–37 Grosvenor Gardens,
Belgravia, London SW1W 0BY

Tel: 0171-828 3156
Fax: 0171-630 7451

Michael Guillem *Partner*

■ Kidsons Impey

Spectrum House
20–26 Cursitor Street
London EC4A 1HY

Tel: 0171-405 2088
Fax 0171-831 2206

Bob Knox *Managing Partner*

Computer Software

■ Master Software Corporation

First Floor, 707 High Road,
North Finchley, London N12 0BT

Tel: 0181-446 2440
Fax: 0181-445 1717
Email: 101657.1612@
compuserve.com

Bryan Hunt UK *Account Executive*

Ask yourself why over 5,700
non-profit organisations have
turned to fund-master. Is it the
comprehensive, user-friendly
fundraising software or the
approachable staff? Find out
by calling for a free demo disk.

Fundraising Consultants

Action Planning
(Ap) *The Charity Specialists*

■ Action Planning

Mid-Day Court,
30 Brighton Road,
Sutton, Surrey SM2 5BW

Tel: 0181-642 4122
Tax: 0181-770 2090
Email: actplan@dircon.co,uk

David Saint *Principal*

The charity specialist Action
Planning provides the best
consultancy and fundraising
management and
communucations. We help our
clients solve problems and seize
opportunities. If you have either
call us now.

■ Collyer Finn Ltd

38 Churchgate Street,
Bury St Edmunds,
Suffolk IP33 1RB

Tel: 01284 762256
Fax: 01284 704190

Timothy Finn *Managing Director*

Fundraising services throughout
Britain in all charitable fields. Our
services include the conduct of
campaigns, lottery and European
applications, strategy, training
and feasibility studies. An initial
consultation is normally free.

■ Donors International Research and Advisory Services Ltd

Post Office Building, Albrighton,
Wolverhampton WV7 3QH

Tel: 01902 374662
Fax: 01902 372288

Mr Ken Bateson *Director*

Solicitors

S J Berwin & Co

■ S J Berwin & Co

222 Grays Inn Road,
London WC1X 8HB

Tel: 0171-533 2222
Fax: 0171-533 20000
E-Mail: info@sjberwin.com

Moira Protani

Investment Management

■ Cantrade Investment Management Limited

4 Chiswell Street, Finsbury Square,
London EC1Y 4UP

Tel: 0171-614 8048
Fax: 0171-454 0888
E-Mail: email@cantrade-
investments.com

Russell Wright

Cantrade Investment
Management Limited, part of
the Union Bank of Switzerland
Group, is a rapidly growing
investment management house.
At Cantrade we currently
manage over £400 million on
behalf of some 85 charity clients,
and specialise in investment
management for charities with
funds over £1 million.

GM

■ Greig Middleton & Co Limited

52–55 Gresham Street
London EC2V 7EH

Tel: 0171-392 4000
Fax: 0171-392 4200

Michael Read

N E W T O N

■ Newton Investment Management

71 Queen Victoria Street
London EC4V 4DR

Tel: 0171-332 9000
Fax: 0171-332 5517
E-Mail: charities@newton.co.uk

Lionel Anderson

**Schroder
Investment
Management**

■ Schroder Investment Management Limited

33 Gutter Lane, London EC2V 8AS

Tel: 0171-382 6668
Fax 0171-382 3870

Matthew Jones